HANDBOOK
OF
TROPICAL FOODS

FOOD SCIENCE

A Series of Monographs

Editors

STEVEN R. TANNENBAUM
Department of Nutrition and Food Science
Massachusetts Institute of Technology
Cambridge, Massachusetts

PIETER WALSTRA
Department of Food Science
Wageningen Agricultural University
Wageningen, The Netherlands

1. Flavor Research: Principles and Techniques   *R. Teranishi, I. Hornstein, P. Issenberg, and E. L. Wick (out of print)*
2. Principles of Enzymology for the Food Sciences   *John R. Whitaker*
3. Low-Temperature Preservation of Foods and Living Matter   *Owen R. Fennema, William D. Powrie, and Elmer H. Marth*
4. Principles of Food Science   *edited by Owen R. Fennema*
    Part I: Food Chemistry   *edited by Owen R. Fennema*
    Part II: Physical Methods of Food Preservation   *Marcus Karel, Owen R. Fennema, and Daryl B. Lund*
5. Food Emulsions   *edited by Stig Friberg*
6. Nutritional and Safety Aspects of Food Processing   *edited by Steven R. Tannenbaum*
7. Flavor Research—Recent Advances   *edited by Roy Teranishi, Robert A. Flath, and Hiroshi Sugisawa*
8. Computer-Aided Techniques in Food Technology   *edited by Israel Saguy*
9. Handbook of Tropical Foods   *edited by Harvey T. Chan, Jr.*

Other Volumes in Preparation

HANDBOOK OF TROPICAL FOODS

edited by

HARVEY T. CHAN, JR.
U.S. Department of Agriculture
Agricultural Research Service
Hilo, Hawaii

MARCEL DEKKER, INC.   New York and Basel

Library of Congress Cataloging in Publication Data
Main entry under title:

Handbook of tropical foods.

  (Food science; 9)
  Includes indexes.
  1. Food supply—Tropics. 2. Food crops—Tropics.
I. Chan, Harvey T., [date]. II. Series: Food
science (Marcel Dekker, Inc.); 9.
TX360.T75H36 1983   631   83-5119
ISBN 0-8247-1880-1

MARCEL DEKKER, INC.
270 Madison Avenue, New York, New York 10016

Current printing (last digit):
10 9 8 7 6 5 4 3 2 1

PRINTED IN THE UNITED STATES OF AMERICA

Preface

The tropics contain some of the most starvation-stricken and nutrient-deficient regions in the world, including many of the developing countries. Postharvest food losses in these countries have been estimated to range as high as 14 to 32%. A great deal of these food losses can be prevented through the application of appropriate food handling and preservation methods. These methods are known about but not used because documentation is not widely disseminated. Only within the past decade have the major scientific journals published to any extent articles on noncash tropical foods. The rejection of many of these articles on tropical foods was justified on the "restricted regional interest of tropical foods." As a result, many tropical food researchers were forced to publish in regional journals, experiment station bulletins, in-house publications, and conference proceedings, all of which have not only a limited distribution, but also in some cases a limited readership due to publication in languages not readily understood by the general scientific community. As a result, there remains a wealth of information lying secluded, scattered, and buried, waiting to be unearthed.

Currently, the most highly developed knowledge of tropical crops concerns the export items of commerce involved in the colonial mercantile-plantation system. Attention to indigenous tropical food systems has been severely neglected; only in recent times have the hunger problems of these areas been recognized and addressed on a worldwide basis. It was not until 1967, at the First International Symposium on Tropical Root Crops, that the role of root crops and their yield potential in comparison to other crops was recognized.

This book contains chapters on two major tropical root crops, cassava and yam, and includes a chapter on the neglected aroids and arrowroots. Other chapters discuss fermented fish products, which are important to the tropical diet but have been virtually ignored due to nonacceptance in occidental fare; amaranth, which has been described by the National Academy of Sciences as an underexploited tropical plant with promising value; palm oil, a cash crop of the tropics whose by-products are an important part of the region's diet; rice, the major staple of the tropics; ginger, an important flavorant, condiment, and confection; tropical fruit wine, a relatively new product with potential economic value; mangoes, papayas, and guavas, which are widely distributed throughout the tropics and whose products have potential value; macadamia nuts, sold at gourmet prices but with tremendous potential as a cash crop for underdeveloped countries; and bananas and citrus, two important cash crops of the tropics.

This book is an attempt to unearth and collect the most recent and available knowledge on selected tropical foods. It was not this editor's intent to develop an exhaustive treatise on tropical foods, as this would be impossible because of the diversity of the subject matter; rather it was this editor's intent to develop a seminal resource book espousing the need for further research in the area of tropical foods.

Harvey T. Chan, Jr., Ph.D.
Research Food Technologist

Contributors

Kurt G. Berger, M.A., F.I.F.S.T. Director, End Use Research and Technical Advisory Service, Palm Oil Research Institute of Malaysia, Kuala Lumpur, Malaysia

Catherine G. Cavaletto, M.S. Department of Horticulture, University of Hawaii, Honolulu, Hawaii

Harvey T. Chan, Jr., Ph.D. Tropical Fruit and Vegetable Research Laboratory, U.S. Department of Agriculture, Agricultural Research Service, Hilo, Hawaii

D. G. Coursey, B.Sc., F.R.S.C., Fl. Biol., F.L.S. Head, Plant Food Commodities Department, Tropical Development and Research Institute, London, England

Pamela A. Lancaster, M.Sc.* Fruit, Vegetable, and Root Crop Section, Tropical Development and Research Institute, London, England

Rowland E. Leverington, F.A.I.F.S.T., F.R.A.C.I. Horticulture Branch, State Department of Primary Industries, Brisbane, Queensland, Australia

Florian Magno-Orejana, M.Sc., Ph.D. Chairman, Department of Fish Processing Technology, College of Fisheries, University of the Philippines in the Visayas, Diliman, Quezon City, Philippines

---

*Mrs. Lancaster is no longer associated with the Tropical Development and Research Institute.

John Marriott, Ph.D.[†] Fruit, Vegetable, and Root Crop Section, Tropical Development and Research Institute, London, England

Albert P. Mossman Cereals Research Unit, Western Regional Research Center, Agricultural Research Service, U.S. Department of Agriculture, Albany, California

Tommy Nakayama, Ph.D. Department of Food Science, University of Georgia Experiment Station, Experiment, Georgia

E. U. Odigboh, Ph.D. Department of Agricultural Engineering and Dean, Faculty of Engineering, University of Nigeria, Nsukka, Anambra State, Nigeria

Olusegun L. Oke Dean, Faculty of Science, University of Ife, Ile-Ife, Nigeria

William S. Sakai, Ph.D. Acting Dean, College of Agriculture, University of Hawaii at Hilo, Hilo, Hawaii

Allan E. Stafford Plant Physiology and Chemistry Unit, Western Regional Research Center, Agricultural Research Service, U.S. Department of Agriculture, Albany, California

S. V. Ting, Ph.D. Florida Department of Citrus, University of Florida Agricultural Research and Education Center, Lake Alfred, Florida

---

[†]Dr. Marriott is deceased.

Contents

HANDBOOK
OF
TROPICAL FOODS

1
Amaranth

Olusegun L. Oke Faculty of Science, University of Ife,
Ile-Ife, Nigeria

I. INTRODUCTION

A. Botanical Description and Varieties

One of the most difficult groups in taxonomy is the genus *Amaranthus L.*
In this genus, which is native to the tropical and temperate regions of
the world, over 50 species have been recognized. According to Singh
(1961) the grain amaranth species belong to the section *Amaranthotypus*
of the genus *Amaranthus* and are characterized by monoecious compound
inflorescences and five-merous flowers with circumscissile utricles.
The basic units of inflorescence are little dichasial cymes, usually called
glomerules, each ordinarily consisting of an initial staminate flower and
an indefinite number of female flowers. There are in all four grain
Amaranthus species, namely, *A. hypochondriacus*, *A. cruentus*,
A. caudatus, and *A. edulis*. They are all annual herbs.

    A. hypochondriacus is the most common one which dominates the
great center of Mexico where it was probably first domesticated, and is
also the species found in Asia. It is characterized by a single, erect,
large flower head which is composed of thick fingerlike projections
(spekes). These spikes are sometimes very thick, measuring over a
foot long or else are shorter, forming a dense flower head. The color
of the flowers varies from green to red, with elliptical leaves. The
plant can attain a height of 1.2 to 2.4 m.

    A. caudatus derived its name from the long drooping taillike inflores-
cence which is characteristic of the species. The spikes are loosely
arranged to form the flower head. Usually the individual flowers are
extremely crowded on the spikes, causing the drooping at advanced
stage of flowering. The color of the flower is normally red but occasionally it can be green. The leaves are elliptical, tapering towards
both ends. The seeds are sometimes light or dark colored. The plant
can attain a height of 1.5 to 2.1 m.

    A. cruentus has a flower head which is composed of loosely arranged
spikes on which the flower clusters on the spike, but they are smaller
than *A. hypochondriacus* and so given an impression of an open flower
head. The flowers are generally yellow-green but occasionally they can
be red. The leaves are thinly elliptical and on a relatively long petiole.
The plant can attain a length of 1.2 to 2.1 m.

    The distinctive aspect of *A. edulis* is the inflorescence with the
branches terminating in a peculiar seven- to nine-merous staminate
flower instead of the indertiminate thyrse commone to the other species.
Apart from the fact that the flowers are generally rust colored, the size.
habit, and leaf shape are similar to *A. caudatus*.

B. Origin and Distribution

There is enough archaeological evidence to indicate that grain amaranth
originated from the New World, and that it was one of the most important staples in Mexico at the time of the Spanish conquest. Other

opposing theories about the origin might have been due to the fact that the cultivation was then concentrated on the highlands which were too remote for the early oriental writers and European travelers. Furthermore, it has been estimated that the grains were domesticated over 2000 years ago since some amaranth seeds were found placed in tombs as food for the dead. The Aztecs made their idols from a mixture of human sacrificial blood and amaranth seed dough. Also before the conquest the Mexicans prepared a cermonial paste called zoale with amaranth seeds formed into idols that were known to appear in at least seven regularly scheduled ceremonies. Zoale was also fed to slaves who were about to be sacrificed to the gods, and hence it is not suprising that the tradition was eventually suppressed by the Catholic church after the conquest. *A. candatus*, for example, was first encountered by the Spanish in the Inca empire and thus was called Inca wheat, but it is believed to be much more ancient than the Incas. It appears that the Spanish introduced the seeds to Europe where it became established as an ornamental plant; and by the nineteenth century it had reached Africa and Asia where it is now cultivated as grain in the mountainous areas of Ethiopia, southern India, Nepal, and the Himalayas. In other places, such as west Africa, it is cultivated mainly for the leaves which are relished as pot herbs. In general it is now grown over a large part of the world extending from Argentina up through the Andes, from Guatemala up through Mexico the the southwestern parts of the United States, from Iran and Ceylon through India and the Himalayas, and through inner China to Mongolia and in east and west Africa.

C. Economic and Nutritional Significance

Amaranth is one of the rare plants in which the leaves are edible and treated as a delicacy, and the seeds are also used as cereals. Very few plants have this double advantage. A member of the Amaranthacene that is very similar to amaranth in many respects is *Celosia argentea,* so similar that farmers believe it is a variety of amaranth. Most of the characteristics, and conditions, and so forth are actually similar except for a few minor variations like sensitivity to attack by pest and fungus. It is very rich in protein, 12 to 16%, increasing with increased nitrogen fertilizer and is exceptionally high in lysine (6.2 g/100 g), about 25 to 30% higher than the high-lysine maize, and similar to milk. This has been attributed to the fact that this species of plant is photosynthesized by the recently discovered C_4 pathway (Hatch and Slack, 1970), yielding asparagine as the major initial product, which is a key intermediate in the biosynthesis leading to lysine (Deuton, 1973). This process, as opposed to the classic C_3 route, could be expected to be exceptionally productive in view of the fact that the C_4 process is characteristic of such plants as millet, sorghum, sugar cane, and other fast-growing plants, and it is very efficient especially under high temperatures, brilliant sunshine, and moisture stress. The fact that most of the seed volume is occupied by the embryo may account for the high-lysine content rather than the C_4 route. Amaranth is therefore an economically fast-growing plant which (as a cereal crop) has helped to sustain untold generations of American Indians in one of the most difficult agricultural regions. This is due to the plant's high resistance to drought, having less than half the water requirement of the major cereals, lack of any serious toxic problems, and production of reasonable yields on poor soils. Although it is now considered overshadowed by the conventional cereals (maize, rice, wheat), it is still cultivated in several countries in the Americas, Asia, and in some parts of Africa Although it is now used as a subsidiary food in India, in some places like the western Himalayas it is still grown at elevations of about 1800 m as a regular crop in infertile and stony soils, and it has continued as the staple cereal in place of wheat (Pal and Khoshoo, 1974). Furthermore, the seeds are hardy and suitable for growing in areas with a short season and deficient soils where the conventional cereals cannot be grown with ease. Thus, they have potentiality as a subsidiary food and could play a major role in feeding the hungry world.

Although the seeds are very small, they are comparable to the improved cereals in minerals, carbohydrate, and protein (Misra et al., 1971). The carbohydrate is easily digestible, and the growth-promoting value is about three to four times that of rice (Singh, 1961). A comparison of the composition of amaranth grain is with various other grains is given in Table 1. On the dry basis the starch content is 62.8%, it is waxy, and it forms a "long" paste that does not gel on standing, thereby resembling the waxy type of starch in cereal grains, which can be of commercial importance. MacMasters et al. (1955) have described a method for the preparation of starch from *A. cruentus*. The plant can be harvested as a whole plant with most of the parts above the ground edible within 20 to 40 days or else the tips of the branches may be picked repeatedly when the plants are older.

II. HORTICULTURAL ASPECTS

A. Cultivation Practices

1. Climatological and Soil Requirements

Amaranth adapts very well to high temperatures and high altitudes, and thus is often found in the hills of the Himalayas and the highlands of Mexico. It is a short-day plant and hence when planted in the winter may bolt early. It is best sown during the rainy season. Trials have been conducted in Ethiopia between 8° and 9° north latitude and 38° and 39° east longitude and at elevations ranging from 1600 to 2000 m above sea level (Schmidt, 1977). The soil type varies from medium-course texture, gray-brown soils with good surface and internal drainage to black and dark-gray cracking clays with slow internal drainage

Table 1 Comparison of Nutritive Value of Amaranth Grains with Some Other Food Grains (Values/Ounce)

Name of food grain	Moisture (g)	Protein (g)	Fat (g)	Mineral (g)	Fiber (g)	Carbohydrate (g)	Ca (mg)	P (mg)	Fe (mg)	Caloric value
Rajgira, sil, or chaulai	2.2	4.4	1.5	0.8	0.6	18.7	63	185	–	106
Wheat	3.6	3.4	0.4	0.4	0.3	20.2	14	91	1.5	98
Rice (raw, milled)	4.1	1.9	0.2	0.2	–	22.0	3	45	0.5	97
Sorghum	3.3	3.0	0.5	0.5	–	21.0	8	79	1.8	101
Rajra (pearl millet)	3.5	3.3	1.4	0.6	0.3	19.1	14	99	3.1	102
Ragi (finger millet)	3.7	2.0	0.4	0.6	–	21.7	94	77	1.5	98
Maize	4.2	3.2	1.0	0.4	0.8	18.8	3	93	0.6	97

after wetting and swelling. The pH can range from 5.0 to 6.6, with reasonably adequate or high supplies of potassium (K), calcium (Ca), and magnesium (Mg) in the soils. In general, the soil should be especially rich for maximum performance. Temperature could range from 10 to 25°C and relative humidity 50 to 90%. Martin and Ruberte (1977) used a mixture consisting of 25% composted sugar cane filter press cake, 25% sand, and 50% loam in pots. The well-mixed soil was thoroughly wetted a day before planting the seeds. Dry sand is placed over the sown seeds to a depth of not more than 3.2 mm. The pots were then watered. The pots should be in a warm place, but not exposed to direct sun or strong breezes.

2. Planting Characteristics

Presently the cultivation of amaranth is on the decline in Mexico, but a few stands can be seen among maize fields. The same situation exists in Guatemala, Peru, Bolivia, and Argentina where it can no longer be seen as pure stands. In India, especially in the Gujarat state, it can be seen mixed with vegetables like chilies, and so forth; and in Afghanistan and Iran, scattered through melon and tobacco fields.

In Mexico amaranth seedlings are still grown on floating gardens, or *Chanapas*, which provided much of the food base for the Aztec civilization. This ingenious system has been estensively discussed by Early (1977), who found that some of the plots have been producing continuously for over 2000 years. The chinampas are built by scooping mud from the canals and piling it up between posts and vine walls. The upper section, which consists mainly of water weeds (serving as compost), is covered with a layer of fresh mud that provides a fertile medium for planting. The bed is cut into small squares and planted with six seeds, with dried cow manure tossed over the top. Watering is done every 2 days with the algae-rich canal water. Weeding is not required. Transplanting takes place 15 to 20 days later to nonirrigated fields, followed by fertilizer application using mineral fertilizer or manure. Harvesting is done by cutting very close to the ground and leaving in the field for 2 to 3 days to dry. The seeds are then separated by beating and sieving. The stubs are plowed under and the field is left to fallow. Usually the soil is depleted after harvesting and so the plot is never used for more than two plantings. There are canals surrounding the chinampa plots, and they contain carp and other fish that are eaten. The canals also provide a rich source of green algae that is skimmed off and used as fertilizer. This system thereby combines agriculture and intensive horticulture and is a system that could usefully be adapted in other parts of the world where traditional systems of agriculture with few labor-saving devices are still practiced.

B. Propagation

In general, there are two main methods of sowing. The seeds are drilled in by hand and mixed with about two to three times its weight

of sand to allow for uniform spread. The seeds are planted at about
5 to 10 kg/ha and are protected from being washed away by rain with
manure and compost. Palm leaves are added to protect the seeds from
the sun until germination. Drilling is done in rows of about 20 to 30 cm
apart, if harvesting is to be done by repeated cutting, or else much
closer at about 7.5 cm if harvesting is by uprooting. After about 3
weeks, when the seeds have germinated, they are thinned down to 3
to 5 cm within a row. Since this process could be cumbersome and may
even result in a big loss of seeds, especially if not mixed with sand,
some farmers prefer to broadcast the seeds on a bed covered loosely
with soil. After 2 to 3 weeks they are transplanted to the other beds
to give plantlets of about 1000 to 2000 plantlets per square meter. The
size of the beds vary but are in general similar to those in Benin, 10
to 50 cm high, 1.2 to 2 m broad, and 5 to 10 m long (Grubben, 1976).
The plants need a lot of watering after transplanting. In the hills of
northern India, the seeds are planted in unirrigated land at the break
of the monsson and harvested anytime from September on, depending
on the altitude (1800 to 2700 m). The practice of transplanting and
manuring is unknown, especially when grown alone. On the other
hand, in southern India it is mainly grown with finger millet and rarely
grown pure. In Gujarat state irrigation is given just after broadcasting and then every 10 to 15 days until the plant is 2.5 to 3 months old.

Since the plants are easily attacked by insects and fungi, they are
usually protected by spraying the leaves with wood ashes or else chemicals such as Gammalin 20 (Lindane) which is effective against grasshoppers; Vetox 85 (a carbaryl insecticide) which is active against
other insect pests; and Dithane M45 (a dithiocarbamate fungicide)
which is active against fungal diseases. Other chemicals which are
used are DDT, HCH, Parathion, and so forth.

Although mineral fertilizers are not used traditionally by gardeners,
manures of compost are used at varying rates. Recent experiments
have been conducted with mineral fertilizers with a nitrogen:phosphorus:
potassium (NPK) of 10:10:20. Weedkillers are not used since weeding is
carried out by hoeing in the weeds or else uprooting by hand.

C. Harvesting

Harvesting is usually done by cutting the seedlings above the second
leaf from the ground, at a height of about 7.5 cm, after they have
attained a marketable size. Cutting is done at various lengths (15 to
23 cm) in the first instance, and subsequently branches are included.
The height from the ground and time intervals between harvests are
not standardized, and these parameters could affect the yield. Alternatively, harvesting is done by uprooting the whole plant at an earlier
stage and bunching together for sale after washing the roots. Whatever happens, the quality of the vegetable is affected by flowering so
as many as possible of those that are flowering are not harvested but
left to seed.

When amaranth is grown for the seeds, harvesting is done when the plant is still at the green stage. In Gujarat state the stems are cut with a sickle and spread on the threshing yard where they are trodden under the feet of bullocks. They are then winnowed and allowed to dry for 2 to 3 days. In some places threshing is done by beating with sticks.

D. Experiments on Yields

One of the major obstacles in the commercial production of amaranth in the tropics is that little work has been done on the optional manure level for maximum yield of the leaves. Kogbe (1978) applied poultry manures at 0, 10, 20, 30, and 40 tons/ha. The seedlings were cut at a height of about 7.5 cm as soon as they attained marketable size, then bulked and weighed immediately. He found that the marketable yield (total fresh wt) and edible yield (fresh wt of leaves including petioles, i.e., part consumed) increased with increased rate of fertilizer application, with the highest yields, 50.7 and 26.1 tons/ha respectively, at 40 tons of manure in the first year (1975) and at 30 tons of manure the following year. The response was much greater and significant between 0 and 20 tons manure applied than between 20 and 40 tons/ha. The dry-matter yields followed the same pattern (5203 kg/ha). The leaf:stem ratio decreased steadily with increasing rate of fertilizer application (from 2.43 at 0 ton to 1.72 at 40 tons/ha), and this was significant in the 1976 trial. The yields, especially at the levels of 10 and 20 tons of manure, were highly significant in 1976, being over 80 and 200% of the control so that 20 tons/ha was regarded as the optional rate of manuring with the best economic returns. This recommendation was similar to the 21 tons/ha being used by the Ministry of Agriculture and Natural Resources in Ibadan, Nigeria. A yield of 30 tons/ha of fresh vegetables has been reported in Taiwan after 30 days of growth.

Wilson and Curfs (1977) compared the cost of production and the likely returns from *C. argentea* under a manual system in which all the work was done by hand tools for land preparation and weeding on a plot of 300 m^2, and a motorized system in which a small 14-hp, four-wheel tractor was used for land preparation and cultivating on a plot of 1100 m^2. The seeds were drilled in 50-cm rows by hand in the manual system and with a small hand-pushed planter in the motorized system. Mineral fertilizer, NPK (15:15:15), at 400 kg/ha was applied prior to planting, and after each cutting a side dressing of 30 kg/ha nitrogen was applied. The first cutting was at 4 weeks after sowing, with three subsequent cuttings at intervals of about 3 weeks. They found that during the dry season the yield for the tractor system (43,788 kg/ha) was nearly twice that of manual 24,740 kg), with no difference in the wet season (71,703 and 73,953 kg, respectively). They attributed the

difference in the dry season to better root development that allowed
for better water and nutrient uptake in the finely pulverized soil which
was mechanically prepared, whereas in the wet season this was not
necessary. Work-hour requirements were higher in both seasons for
the manual than the motorized system, especially in the dry season, resulting therefore in the highest cost per kg ($0.04/kg). No difference
was observed in the cost unit of output in both systems during the
rainy season ($0.02/kg).

Wilson (1971) compared the effect of broadcasting seeds with that of
drilling, using five fertility levels of NPK (15:15:15) from 0 to 800 kg/ha.
He found that broadcasting the seeds is superior to drilling. The response at a level of 200 kg/ha (22,190 kg/ha fresh wt) was optional.
The dry matter followed the same pattern. However, the fertility levels
had no effect on the chemical composition of the leaves.

Enyi (1965) investigated the effects of plant density, height of cutting, frequency of cutting, and the age of seedling at time of transplant on the yield and quality of amaranth, using a basic dressing of
45.3 kg ammonium sulphate, and 13.6 muriate of potash, together with
two headpans of farmyard manure. The plantlets were transplanted 20
days after sowing at various spacings (23×23, 46×46, and 46×92 cm)
and harvesting was done by cutting at various levels from the ground
(75,15,23 cm). At the first harvest, 3 weeks after transplanting,
Enyi found that the yield decreased with increasing height of cutting.
However, at the second harvesting the yield of those cut at 7.5 cm was
lower than those cut at 15 and 23 cm, and the total yield of those cut
at 15 cm was significantly higher than those cut at 23 cm. The yield
also was increased with the closeness of spacing at first harvest but
was lower at subsequent harvests, with the yield of 23×23 and 46×46
cm being significantly superior to that of 46×93 cm. The ratio of the
vegetable:flower weight increased with decrease in the height of cutting
at the first harvest, but increased with the decrease in plant density
and was lower at a 3-week harvesting interval than a 2-week interval.
There was virtually no difference in the total yield between plants
grown at the first two spacings used, but the above ratio and quality
were higher at 46×46 cm than at 23×23 cm. In all the treatments
the yield at second harvest was higher than the others and this decreased with the age of the plants. When transplanting was done at
27, 34, and 41 days, there was a decrease in yield of 51.6, 61.9, and
67.0% compared with that at 20 days. Taking all these factors into
consideration, Enyi suggested transplanting of plants before 27 days,
harvesting by cutting at 7.6 cm height in the first instance, and at
2-week intervals.

E. Pests and Diseases

A major factor in the commercial production of amaranth is the problem
of diseases and pests. Over 50 cultivars have been tried by the

National Horticultural Research Institute in Nigeria, but many have failed due to wet rot of leaves and young stalks caused by *Choenephora cucurbitarum* (Denton, 1979). According to Grubben (1976), the disease often presents itself on the cutting surfaces of the stalks. The young or weak plants die. The larger and more vigorous ones restore themselves by producing secondary branches while the infested part dries up. Yields could be reduced by as much as 50% and so also the quality. This was confirmed earlier by Schmidt (1977). Another disease is caused by *Albugo bliti* and is referred to by Van Epenhuijsen (1974), and a less common one is caused by *Prodenia litura* which can devour the whole of the leaves. Edema (1979) found that grasshoppers and caterpillars all year-round could constitute a big pest and destroy the major part of a field. Van Epenhuijsen (1974) has reported damages caused by a virus transmitted by *Piesma dilutus*. A source of damage often overlooked was pointed out in the field by Denton (1979), who observed that nematodes of the genus *Meloidogyne* cause swellings and tumors in the roots which often are not obvious until the plant is uprooted and the roots torn open. Usually the plants affected have stunted growth with smaller leaves. Edema (1979) has also mentioned the question of bacterial attack in roots and also the stem borer insects which bore tunnels in the stems of the plant. The major pest of the grain is the Rajgira weevil, *Hypolixus truncatulus*. While the larvae dig through the stem, the adults feed on the tender leaves.

F. Breeding

Very few cytotaxonomic studies have been carried out in the tropics on *Amaranthus*. The first cytomorphological investigation in Nigeria was by Olusi (1979) in which five species, *A, spinosus, A. hybridus, A. virdis, A. lividus,* and *A. tricolor,* were studied. The result of the chromosome counts was shown to be $2n = 34$ in all cases and seems to be in agreement with those of other workers elsewhere. One hundred pollen grains of each species were investigated and their size, frequency of occurrence, and fertility were studied. He noted a great range of variation between 10 and 29 μ. *A. spinosus* and *A. virdis* showed little variation with a range of 14 to 25 μ and 14 to 23 μ, respectively. The percentage fertility was very high in all cases, ranging between 82 and 98% with *A. hybridus* as the highest (98%) and *A. viridis* lowest. It was concluded that the genus *Amaranthus* is characterized by a great amount of homogenity in its chromosome number.

Amaranth grains are chiefly self-pollinated, although the stigma of the pistillate flowers is receptive several days prior to opening of the staminate flowers. In spite of the importance of this plant, it is surprising that there is very little work on its improvement. Opeke (1963) compared the characteristics of various local varieties and noted that there was a difference in susceptibility to a fungus disease which caused rotting.

Edema and Fakorede (1978) have pointed out that Nigeria is a center of diversity for most of the horticultural crops, collaborated by the prevalent use of local names and the enormous genetic diversity. In *Amaranthus*, for example, apart from the large number of species, the different species and varieties show several intermediate stages from wild to cultivated, especially with respect to seed production. Also in a given population there is a considerable amount of introgression. In *Amaranthus* and *Celosia* species there are great variabilities in leaf size, leaf shape, bolting pattern, growth and regrowth ability, number of economic branches, and color. There is, however, very little information on these. *A. viridis* var. *olorungbin*, which is unsuitable for cutting, is more preferred as a leaf vegetable to most other *Amaranthus* species and varieties (Van Epenhuiysen, 1974). Some highly similar varieties, some of which are wild, for example, var. *atetedaiye*, can become woody and have very small leaf productions. Some other species such as *A. cruentus*, *A. hybridus*, and *A. tricolor* which have better growth and regrowth ability are not as desirable. The situation occurs in *Celosia* species also.

Only the pale and white seeds are used as grain. Since the pale and colored forms cross in nature through wind pollination, growers tend to preserve their purity by sowing only the white seeds. The various species are reported to respond to changes in photoperiodism and thermoperiodism.

G. Postharvest Handling Methods

If harvesting is done for the leaves, it is traditional in west Africa to soak the whole plant in water before transporting it to the market for sale as this gives the leaves a fresh look. The leaves are arranged in bunches that are usually spread on a raffia tray in market stalls or else hawked about in the street. Since evaporation takes place rapidly, more more water is sprinkled on the leaves at intervals.

After harvest in Mexico, the seeds are traditionally stored in large cotton sacks. To keep out humidity these sacks are placed inside large plastic feed sacks. The seeds keep up to 10 years, and rats and pests cannot get to them; hence; this method offers a big advantage.

III. BIOCHEMICAL AND NUTRITIONAL COMPOSITION

A. Nutritional Composition Tables

Amaranth is one of the very few double-duty plants that can supply tasty leafy vegetables (even preferred to spinach by many people) as well as supply grains of high nutritional quality that can supplement the ammino acids found in a diet that is high in cereals (which are deficient in lysine) and legumes (which are deficient in the sulfur amino

Table 2 Essential Amono Acid Composition of Various Grains (% Protein)

Protein source	Protein (%)	Trp	Met/Cys	Thr	Isl	Ual	Lys	Phe/Tyr	Leu	LAA	EAA
FAO/WHO	—	1.0	3.5	4.0	4.0	5.0	5.5	6.0	7.0	—	—
Amaranth	15	1.4	4.4	2.9	3.0	3.6	5.0	6.4	4.7	67 (Leu)	85
Barley	9	1.2	3.2	3.2	4.0	4.7	3.2	8.2	6.5	58 (Lys)	90
Buckwheat	12	1.4	3.7	3.9	3.8	5.2	5.9	5.8	5.8	83 (Leu)	97
Corn	9	0.6	3.2	4.0	4.6	5.1	1.9	10.6	13.0	35 (Lys)	86
Oats	15	1.2	3.4	3.1	4.8	5.6	3.4	8.4	7.0	62(Lys)	92
Rice	7	1.0	3.0	3.7	4.5	6.7	3.8	9.1	8.2	69 (Lys)	94
Soybeans	34	1.4	3.1	3.9	5.4	5.3	6.3	8.7	7.7	89 (Met-Cys)	98
Wheat	14	1.2	3.5	2.7	4.1	4.3	2.6	8.1	6.3	47 (Lys)	—

Source: Senft (1980).

acids). The amino acid pattern of amaranth grain corresponds closely
to that of the Food and Agriculture Organization/World Health Organization (FOA/WHO) pattern for optimum human nutrition as shown in
Table 2. The grains contain an average protein content of 15%, which
is higher than that of any other cereals. The limiting amino acid is
leucine, with a protein score of 67, as opposed to lysine for the other
common grains with lower scores (except buckwheat). Earlier experiments by Subramanian and Scrinirasan (1952) indicated that the protein
efficiency ratio (PER) was comparable to that of casein, and this has
been supported by the recent trails in the Organic Gardening and
Farming Research Center in the United States and the Central Food
Technological Research Centre in India. In a series of animal experiments, Umoh et al. (1979) obtained a negative PER (-0.4), low biological
value (45 to 46) and net protein utilization (41.7) for *A. caudatus* seeds,
although the total digestibility was high (91.6). The corresponding
PER for *Celosia argentea* was very high (2.1) comparable to the control. The amino acid pattern showed that the amaranth seeds used
were very poor in methionine (0.27 g/16 gN) while those of *Celosia* are
high (1.9 g). Both seeds are high in lysine (5.69 and 4.5 g, respectively). The ratio of arginine plus lysine to proline is an indicator of
the protein utilization of plant foodstuffs. This ratio is about 4 for
rice protein whereas it is about 1 or less for most other cereals. In
contrast, it is 3.4 for amaranth, approaching that of rice, but the protein content of amaranth is about twice that of rice, which is an added
advantage.

The fat content of grain amaranth is about 5%, very similar to that
of maize but higher than other cereals. About 37% of the fat consists
of linoleic (with very little linolenic, 0.87%), 21% oleic, and 15%
palmitic, which indicate the good nutritional quality of the fat (Senft,
1980).

Table 3 compares the mineral content of amaranth grains with those
of other cereals (Schmidt, 1977). The table shows that amaranth is
exceptionally rich in calcium (150 mg%) and magnesium 327(mg%). This
is probably related to the high oxalate content of the plant.

Amaranth is probably the most delicious vegetable grown in Nigeria.
It is relished as vegetable soup, cooked by boiling and mixing with
condiments (pepper, crayfish, onions, palm oil, etc.). It is eaten
with pounded yam, cassava pudding (dodo), cooked beans, and so
forth. Oke (1967) estimated about 100 g is consumed a day. In Ilorin
(middle belt of Nigeria) harvesting is done as much as eight times, resulting in a high yield (Edema, 1979). It could represent about 50 to
80% of the total vegetables in the local market in the southern parts of
Nigeria.

According to Oke (1966) amaranth leaves are an excellent source
of protein (about 30% protein) and could contribute as much as 2 to 5%
of the daily requirement. It is also a very rich source of vitamin C
(420 mg%), iron (287 ppm), β-carotene (25 mg%), and calcium (2.1%).

Table 3 Mineral Element Concentration in Seeds of Seven Grain Crops

	Mineral (mg/100 g) [a]						
	Ca	Mg	Na	Fe	Cu	Mn	Zn
Amaranth, A-53	150	327	9	19.5	0.7	2.6	3.5
Amaranth, Red Top	123	263	6	8.2	0.5	1.7	3.2
Barley, DZ-02-72	46	123	16	6.5	0.7	1.6	2.2
Barley, Handeso	52	157	14	5.1	0.6	2.3	3.3
Triticale, Mex. 68-69	25	126	5	2.9	0.5	1.6	2.0
Wheat, 8156	41	128	5	4.4	0.5	3.0	2.0
Wheat, K4500 L6A4	30	134	5	3.0	0.3	2.1	1.8

[a]Seed samples were composited from crops grown with 0, 40, and 80 kg/ha of fertilizer N, and seeds were air-dried to approximately 10% moisture.
Source: Schmidt (1977).

B. Changes in Nutrient Composition

1. During Development

Oke (1966) reported that the percentage of dry matter of *C. argentea* increased with age. Starting with about 10% during the first week of planting, it increased to about 17% at 10 weeks. The increase in dry matter became significant after 4 weeks. The vitamin C content fluctuates during development but did not vary much. The oxalic acid content rose from an initial value of 10% in the first week to about 13% in the second week and then dropped finally to about 8% by the seventh week. The deleterious effect of oxalic acid could therefore be reduced if the vegetables were harvested after the seventh week. Stafford et al. (1976) reported that the protein content of *A. hybridus* decreased from 15% after 35 days of planting to about 12% after 70 days. A similar trend was obtained when N fertilizer was applied. However, the N content increased markedly from 15% with no fertilizer application to about 29% on application of 225 kg N/ha. Increasing the time before harvest from 49 to 63 days had a small effect on the protein and oxalate content, but it was decisive for the iron content which nearly doubled in amount during the extra 2 weeks of growth (from about 43 to 80 mg/100 g).

2. During Processing and Storage

Stafford et al. (1976) determined the ascorbic acid, iron, protein, and free oxalate content of the leaves of *A. hybridus* after comparing different methods of cooking and found that steaming or boiling for 10 min produced the least loss of nutrients. Under these conditions the ascorbic acid decreased from 153 to 87 mg%. Boiling for 10 min decreased the iron content from 7.2 to 3.7 mg%, but steaming did not affect the iron or free oxalate contents. When the chopped leaves were boiled for 15 min, the free oxalate decreased from 632 to 312 mg%. They therefore concluded that this method of cooking was preferable to the more traditional steaming so as to remove more of the oxalates potentially harmful to children and still retain sufficient nutrients. Scientists at the Rodale Experimental Kitchen found that it is best to cook the leaves with a minimum of water and in the shortest time possible to preserve the vitamins.

IV. PRODUCTS AND USES

A. Seeds and Flours

Amaranth seeds are so tiny that many tend to escape during grinding, and there is also the problem of grittiness or clogging. These problems are overcome by first toasting them lightly before grinding. The flour can be substituted for any whole-grain flour in the baking of foods that do not rise like pancakes, crepes, or cookies. However, if the product requires rising, as in the case of breads, cakes, or muffins, then about 15% of the flour can be substituted conveniently with amaranth flour.

Table 4 Combination of Grains to Improve Protein Quality

	Trp	Met/Cys	Thr	Isl	Val	Lys	Phe/Tyr	Leu
FAO/WHO	1.0	3.5	4.0	4.0	5.0	5.5	6.0	7.0
Amaranth	1.4	4.4	2.9	3.0	3.6	5.0	6.4	4.7
Rice	1.0	3.0	3.7	4.5	6.7	3.8	9.1	8.2
Amaranth:Rice (50:50)	1.2	3.7	3.3	3.8	5.2	4.4	7.8	6.5

The seeds are commonly used in the preparation of cakes or sweet meatballs which are prepared by binding the popped seeds in white or brown sugar syrup. A few recipes from Cole (1979) are given in the Appendix.

B. Leaf Products and Protein Concentrates

Oke (1978) reported utilizing amaranth and *Celosia* for the production of leaf protein concentrate (LPC). In a series of experiments to determine the extractability of LPC from various leaves, Fafunso and Oke (1977) extracted the protein using the IBP Pulper and Press (Davys and Pirie, 1969). The protein was precipitated by passing steam into the juice to give a final temperature of 80°C. The supernatant juice was filtered and the LPC washed with dilute acid. It was then filtered through a muslin bag and allowed to drain at room temperature for 2 days. Samples were then analyzed for nitrogen and digestibility.

The highest protein values were extracted from edible leaves such as *Amaranthus* (73.5%), *Celosia* (72.9%), and *Solanum* (71.4%). Most of the other leaves (most of which are not normally eaten) gave a range of 48 to 68%. Most of the nitrogen extracted in protein extracted in protein nitrogen, with a range of 73 to 90%.

The digestibility of the various LPCs compared with casein (94.6%), were 72.7% for *Amaranthus* and 71% for *Celosia* and cashew. The lowest figure obtained was 50.9% for cocoyam. A yield of about 5 to 10 tons/ha was obtained for amaranth and up to 20 tons/ha for *Celosia*. When the leaves are made into LPC using the IBP Pulper and Press (Davys and Pirie, 1969), the protein content is concentrated severalfold.

As with legumes, the percentage nitrogen in the dry matter and the protein nitrogen increased for up to 7 weeks and then dropped more steeply than with legumes. The total notrogen started to decrease after about 9 weeks. The percentage of nitrogen extracted was very high in vegetables, as high as 90% within 8 weeks of planting. Most of the total nitrogen extracted was true protein (80 to 90%) within 6 weeks of planting, and this decreased to low values (40 to 50%) in 11 weeks.

Details of the amino acid composition are given in Table 5. The amino acid pattern was the same in the different leaves, suggesting that protein of a uniform composition can be extracted from a wide variety of leaves. A comparison of the essential amino acid composition of LPC with other good-quality proteins, such as meat, eggs, cheese and milk, showed that only methionine was consistently lower in LPC (Table 6). Leucine and phenylalanine were occasionally higher while the rest of the amino acids were in favorable balance. Leaf protein contained more lysine than the best high-lysine corn and more methionine than soybean meal. The nonessential amino acids also occurred in a favorable balance, and there was sufficient of each to provide a well-balanced dietary protein.

Table 5 Essential Amino Acid Patterns of Four Nigerian Vegetables (g/100 g)

	Amaranthus caudatus	*Celesia argentea*	*Solanum modiflorum*	*Solanum incanum*
Threonine	5.08	4.95	5.17	5.10
Valine	6.09	6.16	6.12	6.18
Cystine	2.03	1.35	1.55	1.96
Methionine	2.19	2.13	1.76	2.11
Isoleucine	5.37	4.98	5.07	5.13
Leucine	9.51	9.06	9.66	9.07
Phenylalanine	6.06	6.12	6.42	6.04
Lysine	6.75	6.62	6.46	6.57

Source: Oke (1971).

One interesting aspect was that the amino acid patterns of different species of plants at different stages of maturity were very similar, inplying that the protein involved in photosynthesis is of uniform composition. Hence, they may be uniformly of high nutritive

Table 6 Essential Amino Acid Composition of Leaf Protein and Other Good-Quality Protein Sources[a]

	Amino Acid (g/100 g protein)							
	Lys	Phe	Met	Thr	Ileu	Leu	Val	Try
Leaf protein	6.3	6.0	2.1	5.2	9.8	5.3	6.3	1.6
Corn endosperm	3.6	4.5	2.1	3.7	10.5	3.8	5.7	—
Soybean meal	6.4	4.8	0.6	3.7	3.5	6.1	5.0	1.2
Meat, poultry, fish	8.1	4.9	3.3	4.6	7.7	6.3	5.8	1.3
Eggs	7.2	6.3	4.1	4.3	8.0	4.2	7.3	1.5
Milk	8.2	5.7	3.4	4.5	8.5	11.3	8.5	1.6

[a]Amino acid composition of feeds.
Source: FAO, Rome (1970).

value except for the marginal content of methionine. Even so, methionine can now be synthesized cheaply and, if an extreme case is taken in which leaf protein concentrate is supplemented with about 0.5 g/day of methionine, 1 kg (costs about £1.25) will last a person for about 5.5 years (McPherson, 1962).

In a series of feeding trials, Oke and his co-workers have shown that LPC from amaranth and *Celosia* are good sources of protein supplement for rabbits at 10% supplementation (Gbadebo and Oke, 1968), and for chicks at 75% supplementation plus 35% fish meal (Adegbola and Oke, 1973). Omole and Oke (1979a) have used the residual pulp from fractionation of *A. caudatus* as a replacement ration for corn in a rabbit diet, and the results compared with those of Brewer's dried grains (BDG) at levels of 0 to 30%. At the 10% level the daily weight gain (21.1 g) and food conversion ratio of the pulp (2.93) were comparable to the control (22.6 g and 2.90) and better than BDG (21.8 g and 2.98, respectively). Feed intake was similar at levels 0 to 20% but becomes significantly depressed at the 30% level. The liver and kidney weights were similar in all the treatments, but the kidney fat in the 30% level of both the pulp and BDG was significantly higher than those of the 0 to 10% level. There was a gradual reduction in dressing percentage from the control ration to the highest levels.

In another series of experiments Omole and Oke (1979b) fed growing rabbits with leaf protein (LP) from *A. caudatus*, and the performance was compared with fish meal (FM) and groundnut cake (GC) or any mixture of the two as the main protein source in the diet. The daily feed intake and weight gain (71.4 and 22.1 g) were significantly higher in the FM than in the GC or LP (59.4, 15,8, and 58.3, 17.49 g, respectively). The best result was obtained with FM-LP mixture which contributed 50% each of the supplementary protein. This was followed by the FM-GC. The performance of those on LP-GC was significantly lower than those of FM-LP or FM-GC but similar to those of LP or GC alone. Amino acid analysis showed that all the rations were deficient in the three essential amino acids—lysine, methionine, and arginine—required for optimal growth. The methionine content of the GC diet was particularly low, 0.05%, compared with the required 0.45%. The lysine content was also low, 0.38%, compared with 0.93% required. The amino acid pattern of the LP was very similar to that of FM. It was suggested that amino acid imbalance might be responsible for the poor results obtained.

The results obtained for these animal experiments were sufficiently encouraging to justify some clinical trials with leaf protein. As is well known, protein/calorie malnutrition (kwashiorkor) is widely prevalent in the developing countries, including Nigeria. It may be controlled mainly by the addition of protein (usually milk and synthetic proteins) to the diet, and the treatment of skin infections. Not all affected children can be treated in hospitals; the vast majority are sent home with nutrition advice and in some cases a diet sheet. The provision of animal protein is beyond the financial means of many parents and, in any case, there is a cultural reluctance to give meat and eggs to children. Furthermore, milk is believed to induce diarrhea in children who are lactose intolerant. There is therefore a need for a cheap, effective, and culturally acceptable form of protein supplement to overcome kwashiorkor.

An outpatient trial of feeding leaf protein supplements to 22 children with kwashiorkor was conducted, and the preliminary results are given here and reported in more detail elsewhere (Olatunbosun et al., 1972). Clinical diagnosis was established by the presence of peripheral edema, hair and skin changes, and mental apathy. The home diets to which the mothers were instructed to add the leaf protein powder consisted of maize gruel, yam flour pudding, cassava pudding, rice ewedu (*Corchorus clitorius*), and okra soup. The total dose of leaf protein was approximately 10 g/day (7 g protein). Chest infections when present were treated solely with tetracycline. Diarrhea was not treated.

The results showed that within 10 days edema dissappeared, the appetite improved, and the children became more mentally alert. There was a good increase in body weight in view of the fact that the children had to shed a lot of excess water originally accumulated as edema. The serum proteins and albumins also increased markedly. These results indicate that leaf protein supplements may prove to be cheap, effective, and culturally acceptable for the treatment and prevention of protein/calorie malnutrition.

In another series of experiments blood was taken from the femoral vein of 50 children suffering from protein-energy malnutrition (PEM) and analyzed for various parameters (Olusi and Oke, 1979). Control children were taken from the same group that had recovered from PEM. Some of the children were treated by adding leaf protein from *A. caudatus* to their diet to supply an additional 10 g of good protein per day. Apathy usually subsides within 2 weeks of treatment, followed by disappearance of edema.

The mean body weight of the control group was found to be significantly greater than that of the malnourished children. Although the mean hemoglobin concentration of the control children (10.86 g%) was significantly greater than those of the malnourished children, the difference between that of kwashiorkor and marasmus and also the various PCV values were not significant. Total serum protein was not significant among the groups, but serum albumin of control children (4.33 g%) was significantly higher than that of children with marasmus (2.85%). Very high values were obtained for the transferring of control children (343 μg%). Similar results were obtained for serum iron (109.0, 50,1, and 61.7 μg%, respectively).

The most important aspect of the work is the acceptability of the leaf protein concentrates. One advantage in Nigeria is that the villagers are used to taking maize gruel every morning with food mixture

ranging from black to dark green in color, and so the color of the leaf
protein should not be a major problem. Hence, a high supplementation
was acceptable with maize gruel, especially with farmers. It seems the
older they are, the higher the supplementation they can tolerate.
Virtually all the food prepared for lunch and supper is taken with
green vegetable stew which contains many other condiments such as
crayfish, locust beans, peppers, tomatoes, and so forth. The product
has the appearance of a green mass of leaves. Occasionally palm oil is
used. In some cases the pepper soup is cooked separately and a little
bit of it is added to the vegetable soup. Vegetable soups therefore
afford a good medium for supplementation as long as the supplementation does not exceed 60% and there is no change in taste or color.
With certain foodstuffs, especially those that are colored red by palm
oil (e.g., jolloff rice), the green color and gritty feel may create
difficulties with respect to acceptability, but conservation of food
habits is not only a Nigerian problem.

V. PROBLEMS ASSOCIATED WITH AMARANTH

A question often asked is, Why has amaranth been surplanted by the
less nutritious barley and maize in which about 50% of the kernel protein is nondigestible by monogastric animals such as humans? The
first disadvantage is that amaranth seeds are very small, about 1 mm
in diameter. Early seedlings growth from tiny seeds is relatively slow
and weak compared with larger-seeded cereals. Small seeds necessitate rather shallow planting, and on sloping land there is the danger
of being displaced or carried away if heavy rainfall preceded germination and seedling establishment. On the other hand, the small size
may have an economic advantage over the large-seeded conventional
cereals. For example, if 10,000 amaranth seeds weigh 7 g, it would
take about 311 g to plant a hectare at the dense planting of only
225 cm^2 per plant, whereas under the same condition 178 kg (about
600 times as much) maize seeds would be needed (Haptuli, 1977). This
also means that only a miniscule portion of the yield needed to be
saved for future planting, and this becomes even more negligible if
one considers that the yield of amaranth surpasses that of maize and
compares well with other agronomic crops in the United States as shown
in Table 7 by Haptuli (1977).
    The second disadvantage is that the seeds very loosely attached to
the stock are very difficult to handle or harvest mechanically. They
are attacked by birds and scatter when mature, hence they must be
harvested before maturity to minimize losses. It is therefore not surprising that amaranth has been displaced by larger cereals.
    Another reason for the diminished use of amaranth was its cultural
suppression by the Catholic church during the Spanish colonial period

Table 7 Comparative Yields of Grains and Amaranths in 1974

	U.S. average yield (kg/hectare)	World average yield (kg/hectare)
Barley	2000	1910
Oats	1700	1600
Corn	4500	2400
Rice (rough)	5100	2300
Rye	1350	1740
Wheat	1800	1560
Soybean	1580	1370
Amaranth	683-3900 (this report) Weedy Amarantho-typus—same range as cultivated 800-500 (other reports)	

Source: USDA, *Agricultural Statistics* (1974).

in order to eradicate the pagan cermonies of the Aztecs in which these cereals played a central role. At these cermonies the Aztecs mixed blood from human sacrifice with amaranth seed paste and formed it into idols which were distributed to the worshippers. As a result of the church's disapproval, the grain almost disappeared from use in Mexico.

VI. RESEARCH NEEDED

Probably the area in need of most improvement is still getting the word out in order to encourage more research and more use. In general it is lysine that is limiting in cereals, resulting in a low biological value. However, in some of these unconventional cereals, especially amaranth, because of the small size most of the seed volume is occupied by the embryo, and this might account for their unusually high lysine content (Nelson, 1969). This factor may then make it easier for plant breeders to breed varieties of higher nutritional quality. At present there are few plant breeding experiments, and yet there are many varieties with different yields, protein content, height, and so forth. The yields especially are very uneven due to lack of proper selection; some yield about four to five times the others, which should give plant breeders a good opportunity for proper selection for different altitudes and rainfall regions. Similarly, the protein

content of the different varieties ranges from 12.9 to 17.2% which would
make selection easier. Both intraspecific and interspecific crossbreeding
should be attempted. The plasticity (i.e., ability to provide some kind
of yields in a wide range of enviroment) in *Amaranthus* can be exploited
by geneticists to make them respond to added inputs by producing more
tillers, spikelets, flowers, and hence more seeds (Haptuli, 1977). However, this still needs to be described and the factors that cause changes
in biomass allocation studied. In order to be able to study and understand labor requirements, rotation, and cropping patterns of amaranth,
it will be necessary to document the traditional methods of cultivation,
harvesting, and yield under the different agronomic treatments and
climatic zones. Since seed shedding or shattering is a major disadvantage, it will be necessary to breed a nonshattering variety and also
protection factors from birds and other pests.

An important step for further amaranth research is the establishment
of a germ plasm collection for genetic studies, trials in new locations,
and the implementation of an intensive plant-breeding program (USAS,
1975). Apart from selecting the high-yielding varieties with large seeds
for easy packaging, it must also have a high-protein content, balanced
amino acid pattern, and be nutritious and acceptable to people. The
composition of many varieties is not even known nor the nutritional
value. *A. edulis* has been reported to be very rich in lysine, and thus
it is important to findout the reason for this as a step towards breeding
the high-lysine variety of the other grains. The different methods of
utilization should be further documented, especially in India and Latin
America, and methods of imporving on the losses due to processing
verified; at the same time, new methods of preservation should also be
looked into. In view of the above it is probably not suprising that
amaranth has not yet become an economic crop.

VII. FUTURE OUTLOOK

Amaranth is a very cheap crop during the rainy season but becomes
expensive during the dry season. In spite of this many farmers still
look on the more sophisticated temperate vegetables which yield higher
prices. It is now being realized that unless many of these wild or semi-
wild species are cultivated and improved by modern breeding techniques,
many of the useful species that are well adapted to their climatic conditions may be lost. Work is in progress at certain institutions, notably
the University of Ife, International Institute for Tropical Agriculture
(IITA), and the National Hortitute for Tropical Agricultural Research
Institute. In the United States most of the work is in progress at the
Organic Gardening and Farming Research Center.

If research emphasis is shifted a little bit now to such pseudocereals
as amaranth, more food and protein will be supplied to the tropical areas
where protein is in short supply. If in the past enough research on

pseudocereals had been accomplished comparable to that of the major cereals, there would today be better yields, especially of those that can easily adapt to extreme climates like amaranth. These pseudo-cereals would also possess the usual cereal characteristics of bland taste, reasonable bulkiness, ease of cooking, lack of antinutritive factors, good keeping qualities, sufficient blend of minerals and vitamins, and a favorable ND_pCal greater than 5% (Kaul, 1975).

The recognition of amaranth as a valuable food source by Rodale Incorporation in the United States is an excellent beginning. Through such research efforts we hopefully will see the day when amaranth will regain its rightful place among the major cereal crops. Research efforts on improving the production of cereals in the past decade have resulted in a breakthrough referred to as the Green Revolution. At about the same time plant breeders were also searching for genes that could improve both the quality and quantity of major cereal proteins and thereby improve their biological value. This trend has obscured rather than developed the potentials of minor crops. I would like to conclude by advocating that this systematic research now be extended to amaranth as well.

APPENDIX

Amaranth Yogurt Pancakes

1 cup yogurt	1/2 cup unbleached flour
1/4 cup water	1/4 cup whole-wheat flour
1 teaspoon baking soda	1/4 cup amaranth flour
1 egg	Fresh strawberry
1 tablespoon vegetable oil	pancake topping

Combine yogurt, water, and baking soda. Beat together egg and oil, and add to yogurt mixture. Add flour and stir in lightly. Bake on a hot, oiled griddle. Serve with fresh strawberry pancake topping. Yields 12 3-in. pancakes.

Oatmeal and Amaranth Cereal

4 cups water	2 tablespoons wheat germ,
1 cup oatmeal, regular	untoasted
1/2 cup amaranth flour	2 tablespoons sesame seeds,
1/2 cup raisins	untoasted
1 tablespoon honey	1/4 teaspoon cinnamon milk for
1 tablespoon sorghum molasses	serving

Bring water to boil in a 2-quart saucepan. Stir oatmeal into boiling water. Add amaranth flour and raisins. Cook for 10 to 15 min, until the oatmeal is tender. Add honey, molasses, wheat germ, sesame seeds and cinnamon. Serve warm, with milk. Yields four servings.

Amaranth Bread

3 cups whole-wheat flour
2 envelopes dry yeast
1/4 cup carob powder
1/4 cup wheat germ
1/4 cup Brewer's yeast

2 cups water
1/3 cup unsulfured molasses
2 tablespoons butter
1-1/2 teaspoons honey
2 cups ground amaranth flour

In a large mixing bowl, combine 2 cups flour, yeast, carob powder, wheat germ, and Brewer's yeast. In saucepan combine water, molasses, butter, and honey; heat on stove until butter melts. Let cool slightly and gradually add to dry mixture, stirring by hand.

Slowly add the amaranth and remaining whole-wheat flour to make a soft dough. Turn onto a floured board and knead until soft. Cover dough ball with mixing bowl and let rest for 20 min. Punch down and divide dough in half.

Roll out, fold, and shape into two loaves, then place in greased loaf pans. Place in unlit oven with a pan of hot water and let rise until it doubles (about 1 hr). Remove water pan and bake at 400°F for 30 min. Remove from pans to wire racks to cool, covering with a clean cloth for tender crust. Yields two loaves.

Amaranth Corn Muffins

2/3 cup whole-wheat flour
1/3 cup soy flour
2/3 cup corn flour
1/3 cup amaranth flour
1 tablespoon baking powder
1/4 cup honey

1 cup coarsely chopped cran-
  berries, blueberries, or
  raspberries
1 cup milk
1/3 cup melted butter
2 eggs

Grease 12 muffin cups. Combine flour with baking powder in a large bowl. Add honey to berries and add to flour mixture.

Measure milk in 2-cup measure. Add melted butter and eggs; beat with fork to mix well. Mix well in center of flour mixture. Pour in milk mixture all at once, Stirring quickly with a fork just until dry ingredients are moistened. The batter should be lumpy. Quickly fill muffin cups with batter to about two-thirds full. Bake 25 min at 400°F or until golden brown. Yields 12 muffins.

Amaranth Three-Flavor Consumme

3 tablespoons toasted and ground
  amaranth grain
A large handful of shredded,
  young amaranth greens

4 cups boiling water
1 tablespoon tamari soy sauce
2 tablespoons or more popped
  amaranth

Pour boiling water over ground amaranth. Cover and remove from heat. After 10 min, strain and bring to a boil again. Add the greens.

Remove from heat, stir in tamari soy sauce, and sprinkle with popped amaranth. This is an invigorating, delicate first course. Yields three to four servings.

Efo Soup, Nigerian style

Pluck the amaranth leaves, cut into small pieces, wash thoroughly with cold water and drain. Pour boiling water the washed leaves and add a small quantity of salt. Let stand for a few minutes.

Meanwhile, place ground pepper, tomatoes, and onions into a saucepan. Add dried fish and water. Cook for about 15 min. Drain the leaves and squeeze out the excess water. Rinse with cold water, squeeze, and then add the leaves to the sauce in the saucepan. Cook gently until the leaves are tender, add palm oil, salt to taste, rice thoroughly, and leave to simmer until the oil is cooked (i.e., until its raw smell has completely disappeared).

Efo with Melon Seeds

Pluck amaranth leaves and cut into pieces. Wash in cold water and drain. Pour boiling water over washed leaves, add salt, and let stand for a few minutes. Drain and squeeze. Mix ground melon seeds with small quantity of cold water to make a stiff paste. Make sauce in saucepan as above using pepper, onions, canned and fresh tomatoes, and water. To this sauce add ground dried shrimp; simmer for 4 min, and gradually add the melon paste. Add water to cover mixture. Simmer for 15 min. Add the meat or fish. Mix thoroughly and simmer until the meat is well cooked. Add the leaves, salt to taste, then add palm oil. Cover and simmer gently for about 40 min or until oil is cooked.

The main use in Mexico now is in the preparation of alegrias which are little cakes of popped seeds, bound with syrup. The Mexicans also prepare a pleasant drink called atole from the roasted and powdered seeds, mixed with syrup and water. In India the seeds are boiled with rice which makes it almost an ideal food as shown in Table 4, since the amino acid of amaranth compliments that of rice in lysine content while the high content of leucine in rice compliments the low content in *Amaranthus*. The combination therefore approaches better that of the FAO/WHO pattern. In Nepal the seeds are parched, ground into flour, and eaten as gruel with milk or water.

REFERENCES

Adegbola, A. A., and Oke, O. L. (1973). Preliminary observation on the use of leaf protein-fishmeal mixture as supplement for pullets. *Nutr. Rep. Int.* 8:313-318.

Buchanana, R. A., and Byers, M. (1969). Effect of storage and lipid extraction on the properties of leaf protein. *J. Sci. Fd. Agric.* 20:359-363.

Cole, J. N. (1979). *Amaranth,* 1st ed., Emmaus, Pa., Rodale Press, p. 311.

Davys, M. N. G., and Pirie, N. W. (1969). A laboratory scale pulper for leafy plant material. *Biotech. Bioengng.* 11:517-528.

Denton, A. (1979). Personal communication.

Deuton, W. J. S. (1973). *Amaranthis edulis:* a high lysine grain amaranth. *World Crops* 25:20-25.

Early, D. (1977). Amaranth, secretes of the Aztecs. *Organic Gardening* 24:69-73.

Edema, A. A. O. (1979). Personal communication.

Edema, A. A. O., and Fakorede, M. A. B. (1978). *First Ann. Conf. Hort. Soc., Nigeria Proc.*, Ibadan, Nigeria.

Enyi, B. A. C. (1965). Effect of age of seedling height and frequency of cutting growth and yield of African spinach (*Amaranthus oleracena*). *Nig. Agric. J.* 2:35-59.

Epenhuijsen van, C. N. (1974). *Growing Native Vegetable in Nigeria.* Rome, FAO, United Nations.

Fafunso, M. A., and Oke, O. L. (1977). Leaf protein from several varieties of cassava. *Nutr. Rep. Int.* 14:353.

Gbadebo, S. A., and Oke, O. L. (1968). The use of leaf protein as rabbit feed. Unpublished B.Sc. dissertation University of Ife, Nigeria.

Grubben, G. J. H. (1976). *Cultivation of Amaranth as a Tropical Leaf Vegetable.* Amsterdam, Dept. of Agric. Ros of Royal Tropical Institute, Comm. 67.

Haptuli, H. (1977). Agronomic potential and breeding strategy for growth amaranth. *Proc. First Amaranth Seminar,* Emmaus, Pa., Rodale Press.

Hatch, M. D., and Slack, C. R. (1970). The C_4-dicarboxylic pathway of photosynthesis. *Prog. Phytochem.* 2:35-51.

Kaul, A. K. (1975). *Food protein sources. IBP Handbook No. 4* (N. W. Pirie, ed.). London, Cambridge University Press.

Kogbe, J. O. S. (1978). Studies on the manurial requirements of Nigerian local leafy vegetable. Effects of poultry manure on the yield and components of yield of amaranth (*Amaranthus candatus*). *Nig. Agric. J.* 13:84-92.

Martin, F. W., and Roberts, R. M. (1977). *Edible Leaves of the Tropics.* Mayaguez, Puerto Rico, Antillian College Press.

MacMasters, M. M., and Baird, P. D., Holzapfed, M. M., and Rist, C. E. (1955). Preparation of starch from *Amaranthus cruentus* seeds. *Econ. Bot.* 9:300-302.

McClugage, H. B., and Mende, L. B. (1981). Mechansim of $C4$ photosynthesis. *J. Biol. Chem.* 35:353-357.

McPherson. A. T. (1962). The synthesis of food. *Fd. Technol.* 16:34-38.

Misra, P. S., Pal, M., Mitra, C. R., and Khoshoo, T. N. (1971). Chemurgic studies on some diploid and tetraploid grain amaranths. *Proc. Ind. Acad. Sci.* 74(3):155-160.

Oke, O. L. (1966). Chemical changes in some Nigerian vegetables during growth. *W. Afr. Pharm.* 3:122-125.

Oke, O. L. (1967). Chemical studies on some Nigerian vegetables. *J. W. Afr. Sci. Assoc.* 11:42-45.

Oke, O. L. (1970). Leaf protein. In *IPB Handbook No. 20.* London, Blackwell.

Oke, O. L. (1971). Some aspects of amino acid composition of leaf proteins. *Ind. J. Nutr. Diet.* 8:121-125.

Oke, O. L. (1973). Leaf protein research in Nigeria, a review. *Trop. Sci.* 15:139-155.

Oke, O. L. (1978). Leaf protein in Nigeria, past, present and future. *Report to Christian Aid.* London.

Oke, O. L. (1979). Unpublished work.

Olatunbosun, D. A., Adadevoh, B. K., and Oke, O. L. (1972). Leaf protein—a new protein source for the management of protein—energy malnutrition in Nigeria. *Nig. Med. J.* 2:195-199.

Olusi, O. O. (1979). Studies on amaranth. Unpublished B.Sc. dissertation, University of Ife, Nigeria.

Olusi, S. O., and Oke, O. L. (1979). The effect of cyanogenic glucosides in the reporduction and neonatal development in rats. *Biol. Neonates* 36:233-236.

Omole, T. A., and Oke, O. L. (1979a). The use of leaf protein concentrate as rabbit feed. *Nutr. Rep. Int.* (in press).

Omole, T. A., and Oke, O. L. (1979b). The evaluation of leaf protein fibrous residue as rabbit feed. *Nutr. Rep. Int.* (in press).

Opeke, L. K. (1963). Final report of the vegetable breeding programme of the research division of Moore Plantation, Ibadan, Nigeria.

Pal, M., and Khoshoo, T. N. (1974). Evolution and improvement of cultivated amaranth. *vii.* cytogenetic relationships in vegetable amaranths. *Theor. Appl. Genetics* 43:241-251.

Schmidt, D. R. (1971). Comparative yields and composition of eight tropical leafy vegetables grown at two fertility levels. *Agron. J.* 63:546-550.

Schmidt, D. (1977). Grain amaranth. A look at some potentials. *Proc. First Amaranth Seminar.* Emmaus, Pa., Rodale Press.

Senft, J. P. (1980). Personal communication.

Singh, H. (1961). Grain amaranths, buchwheat and chenopods. *India Council of Agricultural Research Cereal Crop Series No. 1,* New Delhi.

Stafford, W. L., Mugerwa, J. S., and Bwabye, R. (1976). Effects of methods of cooking, application of nitrogen fertilizer and maturity on certain nutrients in the levels of *Amaranthus hybridus. Pl. Fd. Man* 2:7-13.

Subramanian, N., and Sriniransan, M. (1952). Vegetable protein from a new source *A. Paniculatis* L. *Proc. Soc. Biol. Chem. India* 10:25-26.

Umoh, I. B., and Oke, O. L. (1974). Nutritive value of leaf protein. A note on *in vitro* and *in vivo* methods. *Nutr. Rep. Int.* 9:453-456.

Umoh, I. B., Ayalogu, E. O., and Oke, O. L. (1979). Evaluation of seeds of amaranth, celosia and cochorus as animal feed. *Nutr. Rep. Int.* (in press).

United States Academy of Science (1975). Underexploited tropical plants with promising economic value. Washington, D.C. National Academy of Science.

Wilson, G. F. (1971). Rood crop report. *Annual Report IITA*, Ibadan, Nigeria.

Wilson, G. F. (1979). Personal communication.

Wilson, G. F., and Curfs, H. P. (1977). Cost of production and estimated income from celosia under tow production systems. *West Ind. J. Agric.* 7:36-38.

2

Aroid Root Crops: Alocasia, Cyrtosperma, and Amorphophallus

William S. Sakai College of Agriculture, University of Hawaii at Hilo, Hilo, Hawaii

I. INTRODUCTION

The most important aroid root crops are probably *Colocasia* and *Xanthosoma*. However, the three genera *Alocasia*, *Cyrtosperma*, and *Amorphophallus* are very important in some areas of the world.

Alocasia, Cyrtosperma and *Amorphophallus* also have the genetic potential of disease resistance and physiology for growth in areas unsuitable for cultivation of *Colocasia* and *Xanthosoma*.

Alocasia appears to be very resistant to insects and disease (although some wild forms are very acrid, the cultivar of New Guinea origin is reported to be very low in acridity). This crop can be grown in areas too dry for most *Colocasia* cultivars. The perennial growth and the above-ground stem make it possible to harvest *Alocasia* in the off-season of other crops. Production is comparable to that of other aroid root crops if fertilized and grown for at least 18 months.

Cyrtosperma is also very resistant to insects and disease, and some forms are also low in acridity. This crop can be grown in deeper water than *Colocasia*, and some forms are also reported to grow in brackish water that kills *Colocasia*. Production compares favorably with other aroid root crops, and some of the fast-maturing cultivars can be harvested annually. The perennial growth of *Cyrtosperma* also makes it possible to harvest it during the off-season of other crops such as breadfruit.

Amorphophallus campanulatus is also reported to be very resistant to insects and disease, and most cultivated forms are low in acridity. Some cultivars apparently have much higher levels of protein than all other aroid root crops. Carbohydrate levels are comparable to other aroids, and carotene content is much higher. This crop can be grown in areas too dry for most *Colocasia* cultivars, and production levels appear to be equal to or greater than *Colocasia* or *Xanthosoma* if proper irrigation and fertilization are used.

A. rivieri, A. oncophyllus, and *A. variabilis* are mostly grown for the glucomannan which has industrial uses and forms the Japanese food konnyaku. Although konnyaku is of questionable or low-nutrient value, it may be of use in low-calorie foods. The liquid fiber nature of konnyaku in the diet may also be of value in lowering plasma cholesterol and glucose levels.

II. ALOCASIA

A. Introduction

1. Origin and Distribution

The genus *Alocasia* (Schott) G. Don. is a member of the subfamily Colocasioideae of the family Araceae (Plucknett, 1976b). *Colocasia* and *Xanthosoma* are also included in this subfamily. *Alocasia* is composed of about 75 species, all of tropical Asia. In the early literature two species were reported, *Alocasia macrorrhiza* (L.) Schott. from Malaysia to the Pacific and *Alocasia indica* Schott. from India to Malaysia. However, these are now classified as *A macrorrhiza* (L.) G. Don. var. *macrorrhiza* and *A. macrorrhiza* (L.) G. Don. var. *violacea,* respectively (Bailey et al., 1976). Another species,

A. cucullata (Lour.) G. Don. is in limited cultivation in India
(Coursey, 1968).

A. macrorrhiza probably originated in Sri Lanka or India (Plucknett,
1976b) and spread eastward as far as the Marquesas Islands in the
Pacific. In historic times it was introduced into South America (Plowman, 1969). It is commonly grown in upland areas, high islands, or
drier areas of atolls. The principal cultivation areas are India,
Bangladesh, and Sri Lanka in Asia and Wallis, Futuna, Tonga, and
Samoa in the Pacific.

2. Description and Common Names

A. macrorrhiza (L.) G. Don. is composed of several varieties differing
primarily in degree of irritation (acridity) and coloration. A general
description (Fig. 1) is as follows: large perennial herb, commonly
1.8 m (6 ft) but up to 4.6 m (15 ft) in height; leaves commonly 1.8 to
2.1 m (6 to 7 ft) long; blades erect or spreading, ovate, sagittate with
rounded basal lobes, commonly 0.6 to 0.9 m (2 to 3 ft) long; petioles,
sheathing in basal half, commonly 0.9 to 1.2 m (3 to 4 ft) long, arranged
spirally on stem; stem, upright, cylindrical, to 1.8 cm (6 ft) or more
in length, commonly 15 to 20 cm (6 to 8 in.) in diameter; inflorescence

Figure 1 *Alocasia macrorrhiza* planted between coconut trees in Tonga.
Plants are probably of the Tonga-Wallis-Futuna cultivar. (Photograph
courtesy of P. Rotar, University of Hawaii.)

with spathe and spadix 23 to 26 cm (9 to 19 in.) long on peduncle to 31 cm (1 ft) long; var. *macrorrhiza* leaf blades, upper surface medium green, lower surface paler, with midrib and main veins greenish cream; var. *violacea* leaf baldes, pale violet (Brown, 1931; Furtado, 1941; Massal and Barrau, 1955; Pancho, 1959; Kay, 1973; Bailey et al., 1976).

Alocasia can be distinguished vegetatively from *Amorphophallus* by the entire leaf, from *Colocasia* by the sagittate leaves, from *Xanthosoma* by the absence of a prominent marginal vein, and from *Cyrtosperma* by the rounded basal lobes (Coursey, 1968).

The large perennial growth of *A. macrorrhiza* is shown in its common English name—giant taro (Kay, 1973). Other common names include: India—alti, arvi, ghuivan (Srivastava, 1972); Sri Lanka—desai ala (Soyza, 1938); Bangladesh—maan kachu (Qudrat-I-Khuda et al., 1960; Plucknett, 1970; Chowdhury and Hussain, 1979; Rashid and Daunicht, 1979); Japan—dokuimo (Doi, 1944); Malaysia—bira-bira, keladi sebaring, senteh (Furtado, 1940); Indonesia—sente or birah (Plucknett, 1970; Sastrapradja, 1970), kei or wire (Barrau, 1957); Philippines—biga (Allen, 1929; Valenzuela and Wester, 1930; Quisumbing, 1951; Plucknett, 1970); Republic of Belau, Palau—biisch or bisech (Barrau, 1957; Migvar, 1968; de la Cruz, 1970); Sonsorol, Pulo Ana, and Merir—morui (McKnight and Obak, 1960); Federated States of Micronesia, Yap Island—lai (Barrau, 1957; Migvar, 1968; de la Cruz, 1970); Ulithi Atoll—fole (Barrau, 1961); Truk-ka (Barrau, 1957; Migvar, 1968; de la Cruz, 1970); Ponape—oht (Glassman, 1952; Massal and Barrau, 1955; de la Cruz, 1970; Lambert, 1970); Kapingamarangi and Nukuoro Atoll—ngaungau (Mahony, 1960b); Kosrae—onnak (Mahony, 1960b); Commonwealth of the Northern Marianas Islands—papau (Migvar, 1968; de la Cruz, 1970) or piga (Barrau, 1957); Marshall Islands Government—wot (Barrau, 1957; Migvar, 1968; de la Cruz, 1970); Papua New Guinea—abir or weriak (Barrau, 1957); Mortlock Islands (Takau or Marqueen Islands)—tekape (Boag and Curtis, 1959); New Caledonia—wave or pindu (Massal and Barrau, 1955; Lambert, 1970); Loyalty Islands—kape (Massal and Barrau, 1955; Lambert, 1970); Republic of Kiribati, Gilbert Islands—kabe or kapi (Luomala, 1974); Fiji—viagaga or viamila (Parham, 1942; Massal and Barrau, 1955; Lambert, 1970); Wallis and Futuna—kape (Massal and Barrau, 1955; Lambert, 1970; Lambert, 1979); Tonga—Kape (Yuncker, 1959; Lambert, 1979); Western Samoa and American Samoa—ta'amu (migvar, 1968; Lambert, 1970); Cook Islands—kape (Lambert, 1970); French Polynesia, Tahiti—ape (Massal and Barrau, 1955; Lambert, 1970); Marquesas Islands—kape (Brown, 1931); Hawaiian Islands—'ape (Neal, 1965); Guyana—hog tannia (Kay, 1973); and Brazil—inhame gigante or toyoea (Plowman, 1969; Kay, 1973).

B. Cultivation Practices

1. Climatological and Soil Conditions

A. macrorrhiza is a tropical species in which temperatures below 10°C (50°F) have been reported to reduce growth (Kay, 1973). It can not

withstand being waterlogged or prolonged drought and grows well
under high rainfall which is evenly distributed throughout the year
(Kay, 1973). In Bangladesh and Sri Lanka it is adaptable to soils
that are well drained (Ahmed and Rashid, 1975) but too wet for cassava or sweet potato (Soyza, 1938). In the Federated States of
Micronesia on Truk and Ponape Islands it is found wild at higher elevations growing among breadfruit or banana (Mahony, 1960a). On
Ngatik, Monkil, and Pinelap Atolls, it grows best in rocky soils next
to dead trees (Mahony, 1960b). And in Wallis and Futuna, on Uvea,
it is cultivated in newly cleared soil with yams (*Dioscorea*) (Kirch,
1978). In general, *Alocasia* grows best in soils too wet for many crops,
but not swampy soil, where *Colocasia* or *Cyrtosperma* might grow
better. *Xanthosoma* and some forms of *Colocasia* can also be grown in
those areas suitable for *A. macrorrhiza*.

2. Cultivars

In the Malaysian-Pacific region, several varieties exist, but only two
are commonly eaten: (a) the first type is probably of Tonga, Wallis,
and Futuna origin (Barrau, 1961; Migvar, 1968), the leaves are green,
the corm flesh is white, and the plant is almost acridfree; (b) the
second type is reported to be of New Guinea origin and brought to
Samoa by the Germans (Varrau, 1961; Migvar, 1968), blades and
petioles are purple-green (Barrau, 1957), the corm flesh is pink
(Watson, 1979), and it is even less acrid than the first type (Migvar,
1968). Several varieties with yellow-green leaves are also eaten in
Samoa, but require special cooking methods to remove the acridity
(Betham, 1982). Other inedible varieties such as chaanu from Truk
(Mahony, 1960a) and eliiche from Palau (McKnight and Obak, 1960)
occur wild in more areas than the two major edible types are grown
in and probably account for the poor reputation of *Alocasia*. These
very acrid wild types, when harvested in times of famine, require
very thorough cooking with several changes of water. On Truk the
edible type of *Alocasia* is considered very tasty and is preferred to
Colocasia (Mahony, 1960a).

In Sri Lanka, eight edible varieties are reported to be grown.
Desai ala, the most commonly grown type, and the two others have
green blades and petioles, three varieties have purplish-green blades
and petioles, and two varieties have mottled petioles (Soyza, 1938).

3. Planting

A. macrorrhiza is usually propagated asexually. It does not commonly
form lateral branches and is propagated by use of: (a) shoot tips
with a few inches of stem and rolled up young leaves; (b) sections of
stem containing two or three buds (Soyza, 1938; Coursey, 1968), less
commonly suckers or offsets (Ahmed and Rashid, 1975). *A. macrorrhiza*
is a perennial and is not seasonal in growth. Planting and harvesting
can take place year around. In Futuna where *A. macrorrhiza* is grown

with yam (*Dioscorea*) to provide stake support for the yam vines, it is planted at the same time as the yam and harvested after 1-1/2 years (Kirch, 1978). In Sri Lanka it is planted in February or July and harvested in December (Soyza, 1938), and in India it is planted in June and harvested in the winter rainy season (Srivastava, 1972). A 6-month-old crop in Bangladesh planted in late March and harvested in late September was reported to have made very little growth and had not reached the harvestable stage (Ahmed and Rashid, 1975).

The shoot tips may simply be planted in the soil to a depth of 10 to 15 cm (4 to 6 in.), or they may be planted in individual mounds. These mounds are prepared by digging a 31-cm (12-in.) diameter hole 20 to 26 cm (8 to 10 in.) deep, filling three-fourths full with compost from *Hibiscus* or legume plants, and making a mound of soil over the hole (Migvar, 1968). In Sri Lanka coconut husk is used as the filling compost (Soyza, 1938). Spacing varies from scattered when interplanted with yam to 0.9 × 0.9 m (3 × 3 ft) in Micronesia (Migvar, 1968); 0.6 to 1.2 m (2 to 4 ft) in Sri Lanka (Soyza, 1938); and 0.6 × 0.6 m (2 × 2 ft) in Bangladesh (Ahmed and Rashid, 1975).

In the Wallis, Futuna, and Samoa area, interplanting with yam (*Dioscorea*) is a common practice. In the Futunan technique yams and *Alocasia* are planted in the central garden area with bananas as a border. After 7 to 8 months the yams are harvested and bananas are planted in place of the yams. After 1½ years the *Alocasia* is harvested. After subsequent harvesting of bananas the area is allowed to regenerate (Kirch, 1978). If *Colocasia* or *Xanthosoma* is planted in place of the *Alocasia* or along with the *Alocasia*, harvesting is after 6 to 10 months for *Colocasia* and 2 years for *Xanthosoma* (Kirch, 1978). In some areas *Colocasia*, sweet potato, or cassava may be planted after harvesting the yam, and several crops of cassava may be harvested before allowing the land to lay fallow to regenerate (Maude, 1970).

4. Nutrition, Weeds, Pests, and Pathogens

Only the organic compost present at planting is used as fertilizer in most of the Malaysian-Pacific area. In the Federated States of Micronesia on Ponape, it is often planted next to dead trees used to support yams (Mahony, 1960b), and on Lukunor Atoll it is known that *Alocasia* grows well when planted where breadfruit trees were cut down for lumber or canoes (Mahony, 1960a). In Tonga the land is allowed to lay fallow between cropping. In areas fallow for 1 to 3 years the fallow vegetation consists of grasses, other herbaceous plants, and shrubs such as lantana (*Lantana camara*) and guava (*Psidium guajava*). When the fallow period is 4 years or more *Hibiscus tiliaceus* and *Rhus simarubaefolia* may grow (Maude, 1970). The longer fallow period usually produces better crops.

In a fertilizer requirement trial conducted in India nitrogen applied at 89.6 and 47.8 kg/ha (80 lb/acre and 40 lb/acre) significantly increased yields at two locations. Phosphorus and potassium at 33.6 and 67.2 kg/ha (30 and 60 lb/acre) had no effect on yield over the 0 kg/ha level (Srivastava, 1972).

Alocasias are considered to be very hardy plants and are resistant to most pests and diseases (Soyza, 1938; Murai et al., 1958; Kay, 1973; Plucknett, 1976b). It has been suggested that when planted with coconut, root secretions from the *Alocasia* may keep away white ants which commonly do considerable damage to coconut seedlings (Soyza, 1938). In India an unidentified bacterial leaf-spot disease has been reported to do considerable damage (Asthana, 1946). In the Philippines a beetle of the family Chrysomlidae eats round holes in the leaves (Quisumbing, 1914). When grown as an ornamental plant in Florida, *Alocasia* is susceptible to root-knot nematode, red spider, mealy bug, and the fungus *Colletotrichum philodendri*, which causes ringlike spotting on older leaves during cool, rainy weather (Reark, 1953).

5. Harvesting and Yields

Because *Alocasia* grows year around, harvesting can take place at any time. In the Wallis and Futuna, Tonga, and Samoa areas the stems are usually harvested after 18 to 24 months, but may be allowed to grow for up to 4 years. These corms are 1 to 1.3 m (3 to 4 ft) in length, about 15 to 20 cm (6 to 8 in.) in diameter, and weigh about 18.2 kg (40 lb) (Coursey, 1968, Plucknett, 1970; Watson, 1979). If spacing is 0.6×0.6 m (3×3 ft) (Migvar, 1968) and an acre is planted entirely to *Alocasia*, the yield would be at least 198 tonnes/ha per crop (90 tons/acre per crop) or 48.4 tonnes/acre/year (22 tons/acre/year). However, no yields for the Pacific region have been reported, primarily due to the predominance of intercropping.

In Sri Lanka where crop time is about 10 to 11 months, yields of 6.6 to 11 tonnes/ha per crop (3 to 5 tons/acre per crop) can be obtained with the variety desai ala grown at spacing of 0.6×1.2 m (2×4 ft). Yield per plant casually averages 1.8 to 2.7 kg (4 to 6 lb) but may be as high 6.8 kg (5 lb) when planted over coconut husks (Soyza, 1938). A 6-month crop planted in late March and harvested in late September in Bangladesh (Ahmed and Rashid, 1975) did not reach the harvestable stage, but yielded about 10.3 tonnes/ha (4 to 6 tons/acre). In the Philippines a crop at least 1-1/2 to 2 years old produced 25 to 30 tonnes/ha (11.3 to 13.6 tons/acre) (Quisumbing, 1914).

C. Preservation Methods

1. Postharvest Handling Methods

A. macrorrhiza is simply harvested by cutting the above-ground portion of the stem (Fig. 2) with a knife or machete (Villanueva, 1979).

Figure 2 *Alocasia macrorrhiza* stems, in center, on sale in market in Tonga. (Photograph courtesy of P. Rotar, University of Hawaii.)

If the stem is washed, it is usually done in the field in standing water. When shipped from Samoa or Tonga to New Zealand, three or four corms 18.2 kg (40 lb) are placed per large clean jute or polypropylene sack. Corms of both the pink and white flesh type apparently ship well and will keep for over 2 weeks at 4.5°C (40°F) (Watson, 1979). *Botryodiplodia theobromae* and *Fusarium solani* are the major pathogens infecting corms of *Alocasia* (Coursey, 1979).

2. Products, Uses, and Dietary Significance

In the Pacific region Alocasia is almost entirely grown as a subsistence root crop. However, about 100 to 200 fresh stems weighing 18.2 kg (40 lb) from Samoa or Tonga are sold in New Zealand every two weeks

(Watson, 1979). And in this Wallis and Futuna, Tonga, and Samoa region *Alocasia* is a major staple of the diet. In the atolls of the Tuamotu Archipelago, the Marshall Islands such as Jaluit Atoll (Barrau, 1961), the Federated States of Micronesia, and Republic of Belau, such as Kayangel and Pelelui (McKnight and Obak, 1960), *Alocasia* is cultivated because other root crops do not do well. In other regions, such as lowland areas of Papua New Guinea (Siki, 1979), *Alocasia* is considered a useful reserve or emergency food and is lightly cultivated or collected from the wild.

In Bangladesh (Rashid and Daunicht, 1979) and many parts of India, particularly Assam and Bengal (Kundu, 1967), *Alocasia* is widely grown as a vegetable for the corm as well as leaves. Leaves and stems are also eaten in Indonesia (Hrishi and Balagopal, 1979b) where it is commonly grown in backyard gardens.

In Brazil and in many parts of the tropics *Alocasia* was used for pig or cattle feed. In the Marquesas Islands the leaves are used for wrapping certain types of packages and for baby bathtubs (Brown, 1931). In the Philippines the petioles are applied as odontalgic (remedy for toothache) (Diguangco, 1950).

3. Preservation Methods and Processes

A. macrorrhiza is not seasonal in growth and can be harvested year-round. Harvesting can also take place from 18 months to 4 years with no apparent effect on quality. However, if the plant is too old, calcium oxalate crystals may occur throughout the stem requiring very thorough cooking to make it edible (Mahony, 1960a). *Alocasia* is thus usually stored in the crop (Siki, 1979). In India, the stem is pulped and washed to yield a pure white starch. This flour is mucilagenous, more digestible than rice, and is a light nutritious food suitable for invalids (Srivastava, 1972). Methods of processing *Colocasia* and *Xanthosoma* could probably be directly applied to *Alocasia*. A study of the value of *A. macrorrhiza* as raw material in the fermentation industry has been made (Doi, 1944).

4. Typical Recipes

A. macrorrhiza is always cooked before eating. Some of the wild types or older stems (i.e., 4 years) may require very thorough cooking with several changes of water to remove the acridity (Quartermaster Corps, 1943; Neal, 1965; Sakai, 1979). Careful peeling to remove all the skin together with the underlying yellow layer of corm apparently removes most of the acridity in the Truk Island types (Mahony, 1960a). Because of the extreme acridity of some wild forms, the stem is considered inedible in Fiji (Parham, 1942) and contact with the acrid sap is also avoided.

In the Pacific the two edible cultivars, the white-fleshed Tonga, Wallis, and Futuna type and the pink-fleshed New Guinea type, are prepared similar to *Colocasia* or *Cyrtosperma*. A common method is to peel the stem, and cut into cubes 1-1/2 in. Four pounds are placed in a pot along with the milk of two coconuts and water to cover the *Alocasia* pieces. After boiling for 1 hr, it is salted, and served to eight people (Owen, 1973). A method used in the Cook Islands and Tahiti was to bake the stems in an earth oven under a layer of ti (*Cordyline terminalis*) tubers. The sugars (mostly fructose: Tu, 1981) of the ti tubers would run down into the *Alocasia* stems making them sweet during the long cooking period (Barrau, 1957).

In the Philippines, vinegar, acid vegetables, or acid fruits such as tamarind, are added to the leaves, petioles, or stems during cooking to reduce the acridity. In Central Java (Sastrapradja, 1970), Assam and Bengal in India (Kundu, 1967), and Bangladesh (Rashid and Daunicht, 1979) the young leaves are cooked and eaten like *Colocasia* A juice drink of central Java called tuwak sente is obtained by cutting the petiole and collecting the juice overnight from the cut end (Sastrapradja, 1970). Three recipes using aroids from Bangladesh, India, Burma, and Sri Lanka are listed as follow.

Curry (Rashid, 1980)

Ingredients: Corms or stems (cut into cubes or sticks), water, curry powder (cumin, coriander, tumeric, hot chili), sliced onion and garlic, oil, salt, and meat or fish (dried or fresh).

Preparation: When fresh fish is used, the spices and pieces of stem are fried in oil until the flavor of the spices starts coming out. Then the fresh fish and water are added and cooked until all ingredients are soft. When meat or dried fish is used, the spices and meat or dried fish are fried in oil until the flavor of the spices starts coming out. Then the pieces of stem and water are added and cooked until all ingredients are soft. Sometimes the pieces of corm or stem are boiled separately to remove the acridity before adding the curry. When *Colocasia* or *Xanthosoma* are used, petioles or stolons may be added.

Fried Leaves: Bhaji (Rashid, 1980)

Ingredients: Chopped leaves and petioles, sliced onion and garlic, green hot chili, oil, and salt.

Preparation: sliced onion and garlic are lightly fried in oil. The chopped leaves and petioles, chili, and salt are added and cooked over low heat until a soft lump is produced. Usually acridfree *Xanthosoma* leaves are used, but young *Alocasia* leaves may be used if from low-acridity types.

Soup Khatta (Rashid, 1980) (Sour Soup)

Ingredients: chopped leaves, oil, sliced onion and garlic, curry powder (optional), hot green chili, tamarind (pieces of unripe fruits or pulp of ripe fruits).

Preparation: onion, garlic, and curry powder are fried in oil until the flavor of the spices starts coming out. Water, chopped leaves, chili, and tamarind are added and cooked until a thin soup is formed. Leaves of *Colocasia* are usually used in this soup, but the tamarind is reported to remove some acridity. Young leaves of less acrid types of *Alocasia* may thus be used.

D. Biochemical and Nutritional Composition

Stems of *A. macrorrhiza* are a good source of carbohydrate (Table 1). Although not as good as *Colocasia*, *Xanthosoma*, and *Cyrtosperma* (Sakai, 1979) (Table 2), it compares with *A. companulatus* corms (Sakai, 1979) (Table 3). The phosphorus, iron, and niacin levels may be adequate if stems are consumed in large quantities (Murai et al., 1958). The protein, fat, ascorbic acid, carotene, and riboflavin levels are low. The calcium may be tied up in the form of calcium oxalate (Murai et al., 1958).

A study of the oxalate content of *A. macrorrhiza* (Srivastava and Krishnan, 1959) showed the total oxalate in 100 g of fresh tissue to be: stems 0.15 g, young leaf blade 0.02 g, petiole 0.28 g, mature leaf 1.24 g, old leaves 1.02 g, and roots 0.32 g. Of these amounts the percentage of total oxalate that was water-soluble was: stems 20.5% young leaf blade 50.0%, petiole 64.3%, mature leaf 14.5%, old leaves 22.6%, and roots 75.1%. For comparison, *C. antiquorum* showed levels in the main corm of 0.35 g with 11.2% water-soluble, cormels of 0.11 g with 72.0% water-soluble, mature leaf of 0.92 g with 14.1% water-soluble, and petioles of 0.25 g total oxalate (Srivastava and Krishnan, 1959). Three strains of oxalate-decomposing bacteria have been isolated from petioles of *A. macrorrhiza* (Yara and Usami, 1968).

The calcium oxalate raphides in stems have been described as of two types: a small needle about 80 μm long (comparable to those in *Colocasia*) and a large needle about 150 μm long (Sakai and Hanson, 1974; Sakai, 1979). Both crystals have two grooves running along most of the length of the crystal and barbs with tips oriented away from the acutely pointed end similar to those found in *Xanthosoma* (Sakai et al., 1972) and *Dieffenbachia* (Sakai and Nagao, 1981).

The acridity of *A. macrorrhiza* may be related to the raphides and/or the presence of a toxin (Tang and Sakai, 1983; Massal and Barrau, 1955) possibly similar to the sapotoxin/tanniatoxin isolated from corms of *X. atrovoriens* (Clark and Walters, 1934).

The starch in *A. macrorrhiza* is 20.8% amylose and 79.2% amylopectin (Chowdhury and Hussain, 1979) compared with 13% amylose and 87%

Table 1 Food Values of *Alocasia Macrorrhiza*

Plant part, location of sample (100-g sample)	Calories	Moisture (g)	Total carbohy. (g)	Starch (g)	Other carbohy. (g)	Fiber (g)	Reducing sugar (g)
Stems fresh							
Marshall Is., Ebon Atoll (18% removed as peel)[a]	70	81	17			1.7	
Surigao, Philippines[b]	143	63		21	11	1.1	
Philippines (2 years old), Talban tuberculo[c]		87		3			
Java[d]				9			
Bangladesh (16% nonedible removed)[e]			27			1.9	
Bangladesh (dry wt basis)[f]		(83)		69		9.5	1.6
Mymensingh, Bangladesh (oven-dry basis)[g]		(84)		63			
Stems, cooked							
Marshall Is., Ebon Atoll (18% removed as peel)[a]	79	79	19			1.8	
Leaf, petiole, fresh							
Bangladesh (14% removed as nonedible waste)[e]			4			1.0	
Leaf, blade, fresh							
Bangladesh (after 38% nonedible waste removed)[e]			6			2.7	

[a] Murai et al., 1958.
[b] Valenzuela and Wester, 1930.
[c] Quisumbing, 1914.
[d] Doi, 1944.
[e] Rashid and Daunicht, 1979.
[f] Qudrat-I-Khuda et al., 1960.
[g] Chowdhury and Hussain, 1979.

Protein (g)	Fats (g)	Ash (g)	Ascorbic acid (mg)	Niacin (mg)	Ribo-flavin (mg)	Thiamine (mg)	Carotene (mg)	Calcium (mg)	Iron (mg)	Phos-phorus (mg)	Oxalic acid (mg)
0.6	0.1	1.1	tr	0.4	0.02	0.10		153	0.5	45	
3.3 1.6	0.2	1.1									
1.8	0.2	1.3	7		0.03	0.09	tr	46	1.0	72	
10.7	2.4	5.8						310	9.0	138	
6.8	0.9	4.4						150	24	390	140
0.6	0.02	1.2	1	0.4	0.02	0.1		169	0.9	46	
0.3	0.1	0.8	5		0.01	0.01	0.9	57	0.6	25	
4.3	0.9	1.4			0.34	0.09	13	235	3.8	99	

amylopectin in *Colocasia* (Hokama et al., 1979). Starch grains from a Philippine sample (Allen, 1929) were small, irregularly shaped, four- or five-sided polygons from 1 to 5 μm in diameter, and averaging 3 to 4 μm. Hilum and rings were not visible and the polarization cross was symmetrical and dim. A sample from Bangladesh had starch grains from 1.3 to 4.6 μm in diameter with 85.2% kernel and 14.8% coat (Qudrat-I-Khuda et al., 1960).

The starch from *A. macrorrhiza* has a swelling power comparable to that of *C. antiquorum*, but less than plantain, sweet potato, or *X. sagittifolium* (Rasper, 1969). The pasting temperature is 73°C (163°F) and the maximum viscosity is 160 (BU) Barbender units, compared to 77°C (179.6°F) and 260 BU for *C. antiquorum* and 77°C (179.6°F) and 350 BU for *X. sagittifolium* (Rasper, 1969).

The total quantity of sterol (mg) from 500 g (wet wt) of tuber is 82.8 for *A. macrorrhiza*, 117.8 for *C. esculenta*, and 56.6 for *X. sagittifolium*. The relative percentage of sterols for each genus, respectively, is: cholesterol 0.1, 2.7, 0.5; campesterol 24.0, 8.6, 17.5; stigmasterol 11.9, 28.1, 9.0; and β-sitosterol 64.0, 60.6, and 73.0 (Osagie, 1977). Cholesterol, stigmasterol, and sitosterol have been reported to reduce membrane permeability (Grunwald, 1971).

A mixture of triglochinin and isotriglochinin was isolated from young leaves of *A. macrorrhiza* (Nahrstedt, 1975). A cyanogenic glycoside is also present in leaf blades, petioles, inflorescence axis, flowers, seeds, and roots, but not stem (Hegnauer, 1963). The young leaves contain up to 0.018% hydrogen cyanide (Plowman, 1969). But hydrocyanic acid could not be detected in the stem (Quisumbing, 1914).

A. macrorrhiza is reported to emit an unpleasant smell (Parham, 1942) that may be volatile amines or skatole produced at anthesis by some arum lily species (Smith and Meeuse, 1966).

III. CYRTOSPERMA

A. Introduction

1. Origin and Distribution

The genus *Cyrtosperma* Griff. is a member of the subfamily Lasiodeae of the family Araceae (Plucknett, 1976b). It is composed of about 11 species (Brown, 1931) native to tropics of the Old and New Worlds (Bailey et al., 1976). Two species occur in Brazil, two in Africa, and the remainder are found in the Southeast Asia-Pacific region. The principal edible species is *Cyrtosperma chamissonis* (Schott) Merr. Probable synonyms include *C. merkusii* (Hasskarl) Schott (this may be a separate species; Plucknett, 1976a; Quisumbing, 1914; Pancho, 1959), *C. edule* Schott, *C. nadeaudianum* Moore, *Apeveoa esculenta* Moerenhaut, *Arisacontis chamissonis* Schott, and *Lasia merkusii* Hassk (Barrau, 1957, 1959; Plucknett, 1976a). Another species, *C. lasioides*

Griff., is reported to be in limited cultivation in Indonesia (Coursey, 1968).

C. *chamissonis* was not domesticated on the Asian continent and is not grown in India or Malaysia (Barrau, 1962; Leon, 1976). The probable origin of the species is Indonesia from where it spread eastwards to the Pacific (Barrau, 1960; Plucknett, 1976b). Its range extends from Indonesia through the Philippines to the north side of New Guinea; in the Solomon Islands and Fiji in Melanesia; in central Polynesia as far as the Marquesas Islands; in the Line. Phoenix, and Gilbert Islands and throughout Micronesia (Catala, 1957; Leon, 1976). The northernmost range is 18° north in the Mariana Islands and the southernmost range is 20° south in the Cook Islands (Plucknett, 1976a).

C. *chamissonis* is commonly grown in fresh water swamps (Quartermaster Corps, 1943) or artificial pits (Kay, 1973) but may also be grown in coastal marshes (Massal and Barrau, 1955; Barrau, 1958). It is a major food crop in Micronesia and is one of the few subsistence crops that can be grown on atolls where *Colocasia* does not grow as well.

2. Description and Common Names

C. *chamissonis* (Schott) Merr, is composed of many varieties. Twenty-six are recognized on Yap alone (de la Cruz, 1970). These varieties differ in mature leaf and corm size; leaf shape; amount of spines on the petiole; color of leaf blade, petiole, and internal tissue of the corm; taste, and time to maturity. A general description (Fig. 3) follows: large perennial herb, up to 4.9 m (16 ft) in height; leaves commonly 1.5 to 1.8 m (5 to 6 ft) long; blades are shiny, dark green, hastate-sagittate to hastate-ovate with acute basal lobes, commonly 0.6 to 0.9 m (2 to 3 ft) in length and 0.45 m (1½ ft) in width; petioles are cylindrical, tapering towards the blade, commonly 10 to 13 cm (4 to 5 in.) in diameter at base, 0.9 to 1.2 m (3 to 4 ft) long, often spiny towards the stem, arranged spirally on stem; stem is a large central corm up to 1.5 m (5 ft) in length and 0.6 to 0.9 m (2 to 3 ft) in diameter, branched at the base forming cormels and sucker shoots; flowers are hemaphroditic on inflorescence of purple-green cylindrical spadix subtended by open spathe; fruit is a berry (Brown, 1931; Massal and Barrau, 1955; Barrau, 1957; Pancho, 1959; Kay, 1973; Plucknett, 1976a). *Cyrtosperma* can be distinguished vegetatively from *Amorphophallus* by the entire leaf, from *Colocasia* by the sagittate leaves, from *Xanthosoma* by the absence of a prominent marginal vein, and from *Alocasia* by the pointed basal lobes (Coursey, 1968).

The large size of C. *chamissonis* is reflected in its common English name—giant swamp taro (Kay, 1973). Other common names include: Philippines—palawan, palauan, or palau (Gesmundo, 1932; Quisumbing, 1960; Barrau, 1961); gallon, galiang, or biha (Gesmundo, 1932); Republic of Belau, Palau Islands—brak (Kim and Defngin, 1960; McKnight

Figure 3 *Cyrtosperma chamissonis* plants growing in Ponape. Small aroids in front are *Colocasia* (taro) plants. (Photograph courtesy of C. H. Lamoureux, University of Hawaii.)

and Obak, 1960; Migvar, 1968; de la Cruz, 1970); Sonsorol, Pulo Ana, Merir, and Tobi—burag (Mcknight and Obak, 1960); Federated States of Micronesia, Yap Island—lak (Kim and Defngin, 1960; Migvar, 1968; de la Cruz, 1970; Ulithi Atoll—lok (Barrau, 1961); Truk—pwuna (Mahony, 1960a; de la Cruz, 1970); puna (Barrau, 1961); pwuwana (Migvar, 1968); pura (Barrau, 1961); pwula (Mahony, 1960; de la Cruz, 1970); pwala (Migvar, 1968); pula, pashon, or fanan (Sproat, 1968); Ponape, Pingelap Atoll, mwahng (Mahony, 1960b; de la Cruz, 1970); mwang (Barrau, 1961; Migvar, 1968); mwong, mwang (St. John, 1948; Kay, 1973); muang (Barrau, 1961); muahng (Glassman, 1952); or muhang (Massal and Barrau, 1956; Lambert, 1970); Kapingamarangi Atoll—puraka (Murai et al., 1958; Barrau, 1961); or purak (Mahony, 1960b); Nukuoro Atoll—taokkeri (Mahony, 1960b); Kosrae (Kusaie)— pashok (St. John, 1948); or pasruk (Mahony 1960b); Commonwealth of the Northern Mariana Islands—baha (Barrau, 1961; de la Cruz, 1970); Marshall Islands Government—iaraj (Murai et al., 1958; Barrau, 1961; Migvar, 1968; de la Cruz, 1970; Lambert, 1970; Kay, 1973); ieraj (Bikajle, 1960); caratz or iaratch (St. John, 1948); Papua New Guinea, Mortlock Islands—tepuraka (Boag and Curtis, 1959; Kay, 1973); Solomon Islands-Malaita—kakake (Massal and Barrau, 1955; Lambert, 1970;

Kay, 1973), or karake (Kay, 1973); Republic of Kiribati, Gilbert Islands—babai (Massal and Barrau, 1955; Murai et al., 1958; Lambert, 1970; Kay, 1973), te babai (Barrau, 1961) or baba (Kay, 1973); Tuvalu—broka or puraka (Barrau, 1961) or baba (Kay, 1973); Fiji—via kana (Brown, 1931; Parham, 1942; Lambert, 1970; Kay, 1973); tao kape (Kay, 1973); Tokelau—pulaka or puaka (Lambert, 1970); Western Samoa and American Samoa—pulaka, puraka, or pula'a (Brown, 1931; Barrau, 1961; Lambert, 1970); Cook Islands—pulaka, puraka, or pula'a (Barrau, 1961; Lambert, 1970); and French Polynesia, Moorea—moata (Brown, 1931; Barrau, 1961; Lambert, 1970); Raiatea—opeves (Brown, 1931); or apeveo (Barrau, 1961); Marquesas Islands—ta'o kape or taa-taa (Brown, 1931).

B. Cultivation Practices

1. Climatological and Soil Requirements

C. chamissonis is a tropical species with the entire cultural range within 20° north or south of the equator. Most cultivation is near sea level, but *Cyrtosperma* may be grown up to an elevation of 150 m (500 ft) (de la Cruz, 1970; Plucknett, 1976a). It is able to withstand higher water tables than *Colocasia* and is commonly grown in fresh-water swamps or in artificial pits dug to a few inches below the fresh water table (Plucknett, 1970) (Fig. 4). Some varieties of *C. chamissonis* apparently can withstand brackish water and are grown in coastal marshes directly inland of the fringing mangrove swamps in the Solomon Islands (Barrau, 1958; Migvar, 1968; Herklots, 1972; Plucknett, 1976b). However, it apparently grows best when abundant rainfall maintains the fresh water lens. In the Gilbert Islands of the Republic of Kiribati, ground-water salinity, which increases during droughts, either stunts or kills the varieties grown there (Luomala, 1974). *Colocasia* grown with the *Cyrtosperma* apparently is stunted or dies at much lower levels of salinity than *Cyrtosperma* (Luomala, 1974). On Ngatic, Mokil, and Pingelap Atoll in the Federated States of Micronesia, sea water washes into the *Cyrtosperma* marshes during severe storms. The salt water is drained and rainfall dissipates the salt sufficiently to replant after 2 to 3 months. During this period stalks are cut and grown temporarily on dry land in less salty areas (Mahony, 1960b). The typhoons of 1905 and 1908, which washed salt water into the *Cyrtosperma* pits have been cited as a possible reason for the decline in *Cyrtosperma* cultivation in the Marshall Islands (Bikajle, 1960).

The soil in the swamps, marshes, or pits is mostly organic and black, due to reducing conditions. On atolls, pieces of coral rock are often present. On the low islands of Losap and Nama of the Truk region in the Federated States of Micronesia, soil is so shallow that individual mounds or ridges are used to provide adequate soil for growth of large corms above the underlying coral (Mahony, 1960a). Humus is

Figure 4 *Cyrtosperma chamissonis* plants growing in standing water in swamp in Kosrae. (Photograph courtesy of L. Stemmermann, University of Hawaii.)

constantly added to the soil as a mulch around the corm or to reduce weed growth. On Kapingamarangi Atoll, soil is constantly being carried into the swamp (Mahony, 1960b). Growth is better in slow-running water about 2 ft deep than it is in stagnant water (Sproat, 1968; Kay, 1973).

2. Cultivars

Since *C. chamissonis* is almost entirely vegetatively propagated, the different types are probably best called cultivars. Fertile seed may form, but it is seldom used (Catala, 1957). Numerous cultivars of *C. chamissonis* are cultivated. In the Ponape region of the Federated States of Micronesia over 50 different cultivars are reported (Mahony,

1960b). Some of these may be the same cultivar with a different name. For example the cultivar simiiten of Truk is the same as simihden of Ponape and probably originated on Ngatic Atoll where six different subcultivars of simihden are found. However, great diversity can be found in the different forms of *C. chamissonis*. One cultivar from Ponape mwahnginmoar is reported to grow well in dry areas (Mahony, 1960b).

The different cultivars of *C. chamissomis* can be separated into two basic cultival types: (a) the group of cultivars which usually are grown for 3 or more years before harvest; (b) the group of cultivars which may be harvested in about 1 to 2 years.

The first group usually matures and first flowers after 3 or 4 years. Production of side shoots or suckers may not take place until about the third year of growth. The corms can be harvested after 1 year, but the flavor of these smaller corms is not as good (Kim and Defngin, 1960). In some areas *C. chamissonis* plants are allowed to grow for 10 to 15 years to produce enormous corms for special celebrations (Migvar, 1968). The cultivar ikaraoi is grown in the Gilbert Islands of the Republic of Kiribati for these large corms. Corms as large as 180 kg (400 lb) have been reported from Ponape (Plucknett, 1976a). Usually they range from 45 to 90 kg (100 to 200 lb) (de la Cruz, 1970).

Cultivars of *C. chamissonis* which mature in 1 to 2 years are apparently not as hardy as the slower-maturing types, but are considered more tasty in some areas such as Truk (Mahony, 1960a). These fast-maturing cultivars usually do not make up a major part of the crop in most areas. Even in areas such as Truk where these rapidly maturing cultivars are favored, the slow-maturing cultivars are grown as a dependable reserve crop for use in times of famine. A rapidly maturing cultivar named sikismont (6 months, Truk) is originally from Ngatik Atoll where it is called sowunpwongwennew a subcultivar of simihden. This cultivar matures in less than 1 year, whereas simihden takes a little more than 1 year (Mahony, 1960a).

3. Planting

Cyrtosperma is typically propagated asexually by use of : (a) tops of mature plants with about 2 cm (3/4 in.) of corm with all the leaves cut back except two to three young ones (termed stalks, setts, or cuttings); (b) tops of cormlets with about 2.5 cm (1 in.) of the cormlet or entire cormlets with two to three young (termed cormlets, suckers, or off-shoots). Apparently the stalks grow faster than cormlets (Mahony, 1960a). On Lukunor Atoll near Truk in the Federated States of Micronesia the stalk is cut to a point with several downward cuts rather than a single horizontal cut. The stalk is then allowed to dry for 3 to 7 days by placement on a taro plant before planting (Mahony, 1960a).

In the slow-maturing varieties the offshoots develop from the base of the main corm in the third year of growth (Boag and Curtis, 1959).

However, the ikaraoi cultivar of the Gilbert Islands only forms offshoots
6 to 9 months after the mainshoot is cut. To increase planting material
of the ikaraoi cultivars, the main corm has to be sacrificed to the developing offshoots (Luomala, 1974). In most areas the stalks are used
preferentially, with offshoots used only to increase plantings; however,
in some areas such as Losap Atoll near Truk in the Federated States of
Micronesia offshoots are preferred (Mahony, 1960a).

Cyrtosperma is not seasonal in growth, and planting and harvesting
may be done at anytime. On Yap Island in the Federated States of
Micronesia harvesting and planting take place constantly so the area is
kept in full production at all times (de la Cruz, 1970). In the Truk
region planting and harvesting usually are done in the dry season from
December to March when the breadfruit is not bearing. New plants
may be planted between older plants or the plot may be completely
harvested before replanting new plants.

The stalks or offshoots are placed into the soft mud or into holes or
furrows prepared with digging sticks or shovels. Planting depth is
commonly from 10 to 15 cm (4 to 6 in.) (Plucknett, 1976a). If the mud
is very deep, as found on Pingelap Atoll, planting is on ridges built up
so the standing water does not completely cover the ridges all the time.
In Yap the water in the Cyrtosperma patches is not allowed to rise to
more than 60 cm (2 ft) in depth (Kim and Defngin, 1960). Apparently
the young plants are more susceptible to flooding than older ones.
Plants are usually not moved after planting. However, the intensive
cultivation method used in the Gilbert Islands commonly involves rooting
in drier areas of the artificial pits to prevent rotting and then transplanting to deeper water after the first two leaves have unfolded
(Luomala, 1974). On Ngatik Atoll large corms for feasts are transplanted into new holes. Plants up to 3 ft in height have been successfully transplanted (Mahony, 1960b). These transplanted corms are
larger but are reported to be less tasty than corms grown in place,
possibly because corms grown more than 3 to 4 years become stringy
and dry (de la Cruz, 1970). Spacing is in relation to mature size of the
plant. On Mokil Atoll plants are spaced 0.5 m (1.5 ft) apart in ditches
1 m (3.5 ft) apart (Mahony, 1960b), whereas in the Truk area spacing
may be up to 1.8 m (6 ft) apart (Kim and Defngin, 1960).

Intercropping with Colocasia was common in the past on Yap Island.
Colocasia was planted first followed 1 or 2 days later by Cyrtosperma.
The Colocasia was harvested about a year later, the patch weeded, and
more Colocasia interplanted. After three crops of Colocasia, the Cyrtosperma was grown alone for 1 year then harvested. In this way three
crops of Colocasia and one crop of Crytosperma could be harvested
every 4 years from the same plot (Kim and Defngin, 1960). Interplanting with Colocasia and rapidly maturing cultivars of Crytosperma
is also common to many other areas where Cyrtosperma is intensively

cultivated (Luomala, 1974; Plucknett, 1976a). However, this practice
has been reported to slow down the growth of *Cyrtosperma* (Mahony,
1960a). On Mokil Atoll, *Colocasia* is planted on one side of a row of
Cyrtosperma and banana on the other side. After about 1 year the
Colocasia is harvested and replanted. The bananas usually start producing fruit after a little more than a year. After two crops of *Colocasia* are harvested, the *Cyrtosperma* is grown for 1 more year then
harvested. The area is then cleared and replanted (Mahony, 1960b).

4. Nutrition, Weeds, Pests, and Pathogens

Only organic mulches have been reported to be used as fertilizer. Dependent on the intensity of cultivation, application may vary from only
one application of fallen branches and leaves trimmed from the over-
hanging branches 6 months after planting in the larger swamps of
Ponape (Mahony, 1960b) to monthly applications in the Gilbert Islands.
These monthly mulches correspond to the production of new leaves.
The mulches are separated from the corm by a layer of soil to prevent
damage to the corm from the heat of the rotting mulch (Luomala, 1974).
In the second year of growth, two layers of mulch are added with each
application. For very large cultivars, such as the ikaraoi on the Gilbert
Islands, grapefruit-sized balls of soil and mulch, wrapped in *Cyrtosperma* leaves, are placed in the spaces on the corm between the leaf
bases in the third and following years of growth. On Tabiteauea in
the Gilbert Islands *Sida fallax* is the most highly valued mulch material
(Luomala, 1974). Other mulching materials include: *Boerheavia dif-
fusa* L., *Guettarda speciosa* L., *Pisonia grandis* R. Br., and *Messer-
schmidia argentea* (L.f.) Johnston in the Gilberts. In other areas,
such as Yap Island, cut grass from the plot is dried in trees and then
used as a mulch. *Hibiscus tiliaceous* leaves, banana leaves, *Barringtonia
asiatica, Morinda citrifolia,* coconut fronds, *Canavalia microcarpa,
Vigna marina, Pandanus,* breadfruit, *Wedelia biflora,* or papaya are
reported to be used as a general mulch over the soil in *Cyrtosperma*
gardens or worked into the soil before planting (Kim and Defngin,
1960; McKnight and Obak, 1960). The corms are thought to taste
better if the plant has been regularly fed (Catala, 1957).

Planted areas are manually kept free of weeds that include: *Cyperus
odoratus* L., *Cyperus javanicus* Houtt, *Jussiaea suffruticosa* L., *Jussiaea angustifolia* Lam., *Eleocharis geniculata* L., and grasses (Catala,
1957; Luomala, 1974). On Yap the grass may be allowed to grow until
the *Cyrtosperma* plants are about 5 ft high to provide some shade, then
regular weeding is done (Kim and Defngin, 1960). Areas neighboring
trees and shrubs are not trimmed until the *Cyrtosperma* plants are
established (Mahony, 1960a).

A 1978 (Stemmermann and Proby) study of the high Caroline Islands
listed the following plants as occurring in taro cultivation areas:

Alternanthera sessilis (L.) R. Br., *Blechum brownei* Juss., Blyxa sp.,
Centotheca latifolia Trim., *Cyclosorus gongylodes* (Schkuhr) Link,
Echinochloa colona (L). Link, *Eleusine indica* (L.) Gaertn., *Fimbristylis
dichotoma* (L.) Vahl, *Fuirena umbellata* Rottb., *Hyptis capitata* Jacq.,
Ipomoea aquatica Forsk., *Ischaemum* spp., *Lemna perpusilla* Torrey,
Lindernia antipoda (L.) Alston, *Ludwigia hyssopifolia* (g. Don.) Exell.,
Ludwigia octovalvis (Jacq.) de Witt, *Paspalum conjugatum* Berg., *Paspalum orbiculare* Forst.f., *Phragmites karka* (Retz.) Trin., and
Rhynchospora corymbosa (L.) Britt.

C. *chamissonis* is reported to be almost insect- and disease-free
(Sproat, 1968), and practically no plant protection practices are used
(Plucknett, 1976a). In the Gilbert Islands a beetle (*Pentodon* species
or *Papuana* species) is reported to attack older tubers, and a cater-
pillar (*Prodenia litura*) is reported to attack leaves of young plants of
Cyrtosperma as well as *Colocasia* (Luomala, 1974). *Botryodiplodia
theobromae* and *Fusarium solani* are the major pathogens infecting corms
(Coursey et al., 1979). *Cercospora* species, which causes leaf spots in
Micronesia (de la Cruz, 1970), caused the complete disappearance of
Colocasia on the low island of Wana Wana in the western Solomon Islands
but apparently has not affected *Cyrtosperma* growing in the coastal
marshes of the nearby island of Malaita (Barrau, 1958). Rats have
been reported to cause serious crop losses on the Mortlock Islands
(Kay, 1973).

5. Harvesting and Yields

Crops times are variable for C. *chamissonis*. It is usually not harvested
until it flowers which is taken as a sign of maturity (Bikajle, 1960;
Mahony, 1960a). Some early maturing cultivars such as oineke and
katutu in the Gilbert Islands and sikismont and simihden from the
eastern Caroline Islands mature and are harvested in less than 1 year
(Catala, 1957; Mahony, 1960a). Most of the longer-maturing cultivars
mature and are harvested after 3 years (St. John, 1948; Barrau, 1958;
Kim and Defngin, 1960; Mahony, 1960a; Coursey, 1968). On Yap
Island areas interplanted with *Colocasia* take 4 years (Kim and Defngin,
1960). In the Philippines the best time to harvest is in 5 to 6 years
(Pancho, 1959). In all areas, plants are usually only grown for longer
periods to develop large corms for prestige in celebrations. These longer-maturing varieties can be harvested after 1 year as in Kapingamarangi Atoll, which has a very thin soil; however, these corms are small,
about the size of a fist, and the flavor is not as good (Kim and Defngin,
1960; Mahony, 1960a). Corm size in Truk averages 2 kg (4.4 lb) and
in Yap 4.5 kg (10 lb) (Plucknett, 1976a). Yields range from 15.9
tonnes/ha per crop (7 tons/acre per crop) on Truk, to 42.5 tonnes/
ha per crop (19 tons/acre per crop) on Palau, and 120.0 tonnes/
ha per crop (53.4 tons/acre per crop) on Yap (Plucknett, 1976a). Crop
time for yap is 4 years which yields 30 tonnes/ha/year. On Palau the

crop time was not specified (Plucknett, 1976a), but if the average of 3 years is taken, the yield is 14.2 tonnes/ha/year. On Truk the rapidly maturing cultivars are favored (Mahony, 1960a), so crop time is probably 1 year or 15.9 tonnes/ha/year. In the Mariana Islands yields of 13.2 to 16.5 tonnes/ha/year (6 to 7.5 tons/acre/year) are reported (Migvar, 1968). The average for all of Micronesia is considered to be 10 tonnes/ha/year (4.5 tons/acre/year) (de la Cruz, 1970).

C. Preservation Methods

1. Postharvest Handling Methods

Harvesting is by hand. The corm is uncovered and pried out. Sometimes this operation requires two men (Villanueva, 1979). The corms are usually washed in the field by dipping in standing water. Generally, no grading is done other than separation of extremely small or damaged corms. If the corm is stored, it is usually left in the field container, but no longer than 2 weeks (Villanueva, 1979). Generally, only 1 week's supply is harvested at a time, governed by the people's needs (Kim and Defngin, 1960). If stored, 4.5°C (40°F) is the recommended temperature (Watson, 1979). Apparently no storage trials are presently being conducted in the Pacific (Lambert, 1979).

2. Products, Uses, and Dietary Significance

Cyrtosperma is grown almost entirely as a subsistence crop. On Yap Island where an estimated 37,000 kg (81,000 lb) were marketed for a value of $7,329 in 1969, the marketed product is the fresh corm. On the low islands or coral atolls of the Federated States of Micronesia, and the Gilbert Islands of the Republic of Kiribati, the Mortlock Islands of Papua New Guinea, and Malaita of the Solomon Islands, *Cyrtosperma* forms a principal component of the diet.

On Pingelap Atoll (St. John, 1948), Kapingamarangi Atoll (Mahony, 1960b), the Mortlock Islands, Papua New Guinea (Boag and Curtis, 1959), and Yap Island, *Cyrtosperma* is the most important food crop. On Yap it is eaten several times a day year-round (Kim and Defngin, 1960). In some areas, such as Truk, *Cyrtosperma* is harvested from December to March in the off-season for breadfruit and in Malaita fish and *Bruguieia* is supplemented by *Cyrtosperma*. In other areas *Pandanus* and coconut may be the principal cultivated plants. On most high islands *Colocasia* or *Alocasia* are the principal aroids. In many areas *Cyrtosperma* is considered a reserve crop and only limited care is given. In other areas it occurs in the wild state as remnants of past cultivation.

3. Preservation Methods and Processes

C. chamissonis is not seasonal in growth and can be harvested at any time of the year with no reported impairment of taste (Mahony, 1960a;

Coursey et al., 1979; Siki, 1979). It is thus generally stored in the crop. If long-term storage is needed, to prevent destruction of the crops due to salt-water flooding of the interior marshes, for example, corms can be stored for up to 2 months after processing by two methods: (a) In the Gilbert Islands (Massal and Barrau, 1955; Kay, 1973) and Micronesia in general (Sproat, 1968), corms are peeled, sliced, and scalded, then sun-dried; (b) In Ngatik, Mikil, and Pingelap Atolls (Mahony, 1960b) corms are baked in earth ovens, cut into slices, and dried in the sun for 2 or 3 days. This dried *Cyrtosperma* is eaten after being boiled in water (Catala, 1957). No processing trials are presently being conducted (Lambert, 1979; Mahony, 1960b). Also, a flour is made by parboiling slices of *Cyrtosperma*, crushing or grinding in a meat grinder, followed by drying. The flour is reported to be stable for a year or longer in the Gilbert Islands (Catala, 1957).

4. Typical Recipes

C. chamissonis is always cooked before being eaten due to the acridity of the calcium oxalate raphides or chemical toxin in the corm (Sakai, 1979; Tang and Sakai, in press). Removal of 1.25 cm (1/2 in.) or more of the outer layer removes much of the acridity (Murai et al., 1958). Also, *Cyrtosperma* does not seem to have the same irritating quality as *Colocasia* when not thoroughly cooked (Murai et al., 1958).

In Micronesia the leaves are usually never eaten (Mahony, 1960a); however, during World War II petioles were peeled, chopped, and boiled in soups (Mahony, 1960a). In the Philippines, the Visayans and some Tagalogs use young leaves and young inflorescences as a vegetable in cooking (Gesmundo, 1932). Leaves are also used for the pot lid to impart a better flavor in the boiled corm in Yap (Kim and Defngin, 1960), and in southeastern Polynesia the outer fibrous tissue of the petiole is peeled into ribbon strips and used in mat weaving (Brown, 1931).

Cyrtosperma is commonly peeled, cut up, and boiled for about 1 hr in water (Kim and Defngin, 1960) or a mixture of coconut milk and water as in the recipe given for *Alocasia* (Owen, 1973). The corms that are boiled in water are often mashed, mixed, and seasoned with grated coconut, coconut milk, and sugar (Bikajle, 1960). The mashing of the boiled corm is often followed by kneading for a long period which probably allows for hydrolysis of the starch, resulting in a dough with a light fluffy texture and a pale mauve, almost pink, color (Massal and Barrau, 1956). The dough is sometimes allowed to ferment, then wrapped in leaves and recooked in ovens to form a dough that keeps for several days.

The fresh corm is also grated, mixed with grated coconut, coconut milk, bananas (Sproat, 1968), or coconut milk and sugar, formed into balls or cakes of up to 2 lb, wrapped in *Cyrtosperma* or banana leaves, and baked (Bikajle, 1960) or boiled (Gesmundo, 1932). The fresh corm may also be baked or roasted whole or cut up, but this generally takes a long time (Kim and Defngin, 1960). On Yap, the fresh corm is peeled, cut into thin slices, fried in deep pork fat, then sugared for flavor (Kim and Defngin, 1960). In the Philippines, *Cyrtosperma* may be substituted for sweet potato in some dishes (Gesmundo, 1932).

On Yap stored corms may develop bitter spots. These spots may be cut out and the good portions soaked in sea water several hours before cooking. An alternative method used to remove the bitter taste is boiling the corms with Polynesian chestnuts (Tahitian chestnut, *Inocarpus fagifer* (Whistler, 1981). This process apparently removes the bitter taste (Kim and Defngin, 1960).

D. Biochemical and Nutritional Composition

Corms of *C. chamissonis* are a good source of carbohydrate, and an excellent source of calories; however, the protein and fat contents are low (Table 2). The phosphorus, iron, and niacin contents are adequate if the corms are eaten in large amounts. The calcium content, although high, may all be tied up in the oxalate form and unavailable (Murai, et al., 1958). The ascorbic acid, carotene, and riboflavin levels are also low. Fiber content is higher than *Colocasia* (Murai et al., 1958; Sakai, 1979). Although the leaves or inflorescences of *Cyrtosperma* are not eaten in most areas, they may contribute more protein in relation to carbohydrate than the corms (Table 2). No measurements of mineral or vitamin contents have been made.

The starch grains have been described as: "medium-sized, rounded, and angular rounded grains from 4 to 18 μm in size, with the average about 11 μm. The grains show pressure facets, resembling a cut stone in may cases. The hilum is visible in very few and is a Y or a straight line. The polarization cross is distinct and is slightly asymmetrical, but centric" (Allen, 1929).

In the Philippines (Diguangco, 1950) a decoction (made by boiling in water, usually in proportion 5 parts to 100 parts of water) of the spadix is used as an emmenagogue (an agent that promotes the menstrual discharge) and ecbolic (a drug that tends to increase uterine contractions and that is used to facilitate delivery).

IV. AMORPHOPHALLUS

A. Introduction

1. Origin and Distribution

The genus *Amorphophallus* Blume ex Decaisne is a member of the subfamily Lasiodeae of the family Araceae (Plucknett, 1976b). It is composed of 90 to 100 species, native to the tropics of the Old World. Thirty-three species are present in Africa, five are found in the

Table 2 Food Values of *Cyrtosperma Chamissonis*

Plant part, location of sample collection (100-g sample)	Calories	Moisture (g)	Total carbohy. (g)	Starch (g)	Other carbohy. (g)	Fiber (g)	Reducing sugar (g)
Corms, fresh							
Tacloban, Leyte, Philippines[a]	143	63		23	11	1.6	
Santo, New Herbrides[b]		60		33		1.0	0.5
Capiz, Philippines[c]	150	62	35			1.4	
San Pablo, Philippines[c]	155	60	36			1.3	
Pila, Philippines[c]	120	69	27			1.4	
Marshall Is., cultivar 'buroro' (36% removed skin)[d]	122	68	29			1.3	
Marshall Is., cultivar 'kaliklik' (36% removed skin)[d]	124	68	30			1.2	
Marshall Is., cultivar 'wan' (26% removed skin)[d]	118	70	28			1.2	
Corms, roasted							
Marshall Is., cultivar 'kaliklik' (32% removed skin)[d]		59					
Corms, baked							
Caroline Is., cultivar 'puna' (skin removed)[d]	149	61	36			1.2	
Caroline Is., cultivar, 'simiden' (skin removed)[d]	141	64	34			1.4	
Young inflorescence, fresh							
Pila, Philippines[c]	35	89	5			1.4	
Young leaf blades, less midrib, fresh							
Pila, Philippines[c]	45	86	4			1.5	
Young midrib and soft portions of petioles, fresh							
Pila, Philippines[c]	25	92	3			1.3	

[a] Valenzuela and Wester, 1930.
[b] Peters, 1957.
[c] Gesmundo, 1932.
[d] Murai et al., 1958.

Protein (g)	Fats (g)	Ash (g)	Ascorbic acid (g)	Niacin (mg)	Ribo-flavin (mg)	Thiamine (mg)	Carotene (mg)	Calcium (mg)	Iron (mg)	Phos-phorus (mg)	pH
0.8	0.1	1.1									
	0.5	1.0					8				
0.9	0.3	1.4									
1.4	0.5	1.6									
0.7	0.4	1.2									
0.8	0.2	1.9	tr	1.2	0.11	0.03		158	1.3	28	
0.5	0.2	1.3	1	0.6	0.08	0.03		598	1.4	57	
0.5	0.3	0.9	tr	1.1	0.10	0.06		301	0.9	79	
				0.6	0.06	0.01					
1.9	0.1	1.5	2	0.9	0.04	0.05		35	1.4	97	6.1
0.7	0.2	0.9	tr	0.7	0.05	0.06		156	0.8	19	5.6
2.4	0.7	1.6									
5.0	0.7	2.0									
2.2	0.3	1.3									

Australia-Pacific region, and sixty-two are native to the Asian continent (Motte, 1932; Chevalier, 1931).

There are two major edible species: *A. campanulatus* (Roxburg) Blume ex Decaisne (Fig. 5), grown from India to Polynesia for the starchy corms (Leon, 1976) and *A. rivieri* Durieu var. *konjac* Engler grown in Japan for the glucomann in the corms. Two other species, *A. oncophyllus* Prain and *A. variabilis* Blume (Fig. 6), are also grown or collected from the wild in Indonesia for the glucomannan content (Ohtsuki, 1967; Kurihara, 1979).

A. campanulatus may have originated in India. It is cultivated from India to Malaysia, where it is grown in backyard gardens or collected from the wild. In Indonesia and the Philippines it is sometimes used as pig feed (de la Pena, 1970). It was probably of ancient aboriginal introduction in Melanesia and Polynesia (Brown, 1931) and is now

Figure 5 *Amorphophallus campanulatus* growing wild in South Pacific. Note the dissected leaves. (Photograph courtesy of P. Rotar, University of Hawaii.)

Figure 6 *Amorphophallus variabilis* plant collected in Indonesia. The corm is about 10 to 15 cm in diameter. (Photograph courtesy of C. H. Lamoureux, University of Hawaii.)

hardly ever used there in human diet. *A. campanulatus* is unknown to Micronesia (Leon, 1976).

A. rivieri originated in the Indochina-southern China region and is still cultivated there. It was introduced to Japan in the early tenth century (Motte, 1932). The variety *konjac* was developed in Japan. In 1979, the area of cultivation was reported to be 15,330 ha (37,865 acres) and production was 91,000 tonnes (100,000 tons) (Kurihara, 1979). Most of these corms are processed into konjak flour and then into a gellike food with an elastic texture called konnyaku (Motte, 1932). *A. oncophyllus* and *A. variabilis* are now grown and collected in Indonesia and processed into iles-iles flour. This flour is composed mostly of glucomannan similar to konjak flour and is also processed primarily into konnyaku (Smith and Montgomery, 1959; Ohtsuki, 1967; Kurihara, 1979).

2. Description and Common Names

Amorphophallus can be distinguished from *Colocasia, Xanthosoma, Alocasia,* and *Cyrtosperma* by the presence of only one or two dissected leaves per plant. Both of the two major species have an annual vegetative and dormant cycle and are not reproductive until the third or fourth years. Descriptions follow: *A. campanulatus* (Fig. 5) herb, commonly 0.6 to 0.9 m (2 to 3 ft) in height, one or two leaves, blade trisected to the base, about 0.9 m (3 ft) in length and width, divisions once or twice branched dichotomously, the ultimate segments oblong or lanceolate-oblong, acuminate, unequal; petiole cylindrical, fleshy, 0.6 to 0.9 m (2 to 3 ft) long, smooth (var. *hortensis*) or rough (var. *sylvestus*), spotted with pale yellowish, gray-green; corm is short, globose, wider than high, commonly 1 to 10 kg (2.2 to 22 lb): inflorescence on peduncle to 10 cm (4 in.) long, spathe funnelform, widely expanded into ovate undulate blade above, green, spotted white outside, reddish purple in throat, to 10.5 cm (8 in.) long and 25 cm (10 in.) across; spadix to 31 cm (12 in.) long, sterile terminal portion, domelike in shape, spongy, deep purple. *A, rivieri* herb, commonly 0.9 to 1.2 m (3 to 4 ft) in height, one or two leaves, blade similar to *A. campanulatus* but up to 1.2 m (4 ft) in length and width; petiole cylindrical, fleshy, 0.9 to 1.2 m (3 to 4 ft) long, brownish green with dark purple spots; corm similar to *A. campanulatus;* inflorescence on penduncle to 50 cm (20 in.) long, spathe funnelform to 41 cm (16 in.) long, the expanded ovate limb blackish red and undulate; spadix much longer than spathe, sterile appendage tapering, to 54 cm (21 in.) long (Brown, 1931; St. John, 1948; Massal and Barrau, 1956; Barrau, 1958, 1962; Kay, 1973; Plucknett, 1976a).

The common names for *A. campanulatus* include: elephant yam, elephant foot yam (Plucknett, 1970); India—suran (Chaugule and Khot, 1963; Koregave, 1964; Chatterjee et al., 1971); Ceylon—kidaran (Senewiratne, 1963; Plucknett, 1970); Bangladesh—ol kachu (Plucknett, 1970; Rashid and Daunicht, 1979); bagh kachu (Chowdhury and Hussain, 1979); Malaya—karak-kavanai (Tamil; Herklots, 1972); Malaysia—mahee (Brown, 1931); Indonesia—(var. *hortensis*) soweg (Ohtsuki, 1967), (var. *sylvestris*) waloer (Ohtsuki, 1967); Philippines—pungapung (Tagalog; Furtado, 1941; Plucknett, 1970); New Caledonia—koe (Paate; Massal and Barrau, 1955), pwea (Camuki; Massal and Barrau, 1956); Fiji—daga; Western and American Samoa—daga (Brown, 1931), teve (Plucknett, 1970); Cook Islands—teve (Massal and Barrau, 1956); French Polynesia, Tahiti—teve; and Marquesas Islands—teve (Brown, 1931; Massal and Barrau, 1955; 1956). Common names for *A. rivieri* include: Japan—konnyaku (Motte, 1932), konjak (Shimahara et al., 1975; Kurihara, 1979); and China—mo-yu (Kay, 1973). In Indonesia common names for *A. variabilis* are iles-iles or kembang banke and for *A. oncophyllus* are at jong or bodoer (Agron. Colon., 1939; Ohtsuki, 1967).

B. Cultivation Practices

1. Climatological and Soil Conditions

A. campanulatus is a tropical and subtropical crop that is seasonal in growth with active vegetative growth in the summer and dormant corms in the winter. Generally warm (77 to 95°F, 25 to 35°C), humid (100 to 150 cm of rain) weather enhances leaf growth and dry weather induces the development of the dormant corms. In drier areas the crop must be irrigated (Kay, 1973). In India it is commonly grown in highlands which receive high rainfall (Abraham, 1969). In the Philippines they are usually found growing in damp, moist, shady areas (de la Pena, 1970). Generally, a deep, loamy, well-worked soil with good drainage produces optimum yields (Kay, 1973).

A. rivieri is a more temperate crop and is generally grown between 34 to 43° north latitude (Kay, 1973). In Japan (Kurihara, 1979) it is grown from Fukushima Prefecture in the north to Miyazaki Prefecture in the south. The altitude varies from 11 m (280 ft) to 380 m (1250 ft), and the annual mean air temperature varies from 12.1°C (54°F) to 14.5°C (58°F). The annual precipitation varies from 2404 mm (94 in.) to 1317 mm (51 in.), with from 1593 mm (62 in.) to 1008 mm (39 in.) falling from May to October and 811 mm (31 in.) to 241 mm (9 in.) falling from November to April. Soil type varies from gravelly to clay and slope may be as high as 35°.

It is thought that introduction of *A. rivieri* into Okinawa may not be successful because of high temperature (Kurihara, 1979). However, *A. oncophyllus* and *A. variabilis* may grow well there. In Java (Ohtsuki, 1967) *A. variabilis* is commonly found at altitudes lower than 700 m (2300 ft) in native gardens or borders of forests, usually in the shade. *A. oncophyllus* usually grows at 800 to 1000 m (2600 to 3280 ft) altitude, and because of the moderate temperature grows slowly with generally smaller tubers 7 to 15 cm (2.7 to 5.9 in.) in diameter.

2. Cultivars

In Java there are two recognizable types of *A. campanulatus,* var. *hortensis* Backer, which has a smooth petiole, and var. *sylvestris,* which has a rough petiole that resembles the skin of an elephant's leg (Ohstuki, 1967). In India 12 cultivars were reported that varied from 5.63 to 10.50% in tuber protein (2-mm peel removed, dried slices) (Shanmugam et al., 1976).

The chromosome count is n = 14 (Krishnan et al., 1970; Darlington and Wylie, 1955) in nature. Seed dormancy is broken by placing the fresh harvested seed in running water for 6 days (Rajendran and Hrishi, 1976). There is high variability in cross seedlings with ranges of 0.1 to 3 kg/plant in tuber yield, 14 to 26% in dry wt, 8 to 18% in starch, 1.4 to 5.0% in crude protein, 0.3 to 1.1% in fiber and 0.05 to 0.36% in oxalic acid (Rajendran et al., 1977). High-yielding mutants can also be obtained by treating small pieces of corm with 2000 to 9000 r of gamma radiation (Abraham, 1970).

In Japan both the original *A. rivieri,* from China, and *A. rivieri* var. *konjac,* developed in Japan, are grown. Breeding and selection of new cultivars are also ongoing. The intent is to develop new types that are more disease-resistant, high in corm weight, high in percentage of mannan content, and early to produce cormels (Yamaga, 1973; Kawakami and Ono, 1971). The chromosome count is 2n = 26 (Gill, 1973).

Since *A. oncophyllus* and *A. variabilis* (Fig. 6) are still mostly collected from the wild, no cultivars probably occur. However, there is some thought of selection and breeding to develop types suitable for growth in Okinawa Prefecture in Japan (Kurihara, 1979).

3. Planting

Both *A. campanulatus* and *A. rivieri* are propagated from cormlets or buds produced below ground from the base of the shoot. These cormlets may be up to 20 cm (8 in.) long, made up of five to six shortened internodes, with black-brown scale leaves and a smaller tip, or they may be much shortened and globose in shape (Motte, 1932; Chaugule and Khot, 1957; Yamaga, 1973). In *A. rivieri* the cormlets are not produced until the second or third year (Yamaga, 1973). In *A. campanulatus* the buds usually do not appear until the fourth year (Chaugule and Khot, 1957). The 1-, 2-, and 3-year-old corms are commonly replanted and harvesting is in the third or fourth year. Both species require a dormancy of 2 to 3 months (Kay, 1973).

In *A. campanulatus* sprouting in storage and emergence and maturing of plants in the fields are much faster in corms after a long atmospheric rest period than after a shorter period. Yields are higher with seed corms with no atmospheric rest period (Chaugule and Khot, 1957). And March-harvested corms are reported to be best for seed pieces (Iyer, 1935). *A. oncophyllus* propagates vegetatively by forming bulbils on the base of branching leaf veins (Ohtsuki, 1967). No reports on *A. variabilis* could be found. However, it does not form bulbils (Ohtsuki, 1967) and probably vegetatively reproduces from cormlets. After the fourth year, *A. campanulatus* corms are sometimes cut into sections containing at least one shoot to produce a crop in 1 year. The yields from these crops are usually slightly lower than the yields from whole corms of the third year (Chaugule and Khot, 1957). A study of *A. campanulatus* in India comparing seed pieces 0.68, 1.1, and 1.6 kg (1.5, 2.5, and 3.5 lb) showed average harvested corms of 4.3, 5.8, and 6.5 kg (9.6, 12.8, and 14.4 lb) and yields of 46.6, 59.6, and 67.2 tonnes/ha (41,535, 53,049, and 59,893 lb/acre, respectively) (Caugule and Khot, 1963). *A. campanulatus* is usually planted from March to June before the rainy season and is harvested when the leaves have whithered, from October to March, 6 to 12 months later (Iyer, 1935; Senewiratne, 1963; Kundu, 1967; Plucknett, 1970; Nair et al., 1974; Ahmed and Rashid, 1975). Crop duration is up to 4 years with annual harvesting, storage, and replanting (Soyza, 1938; Chaugule and Khot, 1957). The cormlets initially weigh about 28 to 57 g (1 to 2 oz), after 1 year 113 to 227 g (4 to 8 oz), after 2 years 0.45 to

0.9 kg (1 to 2 lb), after 3 years 1.4 to 2.3 kg (3 to 5 lb), and after
4 years 6.8 to 9 kg (15 to 20 lb) (Chaugule and Khot, 1957).

   A. campanulatus is generally planted in well-tilled soil (Herklots,
1972) with eight ploughings suggested in India (Iyer, 1935) after paddy culture. Planting depth is 10 to 15 cm (4 to 6 in.) (Kay, 1973).
Spacing may vary from 0.4 × 0.6 m (1-1/2 × 2 ft) to 0.9 × 1.2 m (3 ×
4 ft). The closer spacings, however, require more seed corms. A
study in India using cut 4-year corms comparing spacing of 0.6 × 1.2 m
(2 ft × 4 ft) and 0.9 × 1.2 m (3 ft × 4 ft) showed the spacing of 0.9 ×
1.2 m producing larger corms 5.75 kg (12.78 lb) versus 4.97 kg
(11.04 lb), but the spacing of 0.6 × 1.2 m producing a higher yield
64.6 tonnes/ha (57,562 lb/acre) versus 51.4 tonnes/ha (45,755 lb/acre).
When seed pieces 1.1 kg (2.5 lb) were used, the seed rate was 16
tonnes/ha (14,293 lb/acre) for the spacing of 0.6 × 1.2 m and 10.7
tonnes/ha (9,528 lb/acre) for the spacing of 0.9 × 1.2 m (Chaugule
and Khot, 1963).

   Besides pure crops, *A. campanulatus* may be mix-cropped with no
effect on yield 36.2 tonnes/ha (16.45 tons/acre). The best money returns in India (Koregave, 1964) are in the following order: *Raphanus
sativas* (radish), *Trigonella foenum-graceum* (methi), *Arachnus hypo-
gea* (peanut, groundnut), *Cyamopsis psoralioides* (cluster bean) and
least *Medicago sativa* (lucerne). Other catch or cover crops include:
Zingiber officinale (ginger), *Musa* (banana), *Cyamopsis psoralioides*
(guar), *Dioscorea* (yam), *Crotalaria annum* (sann), and *Capsicum
annum* (chili pepper) (Chaugule and Khot, 1957; Abraham, 1969; Abraham, 1970). *A. campanulatus* can also be intercropped with coconut,
except during the eighth to twentieth year when there is too much
shading from the coconut fronds (Nair, et al., 1974). Spacing of 1 ×
1 m (3-1/4 × 3-1/4 ft) and 8000 plants per hectare (3240 plants per
acre) uses 80% of the area and yields about 12 tonnes/ha (10,500 lb/
acre). In India, after 2 to 3-1/2 months of growth, soil is commonly
trenched in the interrow and mounded up around the plants (Iyer,
1935). A second flush of growth often occurs about 3 months after
planting. Every corm does not produce a second leaf. More second
leaves occur on corms with longer rest periods and with wider spacing.
However, plants with no rest period and only one leaf usually produce
more than those with long atmospheric rest periods and two leaves
(Chaugule and Khot, 1957). Mulching with leaves or straw has also
been shown to be beneficial. A study in India showed an increase in
corm size 4.6 kg versus 2.8 kg (10 lb versus 6 lb) and yield 36.8
tonnes/ha versus 23.7 tonnes/ha with mulching. Corm quality was
also better: 21.2% dry matter, 10.2% carbohydrate, and 1.8% protein
versus 19.0% dry matter, 8.7% carbohydrate, and 1.6% protein (Kumar
et al., 1973).

   In Japan *A. rivieri* is commonly grown in two types of culture
(Kurihara, 1979). Uedama is an intensive cultivation method similar

to that of *A. campanulatus* in India, Bangladesh, and Sri Lanka. Seed corms are grouped by ages and planted separately in the spacing. In the autumn all the corms are harvested and older corms sold. Seed corms are stored on warm shelves in groups by age over winter and are replanted in the spring. The soil is well worked and spacing between rows is commonly 60 cm (24 in.) with the distance between plants in the row varied from 5 to 35 cm (6 to 14 in.), depending on the age of the seed corm. Soil is usually mounded over the plants in the second or third month after planting (Motte, 1932).

Jinenjo culture of *A. rivieri* involves continuous cropping for more than 100 years. Cormlets and older corms are mixed as in natural growth. In late autumn, older corms are harvested and sold. All the remaining corms are left in the fields for regrowth in the spring. Mulching with wild herbs, rice straw, or barley straw is commonly practiced. Jinenjo culture is commonly practiced on hillsides with up to 34° inclination (Kurihara, 1979).

No information is available on the cultural requirements of *A. onco-phyllus* and *A. variabilis* in Indonesia where they are primarily collected from the wild in Java (Ohtsuki, 1967).

4. Nutrition, Weeds, Pests, and Pathogens

High levels of organic manure are needed for growth of *A. campanulatus*. Application of 6 cartloads per hectare (15 cartloads per acre) of cattle manure and leaves of tamarind trees (Iyer, 1935) or 44 tonnes/ha (20 tons/acre) of farmyard manure (FYM) have been recommended (Chaugule and Khot, 1963).

A study of nutrition levels in India showed a control yield of 11.6 tonnes/ha (5.2 tons/acre) and a yield of 34.6 tonnes/ha (15.4 tons/acre) when 25 tonnes/ha (10 tons/acre) of FYM, plus 80 kg/ha (70 lb/acre) each of N and P_2O_5, and 120 kg/ha (106 lb/acre) K_2O was applied. The most economical level in terms of fertilizer cost and yield was 25 tonnes/ha of FYM, plus 40 kg/ha N, 40 kg/ha P_2O_5, and 80 kg/ha of K_2O (Mandal and Saraswat, 1968). If no FYM is applied, top dressing with 45 to 56 kg/ha (40 to 50 lb/acre) of N is suggested in July and again in August for a fourth-year crop in India (Chaugule and Khot, 1963).

Usually the *A. campanulatus* crop requires two to four weedings, dependent on the weed condition before planting and the condition of neighboring fields (Chaugule and Khot, 1957). Usually after the trenching and mounding is done in the third month, little further cultivation is needed (Iyer, 1935). No major pest or disease has been found to affect the crop (Chaugule and Khot, 1957). However, an aphid-borne mosaic virus has been described in India that reduces root growth and causes proliferation of lateral bud and cormlet formation (Chatterjee et al., 1971).

In the Uedama culture of *A. rivieri* in Japan, fertilizer application rates are comparable to those used on *A. campanulatus* in India. In addition, herbicides, pesticides, and mechanical cultivation are employed. Although corm yields have been increased by these methods, damage from *Erwina caratovora, Xanthomonas conjac,* and *Rhizoctonia solani* has also increased (Kurihara, 1979).

In the Jinenjo culture of *A. rivieri,* mulching with 75 to 250 kg/ha (65 to 220 lb/acre) of straws of rice, barley, or wild herbs is the only fertilizer. *Paulownia tomentosa* shade trees may also supply some nutrients since they are legumes. Weeding is by hand, and one or two pesticide sprays per year may be used. Little or no disease has been found in Jinenjo culture of *A. rivieri* (Kurihara, 1979).

5. Harvesting and Yields

Harvesting of *A. campanulatus* is in the dry fall and winter months. Digging of the individual corms (Fig. 7) by hand is usually delayed until sold or consumed, even if additional irrigation is required, since loss of moisture from the harvested corms may be up to 4%/day for the first 4 days (Chaugule and Khot, 1957). Individual tubers usually average 1.4 to 2.3 kg (3 to 5 lb) after 3 years and 6.8 to 9 kg (15 to 20 lb) after 4 years (Chaugule and Khot, 1957). However, corms weighing up to 23 to 27 kg (50 to 60 lb) have been reported (Abraham,

Figure 7 Corms of *Amorphophallus campanulatus* corms on sale in market in Suva, Fiji. (Photograph courtesy of P. Rotar, University of Hawaii.)

1969; 1970). Yields of 16.8 tonnes/ha (15,000 lb/acre) (Iyer, 1935),
44.2 tonnes/ha (39,380 lb/acre) (Ahmed and Rashid, 1975), 34.6 tonnes/
ha (30,820 lb/acre) (Gesmundo, 1932), 67.2 tonnes/ha (59,893 lb/acre)
(Chaugule and Khot, 1963), 36.8 tonnes/ha (32,420 lb/acre) (Kumar
et al., 1973), and 44 tonnes/ha (40,000 lb/acre) (Chaugule and Khot,
1957) have been reported.

A. rivieri is commonly harvested in October. Production in Japan
amounted to 70,000 tons before World War II, 130,000 tons in 1967, and
100,000 tons in 1969 (Yamaga, 1973; Kurihara, 1979). The 100,000 tons
in 1969 was on 1222 ha (3020 acre) of Jinenjo culture and 14,108 ha
(34,850 acre) of Uedama culture (Kurihara, 1979). Collection of *A. oncophyllus* and *A. variabilis* in Indonesia for export to Japan began
during the Japanese occupation (Sastrapradja, 1970) and was restarted
in 1962 to alleviate the shortage of konnjaku flour (Ohtsuki, 1967).

C. Preservation Methods

1. Postharvest Handling Methods

Corms of *A. campanulatus* (Fig. 7) are usually harvested by hand, and
roots and soil are removed by hand or with water. Corms are commonly
stored in the soil with additional irrigation, if necessary, until consumed
or sold. This is because the rate of moisture loss from the harvested
corms for the first 4 days is from 3 to 4%/day and more than 25% can be
lost in the first month (Chaugule and Khot, 1957), and up to one-third
the weight can be lost in 2 months (Iyer, 1935). March-harvested
corms are reported to store better (Iyer, 1935). Corms are often dipped prior to storage in a slurry of cow dung and ash, then stored in a
corner of the house covered with straw (Iyer, 1935; Hrishi and Balagopal, 1979). High humidity and injury during harvesting may lead to
corm decay. Mealy bugs and saprophytic sclerotium have been observed
during storage (Hrishi and Balagopal, 1979), and *Araecerus fasciculatus*
de Geer is reported to infest corms during storage in India (Lai and
Pillai, 1977). Corms may be stored for months at 10°C (50°F) by selling
or consuming those that sprout first (Iyer, 1935; Kay, 1973; Hrishi
and Balagopal, 1979a).

By dipping freshly harvested corms for 1 min in a 4% fungicidal wax
emulsion, the corms could be stored at room temperature for 50 days
with minimal loss in weight or sprout emergence (Food Technology Research Institute, 1960/61). Similarly treated corms stored in soil
tended to sprout and loose weight at a faster rate.

Storage of mature corms of *A. rivieri* prior to sale or consumption
involves drying for 3 to 4 days in the sun, then storage in sacks in a
dry place (Motte, 1932). Those corms to be planted the next year are
also dried in the sun, but for 2 to 3 days. They are then stored on
shelves in beds 15 to 20 cm deep. The shelves are in a shelter protected from freezing and high humidity. If temperatures reach below

-5°C, the corms do not germinate well. In the spring only the vigorously germinating corms are planted in the field (Motte, 1932).

2. Products, Uses, and Dietary Significance

A. campanulatus is almost entirely sold or prepared for consumption
from the fresh corm. Over 800 ha (2000 acre) are reported to be grown
in India where it is grown for sale to the cities as well as for local consumption (Chaugule and Khot, 1957). The India, Bangladesh, and Sri
Lanka region is the only area of major cultivation. Eastward in Malaysia,
Indonesia, and the Philippines most cultivation is subsistence in nature
with mostly small backyard gardens. In Melanesia and Polynesia it appears to have former significance as a subsistence crop but is only consumed presently in emergencies after long cooking (Brown, 1931;
Quartermaster Corps, 1943; Massal and Barrau, 1955). It is also used
for medicinal purposes in the Philippines and India (Diguangco, 1950;
Chaugule and Khot, 1957; Kay, 1973).

    A. rivieri is sometimes prepared for consumption from the fresh
corm in China and Japan (Motte, 1932), and the 1-year-old corms are
reported to be very sweet and succulent (Coursey, 1968). However,
most production in Japan is presently dried and processed into flour.
About 90% of the konjac mannan flour is mostly processed into the food
konnyaku (Motte, 1932). However, konjac mannan flour is also used
to make paste that does not separate when frozen and thawed and is not
eaten by insects. It is also used in the fabrication of paper during the
warm months and in textiles has a use similar to that of starch. Cotton
is also treated by drying and dipping in a dilute caustic soda solution.
After rinsing and drying, the cotton feels similar to linen or hemp.
Coatings of konjac mannan flour, water, and oil or glycerin mixture
when dried and treated with dilute caustic soda solutions produce a
waterproof coating formerly used on umbrellas, raincoats, carriage tops,
and airplane wings. Cosmetics such as those for chapped skin, beauty
creams, and hair pomades also use konjac flour (Motte, 1932).

    The fiber and cell debris, along with some mannan that is separated
from the konjac mannan flour, commonly by air separation, is called
tobiko. Tobiko is mixed with clay and used to cover the boards in walls
of houses. It is also used to form brickets of coal dust, incense sticks,
and is used in some shampoos (Motte, 1932).

    A. oncophyllus and *A. variabilis* collected in Indonesia are presum-
ably all processed into flour. This iles mannan flour is mostly processed
into the food konnyaku (Ohtsuki, 1967). However, iles mannan, extracted by superheated water or the action of a pancreatic enzyme
preparation on the dried ground corms, is reported to be used in the
creaming of rubber latex (Smith and Montgomery, 1959). Both iles
mannan and similarly extracted konjac mannan are valuable beater
additives for augmenting the strength of paper sheets (Wise, 1949;
Smith and Montgomery, 1959).

Konnyaku is commonly eaten by the Japanese more than two times per week. One hundred thousand tons of *A. rivieri* corms were produced in Japan in 1969. These corms contained about 12% or 12,000 tons of glucomannan (Ohsuki, 1967). If 90% of this is processed into konnyaku (Motte, 1932), which is about 3% glucomannan (Wenkam, in press), then this is enough to produce about 320,000,000 kg (700 million lb) of konnyaku.

3. Preservation Methods and Processes

For *A. campanulatus* no preservation methods other than storage of fresh corms have been described. *A. rivieri*, *A. oncophyllus*, and *A. variabilis* are commonly air-dried in the sun and then ground and separated into flour and fiber and cell debris. The dried corms and flour may be stored for long periods. The method described in 1932 and still used in some areas today involves peeling and slicing the corm into 5-cm slices. These slices are skewered onto bamboo sticks 60 to 90 cm long at spaces 2 to 3 cm apart and placed in the sun in groups of six or eight. After about 1 week of drying, the slices are crushed into a material termed *arako*. The arako is then ground in a mortar and pestle run by a water wheel. During the grinding process a flap attached to the pestle blows away the fiber, cell debris, and some mannan flour. The flour is termed *konako* and the fiber and debris are termed *tobiko*. Fresh tubers (100 kg) are dried into 18 kg of arako, and this is ground and separated into 12 kg of flour (konako) and 6 kg of tobiko. The flour contains about 17% water, 68% carbohydrates, 0.6% fats, 2.3% fiber, and 4.5% ash (Motte, 1932).

4. Typical Recipes

A. campanulatus is always cooked before being consumed because of the acridity related to calcium oxalate raphides. Most cultivated varieties are usually low in acridity (Senewiratne, 1963), but some wild forms may be extremely acrid (Quartermaster Corps, 1943; Barrau, 1958; Plucknett, 1970; Herklots, 1972; Leon, 1976). In Indonesia the corms are boiled with sugar and mixed with coconut milk (Sastrapradja, 1970) in a manner similar to the recipes given for *Alocasia* and *Cyrtosperma* (see those sections). In India (Kundu, 1967) and Bangladesh (Ahmed and Rashid, 1975) the pieces of corms are boiled in water and eaten with rice, or a curry is made similar to the recipe given for *Alocasia*. The corms may also be made into chips (Hrishi and Balagopal, 1979b). The leaves or petioles are never eaten in Bangladesh (Rashid and Daunicht, 1979). However, when young they may be consumed in the Philippines (Reantaso, 1935).

A. *rivieri* corms are sometimes used in dishes in place of *araimo* (*Colocasia* corms) (Hegnauer, 1963). Apparently the 1-year-old corms are very sweet and succulent (Coursey, 1968). However, most corms are processed into flour. *A. oncophyllus* and *A. variabilis* are not consumed in Indonesia but are processed into flour. Both konnyaku flour *(A. rivieri)* and iles-iles flour *(A. oncophyllus* and *A. variabilis)* are processed into konnyaku. The method used in Hawaii (Miller, 1933) is outlined below:

1. Water (26.5 to 30 liters) is gradually stirred into 0.9 kg of flour until it becomes uniformly soft and gelatinous.
2. It is allowed to sit for 15 min, then stirred, and allowed to sit again.
3. A mixture of 240 to 360 cc of lime and 2 liters of water is strained and then added with thorough mixing until the gelatinous mass thickens.
4. It is then poured 2 cm deep into trays, allowed to sit, and then cut into 10-cm squares.
5. The squares are boiled for 20 min, allowed to cool in the cooking water, and then stored, refrigerated in the same water. It is reported to last indefinitely if the water is not changed.
6. An alternate noodle form, called shirataki, is prepared by pressing the lime-treated gelatinous mass through a sieve before cooking.

Two recipes using konnyaku follow:

Konnyaku shirai (Miller, 1933)

Ingredients: 3 cups (570 g) konnyaku, 3 cups (0.7 liter) water, 3 tablespoons (36 g) sugar, 3 tablespoons (42 g) shoyu, 3/8 cube (195 g) tofu, 4-1/2 tablespoons (81 g) miso.

The konnyaku is cut into 5-cm-long strips and parboiled in water for 5 min. The konnyaku is drained; the shoyu and sugar are added and cooked until the shoyu is absorbed, then allowed to cool. A paste is made of the mixed tofu and miso, then mixed iwth the konnyaku. The dish is served cold. Makes 3 cups (651 g) which has a total caloric content of 514, distributed 106 to protein, 84 to fat, and 324 to carbohydrate.

Nigome (Miller, 1933)

Ingredients: 1 cup (22 g) aburage, 1/2 cup (58 g) carrots, 1/2 cup (74 g) konnyaku, 1/2 cup (68 g) araimo (*Colocasia* corms), 1/2 cup (68 g) daikon (*Raphanus*), 1/2 cup (40 g) gobo (burdock), 2/3 cup water, 1/4 cup (4 g) dried bonito, 2 tablespoons (24 g) sugar, 1/4 cup (56 g) shoyu (soy sauce).

The vegetables, aburage, and konnyaku are cut into 1/4-in. cubes and simmered for 20 to 30 min with the aburage on top. (The gobo is often cooked and allowed to stand in water for 3 to 4 hr before adding). When the vegetables are tender, the seasonings are added and then cooked for 5 to 10 min more. Dried shrimp or pork may be added for flavor. Makes 2-1/2 cups (452 g) which has a total caloric content of 348 distributed 58 to protein, 46 to fat, and 244 to carbohydrate.

D. Biochemical and Nutritional Composition

Corms of *A. campanulatus* are a good source of carbohydrate (Table 3). And in some samples, it appears these corms may also provide a fair amount of protein. This protein is reported to be evenly distributed in the corms (Shanmugam et al., 1976). A study of digestibility in the Philippines showed the corm contained 0.7% digestible protein and 14.8% total digestible nutrients when fed in a balanced diet (Loosli et al., 1954). All cultivars in Bangladesh are yellow-fleshed and carotene-rich (Rashid and Daunicht, 1979). A meal made from the corms contained 54.9% starch, 8.9% protein, 0.8% fats, 6.2% sugars, 7.8% cellulose, 5.8% lignin, 5% ash, 3.1% pentosans, and 2.7% total mannan, which was not soluble in water 55°C (van Hulssen and Koolhass, 1940).

The starch is 44% amylose and 56% amylopectin (Chowdhury and Hussain, 1979). The grains are 92% kernel and 8% coat, vary from round to polyhedral in shape, and a maximum of 18.7 μm and a minimum of 5.5 μm in size (Qudrat-I-Khuda et al., 1960). The yield of extracted starch from corms is low (4.3%) when compared with sweet potatoes (18.2%) or cassava (28%) (Reantaso, 1935). A yield of up to 24.4% alcohol was obtained by fermentation after treating with 1% sulfuric acid, hydrolyzing for 2-1/2 hr at 120°C and 15 lb pressure, and partly neutralizing with 3% ammonimum hydroxide (Barrau, 1960).

The flowers of *A. campanulatus* at the start of the rainy season emit a fetid odor from the purple appendage. This odor has been related to the attraction of pollinating insects and has been reported to be due to decomposition of protein in the appendage (Herbert and Pacis, 1925). The odor may also be related to the volatile amines produced by some arum lily species (Smith and Meeuse, 1966).

Some extracts of *A. campanulatus* corms include: betulinic acid, β-sitosterol, stigmasterol, lupeol, triacontane, palmitate, glucose, galactose, rhamnose, and xylose (Chawla and Chibber, 1976). These chemicals may be related to *A. campanulatus* use in treatment of dysentery, piles, acute rheumatism, gland enlargement, toothache, and tuberculosis (Chawla and Chibber, 1976).

Trypsin inhibitor and chymotrypsin inhibitor levels (units/milliliter) in *A. campanulatus* corms were low (1.13, 0.07) when compared with *C. antiquorum* (104.69, 4.25) and potato, *Solanum tuberosum* (30.33, 69.00) (Sumathi and Pattabiraman, 1975). Leaves of *A. campanulatus* produce oxalic acid photosynthetically within 1 min of exposure to labeled carbondioxide (Seal and Sen, 1970). Corms of *A. rivieri* contain raphides, which apparently have barbs (Sakai and Shiroma, 1983).

A complete analysis of the corms of *A. rivieri, A. oncophyllus,* or *A. variabilis* could not be found. In *A. rivieri* the corm is reported to consist of 91.67% water, 0.8% fat, 6.47% carbohydrate, 0.3% fiber, and 0.36% ash (Motte, 1932). Flour made from *A. oncophyllus* corms contains: 67% total mannan, 57% soluble (55°C water) mannan, 12.3% starch, 6.5% protein, 3.7% cellulose, 2% lignin, 1.5% sugar, 1.5% pentosans,

0.5% fats, and 3% ash (van Hulssen and Koolhass, 1940). The mannan occurs in many large cells in the corm (Paliwal and Kavathekar, 1972).

Most analyses of *A. rivieri, A. oncophyllus*, and *A. variabilis* are concerned with the polysaccharide content (Table 4). Specific interest is in the glucomannan content because of its uses in industry (see section on products) and the production of food, konnyaku. The analysis of konnyaku is given in Table 5. It is not known whether the flour used was konjac flour or iles-iles flour.

It has long been known that konnyaku is almost completely digested in humans, but probably not assimilated (Kuriyama et al., 1969). The caloric value is still in doubt and is thus not listed in the Japan Nutritionist Association Standard Tables (Table 5). Pancreas secretions apparently release a glucomannan from the konnyaku (Pigman and Goepp, 1948), but the glucomannan is not hydrolyzed until it reaches the large intestine. There intestinal microorganisms, including *Aerobacter mannanolyticus*, produce mannases which break down the gulcomannan (Inoue and Inoue, 1958; Kuriyama et al., 1969). It is not known if the release of glucose and mannan (Altman and Dittmer, 1968) is rapid enough for assimilation. However, studies on degradation and fermentation of other gums by *Bacteriodes* strains from the human colon (Salyers et al., 1977) suggest that some nutrients may be absorbed.

Konnyaku apparently has other beneficial effects when included in the diet. Studies have shown that incorporation of konnyaku powder into a hypercholesterolemic diet markedly lowered the plasma cholesterol level (Kuriyama et al., 1969). However, absorption of iron may also be affected (Truswell, 1977). The glucomannan, termed a soluble fiber, when fed with glucose or in the diet also lowered plasma glucose levels.

The slaked lime added during gelling of konnyaku eliminates a moiety containing a C=O group and causes crystallization of the molecules of konjac mannan in a network structure partially through hydrogen bonding (Maekaji, 1974). This calcium in the gelled konnyaku is probably ultilizable by humans (Nagayama et al., 1975).

The glucomannans from *A. rivieri* (konjac mannan) and *A. oncophyllus* and *A. variabilis* (iles mannan) have been studied extensively (Rebers and Smith, 1954; Wise, 1949; Sugiyama, et al., 1972; Blanshard and Mitchell, 1979). The D-mannose-to-D-glucose ratio in konjac mannan is 2:1 to 1.6:1 (Rebers and Smith, 1954; Smith and Montgomery, 1959; Sugiyama et al., 1972). In iles mannan the ratio is near 1:1 (Wise 1949). The composition of leaf-blade glucomannan may also differ from that in the corm in *A. rivieri* (Murata, 1972). Properties of mannases from *A. rivieri* corms, bacteria, and fungi have also been studied (Shimahara et al., 1975; Sugiyama et al., 1973; Emi et al., 1972; Blanshard and Mitchell, 1979).

Table 3 Food Values of *Amorphophallus Campanulatus*

Plant part, location of sample collection (100-g sample)	Calories	Moisture (g)	Total carbohy. (g)	Starch (g)	Other carbohy. (g)	Fiber (g)	Reducing sugar (g)	Protein (g)
Corms, fresh								
South Pacific[a,b]	79	79	18			0.8		1.2
Bangladesh (11.03% removed as waste)[c]		75	21			0.8		2.5
Bangladesh (dry wt basis)[d]		(71)	70			11.0	1.5	8.8
Mymensingh, Bangladesh (oven-dry basis)[e]		(89)	63					5.3
Philippines[f]	100	75	18			0.6		5.1
Philippines[g]		75	18			0.6		5.1
Philippines[h]		72	24			0.9		1.7
Corms, cooked								
Philippines[h]		84	13			0.9		1.3
Young leaves, fresh								
Philippines[g]			3			4.1		3.4
Old leaves, fresh								
Philippines[g]			3			7.1		2.5
Young petioles, fresh								
Philippines[g]			1			0.8		1.2
Old petioles, fresh								
Philippines[g]			4			1.6		1.0

[a] Massal and Barrau, 1955.
[b] Massal and Barrau, 1956.
[c] Rashid and Daunicht, 1979.
[d] Qudrat-I-Khuda et al., 1960.
[e] Chowdhury and Hussain, 1979.
[f] Hermano, 1934.
[g] Reantaso, 1935.
[h] Loosli et al., 1954.

Fats (g)	Ash (g)	Ascorbic acid (mg)	Niacin (mg)	Ribo-flavin (mg)	Thiamine (mg)	Carotene	Calcium (mg)	Iron (mg)	Phos-phorus (mg)	Vitamin A (IU)
2.1	0.8	tr	0.7	0.08	0.06		50	0.6	20	434
0.2	1.3	3		0.05	0.04	0.9	56	1.4	53	
0.4	3.3						95	7	153	
1.4	2.9						240	11	300	
0.4	0.7									
0.4	0.7									
0.6	1.2									
0.2	1.0									
0.6	1.3									
0.4	1.8									
0.3	0.8									
0.3	0.9									

Table 4 Content of Corms and Leaves of Amorphophallus Species

Species and plant part	G/100 g dry matter									Starch grain sizes	
	Water	Dry matter	Starch	Gluco-mannan	Other polyose	Not hydrolysed	Free sugar	Glucose	Fructose	Compound	Single
A. campanulatus Corms[a]	70.1	29.9	77	0	14.2	8.5	0			20-30	10-15
A. variabilis Corms[a]	78.4	21.6	27	44	0	6	9			20-30	5-6
A. oncophyllus Corms[a]	79.7	20.3	2	55	14	8	0			20-30	2-3
A. bulbifer Corms[a]	80.0	20.0	70	5.5	13	10	0			20-30	4-5
A. rivieri Freshly harvested corm[a]	80.8	20.0	10.6	64	5	5	0			20-30	4-5
Growing corm[b]			8.3	39.8				6.50	6.08		
Mature Corm[b]			18.6	50.4				9.58	5.6		
Dormant corm[c]			18.9	58.8				0.57	1.2		
Withered corm[b]			6.9	36.2				2.82	2.31		
Mature leaf blade[b]			2.9	19.2				7.68	6.63		
Mature leaf petiole[b]			0.4	18.8				15.56	9.60		

[a]Ohtsuki, 1967.
[b]Goto, 1922.
[c]Smith and Montgomery, 1959.

Table 5 Food Values of Konnyaku

Nutrients and units	Hawaii, fresh[a]	Japan, fresh[b]	Japan, canned[a]
	Amount in 100 g, edible portion		
Proximate			
Water (g)	96.60	97.40	96.48
Energy (kcal)	12	—	13
(kJ)	50	—	54
Protein (6.25) (g)	0.09	0.1	0.04
Lipid (fat) (g)	0	0	0.01
Carbohydrate (g)	3.07	2.3	3.28
Fiber (g)	0.06	0.1	0.37
Ash (g)	0.24	0.2	0.19
Minerals			
Calcium (mg)	63	43	63
Iron (mg)	0.30	0.4	0.28
Magnesium (mg)	7	0	3
Phosphorus (mg)	7	5	3
Potassium (mg)	10	—	18
Sodium (mg)	38	10	2
Vitamins			
Ascorbic acid (mg)	0.50	0	0.10
Thiamin (mg)	0.021	0	0
Riboflavin (mg)	0	0	0
Niacin (mg)	0.020	0	0
Vitamin A (IU)	0	0	0

[a]Wenkam, 1983.
[b]Japan Nutritionist Association, 1964.

ACKNOWLEDGMENTS

I thank S. Gusukuma for assistance in obtaining references, R. Okuda and M. Watanabe for photographic assistance, and M. Agag, Jr., and L. Nakamura for typing the manuscript. P. Rotar, C. H. Lamoureux, and L. Stemmermann graciously supplied the photographs. Special thanks to R. Chatelanat of the Food and Agriculture Organization of the United Nations for grant support in 1970 that initiated my interest in aroid root crops.

REFERENCES

Abraham, A. (1969). Tuber crops of India. *Indian Agr. News Dig.* 1(3):111-114. 4 pages of plates

Abraham, A. (1970). Breeding work on tapioca (cassava) and a few other tropical tuber crops. Honolulu, Hawaii. *Proc. Second Int'l Symp. Trop. Root Tuber Crops.* I. pp. 76-78.

Ahmed, G., and Rashid, M. M. (1975). A comparative study of the gross morphological characters and the yield potentialities of the major types of edible aroids of Bangladesh. *Bangladesh Horticulture* 3:15-21.

Allen, R. N. (1929). Photomicrographs of Philippine starches. *Philipp. J. Sci.* 38:242-255.

Altman, P. L., and Dittmer, D. S. (eds.) (1968). *Metabolism,* Bethesda, Md., Federation of American Societies for Experimental Biology.

Arakeri, H. R. (1950). Seed production in suran (*Amorphophallus campanulatus*) *Dharwar Agric. Coll. Mag.* 3:3-4.

Agron. Colon. (1939). Note sur une plante a tubercles amylace's l'Ilis-Ilis de Java (*Amorphophallus campanulatus* Blume), 28(255): 84-87.

Asthana, R. P. (1946). Bacterial leaf-spot on arum. *Curr. Sci.* 15(12):356.

Bailey, L. H., Bailey, E. Z., and staff of L. H. Bailey Hortorium. (1976). *Hortus Third.* New York, Macmillan.

Barrau, J. (1957). Les arace'es a tubercules alimentaires des iles du Pacifique sud. *J. Agric. Trop. Bot. Appl.* 4:34-52.

Barau, J. (1958). Subsistence agriculture in Melanesia. *B. P. Bishop Museum Bulletin.* 219:1-111.

Barrau, J. (1959). The sago palms and other food plants of marsh dwellers in the south Pacific islands. *Economic Botany* 13(2):151-162.

Barrau, J. (1960). The selection, domestication and cultivation of food plants in tropical oceania in the pre-European era. *Symp. on the Impact of Man on Humid Tropics Vegetation.* Terr. of Papua and New Guinea, Goroka, pp. 67-72.

Barrau, J. (1961). Subsistence agriculture in Polynesia and Micronesia. *B. P. Bishop Museum Bulletin* 223:43-67.

Barrau, J. (1962). Les plantes alimentaires de l'Oceanie. *Ann. Mus. Com. Masseille* Ser. F.:1955-1961.

Betham, R. (1982). Personal communication. Western Samoa, Samoan-German Crop Protection Center-Nuu.

Bikajle, T. (1960). Taro cultivation practices and beliefs. Part II. The Eastern Carolines and the Marshall Islands, Taro cultivation in the Marshalls. *Anthropological Working Papers,* No. 6. Guam, M. I., Office of the Staff Anthropolgist, Trust Territory of the Pacific Islands, pp. 133-140.

Blanshard, J. M. V., and Mitchell, J. R. (1979). *Polysaccharides in Food,* London-Boston, Butterworths.

Boag, A. D., and Curtis, R. E. (1959). Agriculture and population in the Mortlock Islands. *Papua New Guin. Agric. J.* 12(1):21-24.

Brown, F. B. H. (1931). Flora of southeastern Polynesia. I. Monocotyledons. *B.P. Bishop Museum Bulletin* 84:128-136.

Cano, O. M. (1974). Evaluation of the fertility of Peruvian soils. Bolete'n T'ecnico, Ministerio de Agricultura, Peru No. 78, pp. 56.

Catala, Rene' L. A. (1957). Report on the Gilbert Islands. Some aspects of human ecology. *The Pacific Science Board, National Academy of Sciences-National Research Council, Atoll Research Bulletin* 59. Washington, D.C.

Chatterjee, S. N., Capoor, S. P., Ram, R. D., and Nimbalkar, M. R., (1971). Effect of mosaic virus on production of corms of *Amorphopallus campanulatus*. *Indian Phytopathology* 24:821-823.

Chaugule, B. A., and Khot, B. D. (1957). Four years with suran. *Indian Fmg.* 7(9):27-31.

Chaugule, B. A., and Khot, B. D. (1963). Effect of size of seed corm and spacing on growth and yield of fourth year suran (*Amorphophallus campanulatus*, Blume). *Indian Journal of Agronomy* 7:310-318.

Chawla, H. M., and Chibber, S. S. (1976). Some extractives from *Amorphophallus campanulatus*. *Indian J. Pharmacy* 38:109-110.

Chevalier, A. (1931). Les amorphophallus et leurs usages. *Revue Bot. Appl. Agric. Trop.* 11(122):809-816.

Chowdhury, B., and Hussain, M. (1979). Chemical composition of the edible parts of aroids grown in Bangladesh. *Indian J. Agric. Sci.* 49(2):110-115.

Clark, A. M., and Walters, R. B. (1934). The presence of a sapotoxin in *Xanthosoma atrovirens*, a tropical food tuber. *Biochem. J.* 28(3): 1131-1134.

Coursey, D. G. (1968). The edible aroids. *World Crops* 20(4):25-30.

Coursey, D. G., Jackson, G., de la Pena, R., Adenuga, A., Chandra, S., Ching, P., de Bruijn, G., Hrishi, N., Miller, S., Nwana, I., Siki, B., Strauss, M., Tanaka, J., Tupuola, T., and Watson, J. (1979). Working group report: handling and storage. In *Small-Scale Processing and Storage of Tropical Root Crops* (D. L. Plucknett, ed.). Boulder, Colo., Westview Press, pp. 15-25.

Darlington, C. D., and Wylie, A. P. (1955). *Chromosome Atlas of Flowering Plants*. London, George Allen and Unwin Ltd.

Dekker, G. H. W. D., and Halewijn, E. K. E. (1940). De bereiding val ilesmannaanmeel uit *Amorphophallus oncophyllus*. (Preparation of meal from *Amorphophallus oncophyllus*). *De Bergcultures* 14(22): 708-718.

de la Cruz, E. T. (1970). Root and tuber crops of the Trust Territory of the Pacific Islands. Honolulu, Hawaii. *Proc. Second Int'l Symp. Trop. Root Tuber Crops. II.* pp. 77-86.

de la Pena, R. S. (1970). The edible aroids in the Asian-Pacific area. Honolulu, Hawaii. *Proc. Second Int'l Symp. Trop. Root Tuber Crops. I.* pp. 136-140.

Diguangco, J. (1950). *Philippine Medicinal Plants.* Manila, University of St. Tomas Press.

Doi, Shinji. (1944). Value of dokuimo as a raw material for the fermentation industry. *J. Agric. Chem. Soc. Japan* 20:457-464; *Chem. Abstr.* 43(3):1146F.

Emi, S., Fukumoto, J., and Yamamoto, Y. (1972). Crystallization and some properties of mannase. *Agric. Biol. Chem.* (Tokyo) 36(6):991-1001.

Food and Agriculture Organization. (1969). *Crop Storage Tech. Rep. 1 Fd. Res. Dev. Unit. Accra.* pp.69.

Fd. Technol. Res. Inst. (1960/61). Effect of waxing on elephant yam (*Amorphophallus campanulatus*) Mysore, *Ann. Rep. Cent.*, pp. 3-4.

Furtado, C. X. (1940). The Malayan Kilades and other edible aroids. *Malay. Agric. Horticultural Assn. Magazine* 10:11-17.

Furtado, C. X. (1941). *Alocasia macrorrhiza* and its varieties. *Gdn's Bull. Straits Settl.* 11(3):244-257.

Gesmundo, A. E. (1932). The nutritive value of "Gallan," *Cyrtosperma merkusii* (Hassk.). Schott. *Philipp. Agric.* 21:106-126.

Gill, L. S. (1973). A note on the karyology of *Amorphophallus rivieri* (Araceae). Baileya 19:42-43.

Glassman, S. (1952). Flora of Ponape. *B. P. Bishop Museum Bulletin* 209:15-32.

Goto, K. (1922). *J. Biochem. (Japan)* 1:210, in Smith and Montgomery, 1959.

Grunwald, C. (1971). Effects of free sterols, steryllester, and steryl glycoside on membrane permeability. *Plant Physiol.* 48:653-655.

Haudricourt, A. (1941). Les colocasiee's alimentaires (taros et yautias). Les alocasia. *Revue Bot. App. Agric. Trop.* 21(1):55-58.

Hegnauer, R. (1963). *Chemotaxnomie der Pflanzen. II. Monocotyledoneae.* Basel und Stuttgart, Birkhauser Verlag.

Herbert, D. A., and Pacis, A. L. (1925). The odor of *Amorphophallus campanulatus. Philipp. Agric.* 13:349-350.

Herklots, G. A. C. (1972). *Vegetables in south-east Asia.* New York, Hafner Press, pp. 401-416.

Hermano, A. J. (1934). Food Values. *Bureau of Science Popular Bulletin* 16:24, in Pancho, 1949.

Hokama, K., Nakasone, Y., and Miyagi, J. (1979). Smith degradation of wet-taro starch amylopectin produced in Okinawa and determination of its average chain length. University of the Ryukyus, *Science Bulletin of the College of Agriculture*, No. 26, 169-181.

Hrishi, N., and Balagopal, C. (1979a). Storage problems in aroids and sweet potato in India. In *Small-Scale Processing and Storage of Tropical Root Crops* (D. L. Plucknett, ed.) Boulder, Colo. Westview Press.

Hrishi, N., and Balagopal, C. (1979b). Processing of root crops in India. In *Small-Scale Processing and Storage of Tropical Root Crops* (D. L. Plucknett, ed.), Boulder, Colo., Westview Press.

Inoue, N., and Inoue, K. (1958). Studies on the mannase of *Aerobacter mannanolyticus*. Inoue et Inoue. *Annual Report of the National Institute of Nutrition* (Tokyo) 52:67-69.

Iyer, N. A. (1935). A note on the cultivation of elephant yam (*Amorphophallus campanulatus*) in Chittoor Taluk. *Madras Agriculture Journal* 23:451-454.

Japan Nutritionist Association. (1964). *Standard Tables of Food Composition*. Tokyo, Dai-Ichi Publishing Co., Ltd.

Jas, J. S., and Bai, K. V. (1978). Chromosome number in *Amorphophallus commutatus*. *J. Root Crops* 4(1):41-42.

Kawakami, K., and Ono, Y. (1971). Essential points for improving production of tropical root crops. *Nettai Nogyo (Japanese Journal of Tropical Agriculture)* 15:163-168.

Kay, D. E. (1973). *Tropical Prod. Institute Crop and Product Digest, No. 2 Root Crops*. London, Tropical Products Institute, pp. 61-66, 71-75, 139-143.

Keleny, G. P. (1960). Notes on the origin and introduction of the Basic food crops of the New Guinea people. *Symp. on Impact of Man on Humid Tropics Vegetation*. Terr. of Papua and New Guinea, Soroka, pp. 76-85.

Kim, D. Y., and Defngin, F. (1960). Taro cultivation practices and beliefs. Part I. The Western Carolines, Taro cultivation in Yap. *Anthropological Working papers*, No. 6. Guam, M.I., Office of the Staff Anthropologist, Trust Territory of the Pacific Islands, pp. 48-68.

Kirch, P. V. (1978). Indigenous agriculture on Uvea (Western Polynesia) *Economic Botany* 32:157-181.

Kitamura, S. (1949). Notes on Araceae of Japan. *Acta Phytotaxonomica et Geolotanica* 14(1):5-8.

Koregave, B. A. (1964). Effect of mixed cropping on the growth and yield of suran (Elephant yam, *Amorphophallus campanulatus* Blume). *Indian Journal of Agronomy* 9:255-260.

Krishnan, R., Magoon, M. L., and Vijaya Bai, K. (1970). Karyological studies in *Amorphophallus campanulatus*. *Can. J. Genet. Cytol.* 12:187-196.

Kumar, C. R., Mohan, C. R., Mandal R. C., and Singh, K. D. (1973). Effect of mulching and plant density on growth, yield and quality of *Amorphophallus*. *Indian Journal of Agronomy* 18:62-66.

Kundu, B. C. (1967). Some edible rhizomatous and tuberous crops of India. *Proc. International Symp. on Trop. Root Crops* 1:124-130.

Kurihara, H. (1979). Trends and problems of konjak (*Amorphophallus konjac*) cultivation in Japan. *JARQ (Japan Norin Suisan Gijutsi Kaigi)* 13:174-179.

Kuriyama, S., Okazaki, Y., and Yoshida, A. (1969). Hopocholesterolemic effect of polysaccharides and polysaccharide-rich foodstuffs in cholesterol-fed rats. *J. Nutrition* 97:382-388.

Lai, S. S., and Pillai, K. S. (1977). New record of Araecerus fasciculatus de Geer on Dioscorea alata and *Amorphophallus campanulatus*
under storage at Trivandrum. *Bulletin of Grain Technology (India).*
15(3):225.

Lambert, M. (1970). Culture, improvement and utilization of root crops
in South Pacific. Honolulu, Hawaii, *Proc. Second Int'l Symp. Trop.
Tuber Crops* II. pp. 70-73.

Lambert, M. (1979). Storage and processing of root crops in the South
Pacific. In *Small-Scale Processing and Storage of Tropical Root
Crops* (D. L. Plucknett, ed.) Boulder, Colo., Westview Press.

Leon, J. (1970). Interchange and maintenance of collections of tropical
tuber and root crops. Honolulu, Hawaii, *Proc. Second Int'l Symp.
Trop. Root Tuber Crops.* II. pp. 90-94.

Leon, J. (1976). Origin, evolution, and early dispersal of root and
tuber crops. *Proc. Fourth Symp. Int. Soc. Trop. Root Crops.*
pp. 20-35.

Loosli, J. K., Villegas, V., and Ynalvez, L. A. (1954). The digestibility of tropical kudzu (*Pueraria javanica*) and poñgapong (*Amorphophallus campanulatus*) by swine. *Philipp. Agric.* 38:491-493.

Luomala, K. (1974). The Cyrtosperma systemic pattern: aspects of
production in the Gilbert Islands. *Polynesian Society, Wellington,
Journal* 83(1):14-34.

Maekaji, K. (1974). The mechanism of gelation of konjac mannan.
Agric. Biol. Chem. 38:315-321.

Mahony, F. (1960a). Taro cultivation practices and beliefs. Part II.
The Eastern Carolines and the Marshall Islands, Taro cultivation in
Truk. *Anthropological Working Papers, No. 6.* Guam, M.I., Office
of the Staff Anthropologist, Trust Teritory of the Pacific Islands,
pp. 69-98.

Mahony, F. (1960b). Taro cultivation practices and beliefs. Part II.
The Eastern Carolines and the Marshall Islands, Taro cultivation in
Ponape. *Anthropological Working Papers, No. 6.* Guam, M.I., Office
of the Staff Anthropologist, Trust Territory of the Pacific Islands,
pp. 99-132.

Mandal, R. C., and Saraswat, V. N. (1968). Manurial requirement of
sweet yam in laterite soils of Kerala. *Indian Agriculturist* 12(1):25-28.

Massal, E., and Barrau, J. (1955). Pacific subsistence crops. . . taros.
South Pacific Commission Quarterly Bulletin 5(2):17-21.

Massal, E., and Barrau, J. (1956). The south sea islanders and their
food plants. *South Pacific Commission, Technical Paper, No. 94,*
1-51.

Maude, A. (1970). Shifting cultivation and population growth in Tonga.
Journal of Tropical Geography 31:57-64.

McKnight, R. K., and Obak, A. (1960). Taro cultivation practices and
beliefs. Part I. The Western Carolines, Taro cultivation in Palau.
Anthropological Working Papers, No. 6. Guam, M.I., Office of the
Staff Anthropologist, Trust Territory of the Pacific Islands, pp. 1-47.

Migvar, L. (1968). How to grow taros, yams, cassava, and sweet potatoes. *Mariana Is. Divn. Agric. Dep. Res. Dev. Trust Terr. Pacif. Is., Agric., Ext. Bull.*, No. 7, pp. 7-8.

Miller, C. D. (1933). Japanese food commonly used in Hawaii. *Hawaii Agriculture Experiment Station Bulletin No. 68*. Honolulu, University of Hawaii.

Motte, M. J. (1932). Le konnyaku in Japan. *Annales du Muse'e Colon., Marseille, 40th anne'e* 10(4):1-22.

Murai, M., Pen, F., and Miller, C. D. (1958). *Some Tropical South Pacific Island Foods*. Honolulu, University of Hawaii Press, pp. 159.

Murata, T. (1972). Studies on konjak mannan biosynthesis. Part I. An analytical study on carbohydrates during the growth on konjak plants. *Agricultural Chemical Society of Japan, Journal (Nippon Nogei Kagaku Kai)* 46:1-7.

Nagayama, S., Nakumura, A., Suzuki, K., and Innami, S. (1975). Studies on calcium in the edible konnyaku. *Report of the National Institute of Nutrition (Kokuritsu Eiyo Kenkyiyo)* 24:124-130.

Nahrstedt, A. (1975). Cyanogenesis in the Araceae. *Phytochemistry* 14(5/6):1339-1340.

Nair, P. K. R., Rama Varma, M., and Nelliat, E. V. (1974). Intercropping for enhanced profits from coconut plantation. *Indian Farming* 24(4):11-13.

Neal, M. C. (1965). *In Gardens of Hawaii*, Honolulu, Bishop Museum Press, p. 156.

Ochse, J. J. (1931). *Amorphophallus campanulatus*. Vegetables of the Dutch East Indies. *Buitenzorg-Java: Archipel-Drukkerij*, pp. 48-51.

Ohtsuki, T. (1928). Studien über das Konjakmannan. *Phytochimica* 4:1-39.

Ohtsuki, T. (1967). Studies on reserve carbohydrates of four *Amorphophallus* species, with special reference to mannan. *Bot. Mag. Tokyo (Nihon Shokurutsu Gakkai)* 81:119-126.

Osagie, A. U. (1977). Phytosterols in some tropical tubers. *J. of Agricultural and Food Chemistry* 25(5):1222-1223.

Owen, H. W. (1973). *Bat soup and other recipes from the South Seas.* Seattle, Washington, Graphics Press, p. 49.

Paliwal, G. S., and Kavathekar, A. K. (1972). Anatomy of vegetative food storage organs. 2. Stems. *Acta Agronomica Academical Scientiarum Hungaricae* 21(3/4):313-318.

Pancho, J. V. (1959). Notes on the cultivated aroids in the Philippines 1. The edible species. *Baileya* (3):63-70.

Parham, B. E. V. (1942). Some useful plants of the Fiji Islands. *Fiji Agric. J.* 13:39-47.

Peters, F. E. (1957). The chemical composition of some South Pacific foods. *Proc. Ninth Pacif. Sci. Congr.* 15:129-138.

Pigman, W. W., and Goepp, Jr. R. M. (1948). *Chemistry of the Carbohydrates.* Academic Press, New York, p. 616.

Plowman, T. (1969). Folk use of new world aroids. *Econ. Bot.* 23:97-122.

Plucknett, D. L. (1970). *Colocasia, Xanthosoma, Alocasia, Cyrtosperma,* and *Amorphophallus.* Honolulu, Hawaii, *Proc. Second Int'l Symp. Trop. Root Tuber Crops.* I. pp. 127-135.

Plucknett, D. L. (1976a). Giant swamp taro, a little-known Asian-Pacific food crop. *Proc. Fourth symp. Int. Soc. Trop. Root Crops.* pp. 36-40.

Plucknett, D. L. (1976b). Edible aroids. In *Evolution of Crop Plants* (N. W. Simmonds, ed.). London and New York, Longman, pp. 10-12.

Quartermaster Corps (1943). Emergency food plants and poisonous plants of the islands of the Pacific. *Technical Manual* 10-420:10-17.

Qudrat-I-Khuda, M. (1960). Properties of certain starch varieties and their sources in East Pakistan. *Pakist. J. Scient. Ind. Res.* 3(3): 159-162.

Quisumbing, F. A. (1914). The cultivated root-producing aroids. *Philipp. Agriculturalist and Forester* 3(4):85-98; 3(5):99-110.

Quisumbing, E. (1951). *Medicinal plants of the Philippines.* Manila, Manila Press.

Quisumbing, E. (1960). Wild species for foodstuffs and their domestication in the Philippines. *Symp. on Import of Man on Humid Tropics Vegetation,* Terr. of Papua and New Guinea, Goroka, pp. 90-93.

Rajendran, P. G., and Hrishi, N. (1976). Breaking seed dormancy in *Amorphophallus. J. Root Crops* 2(2):61-62.

Rajendran, P. G., Hrishi, N., and Maini, S. B. (1977). Genetic variability in *Amorphophallus* seedlings. *Journal of Root Crops* 3(1): 55-56.

Rashid, M. M. (1980). Personal communication. Bangladesh Agricultural Research Institute, Dacca, Bangladesh.

Rashid, M. M., and Daunicht, H. J. (1979). Chemical composition of nine edible aroid cultivars of Bangladesh. *Scientia Horticulturae* 10:127-134.

Rasper, V. (1969). Investigations on starches from major starch crops grown in Ghana. 2. Swelling and solubility patterns: amyloclastic susceptibility. *J. Sci. Fd. Agric.* 20(11):642-646.

Reantaso, C. G. (1935). Puñgapuñg as a source of starch and alcohol. *Philipp. Agric.* 24:239-248.

Reark, J. B. (1953). Cultivation of the genus *Alocasia* in Florida. *Florida State Hort. Soc. Pro., Annu. Meetings* 66:326-331.

Rebers, P. A., and Smith, F. (1954). The constitution of iles mannan. *J. Am. Chem. Soc.* 76:6097-6102.

Sakai, W. S. (1979). Aroid root crops, acridity, and raphides. In *Tropical Foods: Chemistry and Nutrition* (G. E. Inglett and G. Charalambous, eds.). New York, Academic Press, pp. 265-278.

Sakai, W. S. and Hanson, M. (1974). Mature raphide and raphid-idioblast structure in plants of the edible aroid genera *Colocasia, Alocasia,* and *Xanthosoma. Ann. Botany* 38:739-748.

Sakai, W. S., Hanson, M., and Jones, R. (1972). Raphides with barbs and grooves in *Xanthosoma sagittifolium*. *Science* 178:314-315.

Sakai, W. S., and Nagao, M. (1980). Raphide structure in *Dieffenbachia maculata*. *J. Am. Soc. Horticultural Sci.* 105:124-126.

Sakai, W. S. and Shiroma, S. (1983). Relationships between irritation and raphide microstructure and size. *Scanning Electron Microsc.* III:73-85.

Salyers, A. A., Vercellotti, J. R., West, S. E. H., and Wilkins, T. D. (1977). Fermentation of mucin and plant polysaccharides by strains of *Bacteroides* from the human colon. *Appl. Envir. Microbiol.* 33: 319-322.

Sastrapradja, S. (1970). Inventory, evaluation, and maintenance of the genetics stocks at Bogor. *Proc. Second Int'l Symp. Trop. Root Tuber Crops.* II. pp. 87-89.

Sasuke, N. (1949). Breadfruits, yams, and taros of Ponape Island. *Pacific Sci. Congr. Proc. (Honolulu)* 7(6):159-170.

Seal, S. N., and Sen, S. P. (1970). The photosynthetic production of oxalic acid in *Oxalis corniculata*. *Plant and Cell Physiol.* 11:119-128.

Senewiratne, S. T. (1963). *Field Crops of Ceylon.* Lake House, Colombo, Lake House Investments Limited Publishers.

Shanmugam, A., Srinivasan, C., and Selvaraj, P. (1976). Crude protein composition of elephant foot yams (*Amorphophallus campanulatus*). *Agricultural Research Journal of Kerala* 13:211-212.

Shimahara H., Suzuki, H., Sugiyama, N., and Nisizawa, K. (1975). Partial purification of B-mannases from the konjac tubers and their substrate specificity in relation to the structure of konjac glucomannan. *Agric. Biol. Chem. (Tokyo)* 39(2):301-312.

Siki, B. (1979). Processing and storage of root crops in Papua, New Guinea. In *Small-Scale Processing and Storage of Tropical Root Crops* (D. L. Plucknett, ed.). Boulder, Colo., Westview Press.

Smith, B. N., and Meeuse, B. J. S. (1966). Production of volatile amines and skatole at anthesis in some arum lily species. *Plant Physiol.* 41:343-347.

Smith, F., and Montgomery, R. (1959). *The Chemistry of Plant Gums and Mucilages.* London, Reinhold, pp. 627.

Soyza, D. J. de (1938). Yam cultivation in the Kegalla district. *Trop. Agric. Mag. Ceylon Agric. Soc.* 90(2):73-75.

Sproat, M. N. (1968). A guide to subsistence agriculture in Micronesia. Saipan, Mariana Islands, Division of Agriculture, Trust Territory of the Pacific Islands, *Agricultural Bulletin No. 9,* pp. 142.

Srivastava, S. K., and Krishnan, P. S. (1959). Oxalate content of plant tissues. *J. Scient. Industry Res. (India)* 18C:146-148.

Srivastava, S. N. (1972). Fertilizer requirement of alti (*Alocasia indica*). *Indian Agriculturist* 16:105-106.

St. John, H. (1948). Report on the flora of Pingelap Atoll, Caroline Islands, Micronesia. *Pacific Sci.* 2(2):107-108.

Stemmermann, L., and Proby, F. (1978). *Inventory of Wetland Vegetation in the Caroline Islands. Vol. I. Wetland Vegetation Types.* Honolulu, VTN Pacific.

Sugiyama, N., Shimahara, H., and Andoh, T. (1972). Studies on mannan and related compounds. I. The purification of konjac mannan. *Bull. Chem. Soc. Japan (Nippon Kagakukai, Bull.)* 45:561-563.

Sugiyama, N., Shimahara, H., Andoh, T., and Takemoto, M. (1973). Konjacmannase from the tubers of *Amorphophallus konjac* C. Koch. *Agric. Biol. Chem.* 37(1):9-17.

Sugiyama, N., Shimahara, H., Andoh, T., Takemoto, M., and Kamata, T. (1972). Molecular weights of konjac mannans of various sources. *Agriculture Biol. Chem.* 36:1381-1387.

Sumathi, S., and Pattabiraman, T. N. (1975). Natural plant enzyme inhibitors. I. Protease inhibitors of tubers and bulbs. *Indian J. of Biochem. Biophysics* 12(4):383-385.

Tang, C. S., and Sakai, W. S. (in press). Acridity of taro and related plants. In *Taro-Production Practices and Potentials* (J. K. Wang, ed.). Honolulu, University of Hawaii Press.

Truswell, A. S. (1977). Food fiber and blood lipids. *Nutr. Rev.* 35(3): 51-54.

Tu, J. (1980). Personal communication. Department of Food and Nutritional Sciences, College of Tropical Agriculture and Human Resources. Honolulu, University of Hawaii.

Valenzuela, A., and Wester, P. J. (1930). Composition of some Philippine fruits, vegetables, and forage plants. *Philipp. J. Sci.* 41:85-102.

van Hulssen, C. J., and Koolhass, D. R. (1940). Composition of several species of Dutch Indian *Amorphophallus. Ing. Nederland-Indie* 7:29, *Chem. Abstracts* 35:4415 (1941).

Villanueva, M. R. (1979). Processing and storage of sweet potato and aroids in the Philippines. In *Small Scale-Processing and Storage of Tropical Root Crops* (D. L. Plucknett, ed.). Boulder, Colo. Westview Press.

Watson, J. (1979). Importing root corps from the South Pacific Islands for New Zealand markets. In *Small-Scale Processing and Storage of Tropical Root Crops* (D. L. Plucknett, ed.). Boulder, Colo., Westview Press.

Wenkam, N. S. (in press). *Nutritive Value of Hawaii Foods: Vegetable and Vegetable Products—Raw, Processed, Prepared.* Honolulu, Hawaii Institute of Tropical Agriculture and Human resources, College of Tropical Agriculture and Human Resources, University of Hawaii Research Extension Series. University of Hawaii.

Whistler, A. (1981). Personal communication. Honolulu, Department of Botany, University of Hawaii.

Willis, J. C. (1966). *A Dictionary of Flowering Plants and Ferns,* 7th ed., Cambridge, University Press, pp. 1214.

Wise, L. E. (1949). The polysaccharide from Iles mannane. *Arch. Biochem. Biophys.* 23:127-130.

Yamaga, I. (1973). Breeding of Konnyaku in Japan. *JARQ (Japan Norin Suisan Gijutsi Kaigi)* 7:233-235.

Yara, K., and Usami, S. (1968). Studies on oxalate-decomposing bacteria isolated from *Alocasia* plant. *Bot. Mag. Tokyo (Nihon Shokurutsu Gakkai)* 81:425-433.

Yuncker, T. G. (1959). Plants of Tonga. *Bernice P. Bishop Museum Bull.* 220:76.

3

Bananas and Plantains

John Marriott† and **Pamela A. Lancaster*** Tropical Development and Research Institute, London, England

---

†Dr. Marriott is deceased.
*Mrs. Lancaster is no longer associated with the Tropical Development and Research Institute.

I. INTRODUCTION

A. Botanical Description and Varieties

Banana and plantain belong to the family Musaceae genus *Musa*. They are treelike perennial herbs, 2 to 9 m tall, with an underground rhizome or corm. The pseudostem is formed of rolled leaf sheaths which form a terminal crown of leaves. Some 7 to 9 months after planting a sucker (see Sec. II. B), an inforescence is formed at the base of the pseudostem, and about 1 month later, this emerges or is "shot" through the center of the leaf crown after pushing up through the center of the pseudostem. The flowers are arranged in nodal clusters, each cluster being borne on a transverse prominence ("cushion"). In wild, seeded *Musa* species, pollination is essential for fruit development. In edible cultivars, vegetative parthenocarpy results in the formation of fruits with an edible pulp without pollination, and these are usually suitable for harvest 90 to 150 days after emergence of the inflorescence. The fruit bunch consists of 5 to 15 clusters, called hands, which contain 5 to 20 individual fruits or fingers (Simmonds, 1966).

Nearly all edible banana and plantain cultivars, those of the Eumusa series, are derived from two wild diploid species, *M. acuminata* (AA) and *M. balbisiana* (BB). Most cultivars are triploids believed to have been formed as a result of hybridization within or between these species. Simmonds (1966) has proposed a basis for classification in which the difficulties and discrepancies associated with attempting species classification of the genus *Musa* are resolved by classification according to the contribution of the parent species. According to this classification, which has now been widely adopted, the group of Cavendish sweet bananas which dominate international trade are *Musa* (AAA group, Cavendish subgroup) and previous species descriptions such as *M. cavendishi*, *M. paradisiaca* 'French plantain', and *M. sapientium* 'Silk fig' are redundant. The groups contributing major cultivars can then be classified as the diploids, AA, and AB, the triploids, AAA, AAB, and ABB, and one tetraploid, AAAA. The three possible hybrid tetraploids have all been observed but of these only one, ABBB, has even local importance (Richardson, et al., 1965). The remaining edible cultivars belong to a separate series of which the botany is poorly understood and which are described as *Musa* (Australimusa series). This series is characterised by erect fruit bunches and red juice and occurs only in Oceania where it is of minor importance. Simmonds (1966) has described a system of scoring plant and fruit characters which makes it possible to assess and assign *Musa* clones to an appropriate group.

The main cultivars are listed in Table 1, and a full description and discussion has been made by Simmonds (1966). The AA group are less hardy and bear fewer and smaller fruits than triploids, though there are numerous clones. Although the select diploid cultivar

Table 1 Some Widely Distributed Banana and Plantain Cultivars

Group	Cultivar	Notes
AA	Sucrier	Very sweet, thin-skinned fruits, often highly preferred. Short fingers and low yielding.[a]
AAA	Gros Michel	Large fruit, good bunch shape, sweet, and of good eating quality. Very susceptible to Panama disease, which has almost eliminated it as an export banana.
	Highgate	A dwarf mutant of Gros Michel and used as alternate parent in breeding.
	Dwarf Cavendish Giant Cavendish Robusta Lacatan	Members of the Cavendish subgroup, placed in ascending order of stature. Strong flavored, sweet, and of good eating quality. The basis for all major current export trades.[a]
AAB	Mysore	Vigorous, high yielding, and sweet-acid flavor.
	Silk	Less vigorous and susceptible to Panama disease, white flesh, and very attractive sweet-acid flavor.
	French plantain types	Vigorous and high yielding with heavy bunches of numerous medium-sized fingers. Cooking necessary.[a]
	Horn plantain types	Hardy but less high yielding than French types. Bunches consist of few very large fingers in an open and often irregular conformation. Cooking necessary.[a]
ABB	Bluggoe	Vigorous, high yielding, with particularly good tolerance to drought. Fingers straight and blunt-ended. Cooking necessary.[a]
	Pisang Awak	Vigorous and high-yielding dessert type with indifferent flavor. Slightly susceptible to Panama disease.

[a]Resistant to Panama disease.
Source: Simmonds 1966.

Sucrier is grown as a high-quality sweet banana (Table 1), in countries where diploids are grown for subsistence, they are cooked when unripe even though they are possibly palatable when ripe. There are many AAA cultivars, in addition to the widely cultivated Gros Michel and the Cavendish subgroup, and these are eaten mainly as dessert fruit in Southeast Asia. In east Africa they are mainly cooked when unripe, though the cultivars there are all palatable if not necessarily attractive when ripe. Both AAB and ABB groups contain sweet types eaten as dessert fruit and some that are necessarily cooked prior to consumption, either unripe or ripe. AAB dessert types are often highly esteemed (Table 1), whereas ABB types, though locally important, are grown for their productivity and vigor and their quality is often indifferent. AAB cooking types are predominantly of the plantain subgroup and consist of French types, which are prolific with heavy bunches containing many hands and fingers; of Horn types, which bear lighter, more open bunches in which individual fingers are larger though fewer; and of a small number of intermediate forms. Less is known about the cultivars and characteristics of ABB cooking types, hereafter referred to as cooking bananas. These are often incorrectly referred to as plantains, and they are categorized with plantains in Food and Agricultural Organization (FAO) statistics. These types are very important in many areas and are often preferred to plantains both for their vigor and for local preference for culinary characteristics.

The genetic resources available for selection or for breeding have been surveyed recently by the International Board for Plant Genetic Resources (IBPGR, 1978). Banana breeding is technically exceptionally difficult and has only been attempted as a means to producing fruits which will compete with Gros Michel and/or Cavendish subgroup cultivars for exportation to North America and Europe. Breeding has depended on conventional crossing and improvement of diploids selected for disease resistance and fruit characters, and then crossing with Gros Michel or Highgate to produce AAAA group tetraploids. Tetraploids have been produced with resistance to leaf-spot disease as well as Panama disease and with yields and bunch characters to compete with Cavendish subgroup cultivars; however, the best clones have poor shipping characteristics and suffer from fingerdrop after ripening (Menendez and Shepherd, 1975; et al., 1976; Rowe and Richardson, 1975). Plantain breeding has not been undertaken, but recent advances may resolve the technical difficulties and make this practicable (De Langhe, 1976; Rowe, 1976). A further possibility is that mutation breeding could be undertaken for any or all of the *Musa* groups, if the financial resources were available (Menendez, 1973).

B. Origin and Distribution

Wild *Musa* species appear to have originated in Southeast Asia, and their ancestors have probably been used by humans since their arrival there. Both parthenocarpic and seedless forms of *M. acuminata* and edible triploid seedless forms (AAA group) probably originated in or near the Malaysian peninsula. In contrast, hybrids with *M. balbisiana* (AB, AAB, and ABB) appear to have originated on the fringes of this area both in India and the Philippines. While the crop was probably domesticated in the course of early agricultural development in Southeast Asia, which is of uncertain date, the earliest records of the banana indicate cultivation in India about 500 B.C. The date of arrival in Africa is uncertain, but major introductions into East Africa probably occurred by about 500 A.D., bananas were well established in west Africa by 1400 A.D. Bananas spread across the Pacific about 1000 A.D. and to the Caribbean and Latin America soon after 1500 A.D. (Simmonds, 1962, 1966, and 1976).

Banana cultivation is limited by requirements for high temperature and particularly for the ready availability of water (see Sec. II. A.1). Extensive cultivation is practiced throughout Central America and the Caribbean and in South America as far south as Bolivia and most of Brazil. In Africa, cultivation is mainly in the equatorial zone bounded by the Sahara zone in the north and by Angola, the Congo republic, and Tanzania in the south. Cultivation is carried out throughout Southeast Asia and Oceania and in the wetter parts of the Indian subcontinent and eastern Australia (Simmonds, 1966).

In Southeast Asia, there are many sweet cultivars of which the most abundant is Pisang awak (ABB group). With Oceania, Papua New Guinea is by far the largest producer and has traditionally grown diploids (AA group), although these are being displaced by the more vigorous triploids and the most common cultivar is a cooking banana, 'Kalapua.' In the Indian subcontinent, the most common cultivar is an ABB dessert type, 'Poovan,' ('Mysore' of Table 1), which accounts for about half the total production, and a cooking banana 'Monthan' ('Bluggoe' of Table 1) (Bhakthavatsalu and Sathiamoorthy, 1979; Nayar, 1962). In the western part of Africa from Ivory Coast to Zaire, true plantains are mainly cultivated and over 70 types of French, Horn, and intermediate forms are known. In East Africa, most bananas are also used unripe and in the coast these are AA and ABB types, whereas in the central highlands there is a unique cultivation of AAA types for culinary use (De Langhe, 1961; Simmonds, 1966). In the Caribbean and in Latin America north of the equator, Cavendish subgroup cultivars are grown for exportation and plantains predominate for local markets. In Brazil, AAB dessert types have a larger role through Nanica and Nanicão (Dwarf and Giant Cavendish) are very important (Federacion Nacional de Cafeteros de Colombia, 1974; Simmonds, 1966).

A high degree of adaptation to localized ecosystems is observed within the genus *Musa*. It is consequently not necessarily useful to consider major producers such as Brazil and India as single units when they offer diverse habitats which impose different stresses but which are nonetheless suitable for adapted cultivars. The pattern of

Table 2 Production and Exportation of Bananas and Plantains in 1979[a]

Country (1 million tonnes)	Banana		Plantain and cooking banana production
	Production	Exports	
Africa	4.5	0.32	13.3
Burundi	1.0[b]	0	0
Cameroon	0.1	0.08	1.0
Ghana	0	0	1.2
Ivory Coast	0.2	0.12	0.8
Nigeria	0	0	2.2
Rwanda	0	0	2.1
Tanzania	0.7[b]	0	0.7
Uganda	0.4	0	3.2
Zaire	0.3	0	1.4
Latin America	19.3	5.71	5.8
Brazil	6.4	0.13	0
Colombia	1.3	0.63	2.2
Costa Rica	1.1	1.01	0.1
Dominican Republic	0.3	0.01	0.6
Ecuador	2.4	1.39	0.8
Guatemala	0.5	0.27	0.1
Honduras	1.3	0.89	0.2
Mexico	1.9	0.02	0
Panama	1.0	0.60	0.1
Peru	0	0	0.7
Venezuela	1.0	0	0.4
Asia	13.8	1.0	1.5
Bangladesh	0.6	0	0
India	4.0	0	0
Indonesia	2.9	0	0
Philippines	2.4	0.86	0.3
Sri Lanka	0	0	0.8
Thailand	2.1	0	0
Vietnam	0.5	0.01	0
Oceania	1.1[b]	0.005	0
Papua New Guinea	0.9[b]	0	0
World	39.1	7.14	20.6

[a]Includes countries producing more than 500,000 tonnes of bananas plus plantains.
[b]A majority of these are probably used for cooking.
Source: Food and Agricultural Organization (1980a and 1980b).

distribution is thus governed by ecosystems rather than by national boundaries. This is well illustrated by the centers of plantain production which extend from the Ivory Coast to Cameroon in the humid coastal zone of West Africa (Johnston, 1958).

C. Economic and Nutritional Significance

Total world production of bananas and plantains is estimated to be about 60 million tons (Table 2). The division between banana and plantain categories is particularly difficult where AA and AAA dessert cultivars are predominantly used for cooking, and three countries where most of fruit of the banana category are known to be used for cooking are indicated. The data are adequate to show that the quantities of bananas consumed ripe and of plantains and cooking bananas are of similar magnitude but that those for culinary use are grown and consumed within a restricted zone in the humid tropics where they are a significant and often staple component of diet. Dessert bananas are grown throughtout all except the arid zones of the tropics. The level of production is of similar magnitude to that of grapes (57 million tons) and citrus (50 million tons) and far greater than the next most important fruits, apples (21 million tons) and mangos (13 million tons) (Food and Agricultural Organization, 1980a,b).

Exports of dessert bananas comprise about 7 million tons per year and in 1979 were valued at $1141 million (FAO, 1980b). In 1979, the principal importers were North America (2.7 million tons), Europe (2.7 million tons), and Japan (0.8 million tons). Exports of plantains are difficult to estimate but are certainly insignificant when compared with bananas. They were estimated at about 60,000 tons in 1973, nearly all of this being from Colombia, Ecuador, and Honduras to the United States, and about 2500 tons to the United Kindom (Food and Agricultural Organization, 1975).

The economic significance of this trade is considerable in that it represents a major source of foreign exchange to many exporting countries, particularly to some countries in Central America and the Caribbean where bananas are the major export. Thus, in 1978, banana exports represented over 20% of the total exports of Honduras, Panama, and several of the small eastern Caribbean islands (Food and Agricultural Organization, 1980c). Despite the role of this income in the economies of exporting countries, it has been argued that the profits of the trade are inequitably distributed between these countries and multinational companies or other foreign investors and that the internal economic, social, and political consequences of the trade are not necessarily conducive to the general development of the economy and to the improvement of living standards (Beckford, 1972; Clairmonte, 1975).

Soon after 1970, Colombia, Costa Rica, the Dominican Republic, Guatemala, Honduras, Panama, and later Nicaragua, that is the major exporters of Central and South America excepting Ecuador, formed a group to negotiate the terms of trade, Union de Paises Exportadores del Banano (UPEB). UPEB aims to coordinate research, facilitate exchange of technical information, and to improve the returns to producing countries (Pons, 1979; Tarte, 1979).

Despite the economic significance of banana exportation, exports account for only about 15% of world production of bananas and plantains. The most important role of the crop is as a starchy staple in the diet in many parts of the humid tropics. National mean consumption per person per day is estimated to exceed 800 g in Rwanda, and there are 12 other countries where it exceeds 300 g (Table 3) and a further 20 countries where it exceeds 100 g, including Brazil with a population of 106 million (Food and Agricultural Organization, 1974). The mean calorie consumption in most of these countries is about 2100 cal/day, so that for the countries in Table 2, plantains and bananas provide between 9 and 35% of the total calories in the diet. This is consistent with estimates in East Africa that a working person may eat 2.5 kg/day and that school children may eat 800 g/day. Consumption is not distributed evenly on a national level but depends on climatological variation, so that in one of the six zones of the Ivory Coast, mean consumption is as high as 600 g per person per day (Guillemot, 1976).

The economic significance of plantains within forest zones lies in their contribution to subsistence economies. The labor requirements

Table 3 Countries with High Levels of Utilization of Bananas and/or Plantains

Country	Population (millions)	Utilization (g/person/day)[a]
Rwanda	4.1	815
Papua New Guinea	2.7	686
Comoros	0.3	518
Gabon	0.5	430
Dominican Republic	5.0	426
Uganda	11.0	420
Ivory Coast	4.8	292
Samoa	0.2	247
Venezuela	11.9	242
Cameroon	6.3	241
Colombia	25.1	225
St. Lucia	0.1	208
Ghana	9.6	206

[a]Weight of fresh fruit utilized of which about 60% is edible material.
Source: Food and Agricultural Organization (1974).

Table 4 Relative Production Cost of Staple Crops in West Africa

Ranking	Per hectare	Per ton	Per 1000 cal
Cheapest	Plantain	Plantain	Plantain
	Millet	Cassava	Cassava
	Maize	Sweet potato	Sweet potato
	Sorghum	Cocoyam	Maize
	Rice	Yam	Cocoyam
	Cassava	Maize	Sorghum
	Cocoyam	Sorghum	Millet
	Sweet potato	Millet	Rice
Costliest	Yam	Rice	Yam

Source: Johnston (1958).

for plantain are lower than for other crops, even cassava (Table 4), and the cost of production and utilization for plantain is less than for cassava, sweet potato, maize, cocoyam, rice, and yam, whether assessed per 100 cal per kilogram, or per hectare (Johnston, 1958).

The protein content of plantain is low, though not as low as that of cassava (see Sec. III. A), and its protein is deficient in sulfur-con-taining amino acids, as are most plant protein sources (see Sec. III. C. 1). In tests with rats, plantain protein was almost as efficiently utilized as was that of a cereal (maize) and more efficiently than that of cassava, though less efficiently than protein of yam, cocoyam, or sweet potato (Omole et al., 1978). Both plantains and bananas make significant contributions to diet in provision of calcium, iron, and vitamins A and C and several of the B group (see Sec. III. A). It is the role as a source of vitamins and as a cheap and convenient source of calories, requiring no preparation, which gives ripe banana its significance in the diet of the tropical world and in importing countries.

Bananas and plantains do not contain any toxic principles. They do contain a very high level of serotonin and other biogenic amines (see Sec. III. C. 1) and it has been suggested that where high levels of plantains are eaten, daily ingestion of up to 80 mg/day of serotonin may have adverse effects and might be a factor in the etiology of endo-myocardial fibrosis (EMF) which shares a common geographical distribu-tion with plantain diets (Foy and Parratt, 1960). However, Ojo (1969) has shown that serotonin is rapidly removed from circulating plasma and that plantain ingestion is not accompanied by elevated serum serotonin levels in healthy Nigerians. A number of other studies have been made but "there is at present no convincing evidence that the serotonin content of plantains is a factor in the etiology of this condition" (Shaper, 1967).

A banana diet was used from 1924, for a number of years, as a treatment for children suffering from celiac disease, a condition of chronic intestinal malabsorption. It is now known that this disorder results from hypersensitivity to the gluten of wheat or rye, and it is treated by use of a completely gluten-free diet. Bananas apparently function as a source of sugar and gluten-free starch with a low content of soft fiber, which is well tolerated in this condition (Andersen and Mike, 1955).

II. HORTICULTURAL ASPECTS

A. Cultivation Practices

1. Climatological and Soil Requirements

Cultivation practices have been fully described by Simmonds (1966) and practices in the intensive cultivation of bananas described by Champion (1963), Haarer (1964), Purseglove (1972), and Samson (1980). Information on plantains is more restricted, but practices recommended locally have been described for Ghana (Karikari, 1972), Colombia (Federacion Nacional de Cafeteros de Colombia, 1974), and Venezuela (Haddad and Borges, 1973), and an extensive bibliography is available (Lawani et al., 1977; Paradisiaca, 1978).

Banana can be cultivated in a wide range of tropical and subtropical climates. The optimum conditions are monthly means of about 100 mm rainfall and 27°C. Serious checks to growth occur when monthly means are below 50 mm rainfall and/or 21°C. Thus, banana cultivation is largely within the 15°C winter isotherm, corresponding to latitudes of approximately 30° north and south and within 1250 mm isohyets. The cultivar Dwarf Cavendish is considerably more tolerant of temperature than any other, and it is the predominant cultivar grown near the limits of the temperature range. Tolerance to drought is less well understood, but hybrid cultivars (AAB and ABB groups) are more hardy than those of the AAA and AA groups; hybrid cultivars predominate in areas with long dry seasons such as the monsoon countries of Asia (Simmonds, 1966).

The essential requirement for soils is good drainage (Simmonds, 1966; Samson, 1980). This depends on structure and depth and a very wide range of soils can be used. Soil pH between 6 and 7.5 is best, but pH values between 4.5 and 8 are tolerated. Plantain can tolerate and yield on acid infertile soils, and more information is needed on productivity on marginal land (Plucknett, 1978).

Flat terrain is preferred because of its effect on costs of transportation and irrigation and the prevention of erosion. However, in many areas the availability of flat land is restricted, and bananas are extensively cultivated on steep slopes in places such as the Canary Islands, Australia, and many Caribbean islands.

2. Planting and Management

After clearing and planting land, bananas are usually planted in holes or, less commonly, in furrows. Planting is normally carried out in the wet season. Planting density depends on cultivar, especially its potential height, fertility, pruning practice, and marketing requirements. Dependent on these factors, planting density may be between 300 and 3000 plants per hectare, that is planting distances between 2 and 6 m. Good control of weeds, especially grasses, is necessary in the early stages of growth before leaves shade the ground. Manual weed control is by cutting weeds a few inches above ground level, so as to minimize soil erosion and to avoid damage to the shallow roots of the banana. Chemical control is also practical (Feakin, 1971). Irrigation is desirable if there is no rainfall for 2 weeks, and 25 mm/week is normally applied although requirements vary (Salter and Goode, 1967). Where irrigation is carried out, this may be by furrow, flood, or overhead. Nitrogen, potassium, and phosphorus are normally applied for intensive production of bananas; quantities required are determined by soil or foliar analysis (Martin-Prevel, 1980a,b). Other mineral deficiencies arise and symptoms are illustrated by BASF (n.d.). Plantain is usually grown without fertilizer and tolerates adverse conditions well, but it does respond well to close planting, good management, and fertilization (Plucknett, 1978; Federacion Nacional de Cafeteros de Colombia, 1974). Pruning is a critical factor in management, and it is typical of traditional cultivation systems that they are low-density planting with little pruning and poor yield. In contrast, intensive cultivation of banana is usually carried out by permitting establishment of only one sucker (a "daughter") until inflorescence and then allowing a further sucker to develop from the daughter. Unwanted suckers must be removed every 6 or 8 weeks. After inflorescence, a number of other procedures such as deflowering, propping, earthing up, removal of the male bud, bagging of bunches, and removal of small hands may be carried out in intensive cultivation and are described by Samson (1980). The foregoing discussion deals with fruit production in monoculture, although wherever plantain or bananas are grown as subsistence crops intercropping is significant and often predominant (Kouadio, 1979).

3. Productivity

Productivity is extremely variable and has to be considered in relation to the potential productivity of the land utilized, the inputs of fertilizer and agrochemicals, and labor input. Banana on good land, intensively cultivated, can yield 50 tons/ha/year (Purseglove, 1972), whereas plantain cultivated by traditional methods in West Africa yields only about 8 tons/ha/year (Johnston, 1958). Mean world yield is estimated as 12.7 tons/ha/year, and many countries estimate their yield as between 25 and 35 tons/ha/year (Food and Agricultural

Organization, 1974). In Colombia, six cultivars of plantain and cooking banana yielded 7 to 21 tons/ha per crop on one site and 11 to 44 tons/ha per crop on another, showing that hybrid cultivars also have high-yield potential (FNCC, 1974). Most intensive production has aimed to maximize the yield of high-quality, exportable fruit. There is good potential to give very high total yields under intensive production, but the labor requirement is so high and the potential for mechanization so low, the yield under experimental conditions gives little indication of value as a subsistence crop. The true value of plantain and cooking banana is that they give acceptable yields and tolerate pests and drought when grown with a low labor input in tropical forest zones (Johnston, 1958).

4. Diseases and Pests

The development and spread of banana diseases has had a major effect on banana production and on the cultivars grown. Panama disease, a vascular wilt caused by *Fusarium oxysporium* F. *cubense,* was recognized in tropical America soon after 1900 and is now widely established in Africa and Asia as well as Latin America. There are no effective means of chemical control, and this disease has particularly affected production of the susceptible cultivars Gros Michel and Silk though not of the other cultivars listed in Table 1, which are resistant (Stover, 1972).

Banana leaf-spot disease, caused by *Mycosphaerella musicola,* is now the most serious disease of banana. It originated in Fiji and Indonesia, but first spread to the Caribbean after 1930 and now affects all tropical banana-growing areas. It reduces leaf area and retards normal bunch development, so that total yield and fruit quality are reduced. It is controlled by spraying with oil, either alone or mixed with fungicides. At least one and possibly two more virulent forms have developed in Southeast Asia and Oceania and spread to Central America, and these require more frequent spraying and higher standards of management for effective control. Forms tolerant to the benzimidazole fungicides, which are the cheapest effective means of control, have developed and are spreading, necessitating the use of a more expensive fungicide, chlorothalonil. None of the cultivars in Table 1 are resistant to these leaf-spot diseases, though their susceptibility varies. Diploids resistant to *M. musicola* are known, and resistant tetraploid clones have been produced; but it is not known whether there is a good source of resistance to the other *Musicola* races or species (Stover, 1972; Menendez and Shepherd, 1975; Tarte et al., 1979).

A bacterial wilt, Moko disease, nematodes, and a weevil or borer, *Cosmopolites sordidus* are other diseases and pests which are widespread and which require costly forms of control where banana is intensively cultivated. The important cooking banana cultivar, Bluggoe, is particularly susceptible to Moko disease, and this restricts its cultivation in parts of Latin America. These and other pests and diseases have been fully reviewed (Stover, 1972; Feakin, 1971; Wardlaw, 1972).

B. Propagation

Propagation is solely by vegetative methods using whole corms or pieces of corms (bits) or suckers. Suckers can be classified into several types according to their stage of development (Champion, 1963). In the tropics the type of planting material used for intensively cultivated bananas is not critical although larger material has better prospects under adverse conditions. In the subtropics, the stage of development of planting material critically affects the date of flowering of the plant crop and thus the climatic conditions during the critical phase, bunch development, and it is normal practice to control sucker size with precision. Propagation of plantains is often recommended using whole corms, perhaps because these perform better under generally more adverse production conditions (Samson, 1980; Purseglove, 1972; Federacion Nacional de Cafeteros de Colombia, 1974).

All material from plants affected by borers or nematodes should be throughly trimmed and disinfected. Borer control is usually achieved with dieldrin, aldrin, or chlordane and nematode control by hot water treatment.

Planting material may be obtained from plantations being cleared, or pruning can be delayed and suckers cut from growing plants with a small reduction in yield. For plantations in new areas, nurseries can be established using 4000 plants per hectare and multiplication by 100 times per year can be achieved. More specialized systems of rapid multiplication have been developed and have been reviewed recently (Hamilton, 1965; Menendez and Loor, 1979).

C. Postharvest Practices

1. Handling and Transportation

In tropical zones where rainfall is well distributed throughout the year, production of banana and plantain is continuous and largely nonseasonal. Thus systems for banana exportation have been developed in which ships ply continuously between a producing country and a single export market, and shipments are dispatched at intervals usually not exceeding 1 week, so that the maturity of exported bananas can be controlled within close limits (Marriott and Proctor, 1978). The unusual ripening physiology of the banana fruit is exploited to allow transportation of the fruit under refrigeration while still green and firm and to induce ripening uniformly prior to distribution. This avoids the need for storage for much more than the transportation period, which can be up to 7 days at ambient temperature or up to 20 days under refrigeration.

Maturity standards for harvesting vary since fruit bunches are harvested at full maturity for nearby markets and at a less mature stage
for distant ones. Even for local or domestic use, bananas and plantains
are never deliberately allowed to commence ripening prior to harvest,
because tree-ripe fruit have inferior flavor and tend to drop from the
bunch either prior to or during harvesting. Maturity of both bananas
and plantains is most commonly judged by assessing the changes in
angularity as fruit fingers increase in girth from thin fruit to thicker
rounded ones (Fig. 1). For plantation-grown bananas, the girth of
fingers of a selected hand on the bunch may be measured with calipers
(Caliper grade), and in some systems this is combined with color tag-
ging of each bunch to indicate the date of flowering, so that harvesting
can be controlled according to caliper grade and bunch age (Marriott,
1980; Stover, 1972).

For bananas for exportation, the most critical quality factor in
markets in North America and Europe is presentation of well-graded,
fully yellow, unblemished bananas to the retail consumer (Brown, 1972).
Grading standards, types of fruit injury, and methods of packing are
illustrated in advisory publications (Institut de Reserche Fruits et
Agrumes, 1980; Windward Island Banana Growers Association/Tropical
Products Institute, 1977).

There is a heavy investment in export industries in handling systems
and in packaging to minimize abrasion of fruit (Windward Island Banana
Growers Association/Tropical Products Institute, 1977; Stover, 1972;
Coursey et al., 1976). These systems begin with bunch protection in
the field by removal of some leaves and by covering bunches with polyethylene sleeves: Harvesting is normally carried out by resting the
bunch on a padded tray prior to cutting it from the plant. These trays
are carried by field laborers on their heads to a collection point. Various systems are used to transport bunches from the field to central packing stations, from use of monorails, spaced at 100 m-intervals through
plantations (National Institute Agricultural Engineering, 1977), to cut-

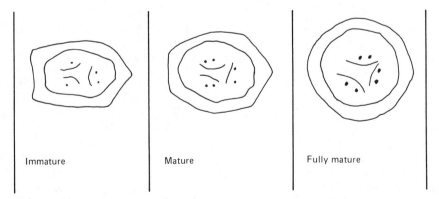

Immature   Mature   Fully mature

Figure 1 Banana maturation changes.

ting and packing hands into a rigid reuseable field box or simply wrapping the bunch with dried leaves and transporting it stacked on a trailer or a truck.

On arrival at a packing station, the fruit hands are cut from the bunch into a delatexing tank to allow initial latex flow and then transferred to a washing tank, in which there is a continuous flow of water. Water availability and pumping capacity are thus critical to the siting and operation of packing stations. After washing, a fungicide, usually thiabendazole or benomyl, is applied by spraying, dipping, or a cascade, and fruits are packed into boxes (15 to 20 kg) after draining but not drying. Where fruits have to be transported for exceptionally long periods, or where transportation is without temperature control, they may be packed into large polyethylene bags to create a modified atmosphere and extend storage life (Badran, 1969; Scott et al., 1971). Where plantains are exported, they are usually cut into separate fruit fingers, then washed, treated with fungicide, and packed in the same manner as bananas. Transportation is normally by sea, in boats specifically designed for the precooling and cold storage of bananas (Deullin, 1970; 1971). The mean shipping temperature is usually between 12 and 14°C, depending on the cultivar and shipping periods, and close control of this temperature is essential to avoid either premature ripening or chilling injury. After shipment, boxed green bananas are normally distributed, while still green, to ripening depots in major population centers.

For bananas and plantains for internal markets, much more rudimentary systems are used (Karikari et al., 1981; Federacion Nacional de Cafeteros de Colombia, 1974; Silvis et al., 1976; Thompson et al., 1972). The most common system is to transport whole bunches neatly stacked in trucks, smaller vehicles, or on top of buses. In some situations, especially in Ghana, individual fruit hands are stacked in an intricately woven stack to increase bulk density for truck transport. Similarly, for plantain bunches with very irregular conformation of fingers, individual fingers may be separated and packed into large sacks (up to 100 kg). All these systems cause extensive abrasion and subsequent blackening of the fruit peel, but as long as the fruits remain green and firm, it is unusual for these injuries to penetrate to the pulp or to cause appreciable loss of edible material. Nevertheless, losses do occur, primarily because of ripening in transit and subsequent damage to soft fruit, and systems have been proposed for marketing plantains in collapsible, reusable boxes.

2. Ripening

For the marketing of bananas imported to industrialized countries, ripening conditions are selected to obtain uniform ripening of boxed fruits with a full development of yellow color and good residual shelf life after removal from controlled conditions. Maximum color development can be obtained by rapid ripening at 20 to 24°C, whereas maximum shelf life is obtained by slow ripening at 16 to 17°C. The technology to optimize ripening conditions has been described in numerous publications, all of which use essentially the same methods (United Fruit Co., 1961; Commonwealth Scientific and Industrial Research Organization, 1972; American Society of Heating, Refrigeration, and Airconditioning Engineers, 1971; International Standards Organization, 1977). Ripening is normally carried out in specially designed rooms, capacity 10 to 20 tons, with precise control of air circulation and air temperatures. Ripening is initiated by treatment with ethylene gas, usually 1000 ppm, for 24 hr, taking precautions to avoid the explosion hazards associated with ethylene levels above 3%. Control of the rate of ripening depends on the temperature during ethylene treatment and then on limiting the rise in the internal temperature of the fruits during the ripening process, when the heat of respiration increases four- to eight-fold. Because the rate of heat removal from fruit stored in bulk is slow, the effects of small variations in temperature are amplified, so that changes in air temperature as small as 0.5°C appreciably affect the rate of ripening. Desirable pulp temperatures for given rates of ripening are shown in Table 5. Control of pulp temperature is achieved by reducing air temperature during the climacteric respiratory rise, which usually occurs on days 2, 3, and 4 of ripening. These temperatures serve as a guide to the rates of ripening which are normally observed, but ventilation, humidity, room design, stacking pattern, and the design of the fruit carton all affect the rate of ripening and need to be controlled to obtain a satisfactory result. A similar controlled method has been described for ripening of plantains using initiation of ripening with ethylene and ripening at 22°C (Sánchez-

Table 5 Banana Pulp Temperatures (°C) during Ripening

Period after initiation of ripening (days)	Total ripening period (days)[a]			
	4	5	6	7
1	18	17	17	16
2	18	17	17	16
3	17	17	16	16
4	16	17	16	16
5		16	16	16
6			15	15
7				15

[a]Period to reach color-stage 4 (more yellow than green).
Source: United Fruit Co. (1961).

Nieva et al., 1970). Controlled ripening of bananas and plantains is normally used for marketing good-quality fresh fruit; however, the same method is used for ripening prior to processing in order to obtain bulk samples of material at a uniform stage of ripeness, and consequently a set of ripening chambers is essential to any industrialized processing operation (see Sec. IV. B. 2).

For internal marketing, artificial induction of ripening is frequently carried out with dessert bananas, cooking bananas, and plantains. Fruits are normally ripened at tropical ambient temperatures by treating, either in a room or in a box, with ethylene, acetylene, or smoke (Pantastico and Mendoza, 1970; Hartshorn, 1931; Salem et al., 1976). Smoke contains a sufficient concentration of ethylene to initiate ripening. Acetylene is usually generated from calcium carbide. Despite the importance of artificial ripening, it is also very common practice domestically to suspend a bunch of green plantains in the shade and to allow slow ripening, using the first fruits green, some yellow-green, and the last ones full ripe, thus taking full advantage of the variety of culinary methods available for utilization of the plantain (see Sec. V).

III. BIOCHEMICAL AND NUTRITIONAL COMPOSITION

A. Nutritional Composition Tables

Proximate analyses in Table 6 are from Paul and Southgate (1978) and are consistent with median values from reviews on bananas (Loesecke, 1949; Simmonds, 1966) and on plantains (Jaffe et al., 1963) and with standard nutritional tables (Watt and Merrill, 1963), excepting for fiber content (see subsequent discussion). Moisture and carbohydrate content are variable between different cultivars and within each cultivar. Typical moisture contents are 60% for unripe plantains and 75% for

Table 6 Proximate Analysis of Banana and Plantain Pulp

Component (%)	Ripe banana[a] (AAA group)	Unripe plantain and cooking banana[b] (AAB and ABB groups)
Water	71-78	57-63
Carbohydrate	16-24	29-35
Fat	0.2	0.2-0.3
Crude protein	1.2	1.0-1.2
Fiber	3.0-4.0[c]	6.0-7.0[c]
Ash	0.8	0.8-1.0

[a]Based on Loesecke (1949).
[b]Based on Jaffe et al. (1963).
[c]Paul and Southgate (1978).

unripe bananas, and they commonly vary within a single cultivar by
±3%. Moisture contents of other types such as the AA group and
sweet bananas of AAB and ABB groups are generally 65 to 70% when
unripe.

The crude fiber content of bananas and plantains has normally been
determined as 0.5 to 1.0%, and this value is established in standard
texts and nutritional tables (Loesecke, 1949; Simmonds, 1966; Watt and
Merrill, 1963). Values of 3 to 7% in Table 6 depend on enzymatic rather
than acid hydrolysis of starch to avoid hydrolysis of hemicellulose and
to give a true measure of available carbohydrate (Southgate, 1969).

Carbohydrates comprise 75 to 80% of the dry matter and are more
than 96% utilizable in fully ripe fruits or in unripe fruits after cooking
(Loesecke, 1949). Calorific values are 79 cal/100 g edible material for
ripe bananas, moisture content 77%, and 112 cal for unripe plantains,
moisture content 67% (Paul and Southgate, 1978). A value more typical
of plantains is probably 136 cal/100 g edible material, derived for a
moisture content of 60%. In estimation of nutritive intake and value,
the ratio of edible pulp to total weight is critical. The proportion of
edible material in mature bananas and plantains is about 60%, but
changes occur during fruit development (see Sec. III. B. 1).

Contents of fat and protein are low (Table 6). The protein content
of 1.2% is lower than that of yam or sweet potato but higher than that
of cassava. Plantain protein makes a significant contribution to human
nutrition in areas where plantain is a starchy staple, but it is very
deficient in methionine and tryptophan (see Sec. III. C. 1).

Bananas and plantains are relatively rich in potassium, magnesium,
and phosphorus and are a fair source of iron and calcium (Table 7).

Table 7 Mineral Content of Banana and Plantain Pulp

Mineral (mg/100 g fresh wt)	Ripe banana	Unripe plantain
Na	1	—
K	350	—
Ca	7	7
Mg	42	33
P	28	35
Fe	0.4	0.5
Cu	0.16	0.16
Zn	0.2	0.1
S	13	15
Cl	79	—

Source: Paul and Southgate (1978).

In contrast to many other foods, the iron content is 100% utilizable for human nutrition (Loesecke, 1949). The potassium content of fruits is variable, dependent on cultural conditions, and whereas most bananas float in water, those deficient in potassium tend to sink, which adversely affects postharvest handling (Johnson, 1979).

Bananas and plantains are an excellent dietary source of vitamin A (carotene). Pulp coloration varies from white to a deep orange, according to cultivar. No study has been published on genetic and environmental influences on this component, but for plantains many samples contain 0.03 mg/100 g or less and many others 1.0 mg/100 g or more (Jaffe et al., 1963). In particular, the large Horn-type plantain cultivars known as Harton (Colombia), Barraganete (Ecuador), simply platano (Venezuela), and platano macho (Cuba) are rich in vitamin A, and it is estimated that in the Venezuelan diet, 48% of this vitamin is derived from plantains.

Bananas and plantains are also an important dietary source of vitamin C. Exported bananas usually contain about 10 mg/100 g (Harris and Poland, 1939), whereas plantains, other cooking bananas, and also dessert bananas of groups AAB and ABB often contain up to 20 or 25 mg/100 g. Two sources cited by Simmonds (1966) where levels of over 50 mg/100 g occurred in plantains are atypical. Bananas and plantains are estimated to contribute 28% of the vitamin C in the Venezuelan diet (Jaffe et al., 1963).

Thiamin (Asenjo et al., 1948), riboflavin (Asenjo et al., 1946), nicotinic acid, and folic acid are present in quantities to supplement other normal dietary sources significantly (Table 8). The content of vitamin B_6 is unusually high compared with other fruits (Polansky and Murphy, 1966).

B. Changes in Nutrient Composition

1. During Fruit Development

The main changes during development are in the content of edible material (pulp) relative to fruit weight and in the contents of moisture and of carbohydrate in the developing pulp. Changes in developing fruits of cultivars Gros Michel (Table 9) have been studied in detail by Barnell (1940). Bananas will ripen to an edible condition even if harvested as early in development as 40 days, but in practice, fruits are usually harvested between 80 days when they reach a reasonable minimum size and a pulp content of 55% and 100 days when they become susceptible to peel splitting and have a pulp content of 62%. Information on plantain is more limited, but in a study in Puerto Rico, pulp content increased from 55% after 60 days to 65% after 109 days; ripening commenced between 122 and 130 days (Sánchez-Nieva et al., 1968).

Table 8 Vitamin Content of Banana and Plantain Pulp

Vitamin (mg/100 g fresh wt)	Ripe banana	Unripe plantain
Retinol	0	0
Carotene	0.20	0.03-1.20 [b]
Ascorbic acid	10	20
Thiamine	0.04	0.05
Riboflavin	0.07	0.05
Nicotinic acid	0.6	0.7
Pyridoxine	0.32 [a]	—
Pantothenic acid	0.26	0.37
Folic acid	0.022	0.016
Inositol	0.034	—
Biotin	0.004	—
Vitamin B_{12}	0	0
Vitamin D	0	0
Vitamin E	0.2	—

[a]Loesecke (1949).
[b]Jaffe et al. (1963).
Source: Adapted from Paul and Southgate (1978).

2. During Postharvest Storage and Ripening

The changes which occur in bananas prior to the commencement of ripening are minimal, whether they are held at tropical ambient temperature (about 25°C) or at an optimal storage temperature (about 13°C). Prior to the onset of ripening, the content of starch

Table 9 Changes in Weight and Composition during Development of Bananas (cultivar Gros Michel)

Period after fruit emergence (days)	Fruit weight (g)	Pulp content (%)	Water content (%)	Carbohydrate content (%)
20	35	25	83	5
40	70	33	78	11
60	100	45	74	16
80	130	55	73	17
100	180	62	74	20
120	240	67	76	14

Source: Barnell (1940).

and of ethanol-soluble carbohydrate is constant, pulp phospholipids
are unchanged, and it is difficult to detect any biochemical changes
(Marriott, 1980).

When ripening commences, there is a rapid conversion of starch to
sucrose, glucose, and fructose which occurs with a minimal loss of carbohydrate due to respiration (Loesecke, 1949). Concurrent with the
increase in sugar content, there is a movement of water from the peel
to the pulp which causes an increase in proportionate weight of pulp
by about 10% and a decrease in the total solids content of the pulp by
3 to 4%. Changes are fully described elsewhere (see Sec III. C. 1)
and are similar in bananas and plantains, although starch hydrolysis
is slower and less complete in plantains.

Ascorbic acid content is the same in unripe and fully ripe fruit for
both bananas (Loesecke, 1949) and plantains (Gomez and Matill, 1949)
although it decreases when fruits become overripe. A decrease in
carotene content of plantain pulp from 1.04 mg/100 g in unripe fruit
to 0.06 mg/100 g when ripe was observed by Asenjo and Porrata (1956).

3. During Processing

The nutritional composition of bananas and plantains is little altered
by processing. Ascorbic acid decreased to about 50% in fresh bananas
about 5 hr after slicing (Harris and Poland, 1939) and to below 50% in
fully ripe plantains when baked or boiled but was stable in partially
ripe plantains (Gomez and Matill, 1949). In plantains, vitamins other
than ascorbic acid are stable when boiled or baked, excepting nicotinic
acid of which is 40% destroyed (Jaffe et al., 1963).

C. Biochemical Composition

1. Carbohydrates, Proteins, Lipids, Acids, Pigments, Phenols, and Amines

The biochemical composition of the banana fruit has been the subject
of numerous studies concerned both with its utilization as a fresh or
as a processed fruit and with the elucidation of the mechanism of control of ripening, and there are comprehensive reviews of the subject
which provide much information additional to that described here.
(Loesecke, 1949; Marriott, 1980; Palmer, 1971).

The main carbohydrate of unripe banana and plantain pulp is starch,
which forms 75 to 80% of the dry matter. The amylose contents of
banana and plantain starches are in the range of 19.8 to 21.2%, and
data on their physiochemical properties and those of their amylose
and amylopectin fractions have been reported (Patil and Magar, 1974).
The rheological properties of plantain starch have been studied by
Rasper (1969a,b; 1971) as part of an investigation of the starches of
staple crops in Ghana; the starches of the seven plantain cultivars
investigated were very similar in granular size and rheological

properties. Plantain starch yields moderately viscous pastes which
form strong gels on cooling. The granule size of plantain starch is
fairly large, with mean diameter between 24 and 28 µm, and it shows a
fairly high resistance to swelling and to degradation by bacterial
α-amylase.

Starch is stoichemetrically converted to sugars during ripening
with formation of sucrose, glucose, and fructose. Other sugars which
have been detected are present in only trace concentrations (Palmer,
1971). Water moves from peel to pulp during ripening, so that the
pulp moisture content of bananas typically increases from 75 to 78% and
that of plantains from 60 to 64% between the unripe and fully ripe
states. Sugars form only 2 to 8% of the total dry matter in unripe
fruit pulp (normally about 1% of fresh wt) rising to 70 to 75% in ripe
bananas (normally 18 to 20% at fresh wt) and to 35 to 60% in ripe plantains (normally 15 to 23% of fresh wt). The composition of bananas at
each color stage during ripening is shown in Table 10, and stage of
coloration may be used as an excellent indication of the probable composition. While bananas approach their maximum sugar content and
minimum starch content as soon as they become fully yellow, starch-
sugar conversion is much slower in plantains and continues until fruits

Table 10 Changes in Percentage Composition of Banana and Plantain
Pulp During Ripening

Color stage	Description	Banana[a]		Plantain[b]	
		Starch	Sugar	Starch	Sugar
1	Green	21.5-19.5	0.1-2.0	34.3	1.1
2	Trace of yellow	19.5-16.5	2.0-5.0	—	—
3	More green than yellow	18.0-14.5	3.5-7.0	—	—
4	More yellow than green	15.0-9.0	6.0-12.0	19.0	11.3
5	Green tip	10.5-2.5	10.0-18.0	—	—
6	All yellow	4.0-1.0	16.5-19.5	13.7	14.1
7	Flecked with brown	2.5-1.0	17.5-19.0	6.7	23.1
8	Large brown areas	1.5-1.0	18.5-19.0	4.0	27.4

[a]Typical ranges for bananas ripened commercially under controlled
conditions (United Fruit Co., 1961).
[b]Means for three cultivars of Ghanaian plantains ripened at 20°C
(Marriott, 1981).

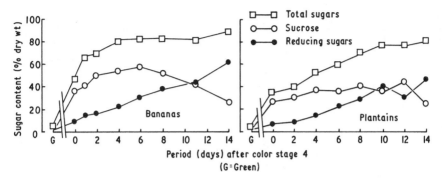

Figure 2 Formation of sugars during banana and plantain ripening at 20°C. (From Marriot et al., in press.)

are black and senescent (Table 10). The ratio of glucose:fructose is approximately constant throughout ripening and values between 1.4:1 and 1:1 have been observed (Poland et al., 1938; Marriot et al., 1981). Sucrose is the predominant sugar in the initial phase of ripening, but in both bananas and plantains the proportion of reducing sugars increases in the later stages of ripening and senescence (Fig. 2).

Unripe plantains contain 5.8% hemicellulose (as hexoses) and 0.3% pentoses in the acid hydrolyzable fraction after enzymatic hydrolysis of starch, and in addition 1.0% cellulose and 0.2% lignin (all percentages based on fresh wt) (Southgate, 1969). Barnell (1943) reported 8 to 10% hemicellulose in unripe bananas decreasing to 1 to 2% in ripe fruits using a relatively crude extraction method. Data for fiber contents in Table 6 were obtained using enzymatic hydrolysis of starch and indicate values higher than those typical of early compositional tables. It is likely that in these earlier reports, the hemicellulose fraction was hydrolyzed and determined as starch rather than as fiber.

The rapid softening which occurs during ripening is presumed to depend on interconversion of pectic substances, and it has been shown that total pectins decrease from about 1.0 to 0.5% fresh wt during ripening of banana, whereas water-soluble pectins increase from about 0.15 to 0.4% (Kawabata and Sawayama, 1974). Banana pectin contained 26.2% anhydrogalacturonic acid and the neutral sugar component contained predominantly glucose, with measurable amounts of galactose, arabinose, and mannose (Kawabata and Sawayama, 1975). Similar changes in total pectin and water-soluble pectin occur in plantains (Loesecke, 1949).

The amino acid composition of pulp tissue after hydrolysis has been examined for banana by Askar (1973) and plantains by Ketiku (1973). Major changes during ripening were not observed by either investigator (Table 11). Two major proteins are present in banana pulp with molecular weights 19,000 and 50,000 (Askar, 1972). Most free amino acids

Table 11 Amino Acid Content of Banana and Plantain Pulp

Amino acid (mg/100 g of dry matter)	Ripe banana[a]	Unripe plantain[b]
His	325	75
Lys	191	89
Arg	145	141
Asp	328	179
Thr	134	66
Ser	195	75
Glu	265	165
Pro	154	103
Gly	116	94
Ala	127	122
Cys	64	0
Val	204	103
Met	31	24
Ilen	127	85
Leu	335	132
Tyr	100	56
Phe	165	94
Total	3006	1603

[a]Askar, 1973.
[b]Ketiku, 1973.

show a complex cyclic change in concentration with a maximum value close to the climacteric peak of respiration (Drawert et al., 1971).

The lipid content of bananas and plantains is very low, and the composition of banana (Wade and Bishop, 1978) and plantain lipids

Table 12 Organic Acid Content of Bananas

Organic acid (meq/100 g fresh wt)	Green	Stage of ripening yellow/green	Fully yellow
Malic	1.36	5.37	6.20
Citric	0.68	1.70	2.17
Oxalic	2.33	1.32	1.37
Other acids	0.19	0.16	0.17
Total	4.43	8.74	10.90

Source: Wyman and Palmer (1964).

(Rao and Bandyopadhyay, 1978) is similar. The total lipid content
remains constant during ripening, although changes occur in the composition of fatty acids, particularly within the phospholipid fraction
where there is an increase in unsaturation (Wade and Bishop, 1978).

The color change from green to yellow in ripening bananas depends
on degradation of chlorophyll, which decreases almost to 0 in yellow
fruit, but no change is measurable in total concentration of carotenoids
(Loesecke, 1949). The total content of carotenoids in banana and
plantain pulp and changes during ripening have been discussed in relation to vitamin A and nutrient content (see Sec. III. A). The carotenoid composition of banana peel and pulp has been studied in detail
by Gross et al. (1976).

The main organic acids of banana pulp are malic, citric, and oxalic
(Wyman and Palmer, 1964). The pH of banana pulp falls during ripening from about 5.4 in unripe fruits to 4.5 when ripe, and the organic
acidity increases, with oxalic acid predominating in the unripe fruit and
malic acid in the ripe (Table 12). The titratable acidity of plantains
is about twice that of bananas at an equivalent stage of ripeness, and
dessert bananas of the AAB group such as Silk and Mysore are also
more acidic than Cavendish cultivars (Marriott, 1980).

Dopamine occurs in very high concentration in banana peel and is
also present in the pulp. It is the primary substrate in enzymatic
browning (Griffiths, 1959). The concentration of dopamine, rather
than that of the polyphenoloxidase responsible for its conversion to
pigment (see Sec. III. C. 3), appears to govern the rate of browning
of bananas (Weaver and Charley, 1974). Tannins and other phenolic
substances have been little studied although Goldstein and Swain (1963)
have shown that the concentration of phenolic compounds soluble in
absolute methanol (assumed to be monomeric and oligomeric forms) decreases during ripening in parallel with the reduction in astringency
which occurs in the ripening process. Problems with the appearance
of astringency during processing by dehydration have been reported
and are ascribed to diffusion of astringency-causing phenolics out of
latex vessels, where they are trapped in fresh fruit (Ramirez-Martinez
et al., 1977).

Bananas and plantains contain unusually large amounts of the
physiologically active amines, serotonin (5-hydroxytryptamine),
dopamine (3,4-dihydroxyphenylethylamine), and norepinephrine
(Table 13) (see Sec. I. C). The peel of the banana is unique in that
it contains exceptional amounts of amines, and banana pulp also has a
high amine concentration; however, some other fruits such as tomatoes
and avocados have comparable though lower levels (Udenfriend et al.,
1959).

2. Flavor Compounds and Flavor Profiles

Recent major investigations on the volatile constituents of bananas
have been made for cultivar Gros Michel (Tressl et al., 1970), for

Table 13 Amine Content of Bananas and Plantains

Amine (μg/100 g fresh wt)	Banana[a] ripe peel	Banana[a] ripe peel	Plantain[a] pulp	Plantain[b] ripe pulp	'Matoke' banana[c] unripe pulp
Serotonin	50-150	28	45	76	16
Tryptamine	0	0	–	–	–
Tryamine	65	7	–	–	–
Dopamine	700	8	–	–	–
Norepinephrine	122	2	–	10	2

[a]Udenfriend et al. (1959).
[b]Foy and Parratt (1960).
[c]Marshall (1959).

cultivar 'Poyo' (Mattei, 1973), and for cultivar Valery (Quast, 1976). The compounds have been listed (Straten and Vrijer, 1973), and work has been reviewed by Palmer (1971), Dupaigne (1975), and Marriott (1980). Of 350 components separated by Tressl et al. (1970), 183 were identified and fell into four groups: esters (80), alcohols (4), carbonyl compounds (23), and phenol ethers (4). For the esters of different acids, the relative concentrations were:

Acetates > butyrates > 3-methyl butyrates > total other acids

and for the esters of different alcohols:

3-methyl butyl > 2-methyl propyl > 1-butyl > 2-pentyl > ethyl 1-propyl

The components present are similar in the three cultivars (all of the AAA group), and once the fruits ripen to reasonable flavor (color-stage 6), esters comprise much the largest group. Mattei (1973) reported 70%. Hexanol and trans-2-hexenal are major volatile components of unripe bananas.

Esters make the main contribution to the characteristic aroma of bananas; amyl esters are responsible for the bananalike note and butyl esters for the fruity note (McCarthy et al., 1963). The phenyl esters contribute to the ethereal note in the aroma. Pentyl and hexyl alcohols and aldehydes and ketones contribute to the green note, important in unripe and partially ripe fruits (Table 14).

Clear changes in volatiles' composition with fruit ripening and between the cultivars Gros Michel and Valery were observed by McCarthy et al., (1963). Baldry (1982) used this technique to compare cultivar Valery with 10 tetraploid clones. Sensory assessments of banana flavor were highly correlated with the absolute and relative concentrations of 3-methyl butyl acetate and butyrate, and amyl acetate and gas chromatography should have predictive value in assessment of the flavor of new clones.

Synthesis of volatiles commences late during ripening relative to starch-to-sugar conversion and tissue softening. The total volatile production increases as an exponential function of temperature over a wide range from 5 to 30°C, but the relative rates of production of individual volatiles differ so that the aroma composition varies according to the temperature selected for ripening (Mattei, 1973). Relative composition also varies through ripening so that after the ester concentration becomes maximal, further increases occur in ethyl esters and then in ethanol, so that ethanol and its esters are minor components when the fruit has its optimal flavor but major ones when the fruit is overripe (Tressl and Jennings, 1972). Volatile formation is markedly reduced by chilling injury even at the marginal storage temperature of 12°C and is evident before symptoms in the peel (Mattei and Paillard, 1973). New flavor constituents are not formed during processing, but changes do occur in the relative proportion of normal volatiles (Uzelac et al., 1975). Baldry (1980) has shown that the composition of volatiles changes rapidly after cutting the fruits, so that a few minutes after slicing higher concentrations of alcohols relative to esters were detectable by gas chromatography and taste panelists distinguished between fresh whole bananas and banana slices. Forsyth (1980) stated in his review of the volatiles of bananas that the flavor research on bananas had been disappointing in that an artificial flavor had yet to be compounded that was equal to that of natural banana flavor.

Table 14 Important Volatile Flavor Components of Bananas

Bananalike[a]	Fruity[a]	Green, woody,[a] or musty	Ethereal[b]
3-Methyl butyl acetate	Butyl acetate	Methyl acetate	Eugenol
Amyl acetate	Butyl butyrate	Pentanone	Elimicin
Amyl propionate	Hexyl acetate	Butyl alcohol	Methyl ether of eugenol
Amyl butyrate	Amyl butyrate	Amyl alcohol	
3-Methyl butyl butyrate	3-Methyl butyl butyrate	Hexyl alcohol	

[a]McCarthy et al. (1963).
[b]Wick et al. (1969).

Sensory studies on bananas have usually been limited to cultivars selected for compact and uniform bunch shape such as the Cavendish subgroup, Gros Michel and its tetraploid progeny. Thus the full range of well-flavored bananas has yet to be explored. McCarthy et al. (1963) found that they could compare the flavor profiles of cultivars Gros Michel and Valery by assessment of bananalike flavor, fruitiness, and sweetness. In an assessment of 31 tetraploid clones relative to cultivar Valery as a standard, it was shown that good bananalike flavor and sweetness were the main factors governing acceptability (Baldry, 1980; Baldry et al., 1981), and negative flavor qualitites such as astringency and off-flavors had relatively less effect on acceptability, except in extreme cases. Flavor profile comparison of cultivars Gros Michel (AAA group), Silk (AAB group), and Sucrier (AA group) in Malaysia showed that Silk was the sweetest and cultivar Gros Michal the most juicy (Choo and Choon, 1972; Choon and Choo, 1972). Sensory evaluation studies in Jamaica of bananas cooked when green show that preference in this situation is based mainly on softness and absence of astringency and that tetraploid cultivars (AAAA group) are generally preferred to cultivars Valery and Lacatan (Baldry and Dempster, 1976).

3. Enzymes

Ripening in bananas is an extremely complex and highly coordinated process which involves synthesis of RNA and of new proteins in the early stages of the climacteric. The major compositional changes of ripening are apparently enzyme-mediated, and the work associated with metabolic control of ripening has been reviewed in detail by Palmer (1971) and by Marriott (1980). Among the metabolically important enzymes which have been purified and studied in banana are pectinesterase (Brady, 1976), invertase (Sum et al., 1980), phosphofructokinase (Salminen and Young, 1975), peroxidase (Nagle and Haard, 1975), and acid phosphatase (De Leo and Sacher, 1970). Enzymes are readily inactivated in the course of homogenization, and polyvinylpyrrolidone may be included during homogenization to aid extraction by protection from phenolics (Baijal et al., 1972). In those cases where enzymes have been purified from plantains, they have been very similar in properties to the banana enzymes.

The enzyme system involved in the browning of the peel and pulp of bananas has been extensively studied. Banana polyphenyloxidase (PPO) has been purified from the pulp and peel of banana fruit (Palmer, 1963). It had a pH optimum about 7.0 and a higher affinity for dopamine than for other substrates and did not oxidize monophenols. Spectrochemical studies indicated that dopamine was oxidized to melanin via indole-5,6-quinone.

Banana PPO activity is higher in the interior than the exterior of the pulp tissue and contains up to 10 isoenzymes, all of which are inhibited by cysteine but only some of which are inhibited by sodium metabisulfite (Montgomery and Sgarbieri, 1975). For processing, browning in bananas and plantains is inhibited by acidification with citric acid to about pH 3.3, where practicable, and by sulfitation or heat inactivation of enzymes (Rodriguez-Soza et al., 1977; Sánchez-Nieva and Mercado, 1978b; Sánchez-Nieva et al., 1975).

4. Biochemistry of Ripening

Bananas and plantains are typical climacteric fruits in that they exhibit a well-defined preclimacteric period after harvesting, during which the fruit remains unripe, the basal respiration rate is low, and ethylene production is almost undetectable. The respiratory climacteric commences spontaneously, and there is a rapid and well-defined rise in respiratory rate which is closely synchronized with evolution of ethylene, with chlorophyll breakdown in the peel and with starch to sugar conversion and tissue softening in the pulp (Palmer, 1971; Marriot, 1980). The close relationship between the respiratory increase, color change, and softening are shown in Fig. 3. The preclimacteric period increases with decreasing temperature between 40 and about 15°C, below which temperature disturbances associated with chilling injury are manifest. Ripening is rapidly initiated by concentrations of exogenous ethylene of 10 ppm or above, and concentrations as low as 0.1 ppm cause a substantial

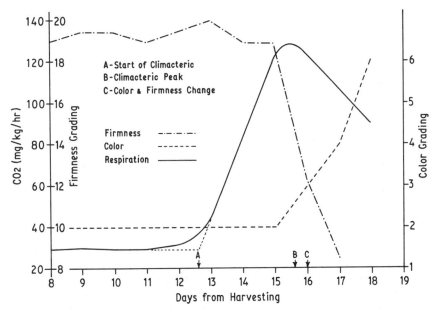

Figure 3 Relationship between respiratory changes and physical characteristics in bananas. (From Peacock, 1966.)

acceleration in the onset of the climacteric. The preclimacteric period is reduced by stresses such as water loss and mechanical injury and is increased by reduction in oxygen concentration and by treatment with gibberellins. Bananas and plantains are extremely susceptible to chilling injury which is observable at 14°C in some cultivars and which is severe at 10°C in all cultivars. The symptoms of chilling injury are initially a discoloration in the vascular tissue underlying the peel surface, known as underpeel discoloration, failure to develop full flavor on ripening, and reduction in starch-to-sugar conversion during ripening, if injury is severe (Marriott, 1980).

The mechanism of control of ripening is related to the role of ethylene in the tissue and to the autocatalytic formation of this hormone during the early phase of the climacteric, which has been studied by induction of ripening using its analogue, propylene. Ethylene is formed from methionine via S-adenosyl methionine and aminocyclopropane-1-carboxylic acid (ACC), and the ripening banana contains appreciable levels of ACC (Hoffman and Yang, 1980). Ripening is preceded by changes in tissue premeability which probably play a role in the control of ripening, though observations are not consistent with a mechanism of control which operates simply through breakdown in cellular compartmentation during senescence (Wade et al., 1980). Similarly, initiation of ripening is linked with redirection of protein synthesis, but there is no evidence that synthesis of any specific enzyme not previously present causes initiation of ripening. The evidence that is available shows that ripening is a highly programmed process in which control is maintained well into senescence but that changes in intracellular compartmentation may play an important role.

IV. PRESERVATION METHODS

A. Traditional Processing

1. Products: Uses and Dietary Significance

Most of the world's bananas are eaten either raw, in the ripe state, or as a cooked vegetable, and only a very small proportion are processed in order to obtain a storable product (Simmonds, 1966). This is true both at a traditional village level with both dessert and cooking bananas and when considering the international trade in dessert bananas. In general, preserved products do not contribute significantly to the diet; however, in some localized areas the products are important in periods when food is scarce.

Probably the most widespread and important product is flour prepared from unripe bananas and plantains by sun-drying, although drying is often regarded simply as a means of preparation as opposed to a preservation method (Simmonds, 1966). In Uganda, dried slices, known as *mutere* are prepared for storage from green bananas, the dried slices being either used directly for cooking or after grinding into a flour (Goode, 1974; Mukasa and Thomas, 1970). *Mutere* is used chiefly as a famine reserve and does not feature largely in the diet under normal conditions. In Gabon, plantains are sometimes made into dried slices which can be stored and used on long journeys (Walker, 1931), and plantains are used in Cameroon to prepare dried pieces which are stored and ground as needed into flour for use in cooking a paste known as *fufu* (see Sec. V) (Tezenas du Montcel, 1979). Dried green banana slices are also used in parts of South and Central America and the West Indies for preparing flour (Fawcett, 1921; Kervégant, 1935).

The other nutritionally important product is beer, which is a major product in Uganda and Rwanda where green banana utilization is particularly high (see Table 3). Banana wines and spirits are also produced in some other areas of the world, but are of fairly minor importance (Fawcett, 1921; Kervégant, 1935).

In Samoa, bananas are preserved by a method similar to that used for breadfruit. The product is a fermented paste which is baked into a breadlike substance called *masi* which can be stored for long periods, until needed, either in the form of the fermented dough or after baking (Cox, 1980). Ripe bananas are also preserved by sun-drying, the product often being known as banana figs, which are eaten as sweetmeats and are very popular in many areas but nowhere making a significant contribution to the diet.

2. Preservation Methods and Processes

Drying. Both ripe and unripe bananas and plantains are normally peeled and sliced before drying, although banana figs are sometimes prepared from whole ripe fruit. Sun drying is the most widespread technique where the climate is suitable, but drying in ovens or over fires is also practiced (Fawcett, 1921; Hayes, 1941; Kervégant, 1935; Mukasa and Thomas, 1970; Simmonds, 1966). In West Africa, plantains are often soaked and sometimes parboiled or boiled before drying (Johnston, 1958).

The slices of unripe fruit are normally spread out on bamboo frameworks or sometimes on a cemented area or simply on the ground (Kervégant, 1935). The technique used in Uganda has been described by Hayes (1941). The bunch is cut from the tree and often left 2 or 3 days to allow some ripening to occur. The fingers are peeled, split lengthwise into two or three slices, and dried in the sun for 1 or 2 weeks on a mat; on a swept-bare patch of earth; on a roof; or sometimes on stone outcrops or sheets of corrugated iron. When dry, the slices are packed into oval-shaped bundles made of banana fiber and hung in the house, or if a large amount is to be stored, millet granaries are used. In Cameroon, plantains are often dried in large ovens (Tezenas du Montcel, 1979).

Banana figs are prepared in a variety of ways, but a detailed description of the method used in the Bombay area of India has been given by

Kulkarni (1911). In this region the preferred fruit for fig preparation is a variety known locally as *rajeli* (a French plantain type). The bananas are harvested green and ripened in a storehouse by piling them in layers covered with plantain leaves. The fruit is ready for drying after about 3 days, by which time a patch of ground has been prepared by beating it until hard and plastering it with cow dung and water. When the earth has dried hard a mat is spread out, and onto this the peeled bananas are arranged in rows. Each night the fruit is gathered in and covered with dry leaves and a mat, and the next day spread in the sun again. This is repeated for 3 successive days and nights after which period the product is ready for the market and is wrapped in leaves for sale. In some areas the fruit is dried on platforms rather than on the ground. In Mexico, ripe bananas are sometimes sun-dried in their peel (Kervégant, 1935).

Oven-drying of ripe bananas is practiced in Polynesia as a means of preserving the fruits, which are then wrapped in leaves and bound tightly to store until needed (Massal and Barrau, 1956). In east Africa a method has been reported that involves drying the peeled bananas on a framework placed over a fire for 24 hr before drying in the sun, to accelerate the process (Kervégant, 1935).

Beverage Production. The typical method of preparation of beer in Uganda and Rwanda is to pick the fruit green and ripen it artificially, by placing in a hole lined with leaves and covered with more leaves and soil. Here the fruit is left for about a week, during which time it ripens and begins to ferment. In Rwanda, heat from a fire or the ashes from a fire are used to aid the ripening process. When ripe, the fruit is removed from the pit, peeled, and placed in a wooden trough. The pulp is mixed with grass and the juice squeezed out; the residue is washed with water to remove all traces of juice, and this liquid added to the main bulk of the juice. To this is added roasted sorghum flour, and the mixture is left to ferment for 1 or 2 days covered with fresh banana leaves. The beer, known locally in Rwanda as *urgwawa*, is then ready for drinking. A more potent beverage, known as *inkangaza* in Rwanda, is prepared by adding honey to the fermenting banana pulp (Adriaens and Lozet, 1951; Champion, 1970; Masefield, 1938). A similar method is used in Benin in West Africa, but the fermentation is initiated by using a little of the drink previously made or a fermented paste made from banana flour, rather than sorghum flour (Kervégant, 1935). Wine can also be prepared from bananas by adding slices of banana to water and leaving for about 3 days, or by mashing bananas in water, leaving for a night, straining, and bottling for a week before drinking (Fawcett, 1921; Kervégant, 1935).

Fermentation. The fermented product masi is prepared in western Samoa with a technique used widely in the Pacific islands for preparing breadfruit (Cox, 1980). A pit is constructed and lined with leaves of

Heliconia paka and also some banana leaves. Unripe bananas are peeled and washed, placed in the pits, and the leaves folded over, forming a relatively airtight pocket. Another layer of leaves is placed on top and finally a layer of soil and rocks. After 34 days the pit is opened up to reveal a homogeneous doughlike paste with a slightly sweet, musky smell. The paste is formed into loaves wrapped in *Heliconia* leaves and baked. On Ta'u in American Samoa, tarpaulin covers are sometimes used as well as soil, and the fruit is placed in plastic bags before burying. On Tanu'eli the baked masi is reburied in three layered baskets and is said to keep for generations, to be uncovered only in times of famine.

3. Product Stability and Storage Problems

There is little experimental data on the storage life of the traditionally made banana and plantain products; however, various storage times are quoted. The banana figs, prepared and dried as described by Kulkarni (1911) in India, are said to keep for 6 months if dried adequately, while Père Labat (cited in Kervégant, 1935) states that banana figs will keep for years. Dried green bananas keep well except that they are liable to insect attack, whereas the flour made from them is less stable, being hygroscopic, and it deteriorates rapidly under tropical conditions (Kervégant, 1935). In Cameroon, processed plantains are normally stored as dried slices and only converted to flour when needed since the flour tends to lose its flavor rapidly (Tezenas du Montcel, 1979).

The fermented dough or masi made in Samoa from unripe bananas is reported to keep for over a year buried in the leaf-lined pits, and on the island of Ta'u bananas are said to be preserved for generations by burying the baked masi in airtight baskets in a deep, covered hole (Cox, 1980).

4. Potential for Scaling Up of Traditional Processes to Industrial Level

Many banana products are now produced on an industrial scale, including the traditional banana figs and flour, and the processing techniques are described in detail in Sec. IV. B. 2. One of the main problems encountered has been the susceptibility of banana products to flavor deterioration and discoloration, and in the past many products reaching the market have been of poor quality. A great deal of research has been directed to overcoming these problems as will be described later, although however good the resultant products are , they cannot compare in flavor and other characteristics with the fresh banana fruit. Indeed, an important constraint on the large-scale development of banana processing is the lack of demand for banana products since the fresh fruit is available throughout the year in most parts of the tropical world.

The production of beer from bananas and plantains has not been scaled up to an industrial level, and while an important product in localized areas of tropical Africa, the market is rapidly declining in favor of European-type brews produced locally (Crowther, 1979). The fermentation technique used in Samoa has also not been adapted for industrial use, although recently fermentation of banana pulp has been studied as a possible means of preservation on a large or small scale (Aegerter and Dunlap, 1980).

B. Industrial Processing

1. Products and Uses

A considerable amount of research has been carried out over recent years concerning the processing of bananas as a means of utilizing the bananas surplus and fruit rejected as unsuitable for export. However, the demand for processed banana products is small, and it has been estimated that the total volume processed in the world does not exceed 100,000 tonnes (Crowther, 1979). Even less enters international trade, the quantity having been estimated at not more than 20,000 tonnes of products using 50,000 tonnes of fresh fruit per year (Wilson, 1975). This is very small in comparison to the 7 million tonnes of fresh banana that appear in international trade (see Sec. IV. C).

The main commercial products made from bananas are canned or frozen puŕee, dried figs, banana powder, flour, flakes, chips (crisps), canned slices, and jams. Of these, the first two are most important in world trade. However, the exports of banana purée amount to only about 12,000 tonnes/year, this mainly coming from Honduras and Panama, while the world exports of banana figs for 1970 to 1972 fluctuated between 2250 and 2500 tonnes/year, of which 95% were supplied by Ecuador. The annual exports of banana powder and banana slices amounted to about 200 tonnes and 100 tonnes/year respectively (Wilson, 1975). The main importers of banana purée are the United States (taking two-thirds of the total), the German Democratic Republic, and the Federal Republic of Germany, while banana figs are imported chiefly by France, the United States, the Federal Republic of Germany, Japan, and Switzerland (Wilson, 1975).

Banana products can be divided roughly into two types—those for direct consumption, such as figs, and those for use in food manufacturing industry, for example purée and powder. Banana figs, or fingers as they are sometimes known, are usually whole, peeled fruit carefully dried so as to retain their shape, although sometimes the fruit is sliced or halved to facilitate drying. The main use of commercially produced banana figs is as a vegetarian food, although they have never been very popular, tending to compare unfavorably with fresh fruit, often being dark and tacky with an altered flavor.

Banana and plantain chips (crisps) are thinly sliced pieces of fruit fried in oil and are eaten as a snack like potato chips (crisps). The product is mainly consumed locally although a small amount of banana chips is sold in the United States as a speciality product. The main use of canned slices is in tropical fruit salads (Lawler, 1967; Wilson, 1975), and only a small amount enters international trade. Banana flakes are small straw-colored particles which taste and smell very much like fresh bananas if properly prepared, and they are used as a flavoring or in breakfast cereals; but again, the demand is small. An advertisement for flakes manufactured in Ecuador states that they reconstitute instantly in hot or cold water to form a smooth flavorful purée suitable for the baby food industry, baking, ice cream, pharmaceuticals, and health foods (*Food Technology*, 1966). Banana purée finds similar use, but mainly in the production of baby foods (Wilson, 1975). Banana flour is said to be highly digestible and is used in baby and invalid foods (Haendler, 1966) but can also be used in the preparation of bread and beverages (Reader, 1950). Banana powder is used chiefly in the baking industry for the preparation and fillings for cakes and biscuits and is also used for invalid and baby foods.

2. Processing Technology

Various reviews on the subject of banana processing have been published, in particular Kay (1967), Reader (1950), and more recently, Crowther (1979). In general, to obtain a good-quality product from ripe bananas the fruit is harvested green and ripened artificially under controlled conditions at the processing factory (*Foreign Commerce Weekly*, 1943; Kay, 1967; Lawler, 1967). After ripening, the banana hands are washed to remove dirt and any spray residues, and peeled. Peeling is almost always done by hand using stainless steel knives, although a mechanical peeler for ripe bananas has been developed, capable of peeling 450 kg of fruit per hour (*Banana Bulletin*, 1974). The peeling of unripe bananas and plantains is facilitated by immersing the fruit in hot water. For example, immersion in water at 70 to 75°C for 5 min has been suggested as an aid for peeling green bananas for flour production (Centro de Desarrollo Industrial del Ecuador, 1966a), while the peeling of green bananas for freezing has been facilitated by immersion in water at 93°C for 30 min (Sánchez-Nieva and Mercado, 1978a).

Banana Figs. Fully ripe fruits with a sugar content of about 19.5% are used and are treated with sulfurous acid (3%) after peeling, then dried as soon as possible afterwards (Loesecke, 1955). Various drying systems have been described using temperatures between 50 and 82°C for 10 to 24 hr to give a moisture content ranging from 8 to 18% and a yield of dried figs of 12 to 17% of the fresh banana on the stem (Centro de Desarrollo Industrial del Ecuador, 1966b; Dupainge, 1957; Gooding, 1958; Loesecke, 1955; McBean and Shipton, 1950; Savage and Arthur, 1935). One factory in Australia uses a solar heat collector on the roof to augment the heat used for drying bananas (*Paradisiaca*, 1978).

Bananas can also be dried by osmotic dehydration, using a technique which involves drawing water from 1/4-in.-thick banana slices by placing them in a sugar solution of 67 to 70° Brix for 8 to 10 hr, followed by vacuum-drying at 65 to 70°C at a vacuum of 10 mmHg for 5 hr. The moisture content of the final product is 2.5% or less, much lower than that achieved by other methods (Brekke and Ponting, 1970).

Banana Purée. Banana purée is obtained by pulping peeled, ripe bananas and then preserving the pulp by one of three methods: canning aseptically, acidification followed by normal canning, or quick-freezing. The last method produces the most acceptable product in terms of flavor and is used commercially in Mexico and Honduras; sales are confined to the United States because of the high cost of transporting the product. Acidification of the purée modifies the flavor and has been attempted on a small scale but does not have widespread acceptance among consumers. The bulk of the world's purée is processed by the asceptic canning technique at La Lima in Honduras by United Brands Company.

A process used for aseptic canning and for freezing is described by Lawler (1967) and Northcutt and Gemmill (1957). Peeled, ripe fruits are conveyed to a pump which forces them through a plate with 1/4-in. holes, then on to a homogenizer, followed by a centrifugal deaerator, and into a receiving tank with 29-in. vacuum, where the removal of air helps prevent discoloration by oxidation. The purée is then passed through a series of scraped surface heat exchangers where it is sterilized by steam, partially cooled, and finally brought to filling temperature. The sterilized purée is then packed aseptically into steam-sterilized cans which are closed in a steam atmosphere. The canning line is capable of handling 29 no. 10 cans per minute. The purée can also be packed in 55-gal drums using a vacuum-filling technique. For freezing, the purée is passed from the heat exchanger into 40-lb fiberboard containers at about 10°C, which are then passed through a tunnel freezer where they are subjected to -37°C air blast. Up to 8 tons of purée can be frozen per day. A similar plant operates in Texas using Mexican bananas with the capacity to freeze 100 tons/day (Crowther, 1979).

Acidified banana purée has been produced commercially in Australia, the Republic of South Africa, Brazil, and Jamaica. A method has been developed in which peeled, ripe fruit is blanched whole in steam, boiling water, or both, until the center temperature of the fruit reaches 88°C, taking 6 to 8 min for medium-sized fruit. The blanched fruit is analyzed for sugar content and pH value and then comminuted with addition of citric acid and sugar, during or after the pulping stage, to reduce the pH between 4.1 and 4.3 and to increase the sugar content to 30 to 35%, in order to mask the slight citric acid flavor. The purée is heated to 100°C and the cans filled hot, closed and inverted to sterilize the lid, after which they are cooled as quickly as possible in running water to 38°C. The whole process must be carried out as quickly as possible to ensure a high-quality product (Guyer and Erikson, 1954). A similiar process for production of acidified purée has been developed in Hawaii, in which the fruit pulp is puréed on a course screen, subjected to heat treatment, then finished on a fine screen prior to acidification and filling (Brekke et al., 1969; Tonaki et al., 1973).

Banana Slices. Several methods for canning of banana slices in syrup have been described (Board and Seale, 1954a,b; Dias et al., 1955; Lawler, 1967; Martin et al., 1975; Smit and Burger, 1957). Best-quality slices are obtained from fruit at an early stage of ripeness. The slices are processed in a syrup of 25° Brix with pH about 4.2, and some processes calcium chloride (0.2%) or calcium lactate (0.5%) are added as firming agents.

Canning plantain slices in syrup was considered to be unsatisfactory by Sánchez-Nieva and Hernandex (1967), who produced frozen slices instead. Ripe slices were cooked in 40° Brix syrup until the concentration of the syrup reached 54 to 60° Brix and cinnamon and lemon juice were added to improve the color. The product was packed in boilable plastic pouches and quick-frozen at -23.3°C and was prepared for serving by boiling the pouches in water for 15 min.

A method for producing an intermediate-moisture banana product for sale in flexible laminate pouches has recently been developed (Ramanuja and Jayaraman, 1980). Banana slices are blanched and equilibrated in a solution containing glycerol (42.25%), sucrose (14.85%), potassium sorbate (0.45%), and potassium metabisulfite (0.2%) at 90°C for 3 min to give a moisture content of 30.2%.

Banana Powder. In the manufacture of banana powder, fully ripe banana pulp is converted into a paste by passing through a chopper followed by a colloid mill. A 1 or 2% sodium metabisulfite solution is added to improve the color of the final product. Spray- or drum-drying may be used, the latter being favored as all the solids are recovered. A typical spray drier can produce 70 kg powder per hour to give yields of 8 to 11% of the fresh fruit (Boulais, 1951; Loesecke, 1955), while drum-drying gives a final yield of about 13% of the fresh fruit (Northcutt and Northcutt, 1948). In the latter method the moisture content is reduced to 8 to 12% and then further decreased to 2% by drying in a tunnel or cabinet drier at 60°C. Other methods of drying have been tested experimentally, including foam-mat-drying (Singhagajen and McBean, 1968), vacuum-oven-drying (Patil and Magar, 1976), and freeze-drying (Brekke and Allen, 1966; 1967), and have been shown to produce good-quality powder with a moisture content of 2% or less.

The possibilities for producing protein-enriched banana powder have been investigated involving either fermentation of the banana pulp itself (Lefrançois, 1970) or the addition of isolated soybean protein to the pulp before drying (Mizrahi et al., 1967). In the former method, crushed banana pulp is divided into two lots, one-half being treated with yeast and subjected to continuous fermentation, and the two lots then mixed together and spray-dried to produce a powder. It has been

estimated that from 1 tonne of banana, the protein recoverable is in
the same order as the amount found in 150 kg of fresh meat (*Food
Trade Review*, 1969). In the second method, soybean protein, within
the range of 4 to 20% on a dry wt basis, is added to banana pulp having
the effect, not only of increasing the nutritional value of the powder,
but also of acting as a spray-drying aid by reducing the adhesion of
the pulp to the walls of the drier and of reducing the moisture absorption of the powder in storage (Mizrahi et al., 1967).

Banana Flour. Production of flour in Ecuador has been carried out
by peeling and slicing green fruit, exposure to sulfur dioxide gas, then
drying in a countercurrent tunnel drier for 7 to 8 hr, with an inlet
temperature of 75°C and outlet temperature of 45°C, to a moisture content of 8%, and finally milling (Centro de Desarrollo Industrial del
Ecuador, 1966a). Similar processes have also been developed in Puerto
Rico with both green bananas and plantains (Rahman, 1963; Rodriguez-
Soza et al., 1977). Unpeeled plantains have also been used satisfactorily
and with no toxic results (Rahman, 1963; Rahman et al., 1963).

Banana Chips (Crisps). A number of processes have been developed to produce good-quality banana chips (Bai and Rao, 1969; Berg
et al., 1971; Jain et al., 1962). Typically, unripe peeled bananas are
thinly sliced, immersed in a sodium or potassium metabisulfite solution,
fried in hydrogenated oil at 180 to 200°C, and dusted with salt and an
antioxidant, such as butylatedhydroxytoluene. Alternatively, slices
may be dried before frying and the antioxidant and salt added with
the oil (Adeva et al., 1968a; Kutty et al., 1978). Similar processes
for producing plantain chips have been developed in Puerto Rico
(Cancel et al., 1962; Gonzalez et al., 1969).

Banana Beverages. A juice can be extracted from banana pulp by
pressing or centrifugation once the pulp has been depectinized, and
although banana beverages are not generally produced on a commercial
scale, several processes have been described (Dupaigne, 1974; Dupaigne
and Dalnic, 1965; Pizarro and Coronel, 1971; Tocchini and Lara, 1977).
In a typical process, peeled ripe fruit is cut into pieces, blanched for
2 min in steam, pulped and pectolytic enzyme added at a concentration
of 2 g enzyme per 1 kg pulp, then held at 60 to 65°C and 2.7 to 5.5
pH for 30 min. In a simpler method, lime is used to eliminate the pectin. Calcium oxide (0.5%) is added to the pulp and after standing for
15 min this is neutralized giving a yield of up to 88% of a clear, attractive juice (Mumyanganizi and Coppens, 1974). In another process
banana pulp is acidified, and steam-blanched in a 28-in. Hg vacuum
which ensures tissue disintegration and enzyme inactivation. The pulp
is then conveyed to screw press, the resulting purée diluted in the
ratio 1:3 with water, and the pH adjusted by further addition of citric
acid to 4.2 to 4.3, which yields an attractive drink when this is centri-
fuged and sweetened (Casimir and Jayaraman, 1971). Methods for

obtaining a nectar (Hernández, 1973) a syrup (Wyk et al., 1978), and a liqueur (Kefford, 1964) have also been described.

Jam. A small amount of jam is made commercially by boiling equal quantities of fruit and sugar together with water and lemon juice, lime juice, or citric acid, until setting point is reached (Loesecke, 1949).

Miscellaneous Products. A number of semiprocessed products based on traditional dishes have been developed recently for sale to the consumer in forms for quick and easy preparation. For example, a dehydrated mix has been produced from which *tatale*, a type of pancake made traditionally in Ghana from soft ripe plantains and fermented wholemeal maize dough by a long and complex process, can easily be prepared. The traditional process is followed for the preparation of the maize dough (see Sec. V), but the ripe plantains are sulfited and blended to purée rather than pounded, and this purée is then mixed with the maize dough. The mixture is dried at 70°C for 12 hr to a moisture content of about 6%, and the final product, in the form of flakes, is packed in polyethylene bags. The flakes can be reconstituted into a paste for frying into tatale by addition of water (Dei-Tutu, 1975).

Peeled, blanched, and sulfited plantain pieces have been produced for the preparation of traditional Colombian and Puerto Rican dishes such as the fried products *patacones* (Colombia) and *tostones* (Puerto Rico) (Delgado et al., 1979; Sánchez-Nieva et al., 1975; Sánchez-Nieva et al., 1975a,b,c). The plantain pieces are packed raw or partially fried and may be stored chilled at about 6°C or be quick-frozen at -42.7°C for storage at -23.3°C. Other products prepared from green plantains in Puerto Rico include a snack called plantain sticks and grated raw fruit as fried chips (Cruz and Gonzalez, 1972), and a method for the production of frozen green bananas has also been developed (Sánchez-Nieva and Mercado, 1978a,b,c).

3. Product Stability and Spoilage Problems

All dried banana products are very hydroscopic and susceptible to flavor deterioration and discoloration, but this can be overcome to some extent by storing in moisture-proof containers and sulfiting the fruit before drying to inactivate the oxidases. The dried products are also liable to attack by insects and mold if not stored in dry conditions, although disinfestation after drying by heating for 1 hr to 80°C or by fumigation with methyl bromide ensures protection against attack (Haendler, 1966; Crowther, 1979). Banana powder is said to be stored for up to a year commercially (*Banana Bulletin,* 1970), and flakes have been stored in vacuum-sealed cans with no deterioration in moisture, color, or flavor for 12 months (Samish and Coussin, 1965). Banana chips tend to have a poor storage life and to become soft and rancid (Adeva et al., 1968a). However, chips treated with an antioxidant have been stored satisfactorily at room temperature in hermetically sealed containers for up to 6 months with no development of rancidity (Adeva et al., 1968a; Jain et al., 1962).

The main spoilage problem of canned slices is discoloration of which Board and Seale (1954a,b) considered there to be three types: enzymatic browing, oxidative browning, and tannin browing, and these are distinguished as follows. Enzymatic browning is caused when oxidizing enzymes in cut and peeled tissues are exposed to the air and can be avoided by minimizing the delays on the processing line. Oxidative browing can be caused in cans containing excessive amounts of residual oxygen in the headspace. Tannin browning occurs as a result of the interaction of carbonyl compounds in the acidified syrup with tannins in the mucilaginous cells of the bananas, which can occur if the syrup is heated too long. However, canned slices have been shown to be still quite attractive with a good texture after 8 months of storage (Smit and Burger, 1957).

Commercially produced, aseptically canned purée can be stored for more than a year at room temperature, while retaining the flavor and color of fresh fruit (Northcutt and Gemmill, 1957), and purée which is not sterile can be stored at 7°C for 6 months or at -18°C for a year or more (Brekke et al., 1969; Tonaki et al., 1973). Spoilage by molds and yeasts can sometimes occur in canned purée, although the purée is said to contain antibacterial substances (Bilenker and Dunn, 1960). A pink discoloration has also been reported in canned banana purée caused by conversion of leucoanthocyanidins to anthocyanidins during heat processing (Ranganna and Parpia, 1974).

4. Quality Control Methods

In general a good-quality product is obtained if fruit is harvested at the correct stage of maturity and, where appropriate, ripened under controlled conditions. For example, in the case of banana figs, the fruit should be fully mature (sugar content of 19.5% or above) or the final product is liable to be tough and lacking in flavor (Roader, 1950). However, if overripe fruit is used, the figs tend to be sticky and dark in color, so the fruit must be fully yellow but still firm. For banana flour, which is prepared from unripe bananas, the fruit is harvested at three-quarters the full-ripe stage and is processed within 24 hr, prior to the onset of ripening. If less mature fruit is used, the flour tastes slightly astringent and bitter due to the tannin content (Centro de Desarrollo Industrial del Ecuador, 1966a).

The optimum maturity of bananas required to produce good-quality fried chips was determined by Kutty et al. (1978). Bananas harvested between 85 and 95 days after the emergence of the inflorescence, with a pulp-to-peel ratio of about 1.7 (see Sec. III. B. 1) were considered to be most suitable for the deep-fat frying. Other criteria suggested for assessing maturity were β-carotene content and reducing sugar content, both of which increase with increasing maturity, and pH which decreases as the fruit ripens, and these should be, respectively, about 2000 µg/100 g, less than 1.5%, and 5.8 or above. Browning was found to occur if the sugar content was higher than 1.5%. The determination of crude fat in processed chips is also considered to be a necessary quality control measure (Bueso, 1974).

It is important to remove all impurities prior to processing of products, and this is done by washing to remove dirt and spray residues and by inspecting peeled fruit on the processing line so that substandard fruit can be removed (Albanese, 1965; Lawler, 1967). There is little information on the quality control methods actually used by the processing industry to check that the end product is of good quality. However, the factory in Honduras which produces aseptically canned purée takes two samples of the canned purée every 2 hr, one being opened immediately and the other 3 weeks later (Lawler, 1967).

5. Byproducts and Processes

The chief waste products of the banana industry are the pseudostem, the peel, and rejected whole bananas. The pseudostem is normally left in the fields to rot after harvesting the fruit; however, while the potash in the stem is useful as a fertilizer, the fiber and gum can be a nuisance, and disposal can be a problem in densely cultivated areas (Subrahmanyan et al., 1963). It has been estimated in India alone that 5.5 million tonnes of banana pseudostem are produced each year (Subrahmanyan et al., 1957). Vast quantities of peel are produced by processing factories, the ratio of pulp to peel in ripe bananas being approximately 1:1; for example, it has been estimated by one of the major companies that about 20,000 tonnes of banana peel are discarded annually from their processing plants in South America (Rios et al., 1975). A number of byproducts can be obtained from this waste material, although in general they are not produced on a commercial scale.

Animal feedstuff is one of the most important potential byproducts of the banana and plantain industries, the whole fruit, peelings, and pseudostem all being usable in this way. Fresh whole ripe bananas, dried green banana meal, and ensiled bananas have been used successfully as pig feed (Clavijo and Maner, 1975; Dividich et al., 1976; Mallesard, 1971), and in Ecuador, green bananas are fed to both beef and dairy cattle (Food and Agricultural Organization, 1969). Both banana and plantain peel have been investigated as sources of animal feed (Goewert and Nicholas, 1980; Mora and Rojas, 1970; Rios et al., 1975). Dried peel from ripe bananas was found to contain 9.16% protein and to be nontoxic when fed at a 20% concentration to rats, chicks, chickens, and pigs, growth rates being almost as high as in the controls (Rios et al., 1975). The use of peelings as an animal feed on a commercial basis does not appear widespread although a banana dehydration factory in South Africa was reported to be utilizing the waste peels in this way (*Commonwealth Production,*

1959) and plantain peels are said to be used locally as an animal feed
in Columbia (Mora and Rojas, 1970). Plantain pseudostems have been
shown to be palatable to cattle, but because of the low-protein and dry-
matter content, 4.52 and 5.87%, respectively, they are recommended
only for use as an emergency food (Arroyo and Rivera Brenes, 1960;
Rivera Brenes et al., 1959).

A high-quality starch similar to potato starch has been extracted
from banana pseudostem (Shantha and Siddappa, 1970a) with yields
varying from 2 to 5% by fresh wt (Subrahmanyan et al., 1963). However, the starch content decreases gradually once the fruit has been
harvested and the pseudostems are left to stand in the field, extraction
becoming uneconomical after 4 days. If the pseudostems are felled and
stored in the shade, the starch content is reduced to such an extent
that even after 2 days extraction becomes uneconomical. It is important, therefore, to extract the starch as soon as possible following the
harvesting of the fruit (Shantha and Siddappa, 1970b). To recover
the starch the stem must be subjected to crushing and tearing; a combination of a can crusher and paper pulp beater have been found to be
suitable for this purpose (Subrahmanyan et al., 1957). The starch is
suitable for use in the food and textile industries.

Fiber can be extracted from the stem of edible bananas, as it can
from the related abaca species, either by hand or by a power-driven
raspador (Jarman et al., 1977). The yield, however, is low, about 1
to 1.5% per stem, 100 tonnes of stems being required for 1 tonne of
fiber; this has been one of the most important factors militating against
the successful commercial production of banana fiber. A fine cloth can
be made by weaving single fibers, or a coarse cloth for matting or
sacking by weaving spun fibers. Mixed with other fibers, banana
fiber can be used for ropemaking for agricultural purposes.

A high-quality pulp with strength properties superior to abaca pulps
has also been obtained from banana fiber by cooking at 170°C with
caustic soda, kraft, or alkaline sulfite, giving yields of 64.6, 63.7,
and 72.3%, respectively (Villanueva et al., 1972). Subrahmanyan et al.
(1963) suggest that minerals could be recovered from the juice pressed
out during extraction of the fibers and returned to the field as fertilizer,
and most of the starch could also be recovered.

There are various micellaneous uses to which waste banana products
could be put. Dried banana peel has been found to contain significant
quantities of a complex mixture of triterpenoids and phytosterols (4 to
7% by weight of the dry peel) (Knapp and Nicholas, 1969; Rios et al.,
1975; Romer, 1973), and at one time it was thought that the peel could
be a useful source of steroids for the pharmaceutical industry. But
because of the structure of the compounds, it has not yet been commercially feasible. Commercial applications, however, may be found
for the banana skin wax, possibly for use as a shoe or furniture polish.
Fermentation of the peel in order to make more efficient use of the

sugars present has been suggested (Goewert and Nicholas, 1980), and recently it has been demonstrated that banana pulp or peel could be used as a substrate for the production of a single-cell protein (Chung and Meyers, 1979). In India a method has been tentatively developed for preparing a fruit cheese from the scrapings of the banana peel (CFTRI, 1963). Finally, waste bananas can be used as a source of vinegar, a small-scale process using fully ripe or overripe fruit having been developed recently (Adams, 1978, 1980).

V. PREPARATION METHODS FOR FRESH BANANAS AND PLANTAINS

The main ways of preparing fresh bananas for consumption are boiling or steaming, roasting or baking, and frying. Boiling followed by pounding into *fufu* is also widely adopted in certain areas of the tropics.

A. Boiling or Steaming

Plantains and bananas are often prepared simply by boiling in water, either in their peel or after peeling, and either ripe or unripe; if unripe, the fruit is scraped throughly after peeling to remove all traces of fibrous material. The boiled fruit is eaten alone or more usually accompanied by a sauce. This preparation technique is widely used in West Africa (Dalziel, 1937; Johnston, 1958; Tezenas du Montcel, 1979; Walker, 1931) and in the West Indies (Kervégant, 1935; Simmonds, 1966). A variety of dishes prepared from boiled green and ripe plantains in Cameroon have been described by Tezenas du Montcel (1979). For example, peeled, washed, and sliced green plantains are boiled for 35 to 45 min and served in a sauce of palm oil with fish, cooked meat, green beans, and haricots, and seasoned. Very ripe plantains are cut in half and boiled for 15 to 20 min, then peeled and served with palm oil or pepper sauce.

In Uganda, where bananas and plantains are an especially important staple, they are normally steamed but, if boiled, then it is usually with other ingredients (Goode, 1974). For example, in the Baganda region, a dish known as *akatogo* is prepared by adding plantain to beans which have been boiled a little first, and boiling for a further 45 min. To this, ghee, pepper, salt, and onions are sometimes added to improve the flavor. A steamed product known as *omuwumbo,* a staple food in Baganda, is prepared by wrapping the fruit in banana leaves and, after steaming it for an hour, pressing it in the hands into one mass, at which stage it can be eaten or resteamed (Goode, 1974; Mukasa and Thomas, 1970).

A soup known as *sancocho* is prepared in Colombia by boiling slices of peeled green plantain with cassava and other vegetables

(Delgado et al., 1979), while in the West Indies boiled green bananas are often served with salted fish or meat (Kervégant, 1935).

B. Roasting or Baking

Unpeeled or peeled fruit, either ripe or unripe, is roasted simply by placing in the ashes of a fire or in an oven. This method is widely used in West Africa (Dalziel, 1937; Tezenas du Montcel, 1979; Walker, 1931), East Africa (Goode, 1974) and the South Pacific islands (Massal and Barrau, 1956). For example, ripe plantains are placed unpeeled in an oven and when partly brown and tender, removed and peeled, then replaced in the oven and roasted evenly. To serve the fruit, it is grated and eaten with avocados, palm oil, or grilled groundnuts (Tezenas du Montcel, 1979). Ripe plantains are also sometimes peeled, and hardened by placing near a fire, then packed into ashes with charcoal on top and left to cook for about 20 min (Goode, 1974).

C. Frying

Ripe or unripe plantains or bananas are often peeled, sliced and cooked in oil, particularly in West Africa (Dalziel, 1937; Johnston, 1958; Tezenas du Montcel, 1979; Walker, 1931) and in parts of South America and the West Indies (Delgado et al., 1979; Sánchez-Nieva et al., 1975a). Similar products are also made in East Africa. Typically, ripe plantains are peeled, cut into slices or split lengthwise, and fried in palm oil or groundnut oil, the pieces being served either hot with a sauce or with fried eggs, or cold as a snack (Tezenas du Montcel, 1979). Tostones, a popular Puerto Rican dish, are prepared by first frying slices of green plantains for several minutes until partially cooked, then pressing the slices, and finally deep-frying until crisp, to be served sprinkled with salt like potato chips (Sánchez-Nieva et al., 1975a). In Colombia, fried green plantain slices are known as *patacones* (Delgado et al., 1979).

D. Pounding

Pounding is a process, used particularly in West Africa, for preparing most perishable staple food crops including plantains, cassava, yams, and cocoyams to obtain a paste or dough known as fufu (Also spelled *foofoo, foutou, foufou*). The plantains are peeled and boiled or peeled after boiling and pounded in a wooden mortar, the resulting paste normally being eaten with soup or a spiced sauce of meat and vegetables, but sometimes after wrapping in leaves and steaming (Johnston, 1958; Lassoudière, 1973). Fufu is also sometimes prepared from a mixture of plantains and cassava (Hartog, 1972; Lassoudière, 1973), and the same term is applied in Cameroon to the paste made by cooking plantain flour in water (Tezenas du Montcel, 1979).

Pounding techniques are also used for preparing bananas in other parts of the world. In the West Indies, semiripe bananas are cooked in water, peeled, then the pulp crushed in a wooden mortar and added to water to from a paste which is normally eaten with soup (Kervégant, 1935). In Samoa, bananas are pounded, mixed with coconut cream, and scented with citrus leaves, the product being known as *poi* and eaten only by chiefs (Massal and Barrau, 1956).

In Ghana, a type of pancake known as tatale is made from a mixture of the pounded pulp of ripe plantains and a fermented wholemeal maize dough (Dei-Tutu, 1975). The maize dough is prepared by steeping maize in water for 2 days, draining off the water, and washing the grain, which is then ground, made into a dough with water, and left to ferment for 3 days. Soft, ripe plantains are peeled and pounded and mixed with the fermented maize dough, and the resulting paste is seasoned with condiments such as ginger, pepper, onion and salt, then fried in palm oil. A variant, *kaklo*, is made in the same way except the paste is made a little thicker so that it can be formed into balls for deep frying. Tatale and kaklo are served alone or with beans as a main meal or as a snack or dessert.

REFERENCES

Adams, M. R. (1978). Small-scale vinegar production from bananas. *Trop. Sci.* 20:11-19.

Adams, M. R. (1980). The small-scale production of vinegar from bananas. *Report G 132*. London, Tropical Products Institute.

Adeva, L. V., Gopez, M. D., and Payumo, E. M. (1968a). Studies on the preparation and storage qualities of banana chips. *Philipp J. Sci.* 97:27-35.

Adeva, L. V., Gopez, M. D., and Payumo, E. M. (1968b). Preparation of banana flakes from lakatan (*Musa sapientum* Linn. var. Lacatan). *Philipp. J. Sci.* 97:139-144.

Adriaens, E. L., and Lozet, F. (1951). Contribution to the study of fermented beverages indigenous to Rwanda. *Bull. Agric. Congo Belge* 42:940-943. (In French.)

Aegerter, P., and Dunlap, C. (1980). Culture of five commonly used acid-producing bacteria on banana pulp. *Appl. Environ. Microbiol.* 39:937-942.

Albanese, F. (1965). Technology for preparing banana powder. *Dtsch. LebensmRundsch.* 61:311-317. (In German.)

Andersen, D. H., and Mike, E. M. (1955). Diet therapy in the celiac syndrome. *J. Am. Diet. Assoc.* 31:340-346.

Arroyo, J. A., and Rivera Brenes, L. (1960). Digestibility studies on Venezuela grass (*Paspalum faciculatum*) and plantain pseudostalks (*Musa paradisiaca*). *J. Agric. Univ. P.R.* 44:103-106.

Asenjo, C. F., and Porrata, E. I. (1956). The carotene content of green and ripe plantains. *J. Agric. Univ. P.R.*, 40:152-156.

Asenjo, C. F., Garcia de la Noceda, H., and Serrano, P. (1946). Riboflavin content of some tropical foods. *Food Res.* 11:137-141.

Asenjo, C. F., Oro de Boringuen Segundo, and Garcia de la Noceda, H. (1948). Thiamine content of some tropical foods. *Food Res.* 13:94-99.

American Society of Heating, Refrigeration, and Air Conditioning Engineers (1971). Citrus fruits and bananas. In *ASHRAE 1971 Guide and Data Book*. New York, Amer. Soc. Heating, Refrig. Air Condition, Eng., pp. 371-380.

Askar, A. (1972). Contribution to analysis of plant proteins: Bananas proteins. *Dtsch. Lebensm.-Rundsch.* 68:259-261. (In German.)

Askar, A. (1973). The importance of amino acids in fruit. Behaviour of amino acids during ripening of bananas. *Gordian,* 73:12-16. (In German.)

Badran, A. M., (1969). Controlled atmosphere storage of green bananas. *U.S. Patent 3,450,542.*

Bai, S. G., and Rao, M. N. (1969). The use of packaging and antioxidants in banana chipping. *J. Food Sci. Technol.* 6:169-172.

Baijal, M., Singh, S., Shukla, R. N., and Sanwal, G. G. (1972). Enzymes of the banana plant: optimum conditions for extraction. *Phytochem.* 11:929-936.

Baldry, J. (1980). Studies on the Comparative consumer acceptability of the fruit of tetraploid and triploid dessert banana clones. Unpublished M. Phil. thesis, University of London.

Baldry, J. (1982). Flavour volatiles and acceptability of tetraploid bananas. *Fruits* 37:699-704.

Baldry, J., and Dempster, F. D. (1976). Green bananas for cooking: a study of taste-panel preferences between certain clones. *Trop. Sci.* 18:219-225.

Baldry, J., Coursey, D. G., and Howard, G. E. (1981). The comparative consumer acceptability of triploid and tetraploid banana fruit. *Trop. Sci.* 23:33-66.

Banana Bull. (1970). Banana powder plant operating, 34:17.

Banana Bull. (1974). Mechanical peeler handles 1000 lb of bananas an hour, 38(12):18-19.

Banana Bull. (1978). Solar energy collector used in Coffs Harbour banana processing factory, 42(2):6-7.

Barnell, H. R. (1940). Studies in tropical fruits. VIII. Carbohydrate metabolism of the banana fruit during development. *Ann. Bot. N.S.* 4:39-71.

Barnell, H. R. (1943). Studies in tropical fruits. XV. Hemicellulose metabolism of the banana fruit during storage and ripening. *Ann. Bot. N.S.* 7:297-323.

BASF (n.d.). *Guide to Diseases, Pests and Principal Deficiencies in Banana.* Ludwigshafen, BASF.

Beckford, G. L. (1972). *Persistent Poverty—Underdevelopment in Plantation Economies of the Third World.* London, Oxford University Press.

Berg, J. R., Berg, R. C., Sarna, E. J., and Bates, B. (1971). Banana and plantain products and process for preparing same. *British Patent 1, 232, 773.*

Bhakthavatsalu, C. M., and Sathiamoorthy, S. (1979). Banana clonal situation in India. A resumé. *Fruits* 34:99-105.

Bilenker, E. N., and Dunn, C. G. (1960). Growth of food spoilage bacteria in banana purée. *Food Res.* 25:309-320.

Board, P. W., and Seale, P. E. (1954a). Canning bananas. *Aust. Food. Manuf.* 23:26,32.

Board, P. W., and Seale, P. E. (1954b). Canning bananas. *Food Preserv. Q.* 14:2-3.

Boulais, J. (1951). Powder from ripe bananas. *Fruits* 6:109-113. (In French).

Brady, C. J. (1976). The pectinesterase of the pulp of the banana fruit. *Aust. J. Plant Physiol.* 3:163-172.

Brekke, J. E., and Allen, L. (1966). Banana dehydration. *Tech. Prog. Rep. 153.* Honolulu, Agric Exp. Stat., University of Hawaii.

Brekke, J. E., and Allen, L. (1967). Dehydrated bananas. *Food Technol.* 21:101-105.

Brekke, J. E., and Ponting, J. D. (1970). Osmo-vac dried bananas. *Res. Rep. 182.* Honolulu, Agric. Exp. Stat., Coll. Trop. Agric., University of Hawaii.

Brekke, J. E., Tonaki, K. I., Cavaletto, C. G., and Frank, H. A. (1969). Stable banana purée for long-term refrigerated storage. *J. Sci. Food Agric.* 20:376-378.

Brown, F. H. (1972). International standards for banana marketing. In Second *Tech. Cof. on Bananas, Guayaguil, Ecuador, 1972, Paper 22B.* Rome, Food Agric. Org.

Bueso, C. E. (1974). A rapid fat test for fried plantain products. *J. Agric. Univ. P.R.* 58:273-275.

Cancel, L. E., Gonzales, M. A., and Sánchez-Nieva, F. (1962). Processing of plantains. *Misc. Pub. 6.* Food Technol. Lab., Agric. Exp. Stat., University of Puerto Rico. (In Spanish.)

Casimir, D. J., and Jayaraman, K. S. (1971). Banana drink. A new canned product. *CSIRO Food Res. Q.* 31:24-27.

Centro de Desarrollo Industrial del Ecuador (1966a). *Preparation of Flour from Green Bananas.* Quito, Ecuador, Centro de Desarrolo. (In Spanish).

Centro de Desarrollo Industrial del Ecuador (1966b). *Dehydrated Bananas (Banana Figs).* Quito, Ecuador, Centro de Desarrollo. (In Spanish).

Central Food Technology Research Institute (1963). Utilisation of banana fruit waste. In *Ann. Rep. 1962-1963.* Mysore, India, Cent. Food. Technol. Res. Inst., p. 80.

Champion, J. (1963). *The Banana*, Paris, Maisonneuve and Larose. (In French).

Champion, J. (1970). Cultivation of the banana in Rwanda. *Fruits* 25:161-168. (In French).

Choo, C. G., and Choon, S. C. (1972). Comparative evaluation of some quality aspects of banana (*Musa acuminata* colla). II. Juiciness and texture. *Malays. Agric. Res.* 1:118-123.

Choon, S. C., and Choo, C. G. (1972). Comparative evaluations of some quality aspects of banana (*Musa acuminata* colla). I. Flavour, sourness and sweetness. *Malays. Agric. Res.* 1:54-59.

Chung, S. L., and Meyers, S. P. (1979). Bioprotein from banana wastes. *Devs. Ind. Microbiol.* 20:723-732.

Clairmonte, F. F. (1975). Bananas. In *Commodity Trade of the Third World* (C. Payer, ed.). London, Macmillan, pp. 129-153.

Clavijo, H., and Maner J. (1975). The use of waste bananas for swine feed. In *Proc. Conf. Animal Feeds of Tropical and Subtropical Origin, London, 1974.* (D. Halliday, ed.) London, Trop. Prod. Inst., pp. 99-106.

Commonw. Prod. (1959). South African banana prospects, 369:33-34.

Coursey, D. G., Burden, O. J., and Rickard, J. E. (1976). Recent advances in research on post-harvest handling of tropical and subtropical fruit. *Acta Hortic.* 57:135-143.

Cox, P. A. (1980). Two Samoan technologies for breadfruit and banana preservation. *Econ. Bot.* 34:181-185.

Crowther, P. C. (1979). The processing of banana products for food use. *Rep. G122.* London, Trop. Prod. Inst.

Cruz, J. R., and Gonzalez, M. A. (1972). Shelf-life studies of plantain sticks. *J. Agric. Univ. P.R.* 56:321-323.

Commonwealth Scientific and Industrial Research Organization (1972). *Banana Ripening Guide, Circ. 8.* Div. Food Res., Commonw. Sci. Ind. Res. Org., N.S.W., Australia.

Dalziel, J. M. (1937). *The Useful Plants of West Tropical Africa.* London, Crown Agents.

Dei-Tutu, J. (1975). Studies on the development of tatale mix, a plantain product. *Ghana J. Agric. Sci.* 8:153-157.

De Langhe, E. (1961). The taxonomy of the plantain banana in equatorial Africa. *J. Agric. Trop. Bot. Appl.* 8:417-449. (In French)

De Langhe, E. (1976). Why is genetic improvement of plantains not possible at present? *Fruits* 31:537-539.

De Leo, P., and Sacher, J. A. (1970). Senescence. Association of synthesis of acid phosphatase with banana ripening. *Plant Physiol.* 46:208-211.

Delgado, D. D., Cruz, M. V., and Monzon, D. A. de (1979). Preparation and preservation of semi-processed products from plantains at different maturity stages. *Rev. Inst. Invest. Technol.* 118:9-31. (In Spanish).

Deullin, R. (1970). Trends in overseas transport of bananas between 1945 and 1970. Part 1. *Fruits* 25:865-876. (In French).

Deullin, R. (1971). Trends in overseas transport of bananas between 1945 and 1970. Part 2. *Fruits* 26:83-102. (In French).

Dias, D. P., Jain, N. L., and Lal, G. (1955). Investigations on the canning of bananas. *Trop. Agric.* 111:37-41.

Dividich, J. le., Geoffroy, F., Canope, I., and Chenost, M. (1976). Using waste bananas as animal feed. *World Anim. Rev.* 20:22-30.

Drawert, F., Heimann, W., and Rolle, K. (1971). About amino acids in fruits and their behaviour during growth and ripening. II. Behaviour of amino-acids during growth of apples. *Z. Lebensm. Unters. Forsch.* 145:7-15. (In German).

Dupaigne, P. (1957). Study on fruit dehydration. *Fruits* 12:317-323. (In French).

Dupaigne, P. (1974). The extraction of juice from banana, with a view to the production of banana beer. *Fruits* 29:821-822. (In French).

Dupaigne, P. (1975). The aroma of bananas. *Fruits* 30:783-789. (In French).

Dupaigne, P., and Dalnic, R. (1965). New beverages based on fruit. *Fruits* 20:571-575. (In French).

Fawcett, W. (1921). *The Banana: Its Cultivation, Distribution and Commercial Uses*, 2nd ed. London, Duckworth and Co.

Feakin, S. D. (1971). Pest control in bananas. *PANS Manual No. 1.* London, Cent. Overseas Pest Res.

Food and Agriculture Organization (1969). *Developments in the Field of Processing and the Use of Bananas in Livestock Feeding. Committee on Commodity Problems Study Group on Bananas. CCP:BA 69/6.* Rome, Food Agric. Org.

Food and Agriculture Organization (1974). *Provisional Food Balance Sheets. 1972-1974 Average.* Rome, Food Agric. Org.

Food and Agriculture Organization (1975). *International Trade in Plantains, Intergovernmental Group on Bananas, 6th Session, Abijan, CCP:BA 75/5.* Rome, Food Agric. Org.

Food and Agriculture Organization (1980a). *FAO Production Yearbook, 1979.* Rome, Food Agric. Org.

Food and Agriculture Organization (1980b). *FAO Trade Yearbook, 1979.* Rome, Food Agric. Org.

Food and Agriculture Organization (1980c). *International Banana Agreements—Further Consideration of Possible Elements. Intergovernmental Group on Bananas, 7th Session, Rome, CCP:BA 80/5.* Rome Food Agric. Org.

Federacion Nacional de Cafeteros de Colombia (1974). *Plantain cultivation.* Bogata. Bol. Ext. 49 Fed. Nac. Cafe. Colombia. (In Spanish).

Food Technol. (1966). Dehydrated banana flake, 20 (April):105.

Food Trade Rev. (1969). Protein recovery from waste bananas, 39:85-86.

Foreign Commerce Weekly. (1943). Dehydrated banana factories, Brazil, 10(13):25.

Forsyth, W. G. C. (1980). Banana and plantains. In *Tropical and Sub tropical Fruits: Composition, Nutritive Values, Properties and uses* (S. Nagy and P. E. Shaw, eds.). Westport, Conn., Avi Pub. Co., pp. 258-278.

Foy, J. M., and Parratt, J. R. (1960). A note on the presence of noradrenaline and 5-hydroxytryptamine in plantain. *J. Pharm. Pharmacol.* 12:360-364.

Goewert, R. R., and Nicholas, H. J. (1980). Banana peel sugars as a source of foodstuff for animals or humans. *Nutr. Rep. Int.* 22: 207-212.

Goldstein, J. L., and Swain, T. (1963). Changes in tannins in ripening fruits. *Phytochem.* 2:371-383.

Gomez, A., and Matill, H. A., (1949). Ascorbic acid and carotene content of plantain. *Food Res.* 14:177-181.

Gonzalez, M. A., Negron, E. D., and Sandoval, A. R. (1969). Studies on the stability of fried plantain chips. *J. Agric. Univ. P.R.* 53: 67-74.

Goode, P. M. (1974). *Some Local Vegetables and Fruits of Uganda.* Entebbe, Uganda, Dept. Agric.

Gooding, E. G. B. (1958). *The dehydration of vegetables and fruits in India. Expanded Tech. Assis. Prog. Rep. 964.* Rome, Food Agric. Org.

Griffiths, L. A. (1959). Detection and identification of the polypehnoloxidase system of the banana. *Nature* 184:58-59.

Gross, J., Carmon, M., Lifshitz, A., and Costes, C. (1976). Carotenoids of banana pulp, peel and leaves. *Lebensm. Wiss. u-Technol.* 9:211-214.

Guillemot, J. (1976). The plantain in the Ivory Coast. *Fruits* 31:684-687. (In French).

Guyer, R. B., and Erikson, f. B. (1954). Canning of acidified banana purée. *Food Technol.* 8:165-167.

Haarer, A. E. (1964). *Modern Banana Production.* London, Leonard Hill.

Haddad, O., and Borges, O. (1973). *The Bananas in Venezuela.* Cagua, Fund. Shell Agric. (In Spanish).

Haendler, L. (1966). Banana products. *Fruits* 21:329-342. (In French).

Hamilton, K. S. (1965). Reproduction of banana from adventitious buds. *Trop. Agric. (Trinidad)* 42:69-73.

Harris, P. L., and Poland, G. L. (1939). Variations in ascorbic acid content of bananas. *Food Res.* 4:317-327.

Hartog, A. P. den. (1972). Food preferences of some secondary school students in Ghana. *Ghana J. Agric. Sci.* 5:23-32.

Hartshorn, R. (1931). Some effects of acetylene on the ripening process of banana. *Plant Physiol.* 6:467-484.

Hayes, T. R. (1941). Plantains. *E. Afr. Agric. J.* 7:75.

Hernández, I. (1973). Preparation and acceptability of banana nectar. *J. Agric. Univ. P.R.* 57:96-99.

Hoffman, N. E., and Yang, S. F. (1980). Changes of 1-aminocyclo-propane-1-carboxylic acid content in ripening fruits in relation to their ethylene production rates. *J. Am. Soc. Hortic. Sci.* 105:492-495.

International Board for Plant Genetic Resources (1978). *IBPGR Working Group on the Genetic Resources of Bananas and Plantains, Rome 1977.* Rome, Int. Board. Plant Genet. Resour.

Institut Reserche Fruits et Agrumes (1980). *Banana Quality.* Paris, Inst. Rech. Fruits Agrumes. (In French).

International Standards Organization (1977). Green bananas-Ripening conditions. *ISO 3959—1977 (E).* Switzerland, Int. Org. Standard.

Jaffee, W. G., Chavez, J. F., and Koifman, B. de (1963). Concerning the nutritive value of bananas and plantains. *Archos Venez. Nutr.* 13:9-23. (In Spanish).

Jain, N. L., Nair, K. G., Siddappa, G. S., and Lal, G. (1962). Studies to improve the keeping quality of fried salted banana chips. *Food Sci.* 11:335-338.

Jarman, C. G., Mykoluk, S., Kennedy, L., and Canning, A. J. (1977). Banana fibre: a review of its properties and small-scale extraction and processing. *Trop. Sci.* 19:173-185.

Johnson, T. J. (1979). Effects of potassium on the buoyancy of banana fruit. *Exp. Agric.* 15:173-176.

Johnston, B. F. (1958). *The Staple Food Economies of Western Tropical Africa.* Stanford, Calif., Stanford University Press.

Karikari, S. K. (1972). Plantain growing in Ghana. *World Crops* 24:22-24.

Karikari, S. K., Pilcher, D., and Marriott, J. (in press). Factors affecting handling and transportation of plantains (*Musa.* AAB Group). *Acta Hortic.*

Kawabata, A., and Sawayma, S. (1974). Changes in the contents of sugars, starch and pectic substances, of acidity of bananas during ripening. *J. Jpn. Soc. Food Nutr.* 27:21-25. (In Japanese).

Kawabata, A., and Sawayama, S. (1975). Constituent sugars of pectic substances from fruits. *J. Jpn. Soc. Food Nutr.* 28:395-402. (In Japanese).

Kay, D. E. (1967). The processing of banana products. *South Pac. Q. Bull.* 17:37-41.

Kefford, J. F. (1964). The CSIRO report on banana juice syrups and liqueurs. *Banana Bull.* 28(11):14.

Kervégant, D. (1935). *The Banana and Its Usage.* Paris, Soc. Edit. Geog., Maritimes Colon. (In French).

Ketiku, A. O. (1973). Chemical composition of unripe (green) and ripe plantain (*Musa paradisiaca*). *J. Sci. Food Agric.* 24:703-707.

Knapp, F. F., and Nicholas, H. J. (1969). The sterols and triterpenes of banana peel. *Phytochem.* 8:207-214.

Kouadio, T. (1979). The plantain in the West Central zone of the Ivory Coast: Examination of production and marketing methods. *Fruits* 34:447-478. (In French).

Kulkarni, L. B. (1911). The drying of plantain at Agashi. *Agric. J. India.* 6:289:290.

Kutty, S. K., Bhat, A. V., and Varkey, A. G. (1978). Determination of the optimum stage of maturity of Nendran bananas for the preparation of deep-fat fried chips. *J. Food Sci. Technol. (India)* 15:68-71.

Kutty, S. K., Bhat, A. V., Varkey, A. G., Menon, K. G. K. and Mookerji, K. K. (1978). Deep fat frying of banana chips: a critical study of factors governing quality production of Nendran banana chips. In *Proc. Symp. Fats and Oils in Relation to Food Products and their Preparation, June 3-4 1976.* Cent. Food Technol. Res. Inst., Mysore. Assoc. Food Sci. Technol. (India), pp. 75-78.

Lassoudière, A. (1973). The plantain banana in the Ivory Coast. *Fruits* 28:453-462. (In French).

Lawani, S. M., Devos, P., and Odubanjo, M. O. (1977). A bibliography of plantains and other cooking bananas. *Paradisiaca* 2:1-95.

Lawler, F. D. (1967). Banana challenges food formulators. *Food Eng.* 39(5):58-63; (6):62-65.

Lefrançois, L. (1970). The production of yeasts or yeast-supplement foods from waste products of the fruit industries. *Fruits* 25:112-114. (In French).

Loesecke, H. W. von (1949). *Bananas.* New York, Interscience.

Loesecke, H. W. von (1955). *Drying and Dehydration of Foods,* 2nd ed. New York, Rheinhold Pub. Corp.

Mallesard, R. (1971). Experiences in Guadeloupe on the feeding of pigs with banana waste products. *Fruits* 26:20-22. (In French).

Marriott, J. (1980). Bananas—Physiology and biochemistry of storage and ripening for optimum quality. *CRC Crit. Rev. Food Sci. Nutr.* 13:41-88.

Marriott, J., and Proctor, F. J. (1978). Transportation and conservation of tropical fruits. *Outlook Agric.* 9:233-239.

Marriott, J., Robinson, M., and Karikari, S. K. (1981). Starch and sugar transformations during the ripening of plantain and bananas. *J. Sci. Food Agric.* 32:1021-1026.

Marshall, P. B. (1959). Catechols and tryptamines in the "matoke" banana *(Musa paradisiaca). J. Pharm. Pharmacol.* 11:639.

Martin, J. Z. de, Bleinroth, E. W., Angelucci, E., Pupo, L. M., and Tosello, Y. (1975). The use of lactic acid and calcium lactate for bananas in syrup, variety "Nanica". *Bol. Inst. Tecnol. Aliment.* 43:49-66. (In Portuguese).

Martin-Prevel, P. (1980a). Mineral nutrition of bananas world-wide, part 1. *Fruits* 35:503-518. (In French).

Martin-Prevel, P. (1980b). Mineral nutrition of bananas world-wide, part 2. *Fruits* 35:583-593. (In French).

Masefield, G. B. (1938). The production of native beer in Uganda. *E. Afr. Agric. J.* 3:362-364.

Massal, E., and Barrau, J. (1956). Musacea. In Food plants of the South Sea Islands. *Tech. Pap. No 94.* Noumea, New Caledonia, South Pacific Commission, pp. 15-18.

Mattei, A. (1973). Analysis of the volatiles of the banana (cv. "Poyo" group "Cavendish"). *Fruits* 28:231-238. (In French).

Mattei, A., and Paillard, N. (1973). Effect of a variable storage period at the critical temperature of 12°C on the aroma of the banana (var. Poyo) at 20°C. *Fruits* 28:319-322. (In French).

McBean, D., and Shipton, J. (1950). *Dehydration of Bananas. Res. Rep. 21.* Homebush, N.S.W., Australia, Div. Food Res. Trans., Commonw. Sci. Ind. Res. Org.

McCarthy, A. I., Palmer, J. K., Shaw, C. P., and Anderson, E. E., (1963). Correlation of gas chromatographic data with flavor profiles of fresh banana fruit. *J. Food Sci.* 28:379-384.

Menendez, T. (1973). Application of mutation methods to banana breeding. In *Induced Mutation Methods in Vegetatively Propagated Plants.* Vienna, Int. At. Energy Agnecy, pp. 75-83.

Menendez, T., and Loor, F. H. (1979). Recent advances in vegetative propagation and their application to banana breeding. In *Proc. Fourth ACORBAT Conf. Panama, 1979* (R. Tarte, S. Pons, and R. Gabrielli, eds.). Panama, Unión de Paises Exportadores de Banano, (UPEB), pp. 211-222.

Menendez, T., and Shepherd, K. (1975). Breeding new bananas. *World Crops* 27:104-112.

Mizrahi, S., Berk, Z., and Cogan, U. (1967). Isolated soybean protein as a banana spray-drying aid. *Cereal Sci. Today* 12:322-325.

Montgomery, M. W., and Sgarbieri, V. C. (1975). Isoenzymes of banana polyphenol oxidase. *Phytochem.* 14:1245-1249.

Mora, C. B. de, and Rojas, A. M. (1970). Chemical and biological properties of the green and ripe peel of Dominica—Harton plantains (*Musa paradisiaca*). *Rev. Inst. Invest. Tecnol.* 64:42-48. (In Spanish).

Mukasa, S. K., and Thomas, D. G. (1970). Staple food crops. In *Agriculture in Uganda*, 2nd ed. (J. D. Jameson, ed.), London, Oxford University Press, pp. 139-153.

Mumyanganizi, Th., and Coppens, R. (1974). Extraction of banana juice. *Ind. Aliment. Agric.* 91:185-191. (In French).

Nagle, N. E., and Haard, N. F. (1975). Fractionation and characterization of peroxidase from ripe banana fruit. *J. Food Sci.* 40:576-579.

Nayar, G. T. (1962). *Banana in India.* Udyogamandal, India, Fact Tech. Soc.

New, S., Baldry, J., Marriott, J., and Dixon, E. A. (1976). Fruit quality factors affecting selection of banana clones. *Acta Hortic.* 57:205-212.

National Institute of Agricultural Engineering (1977). *Banana coveyer.*
O.D. Tech. Bull. No. 7. Silsoe, U.K., Nat. Inst. Agric. Eng.

Northcutt, R. T., Jr., and Gemmill, A. V. (1957). New banana purée.
Food Eng. 29:66-67.

Northcutt, R. T., and Northcutt, R. T., Jr. (1948). Preparation of
dried fruit products. *U.S. Patent* 2,435,842.

Ojo, G. O. (1969). Plantain meals and serum 5-hydroxytryptamine in
healthy Nigerians. *W. Afr. Med. J.* 18:174-175.

Omole, A., Adewusi, S. A., Adeyemo, A., and Oke, O. L. (1978).
The nutritive value of tropical fruit and root crops. *Nutr. Rep. Int.*
575-580.

Palmer, J. K. (1963). Banana polyphenoloxidase. Preparation and
properties. *Plant Physiol.* 38:508-513.

Palmer, J. K. (1971). The banana. In *The Biochemistry of Fruits and
Their Products,* Vol. 2, (A. C. Hulme, ed.), London, Academic
Press, pp. 65-105.

Pantastico, Er. B., and Mendoza, D. B. (1970). Production of ethylene
and acetylene during ripening and charring. *Philipp. Agric.* 53:477-
484.

Paradisiaca (1978). Supplement to the bibliography of plantains and
other cooking bananas, 3:26-33.

Patil, D. L., and Magar, N. G. (1974). Physicochemical properties of
banana fruit starch and starch components. *J. Indian Chem. Soc.*
51:1004-1007.

Patil, D. L., and Magar, N. G. (1976). A comparative study on
chemical examination of banana powders prepared by different
methods. *Indian J. Nutr. Diet.* 13:218-226.

Paul, A. A., and Southgate, D. A. T. (1978). *McCance and Widdow-
son's, The Composition of Foods,* 4th ed., London, Her Majesty's
Stationery Office.

Peacock, B. C. (1966). Relationship between certain physical changes
and the climacteric phase in the banana. *Queensl. J. Agric. Anim.
Sci.* 23:77-80.

Pizarro, S., and Coronel, M. (1971). Manufacture of banana juice.
Politec. 2:165-170. (In Spanish).

Plucknett, D. L. (1978). Tolerance of some tropical root crops and
starch producing tree crops to sub-optimal land conditions. In *Crop
Tolerance to Sub-optimal Land Conditions* (G. A. Jung, ed.), Amer.
Soc. Agron., pp. 125-144.

Poland, G. L., Manion, J. T., Brenner, M. W., and Harris, P. L.
(1938). Sugar changes in the banana during ripening. *Ind. Eng.
Chem.* 30:340-342.

Polansky, M. M., and Murphy, E. W. (1966). Vitamin B_6 components
in fruits and nuts. *J. Am. Diet. Assoc.* 48:109-111.

Pons, S. (1979). Organisation, methodology and objectives of a world
centre of banana documentation at UPEB. In *Proc. Fourth ACORBAT*

Conf., Panama, 1979. (R. Tarte, S. Pons, and R. Gabrielli, eds.) Unión de Paises Exportadores de Banano (UPEB), Panama, Panama, pp. 351-355. (In Spanish).

Purseglove, J. W. (1972). *Tropical Crops Monocotyledons,* Vol. 2, London, Longman, pp. 343-377.

Quast, S. V. (1976). Volatile constituents of ripe banana fruit (*Musa cavendishii* var. Valery). *Cienc. Cult. (São Paulo)* 28:348-352. (In Portuguese).

Rahman, A. R. (1963). Economical method for the production of flour from green plantains. *J. Agric. Univ. P.R.* 47:1-10.

Rahman, A. R. (1964). The development of plantain flakes. *J. Agric. Univ. P.R.* 48:263.

Rahman, A. R., Berrocal, C. M., Cruz-Cay, J. R., and Rivera-Anaya, J. D. (1963). Toxicity studies on flour produced from unpeeled green plantains. *J. Agric. Univ. P.R.* 47:11-13.

Ramanuja, M. N., and Jayaraman, K. S. (1980). Studies on the preparation and storage stability of intermediate moisture banana. *J. Food Sci. Technol. (India).* 17:183-186.

Ramirez-Martinez, J. R., Levi, A., Padua, H., and Bakal, A. (1977). Astringency in an intermediate moisture banana product. *J. Food Sci.* 42:1201-1203, 1217.

Ranganna, S., and Parpia, H. A. B. (1974). Pink discoloration in canned banana (*Musa paradisiaca*) and field bean (*Dolichos lablab* var. lignosus Prain). I. Processing factors contributing to discoloration. *Lebensm-Wiss. u. Technol.* 7:101-110.

Rao, B. Y. K., and Bandyopadhyay, C. (1978). Changes in component fatty acids in pulp lipid of ripening bananas. *Acta Aliment.* 7:35-40.

Rasper, V. (1969a). Investigations on starches from major crops grown in Ghana. 1. Hot paste viscosity and gel-forming power. *J. Sci. Food Agric.* 20:165-171.

Rasper, V. (1969b). Investigations on starches from major starch crops grown in Ghana. II. Swelling and solubility patterns: amyloclastic susceptibility. *J. Sci. Food Agric.* 20:642-646.

Rasper, V. (1971). Investigations on starches from major starch crops grown in Ghana. III. Particle size and particle size distribution. *J. Sci. Food Agric.* 22:572-580.

Reader, D. E. (1950). Dried banana products. *Colon. Plant Anim. Prod.* 1:237-241.

Richardson, D. L., Hamilton, K. S., and Hutchinson, D. J. (1965). Notes on bananas. I. Natural edible tetraploids. *Trop. Agric. (Trinidad)* 42:125-137.

Rickert, E., and Schweigart, F. (1963). The manufacture of fruit flakes. *Food Ind. S. Afr.* 16:43-45.

Rios, A., Abernathy, R. E., and Nicholas, H. J. (1975). Banana peels as a potential source of animal food and other useful products. *Nutr. Rep. Int.* 11:399-408.

Rivera Brenes, L., Herencia, J., Arroyo, J. A., and Cabrera, J. I.
(1959). Palatability trials on Merker grass (*Pennisetum purpureum*),
Venezuela grass (*Paspalum faciculatum*) and plantain pseudostem
(*Musa paradisiaca*). *J. Agric. Univ. P.R.* 43:249-254.

Rodriguez-Soza, E. J. González, M. A., Caloni, I. B. de, and
Parsi-Ros, O. (1977). The preparation of green banana flour.
J. Agric. Univ. P.R. 61:470-478.

Romer, R. (1973). A study into the constituents of bananas with respect to their regional environment. Unpublished Ph.D. thesis,
University of London.

Rowe, P. R. (1976). Potential for genetic improvement in plantain
yield. *Fruits* 31:531-536. (In French.)

Rowe, P. R., and Richardson, D. L. (1975). Breeding bananas for
disease resistance, fruit quality and yield. *Bull. No. 2*, La Lima,
Honduras, Trop. Agric. Res. Serv.

Salem, E. A., Rizk, S. S., Eissawy, M. T., and Yehia, M. M. (1976).
Banana fruit ripening. I. Comparative Study of the conventional
methods used in Egypt. *Agric. Res. Rev.* 54:77-81.

Salminen, S. O., and Young, R. E. (1975). The control properties of
phosphofructokinase in relation to the respiratory climacteric in
banana fruit. *Plant Physiol.* 55:45-50.

Salter, P. J., and Goode, J. E. (1967). Crop response to water at
different stages of growth. *Res. Rev. 2.* London, Commonw. Bur.
Hortic. Plant. Crops.

Samish, Z., and Coussin, B. R. (1965). The production of dehydrated
flakes as a means of utilizing surplus bananas. *Israel J. Agric. Res.*
15:49-51.

Samson, J. A. (1980). *Tropical Fruits.* London, Longmans.

Sánchez-Nieva, F., and Mercado, M. (1978a). Effect of peeling method
on the absorption of aqueous bisulphite by green bananas. *J. Agric.
Univ. P.R.* 62:191-198.

Sánchez-Nieva, F., and Mercado, M. (1978b). Control of enzymatic
browning in green bananas for freezing. *J. Agric. Univ. P.R.*
62:232-240.

Sánchez-Nieva, F., and Mercado, M. (1978c). Effect of peeling method
and sulfitation on the shelf life of frozen green bananas. *J. Agric.
Univ. P.R.* 62:241-248.

Sánchez-Nieva, F., and Hernández, I. (1967). Preparation and preserva-
tion for freezing of ripe plantains in syrup. *Misc. Pub. 7.* Food
Tech. Lab., Agric. Exp. Stat., University of Puerto Rico. (In
Spanish).

Sánchez-Nieva, F., Bueso, C. E., and Hernández, I. (1975). Studies
on the freezing of green plantains (*Musa paradisiaca*) II. Sulfitation
to control browning. *J. Agric. Univ. P.R.* 59:92-106.

Sánchez-Nieva, F., Hernández, I., and Bueso de Viñas, C. (1970).
Studies on the ripening of plantains under controlled conditions.
J. Agric. Univ. P.R. 54:517-529.

Sánchez-Nieva, F., Hernández, I. and Bueso, C. (1975a). Studies on freezing green plantains (*Musa paradisiaca*). I. Effect of blanching treatments on the quality and storage life of raw and pre-fried slices. *J. Agric. Univ. P.R.* 59:85-91.

Sánchez-Nieva, F., Hernández, I., and Bueso, C. E. (1975b). Studies on the freezing plantains (*Musa paradisiaca*). III. Effect of stage of maturity at harvest on quality of frozen products. *J. Agric. Univ. P.R.* 59:107-114.

Sánchez-Nieva, F., Hernández, I, and Bueso, C. E. (1975c). Studies of freezing of green plantains (*Musa paradisiaca*). IV. Effect of cold storage on the quality of frozen sliced green plantains. *J. Agric. Univ. P.R.* 59:239-244.

Sánchez-Nieva, F., Colom Covas, G., Hernández, I., Guadalupe, R., Diaz, N., and Viñas, C. B. (1968). Pre harvest changes in the physical and chemical properties of plantains. *J. Agric. Univ. P.R.* 52:241-255.

Savage, C. G., and Arthur, J. M. (1935). Banana "figs" and banana "coffee." *Agric. Gaz. N.S.W.* 46:199-200.

Scott. K. J., Blake, J. R., Strachan, G., Tugwell, B. L., and McGlasson, W. B. (1971). Transport of bananas at ambient temperatures using polyethylene bags. *Trop. Agric. (Trinidad)* 48:245-254.

Shantha, H. S., and Siddappa, G. S. (1970a). Physicochemical nature of banana pseudostem starch. *J. Food Sci.* 35:72-73.

Shantha, H. S., and Siddappa, G. S. (1970b). Accumulation of starch in banana pseudostem and fruit. *J. Food Sci.* 35:74-77.

Shaper, A. G. (1967). Plantain diets, serotonin and endomyocardial fibrosis. *Am. Heart J.* 73:432-434.

Silvis, H., Thompson, A. K., Musa, S. K., Salih, O. M., and Abdulla, Y. M. (1976). Reduction of wastage during post-harvest handling of bananas in the Sudan. *Trop. Agric. (Trinidad)* 53:89-94.

Simmonds, N. W. (1962). *The Evolution of the Bananas*, London, Longmans.

Simmonds, N. W. (1966). *Bananas*, 2nd ed. London, Longmans.

Simmonds, N. W. (1976). Banana. In *Evolution of Crop Plants* (N. W. Simmonds ed.), London, Longmans.

Singhagajen, S., and McBean, D. M. (1968). Foam-mat drying of bananas. *CSIRO Food Res. Q.* 28:43-45.

Smit, C. J. B., and Burger, I. J. (1957). The canning of bananas and banana purée. *Food Ind. S. Afr.* 10:19-20.

Southgate, D. A. T. (1969). Determination of carbohydrates in foods. II. Unavailable carbohydrates. *J. Sci. Food Agric.* 20:331-335.

Stover, R. H. (1972). *Banana, Plantain and Abaca Diseases*. Farnham, U.K., Commonw. Agric. Bur.

Straten, S. Van, and Vrijer, F. de (1973). *Lists of Volatile Compounds in Food*, 3rd ed. Zeist, Netherlands, Cent. Inst. Voedingsonderz.

Subrahmanyan, V., Siddappa, G. S., Govindarajan, V. S., and Iyengar, N. V. R. (1963). Utilization of cellulosic agricultural wastes: Pulp from banana pseudostem and areca husk. *Indian Pulp Pap.* 17:533-536.

Subrahmanyan, V., Lal, G., Bhatia, D. S., Jain, N. L., Bains, G. S., Srinath, K. V., Anandaswamy, B., Krishna, B. H., and Lakshminaryana, S. K. (1957). Studies on banana pseudostem starch: production, yield, physicochemical properties and uses. *J. Sci. Food Agric.* 8:253-261.

Sum, W. F., Rogers, P. J., Jenkins, I. D., and Guthrie, R. D. (1980). Isolation of invertase from banana fruit (*Musa cavendishii*). *Phytochem.* 19:399-401.

Tarte, R. (1979). The role of UPEB in technical investigation. In *Proc. Fourth ACORBAT Conf., Panama, 1979,* Panama (R. Tarte, S. Pons, and R. Gabrielli, eds.). Union de Paises Exportadores de Banano (UPEB), Panama, pp. 345-350. (In Spanish.)

Tarte, R., Pons, S., and Gabrielli, R. (1979). Symposium I: Sigatoka control programmes in banana growing countries of the Caribbean and Tropical America. In *Proc. Fourth ACORBAT Conf., Panama, 1979,* (R. Tarte, S. Pons, and R. Gabrielli, eds.). Panama, Union de Paises Exportadores de Banano (UPEB), p. 51-66.

Tezenas du Montcel, H. (1979). The plantain banana in Cameroun. *Fruits* 34:307-313. (In French.)

Thompson, A. K., Been, B. O., and Perkins, C. (1972). Handling, storage and marketing of plantains. *Proc. Amer. Soc. Hortic. Sci. Trop. Reg.* 16:205-212.

Tocchini, R. P., and Lara, J. C. C. (1977). Industrial preparation of banana juice, single-strength and concentrated. *Bol. Inst. Tecnol. Aliment.* 51:93-112. (In Portuguese.)

Tonaki, K. I., Brekke, J. E., Frank, H. A., and Cavaletto, C. G. (1973). Banana purée processing. *Res. Rep. 202.* Honolulu, Agric. Exp. Stat., Coll. Trop. Agric., University of Hawaii.

Tressl, R., and Jennings, W. G. (1972). Production of volatile compounds in the ripening banana. *J. Agric. Food Chem.* 20:189-192.

Tressl, R., Drawert, F., Heimann, W., and Emberger, R. (1970). About the biogensis of aroma substances in plants and fruits. VI. Esters, alcohols, carbonyl compounds and phenolether as constituents of banana-aroma. *Z. Lebensm. Unters. Forsch.* 142:313-321. (In German.)

Undenfriend, S., Lovenberg, W., and Sjoerdsma, A. (1959). Physiologically active amines in common fruits and vegetables. *Arch. Biochem. Biophys.* 85:487-490.

United Fruit Co. (1961). *Banana Ripening Manual.* Boston, United Fruit Sales Corp.

Uzelac, M., Martin, Z. de, Silva, E., Kato, K., and Vitali, A. (1975). Volatile compounds in fresh and processed bananas. *Colet. Inst. Tecnol. Aliment.* 6:233-256. (In Portuguese.)

Villanueva, E. P., Visperas, R. V., Estudillo, C. P., Tadena, O. B., and Gabriel, W. S. (1972). Chemical pulps from Giant Cavendish banana fibres: their properties and bleach requirements. *Forpride Dig.* 1(2/3):13-19.

Wade, N. L., and Bishop, D. G. (1978). Changes in the lipid composition of ripening banana fruits and evidence for an associated increase in cell membrane permeability. *Biochem. Biophys. Acta* 529:454-464.

Wade, N. L., Campbell, L. C., and Bishop, D. G. (1980). Tissue permeability and membrane lipid composition of ripening banana fruit. *J. Exp. Bot.* 31:975-982.

Walker, A. (1931). The plantain banana in Gabon. *Rev. Bot. Appl. Agric. Trop.* 11:18-37. (In French.)

Wardlaw, C. W. (1972). *Banana Diseases Including Plantains and Abaca*, 2nd ed. London, Longmans

Watt, B. K., and Merrill, A. L. (1963). Composition of foods. *Agric. Handbook No. 8.* Washington, D.C., U.S. Dept. Agric.

Weaver, C., and Charley, H. (1974). Enzymatic browning of ripening bananas. *J. Food Sci.* 39:1200-1202.

Wick, E. L., Yamanishi, T., Kobayashi, A., Valenzuela, S., and Issenberg, P. (1969). Volatile constituents of banana (*M. cavendishii*, variety Valery). *J. Agric. Food Chem.* 17:751-759.

Wilson, R. J. (1975). The international market for banana products for food use. *Rep. G103.* London, Trop. Prod. Inst.

Windward Islands Banana Growers Association/Tropical Products Institute (1977). *Marketing Top Quality Bananas.* London, Trop. Prod. Inst.

Wyk, P. J. van, Heinen, E. A., and Ackermann, L. G. J. (1978). Preparation of glucose and high fructose syrups from bananas (*Musa cavendishii*). *Lebensm-Wiss. u. Technol.* 11:29-30.

Wyman, H., and Palmer, J. (1964). Organic acids in ripening banana fruit. *Plant Physiol.* 39:630-633.

4

Cassava: Production, Processing, and Utilization

E. U. Odigboh Faculty of Engineering, University of Nigeria, Nsukka, Anambra State, Nigeria

I. INTRODUCTION

Most people in the so-called developed countries regard cassava as a poisonous foodstuff eaten by tropical natives of the world. Up to a few decades ago, most agricultural research workers were not familiar with cassava as a food crop. Prior to 1950 or thereabouts, the cassava crop had been largely ignored by tropical agricultural research scientists who were for the most part nonindigenous to the tropical regions and who had chosen to concentrate their activities on crops exportable in their primary forms. By 1950, the entire world cassava literature must have consisted of a few hundred casual or passing references and articles in farm magazines. Consequently, knowledge about cassava was very limited and acquaintance with it was restricted to varieties grown in a particular locality.

However, by about 1970, the number of individuals and national as well as international institutes researching cassava had increased so much that it had become difficult for a given researcher to keep track of the large volume of cassava scientific literature generated all over the world. Today, thanks to the creation in 1973 of the Cassava Information Centre at Centro International de Agricultura Tropical (CIAT) in Cali, Colombia, worldwide literature on cassava has been collected and collated in a form that facilitates usage. This impressive collection of cassava literature is continuously updated to embody the most up-to-date research information on all aspects of the cassava crop. By the end of 1978, the Cassava Information Centre had collected about 4000 documents on cassava, including major research papers, reputed journal article reprints, monographs and manuals on all aspects of cassava agronomy, breeding, production, pests, and diseases, processing, and utilization.

With so much already done and such a great deal currently being done and written on cassava, it is not possible to present a comprehensive treatment of the subject in one chapter of a book. Were such a comprehensive treatment possible, it would not be a chapter at all but a substantial library. However, a book on tropical foods would be incomplete without a chapter on cassava. The inclusion of this chapter is therefore justified if only to pay tribute to this major food crop of the tropical world.

A. Origin and Distribution of Cassava

The precise center of origin of the cassava plant is unknown. But, it is generally believed to be a native of South America with the Amazon Basin as the most probable center of dispersal. There exists archaeological evidence indicating that cassava was grown by pre-Inca civilizations some 4000 years ago. From the Brazilian Amazon region, cassava spread to the West Indies, Southeast Asia, and later to Africa in the sixteenth and seventeenth centuries (Jones, 1959). Today, the plant is grown in every tropical climate of the world in 1 or more of the over 200 varieties known (Cobley, 1956). The crop thrives between 30° north and south latitudes and at altitudes below 2000 m.

Limited knowledge about cassava in former times may be partially
due to the fact that it goes by various names around the world: *mandioca* or *aipim* in Brazil; *yucca* in the Caribbean; *cassava* or *cassada*
in Anglophone Africa; *manioc* in the Francophone world. To the anthropologist it is most familiar as *manioc*, which is the legendary name given
to cassava in South American folklore (Jones, 1959). Although obscure
and seldon researched prior to 1950, the Cassava Information Centre
(1977) reports the existence of cassava publications that date back as
far as the 1830s and cites two papers written in Dutch in the early
1900s that are still of current relevance (Stock, 1909; Jong, 1913).

B. Importance of Cassava

Cassava is a highly valued crop of the tropics, being one of the highest
yielding plants of the vegetable kingdom. It is particularly valued because of its drought resistance, its unique ability to grow in poor soils,
its tolerance to poor husbandry, and its relative resistance to weeds
and pests (Lockwood, 1969), all resulting in its characteristically high
biological efficiency. It may be the largest single crop of the tropics
and particularly of that part of Africa lying south of the Sahara and
north of the Zambezi where it has become the most important crop in
terms of both the total land area devoted to its production and as a
major component of diet.

1. Importance as Food

Cassava is a basic food for the tropical millions of the world where it
forms the primary source of carbohydrates (Coursey, 1978; Nestel,
1973; Lockwood, 1969). Brazil, reputedly the world's largest producer
of cassava has an estimated 2 million ha planted to cassava, largely for
food. The Food and Agriculture Organization (FAO) (1971) estimated
that 38% of the total cassava production in Latin America is utilized for
human food. In India, especially in Kerala state and the neighboring
states of Tamil Nadu and Andhra Pradesh, the lower- and middle-income
groups consume cassava along with fish as a main wholesome diet. In
the Philippines, cassava is used first as food, that is, about two-thirds
of the cassava grown on about 100,000 ha. The story is similar in all
the producing countries of Asia, America, and Africa. In Nigeria,
which is the largest producer in Africa, about 1.5 million ha under
cultivation supply cassava almost exclusively for human food. Doku
(1969) explained that, on the basis of proportionate distribution of
expenditure on local food crops, more was spent on cassava than any
other, accounting for 12.27% of the total. Thus, the importance of
cassava as a major food crop cannot be overemphasized; while it constitutes a strong hedge against famine at the least, it provides a nour-
ishing basic food for 200 to 400 million inhabitants of the tropics,
especially when properly supplemented.

2. Importance in World Market

In addition to the unchallenged position of cassava as the chief staple food in many tropical countries, its industrial importance is also grow- ing fast. Cassava starch is an important raw material in the manufac- ture of sandpaper, cardboard, charcoal briquettes, dolls, flashlight batteries, molded plastic toys, antihalation powders, photographic films, and so forth (Vries, et al., 1967). Cassava starch represents the best material for the manufacture of adhesives and has a higher efficiency as a beater size in paper manufacture (Friedman, 1950). Cassava starch is much preferred in laundry and textile industries. The bland flavor of the starch and its nonretrogradation tendency and excellent freeze-thaw stability, which make it the favorite of the food processor, also recommend it as a diluent in chemical and drug manu- facturing or as a carrier in cosmetics, pills, and capsules (Odigboh, 1974). The use of cassava in drilling mud or in the manufacture of explosives and such other unusual applications may not be of common knowledge. Thus, beside providing a sure security against hunger, cassava has many nonfood uses with the potential for becoming an im- portant foreign exchange earner for the producing tropical countries.

Currently, the importance of cassava as an energy source is mani- fested by its growing demand in the European Economic Community (EEC) countries as well as other developed countries where cassava is valued as a cereal substitute with a favorable competition in prices for livestock feeds (Walters, 1978). Also, Brazil, the country where cas- sava originated, is prosecuting a national program to replace by 1990 all petroleum consumption with alcohol distilled principally from cassava. With the successful development of that technology, which is nearly assured already, the importance of cassava, particularly as a renewable energy resource, will be at a climax, and many poor tropical countries without mineral oil resources of their own will embrace the cassava plant as a new hope for their energy independence (Hammond, 1977).

C. Description of Cassava

1. Classification and Varieties

All varieties of cassava contain hydrocyanic acid (HCN) in amounts that vary from harmless to lethal. The literature contains discussions on many attempts at the classification of cassava into "sweet" or "bitter" depending on the HCN content (Moore, 1907; Bolhuis, 1954; Doku, 1969). But, the only point of complete agreement seems to be that not enough is known regarding cassava toxicity. However, on the basis of the HCN content, the following two species used to be recognized:

1. Bitter poisonous species: *Manihot esculenta* Crantz.; *M. utilissima* Pohl.
2. Sweet nonpoisonous species: *M. dulcis* Baill.; *M. palmatta* Muell.; *M. aipi* Pohl.

As already stated, this subjective classification of cassava is not generally accepted since no clear distinction exists between the bitter and sweet varieties.

Many researchers think that cassava toxicity is associated primarily with the free HCN readily formed by the enzymatic hydrolysis of cyanogenic glucoside or the so-called manihotoxine the occurrence of which is also generally established to be independent of the particular botanical taxa. Thus, a given variety of cassava may be sweet in one environment and bitter in another, depending on soil fertility status or the soil moisture condition. So, the tendency nowadays is to regard all cultivated cassava as varieties of *M. esculenta* Crantz.

2. Botanical Description

Cassava, *M. esculenta,* belongs to the large and important family of the Euphorbiaceae. The botany of cassava has been discussed by Bailey (1925), Bolhuis (1954), Cobley (1956), and Doku (1969) among others.

In the wild, cassava is a shrubby perennial that grows to heights of 1 to 3 m and over, depending on variety and growing conditions. Present-day cultivated varieties are seldom over 2 m high. Mature stems and branches of the cassava plant are fairly straight and have a uniform thickness of 3 to 8 cm diameter with circular cross sections, whereas immature ones are thinner with pentagonal sections.

As sketched in Fig. 1, the leaves are palmate with five to nine lobes or more depending on variety. The leaves are borne on long slender petioles with varietally characteristic colors of light green, pink, purple, or various shades of these. The base of the petiole bulges out slightly

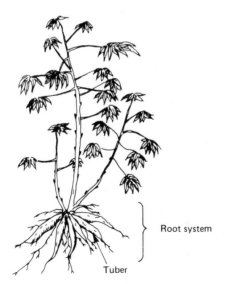

Root system

Tuber

Figure 1   The cassava plant.

at the point of attachment to the stem. When the petioles fall off, these bulges remain as raised scars, forming characteristically prominent nodes of the plant and serving as a protection for the dormant buds. Branching pattern in cassava is a varietal characteristic; there may be several main stems which branch at one-third, halfway, or two-thirds of the main stem, or at the apex of the stem. There are also varieties which do not branch.

The cassava plant flowers and produces fruits that are capsules having six wings that may be contoured or not, according to variety. The fruits have black mottled seeds about 1 cm long that, in cultivated varieties, are not used, except perhaps for breeding experiments, since propagation is generally by stem cutting.

It takes about 7 days for a planted cassava cutting to sprout. Three or four days before sprouting takes place, adventitious fibrous roots are produced at almost all nodes in contact with the soil. The young plant produces a fibrous adventitious root system which develops extensively both laterally and vertically. Varieties differ in length of time taken to mature, some yielding within 6 to 12 months of planting, while others require 18 to 24 months to produce mature tubers. The tubers develop at the base of the stem by a process of secondary thickening initiated in some of the adventitious roots.

II. THE GROWING OF CASSAVA

As mentioned before, cassava is cultivated in nearly all the tropical countries of the world. Presented in Table 1 are the 1968 and 1977 production figures for cassava in countries producing more than 500,000 tonnes. Brazil harvested 26.51 million tonnes of cassava from 2,233,000 ha in 1977 at an average yield of 11.9 tonnes/ha. For the whole of South America, cassava is a leading crop which in 1977 took up 65.56% of the area planted to root crops to yield 72.05% by weight of all the root and tuber crops harvested. In Africa the same year, 6,731,000 ha were harvested to yield 110.17 million tonnes of cassava. This means that Africa is the largest cassava-producing continent in the world. As shown in Table 2, cassava accounted for 58.19% of the area devoted to all root and tuber crops in Africa but represented only 55.16% by weight of all the root and tuber crops harvested.

In Table 2, production figures for all cereals have been included for comparison. It is significant that in Africa, whereas area planted to cassava is only 9.51% that of all cereals, cassava production is 67.34% of all cereals by weight. For South America, corresponding percentages are 7.46% and 50.25%. This should be of particular interest to the government economists concerned with resource development in these regions.

Table 1 1968 and 1977 Production of Cassava in Countries Producing More Than 500,000 Tonnes

Country	Land area (1000 ha) 1968	1977	Yield (tonnes/ha) 1968	1977	Production (million tonnes) 1968	1977
Brazil	1998	2233	14.6	11.9	29.90	26.51
Zaire		1760[a]		7.00	—	12.30[a]
Indonesia	1600	1356	7.4	9.0	11.80	12.17
Congo republic	750	145	10.8	5.3	8.10	0.77
Nigeria	1200	1100[a]	5.6	9.6	6.70	10.60[a]
India	335	392	13.5	16.5	4.52	6.48
Mozambique		450[a]		5.4		2.45[a]
Uganda	350	360[a]	3.8	3.1	2.00	1.10
Thailand	135	697	14.8	15.3	2.00	10.64
Angola	120	120[a]	12.9	13.8[a]	1.55	1.65[a]
Paraguay	100	115	15.0	14.8[a]	1.50	1.7[a]
Ghana	172	300[a]	8.4	8.3[a]	1.45	2.5[a]
Benin	180	—	6.3	—	1.14	—
Tanzania	270	810[a]	4.2	4.8	1.13	4.00
Togo	150	60[a]	7.5	7.9	1.12	0.74[a]
Central Africa	200	304[a]	5.0	3.00	1.00	0.90
Sri Lanka (Madagascar)	280	170	3.3	4.4	0.91	0.75
Colombia	152	251	5.9	8.4	0.90	2.11
Burundi	75	63[a]	11.7	14.4[a]	0.88	0.90
Cameroon	114	191[a]	6.7	4.2	0.76	0.81
Viet Nam	100	180[a]	7.0	8.3	0.70	1.50
Kenya	92	95[a]	6.7	7.9	0.62	0.75[a]
Ivory Coast	200	185[a]	2.7	3.7	0.53	0.69[a]
Peru	42	200	11.9	6.5	0.50	1.30
Philippines	83	100	6.0	6.8	0.50	0.68
World	9794	12,572	8.7	8.8	85.63	110.17

[a]FAO estimate
Source: FAO (1968 and 1977 *Production Year Books*).

A. Traditional Cultivation Practices

Cassava is one of the few food crops, if indeed not the only one, normally propagated by stem cuttings; propagation by seed is used only for breeding purposes as mentioned before. Traditional cultural practices vary widely from region to region. On the average, the

Table 2a   1977 World Hecterage Figures for Cassava, Root, and Tuber Crops and Cereals by Regions/Continents

Region/ Continent	Cassava (A)	All roots and tubers (B)	All cereals (C)	A/B (%)	A/C (%)
		Total area in 100 ha			
World	12,575	51,898	745,704	24.23	1.69
Africa	6,731	11,567	70,773	58.19	9.51
North and Central America	115	1,071	102,853	10.74	0.11
South America	2,759	4,084	36,973	65.56	7.46
Asia	2,951	21,747	321,985	13.57	0.91
Europe	–	6,123	69,691	0.00	0.00
Oceania	19	240	15,281	7.92	0.12
U.S.S.R.	–	7,067	125,149	0.00	0.00

Source: FAO (*1977 Production Year Book*).

stems are cut into lengths of 200 to 300 mm for manual planting.   The cuttings are planted on mounds or ridges to a depth of 200 to 300 mm. They are planted erect or more usually at an inclination of 30° to 90° to the horizontal.   It is essential to ensure that the cuttings are planted with the nodes the right way up, otherwise germination is very seriously impared (Odigboh, 1978a).   Planting the cuttings flat, as practiced in the wetter regions of Nigeria and parts of west Africa, as well as in Brazil where planting on the flat is the pre- ferred system, removes the need to orient the nodes.   However, there is experimental evidence that yields are higher with roots that grow bunched together when the cuttings are planted erect or at an inclination.

The peasant farmers who account for over 90% of the cassava grown in the major producing countries plant their cassava at random, with plant spacings varying from 600 to 1500 mm within and between ill- defined rows.   Almost as a rule, cassava is intercropped with yam, cocoyam, or corn.   Nowadays, however, even the peasant farmers do grow cassava alone with the usual spacing of 900 to 1000 mm between and within rows.

Field operations after planting consist of weeding by hand once or twice, depending on conditions, until a canopy is formed to inhibit

Table 2b   World Production Figures for Cassava, Root, and Tuber
Crops and Cereals by Regions/Continents

Region/ Continent	Cassava (A)	All roots and tubers (B)	All cereals (C)	A/B (%)	A/C (%)
World	110.17	570.21	1459.01	19.32	7.35
Africa	44.26	78.81	65.73	55.16	67.34
North and Central America	0.74	21.85	323.47	3.38	0.23
South America	32.02	44.44	63.72	72.05	50.25
Asia	32.93	224.54	571.38	13.47	14.67
Europe	—	114.68	231.17	0.00	0.00
Oceania	0.21	2.48	15.60	8.47	1.35
U.S.S.R.	—	83.40	187.95	0.00	0.00

Source: FAO (*1977 Production Year Book*).

weeds. But, when grown alone, it is common to find cassava fields
not weeded even once. No weeding naturally leads to low yields.
Weed control is a major cost factor in cassava production. Naturally,
peasant cassava farmers use no chemical controls for weeds, pests,
or diseases. Consequently even where weeds can be controlled by
manual cultivation, farmers sometimes lose the crop to pests and
diseases. The farmers do not apply fertilizer to cassava.

Harvesting of cassava starts from 6 to 12 months after planting, depending on variety. Like planting, harvesting is done manually by
digging up the roots with a hoe or some traditional digger. Harvesting
cassava by hand is tedious and slow. An investigation in Nigeria
(Odigboh and Ahmed, 1979) showed that, with a combination of such
traditional tools as a digger, a hand hoe, and a matchet, a man can
harvest cassava at an average rate of 0.01 ha/hr. It is not therefore
surprising that labor costs for harvesting accounted for well over 40%
of total production cost in Nigeria even by 1970 (Phillips, 1970). More-
over, harvesting by hand leads to substantial loss and damage in terms
of cuts, bruises, or breakage of roots. Luckily, the mature cassava
crop does not have a specific period for harvest and so the farmers
"store" it in vivo, so to speak, and harvest what little they can or
need as and when the roots are required. Thus, it is not uncommon
to harvest a given crop over a period of 1 year.

Cassava yields from peasant farmer fields vary with variety, age, soil type, and growing conditions. The average yields per hectare in the major producing countries, as represented by the FAO production figures in Table 1, show large variations from country to country and from year to year. Whereas the world average was 8.8 tonnes/ha, the lowest yield of 3.0 tonnes was recorded for central Africa and the highest yield at 16.5 tonnes/ha was recorded for India in 1977.

B. Modern Production Technology

Research has positively demonstrated that with simple inexpensive technology, it is possible to double, triple, or even quadruple the yields of both local and improved cassava varieties (CIAT, 1978,1979-1980). The current reported global average yield is a low 8.8 tons/ha and, even at that, some producing countries of Africa and Asia have yields of less than half that figure. This indicates considerable potential for yield improvement worldwide. The cassava farmers of the world must adopt these new techniques.

But what constitutes this modern cassava production technology? The Centro International de Agricultura Tropical (CIAT) in Colombia, the International Institute for Tropical Agriculture (IITA) in Nigeria, the Faculties of Agriculture in producing countries, and the various national agricultural research institutes dealing with root and tuber crops have the answer. This answer has been fairly well documented in research reports, symposium/workshop proceedings, learned journal articles, monographs, and manuals. Whereas the answer is perforce specific to localities, it may be briefly summarized in general terms under certain headings, as presented next.

1. Improved Varieties and Cultivars

The main thrust of world cassava research in the past several decades has been geared towards the breeding and development of high-yielding varieties and cultivars adapted to the local soils and environment. Through breeding, varietal improvements, and selection, certain national institutes and cassava research centers have built up a collection of cultivars which are high yielding, resistant to the prevailing pests, weeds, and diseases, and with other desirable characteristics, such as high dry-matter or starch content, for recommendation to farmers. Recommendations from the research centers are usually based on research carried out on farmers' fields to yield lines and cultivars with stable performance. Many of the centers also undertake the multiplication of recommended planting materials for distribution to interested farmers.

2. Management of Planting Materials

Once the suitable variety or cultivar is selected, the proper husbandry of the planting materials becomes very important. The knowledgeable care and management of the planting materials in terms of the maturity of cuttings, and treatment and storage of planting materials, are essential for attaining the potential yield of the given variety/cultivar.

Maturity of Cuttings. Cassava is highly sensitive to weed competition in the first 90 days of growth, as explained in CIAT 1974 *Cassava Annual Report.* Therefore, early vigor is an important determinant of subsequent yield. On this score, research has shown that cuttings from upper and middle stem sections always germinate well, whereas those from lower stem sections germinate poorly. Plants from upper stem cuttings yield highest. Cuttings from the lowest stem section of vigorous plants are not recommended for planting (CIAT, 1979-1980).

Storage of Planting Materials. Although cassava can be and is harvested year-round, its planting usually follows the pluviometric cycles of the year. This often leads to extended time intervals between harvesting and subsequent planting, during which the planting materials must be stored under conditions that do not expose then to adverse physical damage, dehydration, insect pests, and diseases.

The recommended management is to cut the planting materials into lengths of 1 m or longer, dip-treat them with a mixture of the fungicides BCM (systemic) and captan (nonsystemic) at 3000 ppm each, and then store in a shaded site in the field. When the storage is adequately managed in this manner, germination rate is higher in the stored than in the fresh planting material, independent of storage duration, as demonstrated by experiments at CIAT and illustrated in Fig. 2 (CIAT, 1980). That CIAT field trial also showed that final germination percentage was almost unaffected by storage duration, reaching 95 to 100% at all intervals. It must be pointed out that, although complete germination is achieved by proper storage, there occurs a yield reduction with increasing duration of storage, a fact that is not yet explained. Therefore, fresh planting materials should be used whenever possible for maximum root yield. When storage is inevitable, it should be adequate and for as short a duration as possible.

3. Planting Techniques

There are a number of actual planting specifications that form part of the modern technology package. The specifications deal with the length of cuttings or stakes, treatment of cuttings, angle of cutting the stakes, planting depth, inclination of planted cuttings, plant spacings, and spatial arrangement.

Length and Treatment of Cuttings. As a result of many experiments and field trials, it has been determined that cuttings 20 cm long yield significantly more than other lengths tried. Whether the cuttings are cut square or angled has no significant effect on yield, but a square cut gives more uniformly distributed roots and is therefore considered

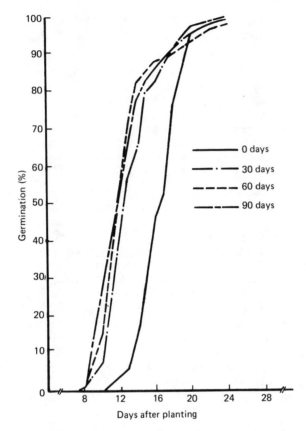

Figure 2 Germination of planting material of cassava variety MC 76 stored for different intervals in a shaded field site. (From CIAT, 1980.)

a better system. It is recommended that the cuttings be dip-treated with fungicide before planting. A mixture of BCM and captan at 3000 ppm each has been shown to give best results of all others tested (CIAT, 1979).

Inclination and Depth of Planting. The decision to plant on the flat or on ridges depends on the soil characteristics, especially the soil moisture conditions. Experiments to determine the best planting depth using cuttings 30 cm long planted vertically on ridges to depths of 10, 20, and 30 cm gave no significant difference on basis of yield and harvest indices. But root development along the buried sections of cuttings was affected. The roots were clumped around the base for cuttings planted 10 cm deep but distributed along the cutting with peduncles for cuttings planted deeper. In angular orientation studies where cuttings are planted horizontally, inclined at various angles to the horizontal and vertically, vertical planting always gives best germination results, with significantly higher yields than other orientations. Rate of shoot emergence is also significantly greater for cuttings planted vertically or slanted than for horizontal planting.

Therefore, for planting and harvesting ease and for the highest yield with best root configuration, it is recommended that stakes should be cut square into lengths of 20 cm, dip treated with fungicide and planted vertically on ridges to depths of 10 cm.

Plant Density and Spatial Arrangement. Studies done to determine optimum plant density indicate that for 10,000 and 15,625 plants per hectare in square and rectangular patterns, there is no significant difference in yield within varieties. This means of course that the higher-density planting gives smaller-sized roots and/or smaller number of roots per plant, which may have some advantage for mechanical harvesting and postharvest handling and processing operations. The rectangular and square planting patterns may have other agronomic implications. For example, a 2-m between-row spacing and 0.5-m within-row spacing, in comparison with a pattern of 1 m × 1 m, make for easier harvesting of mixed crops, and permit uncultivated bands to be left between rows to assist in erosion control. However, the decision on row spacing may have to be determined by the requirements for mechanized planting, weed control, and harvesting.

4. Weed Control

Weed control is the basic factor of cassava production technology and constitutes a major, single cost factor in cassava production. Low cassava yield in traditional farmers' plots may be largely due to inefficient weed control, often resulting from inadequate know-how. Many researchers have worked on weed control in cassava (CIAT, 1980; Onochie, 1978; Akobundu, 1976; Onochie, 1975; Harper, 1974) and have recommended various control measures emphasizing both chemical and cultural approaches. Chemical weed control, though effective, may pose problems of herbicide availability, cost, lack of low-cost applicators and requisite know-how for proper handling, correct application, and safety among the peasant cassava farmers. Therefore, cultural weed control measures, involving variety and planting density, mulching and green covers, manual and mechanical weeding, employed singly or in combination, would appear more attractive, being technically and financially more within reach for the cassava farmers (Doll et al., 1977). Manual weed control by hoeing and pulling is costly and inefficient. More than 50% of farmers' time is spent in weeding cassava in Nigeria. But labor required for weeding cassava crops can be appreciably reduced if weeding is restricted to critical periods for weed competition, namely, during the first 3 months after planting, at early canopy formation, and during early tuberization about the third month after planting. Kasasian and Seeyare (1969) showed that keeping the cassava crop relatively weed-free for the first 3 or 4 months gave as good a yield as when the crop was weeded throughout its life cycle, whereas not weeding throughout the growth period caused a yield loss of 51%. Therefore, if properly timed, a minimum of two weeding operations in cassava crops, the first at 4 to 8 weeks after planting and the second a month later, is enough to obtain near-maximum performance. The effect of weed control systems on weeding cost and yields of cassava is given in Table 3, modified from CIAT (1979) *Cassava Annual Report.* Evidently, the question is not whether or not weed control should be undertaken since that is a must for good yield, rather it is a question of what control measures to adopt—chemical or cultural. In each case, the decision should be based on

Table 3 Effect of Weed Control Systems on Weeding Cost and Cassava Yields

Weed control system	No. of hand weedings	Cost per hectare on a scale of 100		Fresh root yield (tons/ha)
		Labor	Capital	
No weed control	—	—	—	12.9
Preemergent herbicide (Linnuoron, 1 kg/ha fluorodifen 72/ha)	—	2.0	21.0	23.4
Sugar cane bagasse mulch at 17 tons/ha	—	12.0	3.4	27.6
Green cover of phaseolus vulgaris (Black beans intercropped at a seedrate of 120 kg/ha with initial hand weeding)	2	50.0	66.0	26.8
Manual weeding (48 work days for hand weeding)	4	96.0	—	33.2

Source: Modified from CIAT 1979 weed control studies on cassava variety CMC 40 (CIAT, 1980).

the economics of the situation. In general, if deficient weed control is anticipated, yield losses can be reduced by increasing the planting density using genotypically vigorous varieties such as vigorously branching leafy genotypes which have enhanced weed-competing abilities.

C. Mechanization of Cassava Field Operations

Whereas it is generally accepted that better genetic inputs and good agronomic measures contribute significantly toward increases in agricultural production, the major contributions come from timely provision of suitable conditions and environment for plant growth; timely preparation of seedbed; timely planting and subsequent cultivation; timely and proper fertilizer application and weed and pest control; and timely harvesting to reduce losses and adequate provisions for postharvest handling, preservation, storage, processing, and marketing. Mechanization ensures the timeliness of all these operations and the adequacy of the processes in a fashion that removes or at least minimizes the inherent tedium and drudgery (Odigboh, 1976a). Unfortunately, all the cultural field operations for cassava production are at present done manually by the peasant farmers. Consequently, even though the farmers have begun to adopt the modern technology emanating from the cassava research centers, their individual production is still limited to a few hectares which they can manage by hand labor. From what has been done or what is being done worldwide to mechanize the field operations for cassava production, there is a real cause for concern because the probability of mechanizing these operations in the near future is slim (Odigboh, 1978b). Anybody who casually studies the areas of research, research projects, or fields of specialization of researchers in agricultural/cassava research institutions (CIAT, 1978) or just reads through past and ongoing theses on cassava, will come to the same conclusion. The various international, national, and regional centers and institutes for cassava research should do well to pay more attention to engineering research aimed at mechanizing cassava production.

1. Mechanized Planting of Cassava

Machines and equipment for land preparation for cassava production (ploughing, harrowing, ridging, etc.) exist because they are the same as for other crops. Therefore, planting is the first field operation for cassava production which requires special equipment.

The need to mechanize the planting of cassava has long been recognized. As early as 1948, Cardenso reported on "A new planter for sugar cane, potatoes, cassava and similar crops" (Cardenso, 1948), which claimed to be capable of planting 3.8 ha in 8 hr. Kumar (1962) reported trials with a modified Massey-Fergusson ridger-cum-planter using a modified duck-foot cultivator as a six-row cassava planter.

Dimicali (1964) discussed what was called "the sugar cane cassava planter," made by a factory in Caloocan (Philippines), which makes a furrow, drops fertilizer and cutting in the furrow, covers back the cutting as it forms a mound round it, and presses the soil pat. About the same time in Brazil, it was claimed that cassava could be planted perfectly with a stake planter at the rate of 10 ha/day using eight people (Monteiro, 1963). Krochmal (1966), in discussing labor input and mechanization of cassava, mentioned the existence of a Brazilian two-row planter. Beeny (1970) indicated that a sugar cane planter can be modified to plant cassava on the ridge or on the flat. But all these early attempts to design a cassava cuttings planter have not succeeded in putting a commercial machine on the world market. Therefore, the search for commercially viable cassava planter has continued with various levels of success being reported (Echeverria, 1971; Schute et al., 1973; Wahab et al, 1977).

As evident from Fig. 3, cassava cuttings represent very unique planting materials. The cuttings vary considerably among and within varieties in terms of size, girth, straightness, and shape of the cross section, and the number of nodes per unit length. The plantable diameters of cuttings vary randomly between 10 mm or less and 50 mm or more. The variations in the physical properties and especially the presence of nodes scattered on the surface make the cuttings very difficult to handle. This may explain why attempts to adapt planters designed for other crops to plant cassava have not been quite successful or why many researchers have favored the transplanter principles or mechanisms. Odigboh (1978a) discussed a design that attempted to take into

Figure 3 Cassava cuttings showing prominent nodes and randomly varying girths.

Figure 4 Two-row on-the-ridge cassava planter. (a) View with one hopper open to show construction details. (b) Planter being trailed in transport mode.

consideration the unique physical properties of the cassava stem and which yielded the prototype shown in Fig. 4. That prototype is trailed and the cuttings planted at an inclination that may be varied from 45° to 85° and spaced 900 mm on small ridges which are 900 mm apart. Field tests have revealed the desirability of increasing the size of the ridges and of mounting instead of trailing the planter in order to improve maneuverability. In addition, the hopper design is being modified to make manufacture easier and still be capable of handling all the plantable cassava cuttings, their wide variations in size notwithstanding, and at the same time remove the need to feed the cuttings individually, one by one, according to size. The sketch of the modified hopper design is shown in Fig. 5.

In summary, therefore, it is true that mechanization of cassava planting is a problem that has received some attention in the past and is receiving some attention now. Nevertheless, it is still largely an unsolved problem. In view of the growing importance of cassava, especially as a viable renewable energy source, more attention, resources, and effort should be devoted by cassava research workers and institutions to the development of a commercial cassava planter.

2. Mechanized Weeding of the Cassava Crop

It has already been mentioned that chemical weed control poses problems of high cost and oftentimes unavailability of appropriate herbicides and

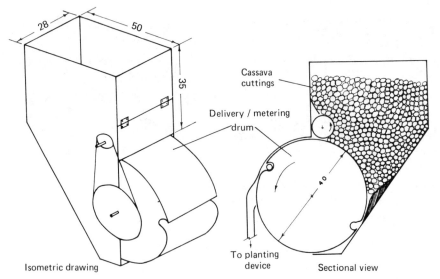

Figure 5 Sketch of experimental hopper for cassava planter.

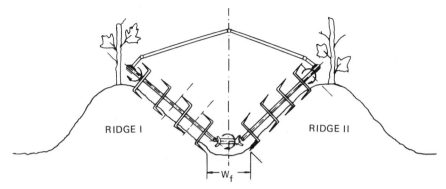

Figure 6 Illustration of ridge profile weeder concept.

herbicide applicators as well as the lack of know-how with respect to the correct and safe handling of herbicides among peasants cassava farmers. It appears then that simple inexpensive mechanical weeders can serve the farmers well. One such weeder, the development of which was requested by the (Nigerian) Operation Feed the Nation (OFN) national committee, has been reported by Odigboh and Ahmed (1980a). The principle or concept of that weeder is illustrated in Fig. 6.

The prototype, called a ridge profile weeder, consists of a rotating short shaft connected by universal joints to two gangs of rotary hoes. With the short shaft nearly at the bottom of a furrow between two ridges, the gangs of rotary hoes lie on the sides of two ridges. The universal joints make it possible to angle the hoe gangs with respect to the horizontal shaft to make the hoes conform to the profiles of the sides of the ridges facing a common furrow. The weeder may be manual, as shown in Fig. 7, in which case the rotary hoes are ground-driven as it is pushed along. Alternatively, the rotary hoes may be powered by a small internal combustion engine. In eithr case, the operator walks in the furrow and simply pushes the weeder along to weed one side each of two ridges. Thus, the weeder can handle the cassava crop, or indeed any crop planted on ridges, irrespective of the height of the plants. The shares on the gangs of the rotary hoe weeder are independently adjustable to facilitate reaching the surface of any ridge. The prototype weeder also easily handles the weeding of cassava crops planted on the flat, provided the planting is in rows. Field tests show that the weeder prototype is very effective in controlling young weeds where light earthing up is required, in keeping with the recommendations made regarding the timing of weed control in a cassava crop. The commercialization of developments similar to the one described here should be encouraged since it has been definitely demonstrated that adequate weed control increases cassava yield significantly.

Figure 7 Photograph of the prototype ridge profile weeder.

3. Mechanized Harvesting of Cassava

It was noted in Sec. II.A that owing to the tedium and slowness of manual harvesting, farmers tend to harvest only a small amount of cassava at a time and as the need arises. But with the emergence of factories processing cassava roots into flour, chips, gari, and other products, manual harvesting is just not adequate any longer. In Nigeria, for instance, there now exist integrated flour and gari processing systems that can handle 50 to 100 tonnes of cassava roots daily. This quantity of roots would be harvested from more than 10 ha at the currently reproted Nigerian average yields. To supply such plants with cassava roots harvested manually at 0.01 ha/hr (Odigboh and Ahmed, 1979) would require an army of workers and would represent a major cost factor, especially nowadays that agricultural labor is very scarce and expensive. Echeverria (1973) quoted manual harvesting of 215 hr/ha). To complicate the situation further, the large cassava processing plants cannot resort to long-term storage since cassava roots do not store well and begin to deteriorate 2 to 4 days after harvest. Therefore, commercial-scale processing and utilization of cassava requires mechanized harvesting to supply the roots economically.

Naturally, mechanization of cassava harvesting, like the mechanization of its planting, has agitated the minds of many research workers. Krochmal (1966) discussed an attempt to use the mold-board plough to harvest cassava. Earlier, Bates (1963) had proposed the adaptation of the potato digger/lifter and the sugar beet harvester for cassava.

Various workers have also experimented with similar adaptations such
as the use of subsoilers, land-clearing blades, groundnut digger/shakers
and so forth (Echeverria, 1971,1973; Hosse, 1971; Makanjuola et al.,
1973). More recently, Wijerwarden (1978), working at IITA in Ibadan,
Nigeria, developed a forklifter for uprooting cassava roots, somewhat
similar to a grip lifter reported by Essais (1954) that is said to reduce
damage and loss without reduction in harvesting time.

Diaz-Duran of CIAT (1979) described a cassava root harvesting aid
that can be attached to a tractor with a hydraulic system. The imple-
ment breaks up the soil and loosens the roots to make their manual
removal easy. Briceno and Larson (1972) discussed a prototype cassava harvester with three-point hitch, 0.95-m-wide blade cutting to a
depth of 0.40 m, and having a field capacity of 0.29 ha/hr at an operating speed of 2 to 3 km/hr, and requiring a tractor of 105-kw-rated
pto power. Kemp (1978) reported on a field demonstration of cassava
harvester designed by Richter Engineering Pty Ltd. of Australia. The
Richter harvester, a Category II, three-point linkage-mounted, pto-
driven machine, has an 810-mm-wide flat share with curved leading
edge, followed by a 162-mm-long chain-web elevator of the same width
as the share. A net work rate of 0.12 ha/hr was recorded with the
harvester at a draught force of 10.8 kN for ridge and 16.4 kN for
flat-planted fields. Another cassava harvester recently developed by
the British firm of Bonfords has been on the field tests at IITA, Ibadan,
and NRCRI, Umudike, both in Nigeria.

The CIAT harvesting aid, the Richter machine, and the Bonford
harvester must have been developed recognizing that adaptation of
existing root/tuber harvesters will not suffice for cassava, which is
unique in many respects. The problems involved in the mechanization
of cassava harvesting are many and varied (Odigboh, 1976b). Apart
from the serious difficulties arising from the random growth patterns
of the roots and the equally random branching of the stems, cassava
has no specific harvesting season. Therefore, the harvester must be
able to work in the parched hard soils of the dry season, the drenched
muddy soils of the tropical rainy season, as well as in soils of consistency varying between the two extremes. At maturity, and depending
on the cassava variety, the above-ground stems, branches, and leaves
are 1.0 to 1.75 m high or higher and have a mass that varies from 1
to 6 kg per plant. The three to eight roots per plant having a mass of
1 to 6 kg together have a depth of penetration of 150 to 450 mm with a
radius of spread of 100 to 250 mm. About 0.25 m^3 of soil is handled
per meter length of ridge to dig and lift the roots. In addition, the
harvester may be required to cut and carefully windrow or otherwise
handle the stems which form the planting material for the next crop.

Taking into consideration these unique cahracteristics of the cassava
crop, Odigboh and Ahmed (1979) designed and built a prototype cassava
harvester shown in Fig. 8. The prototype has a separately powered

Figure 8 Prototype cassava harvester mounted on a tractor. (A) root lifter; (B) Stem cutter/windrower.

rotary knife mounted in front of the tractor to cut the above-ground vegetation. An endless reeling guide is provided to direct and move the cut stems clear of the row and the tractor tires. Behind the 80-kW tractor is the semimounted cassava root lifter consisting of a pto-driven reciprocating hoe designed to "mole" under the cassava roots to dig and lift them. Details of the lifter and hoe design are given in Fig. 9. At 500 reversals per minute, the reciprocating action of the hoe is designed to reduce draught and make it easy to work under different soil types and conditions. The reciprocating action also shakes the roots free of soil and moves and lifts the roots onto a chain-web conveyor just behind the hoe. The conveyor carries the roots backwards to a collection box at the rear of the machine. The harvested roots are dumped in heaps at intervals along the row for subsequent collection. Field tests on the prototype gave a net work rate of about 0.2 ha/hr at an average speed of 2.5 km/hr. The tests, which are still going on, show that the percentages of lost, broken, cut, and skinned roots are very small and less than possible in manual harvesting.

One may conclude that, like the case for the mechanization of cassava planting, a good deal is being done to mechanize cassava harvesting. Development of harvesting aids such as reported by Wijerwarden should be encouraged for the benefit of the peasant cassava farmers. Work on complete harvesters should be intensified because, until the harvesters are on the market, the job is not yet done.

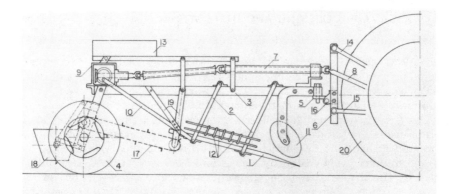

(a)

(b)

Figure 9 (a) Details of cassava root lifter design. (b) Close-up photograph showing hoe of the lifter.

III. CASSAVA PROCESSING AND UTILIZATION

A. Publications on Cassava Processing

Since 1973, there have been at least five major international and inter-disciplinary workshops dealing specifically with sundry aspects of cassava processing and utilization. These workshops have involved scientists, researchers, and technologists who are interested in cassava both as a source of food for millions of humans and as a raw material for numerous food and nonfood industries. The proceedings of a workshop held in London, England in January 1973, dealing with chronic cassava toxicity, was edited by Nestel and MacIntyre (1973) and published by the International Development Research Centre (IDRC) in Ottawa, Canada. The report of a consultant study by Dr. Truman Phillips formed the basis of discussion of the next specialist workshop; the report as reviewed and modified by that workshop was also published by IDRC as *Cassava Utilization and Potential Markets* (Phillips, 1974). In April the same year (1974), another workshop entitled *Cassava: Processing and Storage*, was held in Pattaya, Thailand. The proceedings, edited by Araullo et al. (1974) was also published by IDRC. In 1977, a meeting was held in Guelph, Canada, which dealt with cassava as an animal feed (Nestel and Graham, 1977). Then in April 1978, a workshop entitled *Cassava Harvesting and Processing* was held at CIAT, Cali, Colombia. The workshop proceedings, edited by Weber et al. (1978) was published by IDRC. In addition,there have been many national and international workshops, seminars, and symposia on tropical root crops in which cassava processing and utilization always featured prominently. One such is the workshop entitled *Small-Scale Processing and Storage of Tropical Root Crops* held in Honolulu, Hawaii, in June 1978. The proceedings of the workshop, edited by Plucknett (1979) were published by Westview Press, Boulder, Colorado. Many other reports and publications on cassava processing and utilization from cassava research centers and institutions around the world exist. This series of reports and publications are highlighted here because they represent a summarization of a great deal of important information accumulated and documented by experts in the field; the tropical food technologist or research student should do well to consult this series. The *Cassava Newsletter* is of course an invaluable medium which often carries detailed descriptions of recipes and processes for unique cassava foods.

B. Integrating Cassava Processing and Utilization

It is natural to discuss processing of cassava together with its utilization because the intended use and level of application oftentimes predetermine the processes employed. New and large-scale processing technology, while favoring large cassava producers and processors with

perhaps increased efficiency due to economy of scale, may create serious economic difficulties for the millions of small producers. Therefore,
developments on or improvements of cassava processing techniques
should consider the economic interests and improved quality of life and
standard of living of the peasant cassava farmer as a first priority.
The functional linkage between processing and utilization may be highlighted by the classic definition of agricultural product processing as
any activity which increases the economic value of a crop by improving
its consumer appeal, its quality, or its storability by a change in form
or composition, thereby extending its uses or its availability over time
and space. This definition also emphasizes the economic implications
of processing. Thus, if cassava root storage is contemplated, storage
must meet the requirements of time utility; if the roots are to be transported, spatial or place utility must be ensured; and if the roots are
to be processed into other forms, transformation utility must justify the
economic inputs. The price elasticity of demand for cassava as a staple
food tends to be negative, that is, purchases/sales vary inversely with
price. Therefore, improvements on and technological inputs to processing cassava for food must not lead to price increases that will threaten
the status of cassava as a hedge against hunger for the consuming
millions of the tropics.

C. Unit Operations in Cassava Processing

Cassava roots have to undergo some transformative processing before
they can be used in any form. Processing is usually required to
achieve the detoxification that is necessary to varying degrees with
different cultivars or different products. Processing costs vary with
the degree of transformation and the scale of operation. Space limita-
tion does not allow for detailed descriptions of methods for the processing of cassava roots into different food forms and products. Such
details may be obtained from the references cited earlier. But, there
are a number of unit operations to which cassava roots are commonly
subjected to produce a given food or product, as illustrated in Fig. 10.
Each step or unit operation indicated in Fig. 10 can be mechanized but
is largely done by hand at the village level. Apart from the high labor
intensity and tedium involved in manual processing, the conditions
during the process are generally unsanitary and often unhygienic and
unwholesome. Little or no attention is paid to quality control at that
level of operation. Consequently, the products are of variable and uncertain quality. It is, therefore, essential that efforts should be devoted to the development of appropriate equipment for the various unit
operations to minimize the drudgery, improve the sanitation of the
process conditions, and ensure wholesomeness by establishing simple
techniques of quality control to measure compliance with unambiguosly
defined criteria for good quality.

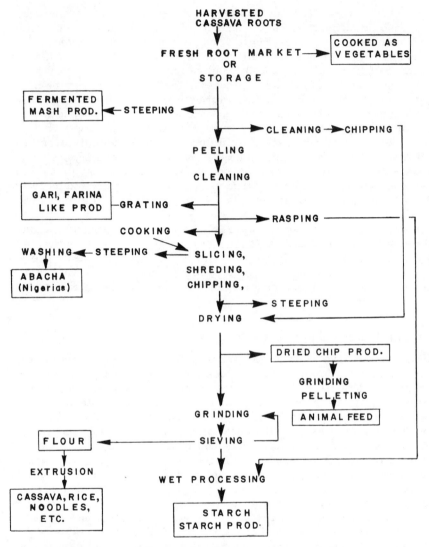

Figure 10 General sequence of unit operations for processing cassava roots into various products.

D. Processing Cassava for Human Food

In a text such as this, one is justified in emphasizing the processing of cassava for human food since as much as 80% of world cassava production is processed for human consumption. As already mentioned, there are numerous processing methods for various cassava foods, with wide differences from one country to another. But, in terms of number of consumers, the most important or at least the most common processed foods from cassava are *farinha de mandioca* based in Brazil and *gari* in west and central Africa. Gari as well as farinha has a scale of process-ing that ranges from 0.5 to 5 tonnes of roots per day for individual family units and small-scale village processors (Plucknett, 1979) to 50 to 100 tonnes/day for large-scale commercial processors. More than 200 million people consume gari/farinha in varying amounts; for the majority of people from west Africa, gari forms the main meal of the day that the majority of the people, rich or poor, like to eat at least once a day.

The technological requirements for large-scale gari/farinha process-ing differ from the technologies for small-scale operation. Large-scale gari processing technologies are, in the main, available and already in use as exemplified by the PRODA, Fabrico, and Newell Dunford process-ing systems. But, technologies appropriate for small-scale processing of gari/farinha are not as well developed, even though there is evidence to show that the small-scale operations may have points of efficiency and certain advantages over the large-scale enterprises (Ngoddy, 1976, 1978). Gari processing may be used to give specific examples from the author's experience of what may be considered desirable or appropriate developments for small-scale production according to the processing flowchart shown in Fig. 11.

1. Peeling the Roots

Peeling of cassava roots is a major bottleneck in cassava processing for which a mechanical device is very desirable. Excepting for processing of cassava chips, in which the roots are sometimes cut up without peeling as shown in Fig. 10, nearly every other cassava product proc-essing starts with the peeling of the roots. This is probably because the concentration of HCN responsible for cassava toxicity is known to be highest in the peel. Peeling of cassava with hot lye has been tried but has not been found suitable due to the contamination of the roots, partial gelatinization of outerlayers of the roots, the inconvenience of handling, and the cost of the process.

Mechanical peeling is problematic because cassava roots vary widely in size and shape; most varieties have carrotlike shapes but elongated ovoid and barrel shapes are also common. The roots are often irregular-ly curved lengthwise and have cross sections that deviate considerably from a circle, having a roundness of transverse section of about 0.85 (Odigboh, 1976b). Furthermore, the thickness of the cassava peel, and the texture and strength of adhesion of the peel to the root flesh vary with variety. All these physical and mechanical properties also vary with the age of the roots as well as the time of the year when harvested.

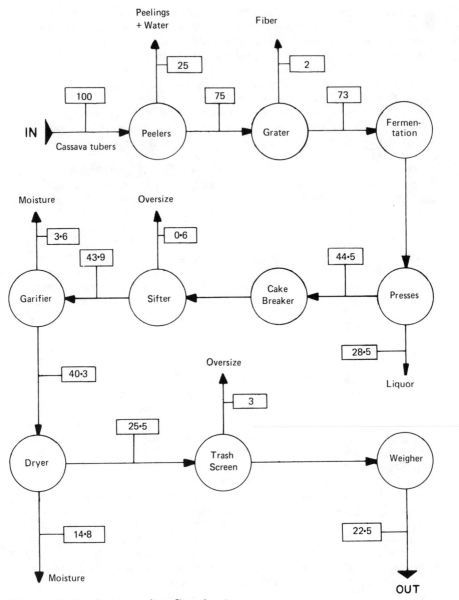

Figure 11 Gari processing flowchart.

An effective cassava peeler must be capable of handling all these variations mentioned. Two such functional prototype cassava peelers were developed by the author. One, a continuousprocess machine, consists of a cylindrical knife assembly (Fig. 12a) and a solid cylinder

Figure 12 Continuous-process cassava peeling machine (prototype).
(a) View showing the knife assembly. (b) View showing rough
cylinder, B.

(Fig. 12b) both mounted parallel and 20 mm apart on a frame inclined at 15°. The unpeeled roots, cut into 100 mm pieces, are introduced lengthwise through the feed channel, J. In operation, (a) and (b) are both rotated in the same direction at 200 rpm and 88 rmp, respectively, while the cassava root pieces rotate in an opposite direction and move down the incline as the knives of (a) progressively peel them. There is a continuous flow of the cassava root pieces which enter one end of the peeler unpeeled and come out of the other peeled, with a peeling efficiency of over 95% at 185 kg/hr when handling sized lots of cassava root pieces (Odigboh, 1976c).

To obviate the need to cut the cassava roots into short lengths and then size them before peeling, a batch-process abrasion peeling machine for whole cassava roots was designed. The prototype shown in Fig. 13, consists simply of a 210-liter oil drum eccentrically mounted on a shaft in the long axis. The inside surface of the drum is covered with a small guage expanded metal sheet. To operate, the drum, loaded with a mixture of roots and some inert abrasive materials such as graded course river sand or quarry stone pulverized to suitable sizes, is rotated at an optimum speed of 40 rpm that can be obtained through a belt speed reduction system driven by a small internal combustion engine or a small electric motor of about 0.56 kW. As the drum rotates, the complex

Figure 13 Batch-process cassava peeler prototype.

Figure 14 Sample of cassava roots peeled by the batch-process peeler.

side-to-side and up-and-down motions of the drum resulting from the eccentric mounting lead to the complete peeling of roots. During the process, water is continuously sprayed onto the roots and abrasives to wash and carry away the finely abraded peels. As reported by Odigboh (1979a), uniform and thorough peeling, which is even better than possible by manual peeling, is achieved at about 180 kg/hr, ir-respective of the sizes or shapes of the roots. The peeled roots from this prototype peeler are shown in Fig. 14 to illustrate that peeling is achieved with negligible loss of useful root flesh and that trimming by hand is virtually eliminated; this is important because manual peeling as done in most gari factories leads to losses of 10 to 15% of the useful root flesh. The abrasion peeler is simple to construct and may be said to be the answer for the elimination of the drudgery and waste inherent in manual peeling of cassava roots. Developments of this nature can encourage rental or cooperative ownership of cassava peelers to the benefit of small-scale cassava processors.

2. Grating the Peeled Roots

The next unit operation in gari production is the grating of the peeled cassava roots. Traditionally, grating is done by manually rubbing the peeled roots against a roughened surface, usually a perforated 3-mm-thick piece of galvanized mild steel plate mounted on a wooden frame. Manual grating is tedious and time-consuming and usually involves scrapes and bloody injuries to the hands of the operator. Thus, manual grating is not hygienic and leads to nonuniform particle sizes as well as losses arising from the inability to hold small pieces of cassava roots for grating.

However, there now exist various versions of mechanical cassava graters that are driven by small electric motors, as shown in Fig. 15, or by small internal combustion engines. Recently, the author also developed a manually operated cassava grating machine (Fig. 16) whose throughput at 125 kg/hr and quality of product are just as good as for the motorized graters, while costing much less to own and operate. This new design compensates for the lower revolutions per minute of

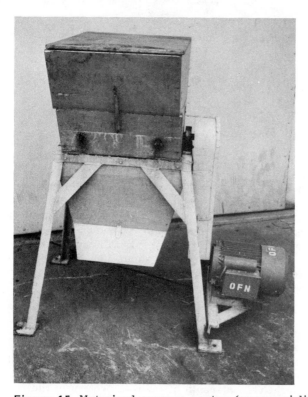

Figure 15 Motorized cassava grater (commercialized).

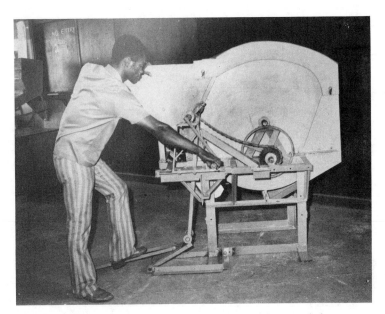

Figure 16 Manually operated cassava grater prototype.

the manually operated machine (25 to 30 rpm) by the increased diameter of its grating drum which is 1.0 m versus the 0.2 to 0.25 m diameter of the motorized graters. It may be said that cassava grating for small-scale gari processing has been effectively mechanized. In Nigeria, for example, local artisans are able to fabricate the mechanical graters that are found in common use alongside the popular corn mills in village squares and markets.

3. Fermentation and Dewatering of Gari Mash

In the traditional processing method, the mash resulting from the grated cassava roots is put in bags of jute, muslin, or baft. The bags are tied or roped up and stones or other heavy objects are placed on them. The mash is left for 4 to 5 days to ferment. During this period and as fermentation progresses, the mash softens and the weight of the heavy objects presses out a juice called liquor from the mash. Therefore, fermentation and dewatering takes place simultaneously. Fermentation of the gari mash achieves the two objectives of a nearly complete removal of the HCN content, referred to as detoxification, and the imparting of the unique characteristic gari flavor to the product. The main difference between gari and farinha de mandioca of Brazil is that dewatering of the farinha mash is done using powerful presses in 4 to 5 hr so that practically no fermentation and, therefore, no flavoring of

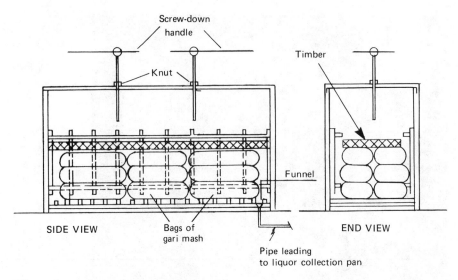

Figure 17 Press for in situ dewatering of fermenting cassava mash. (Developed at U.N.N.)

the product take place before frying or toasting. It has been found through research that inoculation of the fresh gari mash with liquor from earlier mash cuts down the time duration necessary for fermentation to 6 to 18 hr, depending on the amount of liquor or the so-called ferment added. With this discovery and the provision of presses such as shown in Fig. 17, the quality and uniformity of the resultant product are immensely improved while drastically reducing the time and effort involved.

4. Pulverization/Sifting of Dewatered Gari Mash

The product of the fermentation and dewatering processes on the grated cassava is a cake of gari mash having a moisture content of about 40%, wet basis. This cake has to be pulverized and sifted to remove oversize particles and chaff to give the product that is fried to yield gari. Pulverization and sifting of the dewatered gari mash are accomplished together in the traditional processing method by manually pressing and rubbing the cake against sieves of wire mesh or raffia mat. Manual pulverization and sifting of the cake are tedious, time-consuming, and unhygienic. In large-scale operations, the cake is first passed through a cake breaker and then through a sifter. In Fig. 18 is a prototype machine for the pulverization and sifting of fermented and dewatered gari mash. This machine accepts the gari mash cake, cuts up and pulverizes the lumps, and delivers the pulverized mash by a belt conveyer onto a reciprocating sieve for sifting (Odigboh, 1979b). The prototype has a throughput of 125 kg/hr which is more than 15 times the average manual rate and gives a better, more uniform, and more wholesome product.

5. Frying of Gari (Garification)

Gari frying is a complex process. Mere stirring of the pulverized and sifted mash in a vessel over a fire would yield a product which, though

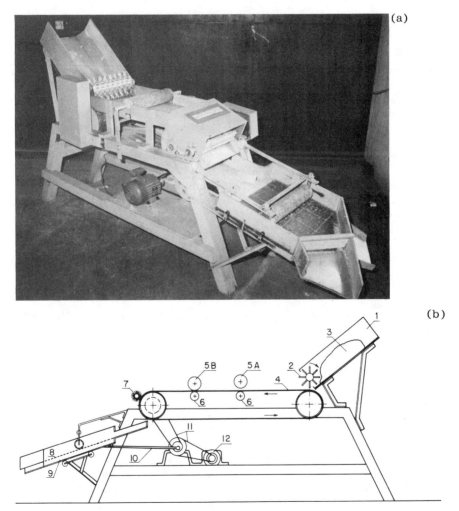

(a)

(b)

Figure 18 (a) Photograph of prototype machine for pulverizing and sifting dewatered gari mash. (b) Sectional view of gari mash pulverizing and sifting machine.

resembling gari visually, would not in fact be gari. Traditionally, gari is fried in shallow earthenware or cast-iron pans over a wood fire. Spatulalike paddles of wood or calabash sections are used to press the sifted mash against the hot surface of the frying pan, quickly scrape the mash off the hot surface to avoid burning, vigorously stir the mash, and then repeat the series of operations. Thus, frying gari involves repetitive pressing, scraping, and stirring of the sifted mash in a frying pan over a fire. The pressing of the mash against the hot surface of the frying pan results in the toasting of the gari particles; starch thus pressed out from the starch granules coats the gari particles and is partially gelatinized to form a thin enveloping film. Thus, under the microscope, a gari particle is seen to be composed of a small grain of cassava coated by a thin film of gelatinized or partially gelatinized cassava starch. When placed in water or otherwise wetted, the grain absorbs moisture through the partially gelatinized starch film and swells. Unless the frying is correctly done, the product will not exhibit this characteristic swelling as some early workers researching the mechanization of gari frying found out. In this respect, the term garification has come to be used to call attention to the fact that the process involves more than drying over a fire.

Sometimes, about halfway through the 45 to 60 min of the manual frying process, some palm oil is added to give the gari a color, which may be various shades of yellow depending on the amount of oil added. It is said that the oil prevents the burning of the gari and imparts a flavor favored by some consumers. After frying, the hot gari is spread out to cool and has a moisture content of 13 to 16% (wet basis), which is the usual range of moisture content of fresh gari found in the local markets. At this range of moisture contents, the gari can keep for about 1 week without deteriorating, provided that the gari is initially uniformly cooled and subsequently stored under conditions that do not permit readsorption of moisture from the ambient environment. Gari can keep for much longer periods, even for over 1 year, if dried down to 8 to 11% moisture content, wet basis, and stored in an airtight container (Odigboh, 1968).

As can be appreciated from the description of the process, manual frying of gari is a hot business; the person sits near the fire for the hour-long batch process sweating profusely, and pressing, scraping, and stirring continuously to obtain an average of 3.5 kg of gari (Ibe, 1979). Naturally, the manual frying process is not quite hygienic as there is ample opportunity for contamination from sundry sources including drops of sweat from the body of the operator. The large gari processing systems mentioned previously have, of course, mechanized the garification process. Still, there is a need to develop a gari frying machine suitable for the small- and medium-scale processors who account for over 90% of the gari consumed in most of Africa.

To serve this group of small processors, a prototype gari frying machine (Fig. 19) was recently developed (Odigboh and Ahmed, 1980b).

Figure 19 Prototype continuous-process gari frying machine.

The prototype simulates the manual frying technique previously described. It consists of 16 spring-loaded paddles carried on 1.75-m-
long shaft that is mounted axially so as to locate the paddles in a 1.70-
m-long semicircular trough of 57 cm diameter. The paddles shaped
as shown in Fig. 20, are spaced with a small overlap, one over the next,

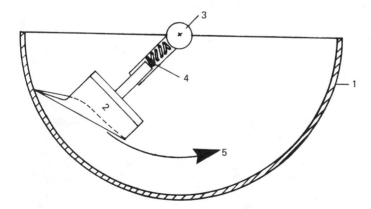

Figure 20 Sketch showing a paddle as mounted within the gari frying
trough.

and are angled relative to the axis of the trough in such a fashion as to form discontinuous flights of a conveyor. The trough is set at a small axial inclination that may be adjusted between 0° and 10° to the horizontal. The paddles oscillate within the frying trough through a semicircle at 40 reversals per minute. The oscillating mechanism of the paddles also actuates a metering device which continuously meters the sifted gari mash from a hopper into the raised end of the frying trough once every two reversals. The frying machine may be fired by a gas or wood fire.

As the paddles swing back and forth, and due to their shape and orientation, they press the gari mash against the hot surface of the trough when moving in the direction shown in Fig. 20, whereas in the opposite direction, the paddles scrape the mash off, stir it, and move it down the slope of the trough. By appropriately adjusting the amount of mash metered, the inclination of the frying trough, and the intensity of the fire, frying is completed when the mash traverses the length of the trough and reaches the outlet. Thus, the prototype is a continuous-flow gari frying machine with an average capacity of 55 kg of gari per hour. The prototype is driven by a 0.75 kW electric motor. But with a modification of the drive train, the machine can be manually operated, and this is the ultimate objective which is currently receiving attention.

E. The Myraid Food and Feed Uses of Cassava

Whereas gari or its Brazilian analogue, farinha, may be the most popular food product of cassava, there are hundreds of its other forms that would not be found in the literature since most of them are specific to given localities outside of which they may not be known even in the same country. Gari itself is eaten in may different ways and forms.

1. It may be eaten dry with palm kernels, coconuts, or fish.
2. Mixed with enough cold water, it is made into a sort of gruel eaten with fish, groundnuts, or coconuts.
3. Enough cold water is added to make it swell, the grains become softer but retain their individuality and, in that form, it is eaten with bean stew.
4. As *gari fortor,* a sophisticated and very delicious preparation in Ghana, the swollen meal prepared as in (3) is thoroughly mixed with an oily stew containing slices of tomatoes, onions, and sometimes eggs or fish, and the mixture is fried with pepper added to taste.
5. By far the most common form in which gari is eaten is prepared by mixing in boiling hot water to make a paste generally known as *eba* in Nigeria. In this form, it is eaten with various types of thick soups prepared with vegetables, plenty of meat or fish, or stockfish, and forms a main meal of the day.

Fresh cassava roots, especially of the sweet variety, are used as vegetables; boiled or roasted and eaten alone or with some stew; or the boiled roots are pounded in a mortar into a paste called *akan* in Ghana and taken with soup. The roots may be peeled, cut into pieces, dried, and stored. The dried roots are milled into a flour which is used in many different meal forms under different names such as *kokonte* in Ghana, *carima* in Brazil, *oke-akpu* in the Igbo land of Nigeria, and *gaplek* in Java.

Another type of cassava meal is prepared by putting the fresh roots to soak for 3 or 4 days in pools at the edge of a stream or fermented in water in large earthenware pots. The resultant roots are soft and, after removing the peels, are easily reduced to a pulpy mash mixed with water in a jute bag. The water is pressed out to give a wet meal which is prepared into a stiff paste by cooking and pounding in a mortar. The stiff paste, called *fufu* in Sierra Leone and Ghana, is eaten with soup. This sort of meal is called *Farinha d'agua* in Brazil and *apalapa* or *akpu* in the Ibo land of Nigeria.

An important food form of cassava is cassava starch, traditionally obtained by stirring grated roots in several washings of clean water. The starch settles at the bottom of the vessel. The product is very good starch. When sifted and toasted while damp. the starch granules become gelatinized or partially dextrinized causing the starch particles to adhere, forming milky white balls known as tapioca. This is the tapioca of commerce, also known as pearl tapioca, used a great deal for puddings in the United States and elsewhere. Though a very important product of commerce as laundry starch, a source for sugars, alcohol, and acetone, as well as important to the adhesive industry, most of cassava starch produced by the local farmers is consumed directly as food in various local forms.

Juice pressed from the raw grated roots in the production of gari, farinha, or starch can be boiled down to concentrate it and destroy the poisonous property. The resultant thick fluid known as *cassareep* in the West Indies and *manipuera* in Brazil is used to make a stock for soups used in many commerical meat sources.

There are many delicious snack food forms of cassava such as *yakayake* in Ghana, *agbeli kaklo* in Sierra Leone, *abacha* in Nigeria, cassava *pulav* in India, cassava crab fritters in Colombia, and so forth, all produced by unique processing techniques.

Cassava leaves and young parts of the stem are relished by sheep and goats and even humans eat the tender green leaves as spinach. The fresh or dried cassava peelings are fed to sheeps and goats. Cassava has always been widely used in most tropical countries for feeding livestock. Cassava provides good-quality carbohydrates and is now valued as an ideal cereal substitute for livestock feeds in the world market where it is in great demand, especially in the highly developed compound animal feed industry of the European Economic Community (Grace, 1977).

Apart from the numerous types of meals, starch, flour, snack foods, stock for soups and sauces and livestock feed, researchers are finding other sophisticated and nontraditional food forms for cassava. Thus, cassava bread is now produced and accepted in many cassava-producing countries (Kim and de Ruiter, 1968; Crabtree, 1978; Crabtree et al., 1978). It may not be long now before cassava rice, cassava spaghetti, and cassava noodles such as shown in Fig. 21 find their way to supermarket shelves in urban centers.

Although cassava roots are known to be low in protein, Rojanarid-piched (1977) reported on the production of cassava leaf pellets as a protein source in Thailand. Cassava has also been shown to be a very good energy source for growing single-cell proteins as a means of greatly increasing the level of available protein in tropical countries (Khor, 1976; Rattakul, 1976). The production of alcohol from cassava was mentioned previously. To complete the picture, mention should also be made of the existence of beer and other drinks brewed from cassava.

The food and feed uses of cassava really appear to be limitless, but it is unfortunate that no standard or special-purpose machinery exists for its processing. Traditional and manual methods of processing which are inherently slow, tedious, and generally unwholesome are still practiced. Even with the growing, relatively affluent, class of urban dwellers in the tropical countries demanding these foods in better forms and packages, standard machinery of European or American manufacture is still not available. Therefore, producing countries of Asia and Africa should invest into the manufacture of the processing machinery themselves. Perhaps no argument in support of this view will be stronger than the one presented pictorially in Fig. 22.

CASSAVA RICE   CASSAVA NOODLES

Figure 21 Samples of experimental cassava rice and cassava noodles produced by extrusion.

F. Storage of Fresh Cassava Roots

In Nigeria, as in many of the producing countries of Africa, direct use of fresh cassava roots for food is very limited; the roots are nearly always converted into a processed product shortly after harvest. But in many other parts of the world, especially Latin America, a large proportion of the total cassava crop is consumed fresh. Therefore, the subject of fresh cassava root storage is very important because the fresh roots are very perishable and cannot keep for more than a few days without deterioriation. In the past, this situation was tolerated because cassava can be stored in the ground for six months or more after optimum harvest maturity. But nowadays, due to the demands of increasing urbanization in the producing/consuming countries, coupled with the increasing industrial-scale utilization of cassava for food and feed processing as well as for nonfood applications, the old solution of in vivo storage no longer suffices. The alternative of quick transportation from farm sites to the market and processing locations is often not tenable considering the very inadequate transportation facilities in the rural areas of the producing countries. At any rate, when possible, cassava roots for industrial use are normally transported in bulk in trucks or trailers and then stored in large piles of several tonnes while awaiting processing. And, after handling in this manner, cassava deteriorates very rapidly.

Consequently, a good deal of research effort has been devoted to the solution of the problem of fresh cassava root storage. Various techniques such as refrigeration (Singh and Mathur, 1953), storage in clamps and boxes using different perservation/curing media, such as moist straw, sawdust, sand, or coir dust (Booth, 1977, Mariot et al., 1974; Aiyer et al., 1978), as well as coating with paraffin or fungicidal wax (Subramanyan and Mathur, 1956), have been investigated. Several applied studies on the etiology and control of postharvest deterioration of cassava have also been reported (Booth, 1976a; Mariot et al., 1978, 1979; Noon and Booth, 1977; Rickard et al., 1979). These studies show that cassava deterioration is due to an internal discoloration which spreads along the vascular stytem from wounds sustained during harvesting and subsequent handling prior to storage, after which comes microbial rotting. The extent or rate of deterioration of the roots depends on the variety, the growing conditions, and above all, on the extent and nature of harvesting/handling damage. A number of procedures established for reducing the rate of cassava deterioriation to extend its storage life, based on recent findings by various workers and institutions, notably CIAT and the Tropical Products Institute (TPI) in the United Kingdom, are briefly summarized as follows.

1. Pruning plants prior to harvest: All the branches and leaves are removed from the aerial part of the plant by cutting the stem to

Figure 22 Pictorial description of manual (traditional) gari production processes. (a) Grating by hand. (b) Fermenting/pressing of gari mash.

15 to 30 cm above the ground, leaving sufficient stem to assist with the eventual harvesting operation. Pruning can be carried out mechanically or mannually. The pruned plants are left in the ground and for maximum effect are harvested 3 weeks after pruning. This method has been consistantly successful in tests in Colombia, and storage without any further treatment can usually be obtained for five days when plants are pruned 3 weeks before harvest.

2. Reduction in mechanical damage: Both discoloration and rotting originate from cuts, breaks, or scuffing of roots. The most severe

(c) Pulverizing/sifting of gari mash. (d) Manual frying of gari.

site of damage is usually the neck of the root where it is attached
to the plant stem. For industrial use, it is very difficult to reduce
mechanical damage economically. However, there is evidence that
if the individual cassava roots are left attached to the plant stem
during storage, then deteroiration is reduced. This might be
practicable although it would involve a reduction in bulk density of
loads in transit and of roots in storage.
3. Reduction of water loss during storage: This has been variously
achieved by waxing, by storage in the field in clamps, by packing

into boxes containing a moistened packing material such as sawdust, or by storage in polythenelined sacks. Any reduction in water loss reduces the development of internal root discoloration, although it may enhance microbial rot. It would probably be worthwhile to cover stacks of cassava with heavy plastic sheets, although this is not known to have been tested. Cassava can also be stored immersed in water, and this might be practicable for small-scale processing operations. Purpose-built storage rooms, with or without temperature control, would be technically possible but are unlikely to be economical, especially for industrial use. It is not known whether evaporative-cooled storage would be effective, practical, or economical for cassava roots. But considering the facts in 5 which follows, it may be worth investigating, especially if fumigation with HCN is incorporated.

4. Use of fungicide: Ambient temperature storage of cassava roots packed in polythene bags has been extended from 10 days to more than 20 days using Maneb (Manzate) in trials at CIAT.

5. Storage in interlayered cassava leaves: This procedure, reported by Aiyer et al. (1978), involves stacking of high-quality roots in between layers of cassava leaves in a volume ratio 1:3.6. The technique gives the optimum temperature of 35 to 40°C and relative humidity of 85 to 90% recommended for would healing in cassava roots (Booth, 1976a). The technique provides a microenvironment that has a high level of HCN said to be slowly liberated as the cassava leaves dry; the presence of significant amounts of HCN in the storage air during the first 7 to 8 days is suspected to have an inhibitory effect on the would pathogens. It is claimed that storage in interlayered cassava leaves is significantly superior to both sawdust and sand as curing/preserving media for a 4-week storage period. This storage technique is also said to be effective in reducing the breakdown of starch to sugar—a troublesome phenomenon that usually occurs early in the storage of cassava roots that leads to a reduction in the eating quality of the fresh roots (Booth, 1976b).

It should be noted that the storage procedures and techniques briefly discussed here are recommended for local trials only but not yet for commercial use. Techniques that are locally practicable and economical may be used separately or in combination. Fuller information on the techniques may be obtained from the authors of the references cited as well from CIAT or TPI.

G. Nutritive Composition of Cassava

Cassava is primarily a source of carbohydrate. Its food composition is similar to that of other starchy roots and tubers such as potatoes, sweet potatoes, and yams, but its protein content is even lower. Probably, this is why there is a certain interest in protein fortification for cassava foods even though that is hardly justified since traditionally cassava is always consumed together with other natural sources of protein. Nevertheless, cassava is relatively rich in calcium and ascorbic acid (vitamin C), with nutritionally significant amounts of thiamine, riboflavin and niacin. Table 4 gives the food composition of fresh cassava per 100 g of the edible portion, along with three other tubers for comparison. It is, however, important to note that the minerals and vitamins found in the fresh roots may be dissipated and lost when the roots are processed for consumption. Also, the protein may be denatured or altered. Unfortunately, cassava is never eaten raw but always subjected to some heating, soaking, grating, or some other process traditionally evolved to achieve detoxification or the removal of prussic acid (HCN) that all varieties of cassava contain in amounts that vary from harmless to lethal.

Prussic acid does not exist free in unharvested cassava roots. The roots contain a cyanogenic glucoside which, in its decomposition, furnishes the prussic acid (Jones, 1959). Cyanogenic glucoside of cassava was identified in 1866 by Theodoro Peckolt who named it manihotoxine. Cyanogenic glucoside is highly soluble in water. It decomposes at 150°C. It exists along with an enzyme called linase. The freeing of prussic acid is accomplished by the enzymatic action of linase.

Table 4 Food Composition of Fresh Cassava and Three Common Tuber Vegetables for 100 g of Edible Portion

Item	Unit	Cassava	Yam	Sweet potato	Potato
Food energy	Calories	146	105	117	82
Water	g	62.5	72.4	70.0	78.0
Carbohydrate	g	34.7	24.1	27.3	18.9
Protein	g	1.2	2.4	1.3	2.0
Fat	g	0.3	0.2	0.4	0.1
Calcium	mg	33.0	22.0	34.0	8.0
Iron	mg	0.7	0.8	1.0	0.7
Vitamin A	IU	trace	trace	500.0	trace
Thiamin B_1	mg	0.06	0.09	0.10	0.10
Riboflavin B_2	mg	0.03	0.03	0.05	0.03
Niacin	mg	0.6	0.5	0.6	1.4
Vitamin C	mg	36.0	10.0	23.0	10.0

Source: Extracted from *FAO Food Composition Tables for International Use,* 2nd ed., Jan. 1953, pp. 23-24 and *FAO Food Composition Tables—Minerals and Vitamins—for International Use,* March 1954, pp. 30-31.

Hydroysis under linase influence is accelerated by soaking in water and by heating below 75°C. The various traditional methods of processing cassava for human food ensure the complete or nearly complete removal of the glucoside. Mechanization of cassava processing must, therefore, ensure that any heat treatments do not lead to temperatures in excess of 75°C before all the glucoside is eliminated, else the linase is destroyed and the remaining glucoside can still be broken down by enzymes of the digestive juices and lead to poisoning.

H. Engineering Properties of Cassava

To be able to predict or evaluate the behavior of cassava and its products under conditions of applied load, force, thermal stress, or any other stress in order to design for the mechanization of the various processing operations or analyse the industrialization processes and systems, knowledge of the physical characteristics, mechanical, rheological, thermal, and other engineering properties of the material is essential. Unfortunately, very little work, if any, has been done or reported in this area of engineering characterization of cassava and its products. The situation is made worse by the fact that there are over 200 cultivated varieties of cassava which have wide variations in their composition and properties and, even within the same variety, exhibit big differences under different soil types, climatic conditions, cultural practices, and husbandry. To illustrate the nature of data needed for the engineering characterization, some data on the properties of cassava from very limited tests by the author are presented in Table 5 (Odigboh, 1976b).

The mature cassava tuber consists of three distinct regions as illustrated in Fig. 23, namely, the outer periderm, the cortex, and the central pith. The central pith is the main storage region consisting of a mass of parenchyma cells mixed with some vascular elements and lactiferous tubes. It is white in most varieties, but in some varieties it has a cream color. The chief storage material is starch of medium-sized granules unique among other root and tuber starches in having a stellate hilum. Starch forms about 30% of the contents of the central pith; younger immature roots contain up to 6% of sucrose as well, while older roots tend to become lignified and are more difficult to process for food. At the center of the pith is a fibrous cord that runs through the whole length of the root. As shown in Fig. 23, the central pith shows a distinct differentiation into a medullary zone in the pith proper, separated by a salient vascular ring.

I. Cassava Starch

Although not as important a food form as the meals in the traditional diets of the cassava producers and consumers, cassava starch is

Table 5 Some Engineering Properties of Cassava Roots

Property	Value[a]	Method of Determination
Shape of roots	Spindle shaped; elongated ovoid; barrel shaped with rounded ends; conical with rounded ends, (conical with rounded head ends)	Comparision with known geometrical shapes (Mohsenin, 1970)
Roundness of transverse section of roots	0.65 to 1.0 (0.85)	A_p/A_c where A_p = actual area of section A_c = area of circumscribing circle
Length of roots	10 to 55 cm (25 cm)	Direct measurement
Average straight length of root	(10 cm)	Direct measurement
Maximum diameter of root	2.5 to 15 cm (6.3 cm)	Direct measurement
Mass of individual root	25 to 4000 g (175 g)	Direct measurement
Mean specific gravity of whole root	(1.025)	Water displacement
Moisture content (% wet basis)	Tail and midportion 85 to 93 Head portion: 78 to 86 (88)	Aerated oven
Solid density (g/cm^3)	1.92 to 2.3 (2.0)	Air comparison pycnometer using ground bone-dry roots average particle size under 250μ
Thickness of outer periderm	0.25 to 0.3 mm	Instron testing machine, time-displacement recording
Thickness of cortex	1.0 to 2.0 mm (1.5 mm)	Instron testing machine, time-displacement recording
Modulus of deformability or apparent modulus	3.45 E + 06 - 4.82 E + 06 Pa	Tangent to stress-strain curve at designated stress

Table 5 (Continued)

Property	Value[a]	Method of Determination
Bioyield strength	(9.13 E + 05 Pa)	Force-deformation curve in a compression test
Shear strength	Medullary zone: 6.76 E + 05 Pa Central pith zone: 96 E + 05 Ba Section with chord: 2.14 E + 06 Pa	Double shear test using instron machine
Specific heat	(0.94 J/kg.K)	Calorimeter method of mixtures
Thermal conductivity of root flesh	(0.285 W/m.K)	Modified Fitch Apparatus (Odigboh, 1978c)
Thermal conductivity of white gari at 610 kg/m³ bulk density	(0.161 W/m.K)	Thermal conductivity probe (Odigboh, 1978c)

[a]Mean values in parentheses. Tests on unidentified variety of cassava from University of Florida Agric. and Education Center (Odigboh, 1973).

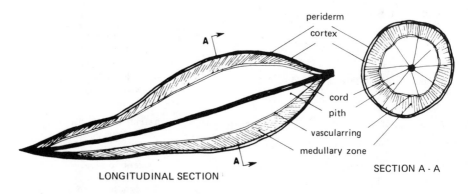

LONGITUDINAL SECTION

SECTION A - A

Figure 23 Section through a cassava root showing salient parts.

perculiarly adapted for food manufacture and is preferred to other starches in many industrial food applications. Due to its unique characteristics, it is said to be superior to corn, wheat, or potato starch for culinary purposes (Rose, n.d.). Cassava starch has 83% amylopectin content which is responsible for its pastes being clear, fluid, nongelling, and having little retrogradation tendency (Friedman, 1950; Glicksman, 1969). Work on the viscometric characterization of cassava starch pastes (Odigboh, 1974) established the following properties and attributes.

1. Cassava starch pastes exhibit plastic fluid flow behavior.
2. Stable pastes are formed about 60 to 65°C during the cooking phase, making it the starch with the lowest temperature of gelatinization among the starches commonly used in the food industry (Osman, 1965). The pastes are translucently clear and have a suave flavor, both of which are properties favored by the food industry.
3. The pastes have high hot-paste peak viscosities, particularly at high concentrations. Starch dried at 70°C or more give lower viscosities, peak or otherwise (Odigboh and Mohsenin, 1975).
4. The freeze-thaw stability of cassava starch pastes is significantly affected by the temperature at which the starch is dried as well as the concentration. While the stability is decreased with increase in concentration, it is increased with higher (starch) drying temperature. Overall, cassava starch pastes have very good stability for freezing and thawing, a useful quality for frozen-food processing applications.
5. Cassava starch pastes exhibit pronounced setback on cooling, expecially for paste concentrations of 4% and above. However, application of shear during the cooking of the paste reduces the extent of retrogradation drastically.
6. The pastes exhibit considerable work-softening or shear-thinning. Shear-thinning in cassava starch pastes is not a phenomenon of true thixotropy but represents a case of irreversible work-softening termed rheomalaxis (Scot Blair, 1969), resulting from the disruption of the fundamental structure of the paste, namely the starch granules. Therefore, maximum shear degradation occurs about the temperature of the peak viscosity (Odigboh and Mohsenin, 1975).
7. Cooked beyond the temperature of the peak viscosity, cassava starch pastes have long cohesive textures, whereas below that temperature the texture of the pastes is less sticky. Therefore, for food applications where long cohesive textures may be undesirable, pastes should be cooked below 80°C.
8. Cassava starch dried at 70°C or higher temperatures yields short-textured pastes with lowered viscosities and as such, is preferred for pie fillings, cream puddings, and baby food manufacture.

It is clear that, in addition to the traditional cassava food forms, cassava starch forms an excellent base for numerous foods. One simply marvels at the vastness, scope, and branches of the corn starch industry. Reading about the activities of the Corn Industries Research Foundation, Inc. of the United States, it is easy to appreciate what minor miracles research on cassava starch can bring about. The natural qualities of cassava starch make it a good substitute for the cereal starches in the textile industry, in paper mills, tobacco and cigarette plants, rubber factories, foundries, in chemical and drug manufacture, the mining industries, the manufacture of adhesives, and in the various food processing plants. Recent research presents numerous possibilities using starch derivatives such as starch aldehyde reaction products, starch alkoxides, deoxystarches and so forth, for which the cereal starches have so far captured most of the market.

Production of good-quality cassava starch may be beyond the means of the peasant farmers since it depends upon good quality control. Adequate amounts of clear, potable water must be available for washing the roots, rinsing the wet ground pulp, and for extracting the starch. The machinery and other equipment must not be subject to rusting and must be easy to clean. The process of starch extraction should be such that the raw material and the product are handled quickly to allow no opportunity for deterioration or spoilage. The final product should be dried well and uniformly to give the desired appearance and low bacterial, mold, and yeast counts in order to give starch that is a white powder, odorless, tasteless, and neutral. The final product should have a low moisture content (11 to 13%, wet basis), ash (0.2%), and neutral pH (6.3 to 6.5), and a high vicosity (Ayres, 1972). Kaufman (1950) published specifications for commercial cassava starch, such as mesh size, moisture content, ash content, degree of foreign contamination, and so forth. The demand for good-quality cassava starch far exceeds the supply; investment into industrial cassava starch manufacture is recommended to entrepreneurs in the producing countries as a really profitable venture.

IV. SUMMARY

The importance of cassava as a major food crop of the tropics has been discussed in terms of the size of the crop and its many food and feed uses. The industrial applications and the tertiary processed food potentialities are cursorily discussed for completeness. The need to improve the yield of cassava on the peasant farmers' fields is emphasized as being a probelm of both agronomy and engineering. The labor intensity of all aspects of the cassava culture and husbandry is highlighted, and cassava researchers are called upon to intensify work and effort to put on the market viable cassava planters, weeders, and harvesters. Almost all aspects of the traditional processes for producing the various cassava foods manually are shown to be tedious, time-consuming, and largely unwholesome. Cassava research programs and workers should pay a lot more attention to the mechanization of the various unit operations involved in processing cassava into its many food forms. Applied research to quantify the mechanical, rheological, and other engineering properties of cassava and its products is not much in evidence in the literature. The potentials of cassava as food, feed, and industrial raw material are not yet being fully utilized. A great deal more engineering research on all aspects of cassava production and processing is needed to maximize its utilization with less waste and enhanced product quality at lower costs to the family or industrial, domestic, or foreign consumers.

REFERENCES

Aiyer, R. S., Nair, P. G., and Prema, L. (1978). No cost method of preserving fresh cassava roots. *Cassava Newsl. (CIAT Series OIEC-4* 4:8-9.

Akobundu, I. O. (1976). Weed control in root and tuber crops. Paper presented at First National Cassava Workshop. National Root Crop Research Institute, Umudike, Nigeria, (unpublished).

Araullo, E. V., Nestel, B., and Campbell, M. (eds.) (1974). *Cassava processing and storage. Proceedings of an International Workshop, Pattaya, Thailand.* Ottawa, Canada, IDRC-031e.

Ayres, J. C. (1972). Manioc and its products. *Food Technol.* 26(4): 128-138.

Bailey, L. H. (1925). *Manual of Cultivated Plants.* New York, Mcmillian.

Bates, W. N. (1963). *Mechanization of Tropical Crops.* London, Temple Press Books, Ltd.

Beeny, J. M. (1970). Mechanization for tapioca. In *Crop Diversification in Malaysia* (E. K. Blencowe and J. K. Blencowe, eds.). Malaysia, Incorporated Society of Planters, pp. 167-182.

Bolhuis, G. G. (1954). The toxicity of cassava roots. *Neth. J. Agric. Sc.* 2(3):176-185.

Booth, R. H. (1976a). Storage of fresh cassava (*M. esculenta*). I. Postharvest deterioration and its control *Exptl. Agriculture* 12(2):103-111.

Booth, R. H. (1976b). Changes in quality of cassava roots during storage *J. Food Technol.* 11(3):245-264.

Booth, R. H. (1977). Storage of fresh cassava (*M. esculenta*). II. Simple storage techniques. *Exptl. Agriculture* 13(2):119-128.

Briecno, P. R. H., and Larson, G. (1972). Research on developing a cassava harvester. *Revista ICA* 7(2):139-150. (In Spanish.)

Cardenso, B. R. (1948). A new planter for sugar cane, potatoes, cassava and similar crops. *Agricultura Tropical (Colombia)* 4:33-38. (In Spanish.)

CIAT (1977). Looking back—cassava cultivation yesterday. *Cassava Newsl. (CIAT, Cali)* 2:11.

CIAT (1978). *Cassava Workers Directory.* Cassava Information Centre Publication 20 NC-1. Cali, Colombia, Centre International de Agricultura Tropical.

CIAT (1979-1980). *Cassava Annual Report(s).* CIAT Series No. 02EC1-78 and 02EC1-79. Cali, Colombia, Centro International de Agricultura Tropical.

Cobley, L. S. (1956). *An Introduction to the Botany of Tropical Crops.* London, Longmans.

Coursey, D. G. (1978). Cassava: a major food crop of the tropics. Paper presented at workshop of Cyanide Metabolism, sponsored by The European Molecular Biology Organization. Canterbury, U.K., August 14-18.

Crabtree, J. (1978). The breadmaking potential of products of cassava as partial replacements for wheat flour. *Nutr. Rep. Int.* 18(2):397-407.

Crabtree, J. , Kranner, E. C., and Baldry, J. (1978). Technical note: the incorporation of fresh cassava into bread. *J. Food Technol.* 13:149-153.

Diaz-Duran, A. (1979). *A Cassava Harvesting Aid.* Cassava Information Centre publication, Series No. 05EEn-3. Cali, Colombia, CIAT.

Dimicali, A. (1964). The sugar-cane cassava planter. *Agricultural and Industrial Life* 26(8):12.

Doku, E. V. (1969). *Cassava in Ghana.* Accra, Ghana University Press.

Doll, J., Pinstrup-Anderson, P., and Diaz, R. O. (1977). An agro-economic survey of weeds and weeding practices in cassava (*Manihot esculenta* Crant 2) in Colombia. *Weed Research* 17:153-160.

Echeverria, R. H. (1971). *Feasibility Study for the Mechanical Planting and Harvesting of Cassava.* Monograph. Maracay, Universidad de Venezuala, Instituto de Inginiera Agricole. (In Spanish.)

Echeverria, R. H. (1973). Mechanization of cassava cultivation. In *Primer Seminario National Sobro Yuca. Revista de la Facultad de Agronomia (Venezuala) Alcance* 22:45-49. (In Spanish.)

Essais, D. E. (1954). Trails with a cassava grip lifter. *Bulletin d'Information de L'INEAC* 3(6):343-345.

Food and Agriculture Organization (1971). *FAO Food Balance Sheets 1964-1966.*

Friedman, A. (1950). Starch adhesives. In *Chemistry and Industry of Starch* (R. N. Kerr, ed.). New York, Academic Press.

Glicksman, M. (1969). *Gum Technology in the Food Industry.* New York, Academic Press.

Grace, M. R. (1977). Cassava processing. *FAO Agric. Services Bull. No. 8* Rome, FAO.

Hammond, A. L. (1977). Alcohol: a Brazilian answer to the energy crisis. *Science* 195:564-566.

Harper, R. S. (1974). Chemical weed control in cassava using paraquat. *PANS* 20:185-189.

Hosse, G. A. J. (1971). A study of mechanizing the harvesting of cassava. Unpublished thesis, National College of Agric. Engineering, Silsoe, Bedford, England.

Ibe, D. G. (1979). A partially mechanized village-scale gari production system. *Proceedings of Nigerian Society of Agricultural Engineers* 3:223-229.

Jones, W. O. (1959). *Manioc in Africa.* Stanford, California. Stanford University Press.

Jong, A. W. G. (1913). Het zetmeelgehalte van den cassave wortel (the percentage of starch in cassava roots). *Mededelingen van het Agricultuur Chemisch Laboratorium* 5:1-18.

Kasasian, L., and Seeyare, J. (1969). Critical periods for weed competition *PANS* 15:208-212.

Kaufman, C. W. (1950). This 10-Test plan clinched tapioca quality. *Food Industries* 22(4):614-617.

Kemp, D. C. (1978). Harvesting: a field demonstration of two machines. In *Cassava Harvesting and Processing* Proceedings of a Workshop. (E. J. Weber, J. H. Cock, and A. Chounard, eds.). Ottawa, Canada, IDRC-114e.

Khor, G. L. (1976). Nutritive value of motolervant fungi grown on cassava. *Canadian Instutute Food Sci. Technol. J.* 9(3):139-143.

Kim, J. C., and de Ruiter, D. (1978). Bakery products with non-wheat flours. *Baker's Digest* 43(3):50-63.

Krochmal, A. (1966). Labor input and mechanization of cassava. *World Crops* 18(3):28-30.

Kumar, H. (1962). Mechanization of cassava planting. *Ghana Farmer* 6(3):102-104.

Lockwood, R. B. (1969). Poisonous food for millions. *Pacific Discovery* 22(3):28-31.

Makanjuola, G. A., Onochie, B. E., and Schulte, E. E. (1973). Preliminary studies on the mechanical harvesting of cassava roots in Nigeria. *Paper presented at Third Internation Symposium on Tropical Root Crops. University of Ibadan, Nigeria.*

Marriot, J., Been, B. O., and Perkins, C. (1974). *Storage of Fresh Cassava Roots in Moist Coir Dust.* Kingston, Jamaica, Ministry of Industry.

Marriot, J., Been, B. O., and Perkins, C. (1978). The aetiology of vascular discoloration in cassava roots after harvesting: association with water loss from wounds. *Physiol. Plant* 44:38-42.

Marriot, J., Been, B. O., and Perkins, C. (1979). The aetiology of vascular discoloration in cassava roots after harvesting: development of endogenous resistence in stored roots. *Physiol. Plant* 45:51-56.

Mohsenin, N. N. (1970). *Physical Properties of Plant and Animal Materilas, Vol. 1.* New York, Gordon and Breach Science Publishers.

Monteiro, F. P. (1963). The economic value of cassava and merchanized cultivation systems. *Rural (Brazil)* 511(43):16. (In Spanish.)

More, C. C. (1907). Cassava: its content of HCN, starch and other properties *U.S. Bur. Chem. Bull.* 1:6.

Nestel, B. (1973). Current utilization and future potential for cassava. In *Chronic Cassava Toxicity Proceedings of an interdisciplinary workshop.* (B. Nestel, and R. MacIntyre, eds.). Ottawa, Canada, IDRC Publication, pp. 11-26.

Nestel, B. and Graham, M. eds. (1977). *Cassava as Animal Feed, Proceedings of workshop University of Guelph.* Ottawa, Canada, IDRC 095.

Nestel, B., and MacIntyre, R. (eds.) (1977). *Cassava as Animal Feed. Proceedings of workshop University of Guelph.* Ottawa, Canada, IDRC 095e.

Nestel, B., and MacIntyre, R. (eds.) (1973). *Chronic Cassava Toxicity. Proceedings of an Interdisciplinary Workshop, London, England, January 1973.* Ottawa, Canada, IDRC 010e.

Ngoddy, P. O. (1976). Gari mechanization in Nigeria: the competition between intermediate and modern technology. In *Appropriate Technology Problems and Promises* (E. Jequier, ed.) pp. 260-275.

Ngoddy, P. O. (1978). Determinants in the development of technology for processing roots and tubers in Nigeria. In *Proceedings of the First National Seminar on root and Tuber Crops* (L. S. O. Ene, ed.) Umudike, Nigeria, NRCRI, pp. 134-151.

Noon, R., and Booths, R. H. (1977). Nature of Post harvest deterioration of cassava roots. *Trans. Br. Mycol. Soc.* 69(2):287-290.

Odigboh, E. U. (1968). Results of some gari storage experiments. Nigerian Civil War Food Notes (unpublished).

Odigboh, E. U. (1973). Engineering properties of cassava roots. Unpublished research report (Res. Project 1901 SE/PSU 1972-74). University Park, Penn., The Pennsylvania State University.

Odigboh, E. U. (1974). Viscometric characterization of cassava starch pastes. Unpublished Ph.D. dissertation. University Park, Penn., The Pennsylvania State University.

Odigboh, E. U. (1976a). Engineering the mechanization of Nigerian agriculture: technological and sociological implications. In *Appropriate Approaches for Accelerated Food Production in the Rainforest Zones of Nigeria* (U. G. N. Anazodo and E. U. Odigboh, eds.). Symposium Proceedings. Agricultural Engineering Department, Nsukka, University of Nigeria, pp. 120-130.

Odigboh, E. U. (1976b). Mechanization of Nigerian cassava production and processing: research needs and interests. *The Agricultural Engineer (J. Proc. Brit. IAgrE)* 31(1):20-23.

Odigboh, E. U. (1976c). A cassava peeling machine: development, design construction. *J. Agric. Enginneering Res.* 21(3):361-469.

Odigboh, E. U. (1978a). A two-row automatic cassava cuttings planter: development, design and prototype construction. *J. Agric. Engineering Res.* 23:109-116.

Odigboh, E. U. (1978b). Problems and progress in field mechanization of Nigerian roota and tuber crops. *Proceedings of the First National Seminar on Root and Tuber Crops L. S. O. ed.).* Umudike, Nigeria, National Root Crop Research Institute, pp. 113-120.

Odigboh, E. U. (1978c). Instruments for measurement of thermal conductivity of solid food materials. *Nigerian J. Enginnering Technol.* 1(1):1-14.

Odigboh, E. U. (1979a). Mechanical devices for peeling cassava roots. In *Small Scale Processing and Storage of Tropical Root Crops* (D. L. Plucknett, ed.). Boulder, Colorado, Westview Press.

Odigboh, E. U. (1979b). Machine for pulverization and sifting of dewatered gari mash. In *Broachure for National Exhibition of Locally Developed Agricultural Equipment.* Agricultural Engineering Department, Nsukka, University of Nigeria.

Odigboh, E. U., and Ahmed, S. F. (1982). A cassava harvester: design analysis and prototype development. Nigerian Council of Operation Feed the Nation (OFN) sponsored research project report. Agricultural Mechanization in Asia, Africa, and Latin America (AMA) 13(4):15-20.

Odigboh, E. U., and Ahmed, S. F. (1980a). Development of a ridge-profile weeder. *Nigerian J. Technol. (NIJOTECH)* 4(1):1-7.

Odigboh, E. U., and Ahmed, S. F. (1980b). Design and development of a continuous-process gari frying machine. Research report prepared for publication in a journal. (Unpublished.)

Odigboh, E. U., and Mohsenin, N. N. (1975). Viscosity characterization of cassava starch pastes. *J. Texture Studies* 319-328.

Onochie, B. E. (1975). Critical periods for weed competition in cassava in Nigeria. *PANS* 21(1):54-57.

Onochie, B. E. (1978). Weed control in root and tuber crops. In *Proceedings of the First National Seminar on Root and Tuber Crops* (L. S. O. Ene, ed.). Umudike, Nigeria, National Root Crop Res. Inst. (NRCRI), pp. 12-23.

Osman, E. M. (1965). Starch in the food industry. In *Starch Chemistry and Technology* (R. L. Whistler, and E. F. Paschall, eds.). New York, Academic Press.

Phillips, T. P. (1970). *An Agricultural Note Book.* Longmans Nigeria, Ltd.

Phillips, T. P. (1974). *Cassava Utilization and Potential Markets,* Ottawa, Canada, IDRC Publication IDRC 020e.

Plucknett, D. L. (ed.) (1979). Small-scale processing and storage of tropical root crops. *Westview Tropical Agriculture Series, No. 1.* Boulder, Colorado, Westview Press.

Rattakul, B. (1976). Single cell protein production from cassava starch by yeast. Unpublished Ph.D. thesis. Provo, Utah, Brigham Young University.

Rickard, J. E., Marriot, J., and Gahan, P. B. (1979). Occlusions in cassava xylem vessels associated with vascular discoloration. *Ann. Bot.* 43:523-526.

Rojanaridpiched, C. (1977). Cassava leaf pellets as a protein source in Thailand. *Cassava Newsl.* (1)5.

Rose, R. E. (n.d.). Cassava growing and starch making in Florida.

Schulte, E. E., Makanjuola, G. A., and Onochie, B. E. (1973). Mechanization of cassava production I: Planting. *Paper presented at 3rd International Symposium on Tropical Roots Crops, University of Ibadan, Nigeria.*

Scot Blair, G. W. (1969). *Elementary Rheology.* London and New York, Academic Press.

Singh, K. K., and Mathur, P. B. (1953). Cold storage of tapioca roots. *Bull. Mysore Centeal Food Technol. Institute* 2:181-182.

Stock, J. E. Van Der (1909). Bibitproefbij cassava *Manihot utilissima* Pohl (selection of stem cuttings). *Teysmannia* 20:730-734.

Subramanyan, H., and Mathur, P. B. (1956). Effect of fungicidal wax coating on the storage behaviour of tapioca roots. *Bull. Mysore Central Food Technol. Res. Inst.* 5(5):110-111.

Vries, C. A. de, Ferwerda, J. D., and Flach, M. (1967). Choice of food crops in relation to actual and potential production in the tropics. *Neth. J. Agric. Sc.* 15:241.

Wahab, A. H., Robinson, P. F., and Hassan, I. (1977). Mechanized planting of cassava stem cuttings on Guyana's light peats and peaty clays. *Turrialba* 27(2):137-141.

Walters, p. R. (1978). Cassava poised for major UK compound role? *Cassava Newsl. (CIAT, Cali)* 3:7. (Abstracted from an article in Agr. Trade, London.)

Webber, E. J., Cock, J. H., and Chouinard, A. (eds.) (1978). *Cassava Harvesting and Processing. Proceedings of a Workshop at CIAT, Cali, Columbia.* IDRC Publication IDRC-114e. Ottawa, Canada.

Wijerwarder, R. (1978). Notes on tools for productivity. Kaduna, Nigeria, National Committee of OFN sponsored seminar on mechanization of crop production. 30, 31 October.

5
Citrus Fruits

S. V. Ting Florida Department of Citrus, University of Florida
Agricultural Research and Education Center, Lake Alfred, Florida

I. GEOGRAPHIC DISTRIBUTION

As an evergreen plant, susceptible to damage from the cold, *Citrus* is the only genus grown in the tropic and subtropical regions of both the northern and southern hemispheres. In the extreme north of these regions, only the cultivars most tolerant to the cold can survive or be commercially produced. In the tropical region, the excessive rainfall and constant high temperatures and humidities are also unsuitable for commercial citrus growing. The citrus-producing areas in the northern hemisphere include the following: northern Mexico, southern United States, and the Mediterranean, including northern Africa and southern Asia. In the southern hemisphere they include the southern part of South America, South Africa, and most of the continent of Australia.

The entire citrus fruit production for the years 1968 and 1969 was 27 million tonnes, and in 1972 and 1973 it had increased to 35.6 million tonnes (USDA, 1976b). These figures are reported by the Foreign Agricultural Service represent 24 countries or areas and an estimated 80 to 85% of the total world citrus output. Orange and mandarins are by far the major citrus fruit produced, nearly 83%, with grapefruit and lemon making up the remainder. The average citrus production between the years 1968 and 1974 is shown in Table 1.

II. BOTANY AND HORTICULTURAL CULTIVARS

Citrus fruits contain a number of genera and species but only three genera are grown commercially. These are *Citrus, Poncirus,* and *Fortunella* in the family Rutaceae. Among these genera, *Citrus* is by far the most important and has the most cultivars.

A. *Poncirus*

Poncirus have small spiny trees or shrubs. One single species, *P. trifoliata,* is of economical importance. The fruit is not used as food, but the seed is in great demand for the production of rootstock. Of all citrus rootstocks, *P. trifoliata* is the hardiest to cold weather, as well as the most resistant to heat. It has been reported that such characteristics may be imparted to the budded portion of a tree (Hume, 1957).

Table 1   World Citrus Production Between 1968 and 1974

Fruit (million tonnes)

Area	Orange and tangerine		Grapefruit		Lemon	
	1968/69	1973/74	1968/69	1973/74	1968/69	1973/74
North America and Caribbean	8.56	10.13	2.07	2.52	0.54	0.60
Mediterranean area	7.16	9.37	0.39	0.55		1.41
Far East (Japan and Taiwan only)	2.99	4.10	—	—	—	—
South America	2.70	4.89	0.11	0.18	0.32	0.64
Other southern hemisphere	0.72	1.00	0.11	0.12	0.04	0.06
Total	22.14	29.49	2.69	3.36	2.20	2.72

[a] 26 reported countries.
Source: USDA (1976).

B. *Fortunella*

The most popular fruit in the genus *Fortunella* is the kumquat. It was
first introduced to Europe from China and Japan in 1846 by Robert
Fortune, an English horticulturist. It was later introduced to America.
The small and colorful oval fruit are eaten fresh or candied. No world
production figure is known. The trees are also grown as ornamentals
for their small orange-colored fruit in the fall.

C. *Citrus*

Citrus is the genus in which all commercial citrus fruit belong. It
also contains some less familiar species. Some of the common cultivars
of each species are shown in Table 2. Predominant cultivars, especially
oranges, are generally grown in all subtropical and tropical areas
around the world.

Many species of *Citrus* originated for Southeast Asia. China and
the Cochin China region are also contributed greatly to their origin.
Some *Citrus* species were reported to have been introduced to Europe
as early as the third century B.C. (Cooper and Chapot, 1977). Later,

Table 2 Principal Commercial Cultivars of Different Species of Citrus

Common and botanical names	Cultivars	Principal regions grown
Sweet orange *(C. sinensis)*	Valencia, Pineapple, Parson Brown, Hamlin	All regions
	Pera	Brazil
	Jaffa, Shamoutti	Israel
	Marrs	Texas (U.S.)
	Biondo Comune	Mediterranean
	Doblefina, Moro, Natal, Tarocco, Malteseblood	
	Washington Naval	All regions
	Australian Naval	Australia
Mandarin *(C. reticulata)*	Dancy	All regions
	Clementine, Cleopatra	Mediterranean
	Robinson, Page	U.S.
	Ponkan, Tankan	Far East
	Murcott	U.S.
Grapefruit *(C. paradisi)*	Marsh, Ducan	All regions
	Ruby, Thompson Star Ruby, Burgundy, Red Blush	Texas (U.S.)
Tangelo and tangor *(C. reticulata × C. paradisi)* and *(C. reticulata × C. sinensis)*	Oralando, Mineola, Nova, Temple	North America
Pomelo *(C. grandis)*	Mammoth, Pink	All regions
	Mati	Far East
Sour orange *(C. aurantium)*	Bitter sweet, Sour	All regions, Mediterranean predominant
Lemon *(C. limon)*	Lisbon, Eureka, Sicily, Villafranca, Ponderosa, Meyer, Rough, Bearss	All regions, especially Mediterranean and California (U.S.)
Lime *(C. aurantifolia)*	Tahiti	Caribbean
	Mexican, Key	North America

Source: Cooper and Chapot (1977).

oranges and lemons were extended to the Mediterranean. From there, Columbus took them to the Americas. Today citrus fruits are grown throughout the warmer areas of the United States.

III. CITRUS FRUITS AS HUMAN FOOD

No fruit is more popular and desired than the citrus fruit. It has many unique qualities, such as its distinct, pleasant aroma that is characteristic of the citrus essential oils and its typical colors due to the presence of various carotenoids in the plastids. With the exception of acid citrus fruit, most have a combination of sour and sweet that delights the palate of people of all ages. The acid fruits, such as the lemons and limes, are natural ingredients for refreshing beverages when combined with appropriate amounts of nutritive or nonnutritive sweeteners.

Before the middle of this century, most of the tangerines, oranges, and grapefruit were used fresh. Outside the region of their production, they commanded relatively high economic value because they were easily perishable. With increasing knowledge of storage, transporation, and disease control, both distance and storage life have been extended, and the marketing of citrus fruit has become more profitable.

The canning of citrus juice makes possible the utilization of portions of fruit that cannot be marketed fresh. The quality of the canned products in early days had much to be desired, and the economy of citrus fruit was still largely dependent on fresh trade. With the advance of knowledge of human nutrition and of processing and handling technology, citrus fruit and citrus juice soon became important items in the human diet.

Today citrus fruit is considered to be one of the most important sources of vitamin C. Early in the eighteenth century a Hungarian physician, Kramer, treated patients with scurvy with the pulp of citrus and green vegetables. The British navy, about 100 years later, adopted citrus fruit in the ration of sailors after so many had succumbed to the dreadful disease earlier. It was not until 1928 that a substance was isolated from citrus fruit and green pepper which possessed this antiscorbutic activity. Albert Szent-Gyorgyi is generally credited with the dicovery of vitamin C (Szent-Gyorgyi, 1928).

Many vegetables and fruits, other than citrus, contain ascorbic acid. However, citrus fruits and citrus products supply a major portion of the vitamin C requirement for a large percentage of the population of the developed countries. Citrus fruits and tomatoes provided only 18% of the total vitamin C intake in the diet of the American people in the period between 1910 and 1920. By 1955 and 1958, those two fruits supplied 41% of the vitamin (Friend and Clark, 1959), and today it is reported that citrus products alone provide nearly 60% of the U.S. recommended daily allowance (RDA) of vitamin C in the American diet (Araujo, 1977). The RDA of vitamin C as recommended by the Food

Table 3 The Recommended Dietary Allowance for Vitamin C for People of Different Ages and Under Different Conditions

Ages and condition	RDA of vitamin C (mg)
Infants	
0-1 year	35
Children	
1 to 11 year	45
11 to 14 year	50
Male	
14 year and over	60
Female	
14 year and over	60
Pregnant	+20
Lactating	+40

Source: Adapted from Food and Nutrition Board (1978).

Table 4 Vitamin C Content of Several Citrus Fruit as Compared with Other Fruits and Vegetables

Product	Vitamin C (mg/100 g)
Orange	50
Grapefruit	40
Tangerine	25
Lemon	50
Apple	10
Banana	10
Peach	4
Pineapple	25
Guava	300
Tomato	25
Broccoli, turnip greens	300
Green pepper	120
Cabbage	60
Potato	30

and Nutrition Board, National Academy of Science for people of various ages is shown in Table 3. The RDA has replaced the older terminology, minimum daily requirement. The MDR is that amount of a nutrient that, if taken daily, could prevent the development of deficiency symptoms, whereas the RDA is the amount that would maintain an individual in good health.

Citrus does not have the highest vitamin C per unit weight, but it probably is the most pleasant tasting and appealing food source for it. A comparison of the vitamin C content of several types of citrus fruit together with other fruits and vegetables is shown in Table 4. A daily serving of any of the citrus products adequately supplies the U.S. RDA of vitamin C.

IV. HORTICULTURAL ASPECTS OF CITRUS

A. Temperature Requirement

The limiting factor for citrus growing is the climate because it is mainly a subtropical crop and because the fruit, as well as the trees, may be damaged by cold. Temperatures lower than -3°C for 4 or 5 hr will cause ice crystal formation in the fruit with subsequent internal drying and loss of quality. Temperatures around -8°C for a period of 6 to 8 hr can cause tree damage. The degree of damage to fruit depends on fruit maturity and variety. The unripened fruit can withstand lower temperatures than fully matured ones. The freezing points of fruit of different varieties vary only within 1°C (Hume, 1957). The tree toler- ance to cold on the other hand may vary greatly. Trifoliata orange has been reported to grown where temperatures may reach as low as -10°C. In cultivated citrus, in order of cold hardiness is as follows: *Trifoliata,* Satsuma, kumquat, sour orange, tangerine, sweet orange, grapefruit, lemon, lime, and pomelo (Hume, 1957).

In world citrus-producing regions, extremely low temperatures in winter may vary from -10 °C to above 0°C. Oranges growing in trop- ical regions where low temperatures seldom fall below 10°C usually do not have the characteristic orange color and remain green. The juice of these oranges may be low in acid and have a bland taste with low soluble-solids content. The arid producing regions, such as California and Arizona in the United States, the Mediterranean, South Africa, and central China, the low moisture during the fruit-ripening period and the ideal combinations of day and night temperatures produce oranges with high color, high acid, and thick rind.

B. Soil and Topographical Requirement

Citrus trees can be grown on any soil, although well-drained and relatively flat lands are most desirable. Throughout the world, citrus

trees have been planted on hills, valleys, flat lands, deserts, and low-
lands. In each case, special operations must be used to suit the
conditions. In areas where spring frosts may occur, good air drainage
would be beneficial to avoid flower damage. Irrigation, drainage, ter-
racing, cold protection, such as planting near a large body of water,
and wind break are some of these operations.

C. Production of Citrus

1. Propagation of Citrus Trees

Methods of Propagation. Citrus are polyembryonic, unlike many
deciduous fruit such as apples and pears. Citrus can be successfully
propagated from seeds. Indeed, many early plantings originated from
seeds. As late as the latter part of the nineteenth century, most
plantings were started from seeds. Seedling trees may be quite dependable to produce fruit of good quality; however, they are not
uniform, and the yield of trees is not consistent. Selections of variations can be made to discover new varieties.

Citrus species are also easily cross-fertilized, yielding new selections. The most evident results are some of the new cultivars that have
become available commercially. New cultivars can also be obtained by
seed radiation. A new red variety of grapefruit, the Star Ruby, was
originated in this manner (Hensz, 1971). Tangerine (*C. reticulata*),
when crossed with either orange or grapefruit, has produced several
new commercial cultivars with excellent quality and desirable special
characteristics.

Other means of propagation are by budding, grafting, layering, or
cutting. Of these propagation methods, budding is the most popular.
Grafting is generally the choice of top-working an existing orchard to
a new cultivar. However, as a method of commercial tree production,
it is slow and uneconomical. The rootstock can only be used once;
unlike budding, the rootstock cannot be used again if the propagated
plant was unsuccessful. A variation of the grafting is inarching. In
this practice, where the tree is girdled by disease or injury, several
seeds are planted around the tree to be grafted, and the stem of the
rootstock is grafted to the tree above the injury. For top work, cleft
grafting on large trunks is practiced. Layering is not practiced
commercially.

Cuttings can be successfully used on lemons and trifoliata oranges.
Sweet oranges and grapefruit stems are difficult to root. Cuttings
should be made from mature 1- or 2-year-old wood, and each cutting
of about 5 in. long should have four or five well-developed buds. The
cuttings are placed in sterilized soil in flats. As soon as they form
roots, they may be transplanted. These plants can be used as stocks
or be transplanted and allowed to develop into maturing trees.

Budding is by far the most popular method of propagating citrus. The bud from a desired cultivar is inserted under the bark of a rootstock of another cultivar. The rootstock is usually chosen for the adaption of soil and climate requirements as well as for compatibility to the scion cultivar and to pest resistance.

Selecting Rootstock. Some of the more popular rootstocks are rough lemon *(C. limon)*, sour orange *(C. aurantium)*, sweet orange *(C. sinensis)*, grapefruit *(C. paradisi)*, trifoliate orange *(P. trifoliata)*, and Cleopatra mandarin *(C. reticulata)*. As can be seen, most of the popular genera have some cultivars more suitable for rootstocks. No rootstock can adapt to all environments. It is important to know the characteristics of each rootstock for the best result in specific conditions. The compatibility of stock and scion are important factors to be considered in selection of rootstock resistance to disease. Especially in terms of virus diseases, new cultivars of rootstocks are being tested. Several of these are the Rangpur lemon, Troyer citrange, and Milam. Dwarfing rootstock is being tested for commercial plantings. With ease of caretaking and harvesting, dwarf trees should prove to be feasible for large-scale development.

Generally, Cleopatra mandarin probably is a most adaptable stock for nearly all climate and soil conditions, and it is most suitable for Dancy tangerine or Temple oranges. Since its introduction in 1917, it is increasing in use. Some of the disadvantages are slow-to-reach maximum crop production, and the fruit tend to be smaller as compared with those grown on other rootstock.

Trifoliata is the hardiest rootstock. There has been no certainty as to whether its hardiness is imparted to the scion to which it is budded. General observation has been that young trees on this rootstock are more tolerant to cold than those on sour orange and rough lemon, in that order (Hume, 1957). It is grown in colder regions of the citrus belt and not suitable on dry or calcareous soils. It is most adaptable to soil with high moisture and organic matter. Satsuma and Dancy tangerines grow well on this rootstock, but Marsh seedless is not successful. For sweet oranges, the fruit is smaller but the size of the crop is comparable to the other rootstocks. Trifoliate orange is also susceptible to the virus disease exocortis which dwarfs the trees.

Two of the most common and popular rootstocks for orange and grapefruit production in the United States, especially in Florida, are the sour orange *(C. aurantium)* and rough lemon *(C. limon)*. Perhaps next to trifoliate orange, sour orange is the most tolerant to low temperature. Like trifoliate rootstock, sweet oranges grown on this rootstock also tend to tolerate cold better than the others. Sour orange rootstock also tend to tolerate cold better than the others. Sour orange rootstock is also more adaptable to heavy soil and will withstand some wet and waterlogged soil. Fruit from trees on this stock are of high quality with higher soluble-solids content, but the crop yield on young

trees of comparable age is lower than on other rootstocks. This deficiency is generally made up when the tree is fully mature. One of the
disadvantages of this rootstock is its susceptibility to a virus disease,
the tristeza, which is prevalent in South America but has also been
found in other citrus-producing regions of the world. In California,
a disease known as *quick decline* has been reported to be a slightly
different strain from that found in South America. Even with this
disadvantage, sour orange remains to be the rootstock for heavy and
sometimes wet soil.

For light sand, such as that found in the central part of Florida,
rough lemon is most suitable. Trees obtain full size quickly, but the
fruit is lower in quality than those on sour orange rootstock, although
the yield is usually higher. It does not tolerate wet and heavy soil
but will tolerate drought and is resistant to tristeza virus.

Both grapefruit and sweet orange are also commonly used as rootstock. Like the sour orange, they are adaptable to somewhat heavier
soil. Satsuma on sweet orange does not yield well; but other varieties
on this rootstock produce fruit with good yield and quality. If the top
is frozen back by cold, the rootstock sprouts readily and the trees can
be reestablished. Grapefruit rootstock is satisfactory but has no special advantages either in tree growth or in production. Its use as
rootstock has not been promoted greatly by nurseries as other
cultivars. Because of the susceptibility of citrus to various disease
and nematode attacks, the search for resistant rootstocks that may
reduce losses have been attempted. Milam is one of these rootstocks
found to be tolerant to the burrowing nematode infection also known as
the *slow decline* disease found in Florida during the 1950s (Ford and
Feder, 1964). Damage by tristeza or quick decline can be somewhat
abated by the use of Rangpur lemon. Other rootstocks that have been
tried experimentally are Troyer citrange, which is a hybrid (Wallace,
1978).

Selecting the Bud Cultivars. The selection of budwood is also very
important. Only disease-free trees should be the source of buds. The
varieties chosen will depend on the marketing conditions. For the
fresh-fruit market, the mandarin-type orange and hybrids are most
suitable. Their loose skin makes them easy to peel, and the sections
can be easily separated and eaten out of hand. Varieties of tangelos
and tangor are becoming popular. With better disease and quality control and improvements in refrigerated transportation, these fruits
should become more available in the market place. Temple orange,
which is either a tangor or a hybrid of orange and some mandarin, is
a new variety. It is generally classified as a mandarin-type orange,
and has a fine flavor different from oranges and a distinct aroma. Its
oil is in high demand. Murcott has excellent flesh color.

Tangelos should prove to be another selection for the fresh-fruit
market. They are selections from hybrids of tangerine and grapefruit

or pomelo. Seminole, Orlando, and Mineola are the main cultivars of this particular hybrid. They have high flavor and aroma.

Besides the Dancy, several new cultivars of mandarin hybrids hold good prospects, both because of their early season maturity and their seedlessness characteristic. Robinson, Page, and Nova are examples. One of the earlier-maturing tangerines is the Satsuma. It is more cold-resistant than other tangerines, but the texture is coarser and the flavor is more bland.

Grapefruit is also grown extensively in regions where the temperature is slightly higher than for orange and where water is sufficient. It is grown mainly as fresh fruit. With increasing production, much of it is diverted to the processing channel. The colored grapefruit, such as Ruby and Pink Marsh, are very popular as fresh fruit. Its processed products are of low quality because the pink color, which is not stable, turns to a muddy color. The flesh color also tends to decrease with maturity. A new cultivar, the Star Ruby, was developed through mutation by seed irradiation (Hensz, 1971). Its color has been found to be more stable with maturity (Ting et al., 1980).

Two of the largest orange-producing areas, Florida and Brazil, produce most of the oranges for processing. In Florida, nearly 92% of the 9 million tons which comprised the 1979 and 1980 crop was processed; in Brazil, nearly 5 million tons were processed. But the consumption of oranges as fresh fruit still maintains its share of the market. Among the orange cultivars, the navel oranges, especially the cultivar Washington, enjoy its superior position. It ships well, and with the development of new storage and disease control procedures, it suffers less loss. Valencia and the early maturing cultivars, such as Hamlin and Parson Brown, are also popular, especially as processing fruit.

Citrus grown in semiarid areas with cooler nights and low moisture have much better color and thicker rind with less juice content. The soluble solids, as well as the titratable acids, tend to be higher. With a thicker rind, they are more suited for the fresh-fruit trade. In areas where rainfall is high, such as Texas and Florida in the United States and São Paulo in Brazil, the rind is smoother and thinner and the juice content higher. These fruits are more suitable for juice production. Cooper et al. (1963), studied the characteristics of Valencia oranges produced in Arizona, California, Texas, and Florida. In addition to the lower carotenoid content in fruit produced in the more humid regions, the delay in chlorophyll disappearance also detracts from fruit quality, from a fresh trade point of view. Miller et al. (1940) found that high humidity and temperature during the winter season delay the breakdown of chlorophyll and formation of carotenoids. The carotenoid content of juice of fruit produced in more arid areas is also higher than in the more humid regions.

Planting the Seedbed. After deciding the variety of rootstock to be used, a seedbed with rich soil should be prepared. The seeds are

sowed in rows 45 to 60 cm wide and covered with 2.5 to 5.0 cm soil.
The seeds will generally germinate in 3 to 4 weeks when temperatures
of about 32°C and sufficient moisture are available. The seedlings are
then transferred to a nursery row in 12 to 18 months when they are
about 0.5 to 0.75 cm in diameter. Only the best plants are used. The
nursery row should be 1 to 1.25 m wide and the trees about 30 to 35
cm apart. A hectare can hold as many as 30,000 trees. From 1 to 2
years after transplanting the trees, now about 1.25 to 1.5 cm in diameter, they are ready for budding. This means that from the seed, the
rootstock is about 3 years old. Only the best rootstock should be
budded. A liter contains about 2500 orange seeds. Depending on the
germination rate, one and one-half times the seeds should be planted
as the number of seedlings to the nursery row. The taproots are cut
and the tops are also trimmed off during transplanting.

Budding. Budding is done in the nursery row. After the bud is
attached to the stock, it is wrapped with plastic strips to prevent
drying out. After the bud begins to "take," the remainder of the
leaves from the rootstock can be trimmed off. An experienced worker
can bud several trees an hour. They are ready to plant after 1 year.

2. Preparation and Planting

The layout of an orchard is important because, unlike annual crops,
once it is planted the arrangement cannot be changed without economic
and time loss. The orchard plan must be such as to facilitate orchard
operations. All other trees and plants must be completely removed
first. The rows must be spaced wide enough for machinery and allowances anticipated for future requirements.

Grapefruit should not be interplanted with oranges or tangerines
where physiological sprays of grapefruit to reduce acidity are practiced (University of Florida, 1980). Interplantings are generally not
recommended because trees of different species have different growing
characteristics and requirements. Citrus trees will start to bear a few
fruits after 4 or 5 years and can become commercially productive within 10 to 12 years. Citrus trees have been known to produce for over
100 years.

D. Harvesting and Postharvest Handling

1. Harvesting Methods

Citrus fruit in all producing countries is still harvested by hand,
although research in mechanical harvesting has made an inroad during
the last 20 years (Coppock, 1978). In harvesting by hand, the fruit
is carefully clipped with various types of clippers (Hume, 1957). Alternately, the fruit can be removed by severing the abscission layer between the stem and the fruit by grasping the fruit in the hand and

applying a simultaneous twist and pull. The force required to sever the fruit at that layer is called the fruit removal force (FRF). As much as 9 kg may be needed to break the fruit away in a normal mature fruit (Cooper and Chapot, 1977). With such force it is not uncommon to break the peel from the fruit (plugging) if the picking is not skillfully done. Usually one can become quite proficient after a short training. Presently, harvesting with clipping is only practiced with mandarin fruit for the fresh market.

Mechanical harvesting by tree or limb shakers or by other forces is not feasible until the FRF is lowered in the abscission layer. Various abscission chemical sprays have been used to reduce this force. Among the most prominent ones is a cyclohexamide. A solution of 10 to 20 ppm sprayed on the tree can render the fruit easily separated from the stem (Wilson et al., 1977) within 3 to 6 days. Caution should be taken to avoid too strong a spray as to cause the leaf, and in the case of Valencia, the young fruit of the succeeding season, to drop. When the fruit is chemically loosened, it may be detached from the tree by a tree shaker or other means, such as an air blower or water hose. Use of chemicals to loosen fruit also facilitates manual picking, and in the case of madarin fruit to avoid plugging. Mechanical harvesting of citrus fruit is still in the developmental stage. In labor-sufficient citrus-growing regions, it probably will not be practical for a long time. However, the use of chemicals for loosening fruit definitely has its place in the harvesting of soft-peel fruit. Abscission chemicals also hasten the aging of the peel (Moshanos et al., 1977; Cooper and Henery, 1973) and reduce the resistance of the peel to decay.

The choice of harvesting methods and handling of citrus depends upon the channel to which the fruit is to be directed. Extreme care of picking is important if the fruit is intended for the fresh-fruit market. A fruit with a piece of peel pulled off (plugged) is not suitable for marketing as fresh fruit. Stem punctures, crushing, splitting are some of the other fruit injuries that must be minimized, regardless how the fruit is to be used.

2. Maturity and Quality Standards

In order to have uniform standards of quality, only fruit that has reached palatability should be harvested. Unlike much deciduous fruit, citrus fruit does not continue to ripen once it is severed from the tree (Harding et al., 1940). In order to prevent immature fruit from reaching the market, strict quality standards should be promulgated by authority to safeguard against unpalatable fruit going to the consumers. Only mature fruit should be harvested. The best index of maturity is the internal quality measurement of the soluble-solids content, the juice content, the titratable acidity, and the soluble-solids-to-acid ratio (Wardowski et al., 1979).

Soluble Solids and Soluble-Solids-to-Acid Ratio. Whereas the
soluble-solids-to-acid ratio (S:A ratio) only describes the taste of a
fruit, it is the best index of maturity available that is easy to determine and approximates the degree of fruit ripeness. In most countries
where strict quality requirements are enforced, the S:A ratio is one of
the criteria widely used. That the ratio alone does not describe the
juice quality is evident because the total amount of soluble solids and
acids is not indicated by it. Juice with different amounts of acids and
solids may have the same ratios. Thus, the soluble solids are also a
major criteria in defining the taste.

Soluble solids are composed of all constituents of a fruit that are
dissolved in the water portion of the juice. It can be measured by a
specific gravity hydrometer or a Brix hydrometer, and the results are
expressed as degrees Brix (percent soluble solids by weight). Soluble-
solids content in the juice are also measured by the use of a sugar
refractometer. About 70 to 80% of the soluble solids in oranges, tangerines, and grapefruit are sugars. Suitable corrections must be applied to compensate for the nonsugar-soluble solids that have a slightly
different refractive index from that of sugar (Stevens and Baier,
1939).

Acidity and pH. The citrus juices attribute their sourness to the
organic acids they contain. The main acid of the juice is citric acid
(Sinclair, 1961). Total acidity is determined by titration with standard
alkali and expressed as grams of citric acid per 100 g of juice. The
pH or hydrogen ion concentration is a measure of the active acidity.
Citrus juices with equal titratable acidity became more sour if the pH
is lowered (higher hydrogen ion concentration). Similarly, maintaining the same pH, juice with higher total acidity is more sour. As the
fruit ripens, the total acidity decreases and pH increases. A decrease
in total acidity exerts more influence on the decrease of sourness than
increase in pH, as can be measured routinely in the laboratory. When
citrus fruit matures, there is an increase in total soluble solids (° Brix)
and a corresponding decrease in titratable acidity resulting in a significant increase in the B:A ratio.

Other Quality Factors. The quality of fruit improves with fruit
maturity. While taste is a major quality factor, other attributes, such
as aroma, flesh texture, rind and juice color, and juice viscosity, all
contribute to the total quality of the fruit. In addition to the aroma of
the orange oil, the flavor of the fruit and juice can be adversely affected by immature and overmature flavors. When a fruit reachs a
certain Brix:acid ratio, the immature flavor generally disappears.
This flavor has been attributed to certain constitutents in the essential
oil. Overmature flavor generally develops when the fruit has passed
senescence. Thus, a maturity standard should consist of a minimum
and a maximum soluble-solids content as well as a minimum total acidity.

The color of the rind, which is greatly influenced by climatic factors, is not a criteria of the internal juice quality, and needs to be considered only if the fruit is to be used for fresh-fruit trade.

Harding and his co-workers (1940,1945,1953) have shown that the cultivars of the scion and rootstock all have significant effect on the soluble-solids and B:A ratio of the fruit. Certain physiological sprays also have an effect in decreasing the acid content (University of Florida, 1980). Maturity indexs designed to regulate harvesting of fruit of local cultivars should consider these variations as affected by local conditions. Only fruit meeting the minimum legal maturity standard should be permitted to be marketed in order to prevent the selling of immature fruit of undesirable quality.

Juice Volume. Volume of juice has also been used as a maturity index, especially in grapefruit. The Florida citrus code (Florida Department of Citrus, 1974) specifies milliliters of juice required for various grapefruit sizes. Fruit with a thick rind will have less juice than those with a thin rind of equal size.

3. Packinghouse Operations (Fig. 1)

Degreening. In a climate with high temperature and humidty during the fruit-ripening season, the fruit does not lose its green color until some cold weather has occurred. Young and Erickson (1961) showed

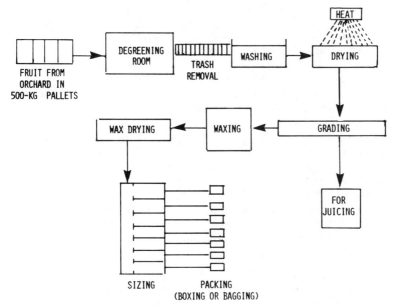

Figure 1 Schematic description of a fresh citrus fruit packinghouse operation.

that temperatures below 10°C are generally needed to cause the decomposition of chlorphyll. There are certain regions in the tropics where citrus are grown, and the fruit never lose their green color.

In semitropical regions, such as Florida, the 10°C or lower temperature does not generally occur until December. Some early cultivars would reach maturity before that. When there is not sufficient cold weather, the fruit remain green. For a late-season cultivar, such as Valencia, the humid and hot climate in the spring tends to cause the fruit, which has lost its chlorophyll, to regreen (Harding et al., 1940). The fruit are usually treated with ethylene to hasten the disappearance of green color. The process is called degreening. Citrus fruit produces ethylene slowly (Wheaton and Stewart, 1973) in storage, and green citrus fruit can be induced to lose its green color. But the process takes a long time and is not practical. Only fruit directed for the fresh-fruit market need go through the degreening process since consumers have a resistance to purchase poorly colored oranges. The degreening process can be eliminated if the fruit is well-colored naturally. On degreened fruit, color may be added.

Washing, Waxing, and Decay Control. Whether degreened or not, the fruit must be washed. The fruit washer consist of a row of rollers which convey the fruit to a water tank. The leaves and small twigs are separated from fruit during this operation. The water completely wets each fruit and loosens all adhered dirt. Sometimes the wetting is done by a water spray. A film of detergent is applied to the fruit, and the fruit are rotated on a row of brushes. The rotating rollers advance the fruit and keep the rows of fruit rolling. The detergent is washed off with a fresh water spray, and the fruit are dried of excess water by a blast of air. A layer of wax is applied. The purpose of the wax is to reduce water loss from the fruit and to maintain a fresh appearance. The fruit are dried under a blast of warm air, and a row of brushes polish the fruit to a shine. Newhall and Grierson (1955) developed a water wax which is self-shining. The wax is generally applied as a paraffin or carnauba wax emulsion. Where fruit decay is severe, fungicides are incorporated with the wax (McCornack and Wardowski, 1972). The fruit are then run through a sizer which divides the fruit to predesignated sizes accord to their diameters. In the United States, the size designation is determined by the number of fruit of each size that can be packed into a standard box (Florida Department of Cirtus, 1974). Undersized and oversized oranges are generally not used in the fresh-fruit trade, and they are sent to the cannery for processing.

Packing. The packing of fruit in standard boxes follows certain patterns so that the maximum number of fruit of each size is placed in the box. Careful packing also reduces injuries during shipment to the market. If the fruits are graded, the grading is done prior to packing the fruit in the box. Some of the factors used in grading are the external appearance, injuries of the peel, insect and disease lesions, and off-color. The grades may be designated by government regulations which allow certain tolerances to each grade (Grierson and Ting, 1978). The grade is stamped on the box and the fruit is ready for market.

V. CITRUS FRUITS AND THEIR BIOCHEMICAL COMPOSITION

A. Description of Fruit

Botanically, citrus fruits or the hesperides are calssified as modified berry. The fruit is covered by a layer of peel which is composed of the outer colored layer or the flavedo and the inner layer of white spongy parenchymatous tissue known as the albedo. The flavedo contains the oil sacs in which the essential oils develop. It also contains a colored epidermal layer which contains the chromatophores (Miller et al., 1940).

The inner pulp portion of the fruit contains the segments, usually 10 to 13 in nimber. Within the segments are the juice vesicles attached to the dorsal vein on the segment and the seeds, which are connected to the center portion of the fruit. Figure 2 shows a schematic diagram of a cross section of a citrus fruit showing the juice vesicles. During fruit development, the various components of fruit change in their percentage of the total fruit as shown in Table 5 for Marsh seedless grapefruit and Hamlin oranges. Both cultivars are considered as seedless, although in some fruit up to five seeds may be found. The weight of the seeds which was not significant was included in the weight of the juice vesicle.

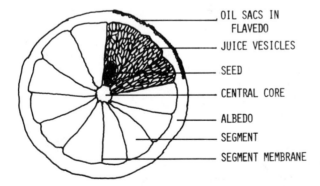

OIL SACS IN FLAVEDO
JUICE VESICLES
SEED
CENTRAL CORE
ALBEDO
SEGMENT
SEGMENT MEMBRANE

Figure 2 Cross section of a citrus fruit showing the various components.

Table 5 Changes in Percent Distribution of Component Parts of
Hamlin Orange and Marsh Grapefruit

Fruit	Maturity	Fruit components			
		Flavedo	Albedo	Membrane	Juice vesicles
Hamlin orange	Immature (August)	11.9	33.6	5.2	49.4
	Mature (December)	12.9	24.4	3.8	59.0
Marsh grapefruit	Immature (August)	12.6	38.1	4.9	44.4
	Mature (December)	14.5	29.6	3.5	52.4

Source: Ting and Vine (1966).

B. Biochemical Composition

Myriads of chemical constituents can be found in a citrus fruit, but
those affecting the quality and nutritional values of the citrus fruit are
of more interest to food technologists. Citrus fruits are one of the
best food sources for vitamin C, but other nutrients and chemical constituents contribute to the demands and acceptance of citrus fruit in
the human diet. A USDA publication (1956) listed some 11 classifications of chemical constituents and numbered about 150 that can be
found in orange juice. Many more have been isolated and identified,
but some of these newly identified compounds are not known to contribute to quality (Horowitz, 1977; Chandler and Kefford, 1970; Ting
and Attaway, 1971; Tatum et al., 1978). Some compounds are characteristic for a particular group of citrus fruit. For instance, hesperidin
is the major flavonoid of sweet oranges *(C. sinensis)* and mandarin
(C. reticulata), but naringin is the major flavonoid of grapefruit
(C. paradisi) and pomelo *(C. grandis)*. Other classes of compounds
may be common to all citrus fruits.

1. Carbohydrates

The major carbohydrates in citrus fruit are the soluble sugars. The
three major sugars in orange juice are identified to be glucose, fructose, and sucrose (McCready et al., 1950). The same three sugars
were also the major soluble carbohydrate found in the peel (Ting and
Deszyck, 1961). The proportion of these three sugars in juices of

different cultivars varies (Ting, 1980). Generally, the more acid juice has less nonreducing sugars than the less acid juices.

Complex carbohydrates of citrus include cellulose, hemicellulose, and pectin. These are important as dietary fibers. The peel of citrus is a rich source of pectin. Pectin has been prepared from peels of oranges, grapefruit, lemon, and lime, with jellying power (IFT Commitee, 1959) increasing in that order (Rouse, 1967). The carbohydrate monomers of hemicellulose and cellulose fractions of various components were reported by Ting (1970) and Ting and Deszyck (1961).

2. Organic Acids

Although not a carbohydrate, organic acids are measured in the soluble-solids determination using a Brix hydrometer. In measuring the soluble solids by refractive index a corrective of nearly 0.2° Brix must be added for each 1% acid (Stevens and Baier, 1939).

The main organic acid of all citrus juice is citric, with malic acid occurring in various portions with juices of different fruits and at different stages of maturity (Sinclair, 1961; Ting and Vines, 1966). Other organic acids found in much smaller amounts are tartaric, benzoic, succinic, malonic, quinic, isocitric, and aconitic (Vandercook, 1977a). The organic acids in citrus juice are a juice quality factor since they impart a refreshing, tart taste to the product when in combination with sugars. The low pH of the juice is also a plus factor in reducing spoilage of the product by certain microorganisms (Patrick and Hill, 1959).

3. Nitrogenous Compounds

The majority of the nitrogenous compounds of citrus juices is in the form of the free amino acids. Individual amino acids can be separated and measured by amino acid analyzers. Brenoe (1971) quantitatively analyzed 18 amino acids of oranges picked in January through March of 2 years from various regions in Greece. True protein in oranges and grapefruit juices is relatively low. Clements (1966) found that only 20% of acetone powder made from juice is protein. The true protein determined by Kjeldahl's method of the alcohol-insoluble solids averaged about 0.15% (Attaway et al., 1971). Most of this protein found in the alcohol-insoluble solids is contents of the cell organells, including all the enzymes. Enzymes found in citrus are listed by Vandercook (1977b). Perhaps the most important citrus enzymes that may affect the quality are pectic enzymes which may cause the citrus juice to lose its characteristic opaque appearance, or the "cloud."

Citrus juices also contain a number of nitrogen bases (Stewart and Wheaton, 1964), and synepherine, a decongestant, was reported to occur in pharmaceutically significant quantities in a normal serving of tangerine juice (Stewart et al., 1964).

4. Pigments

The color of both the peel and juice of oranges is due to oil-soluble carotenoids. The carotenoid that has the most intensive orange color in the peel is β-citraurin (Curl, 1965; Stewart and Wheaton, 1973). Most other carotenoids, especially violaxanthins, are responsible for the characteristic yellow color. The red color of pink and red grapefruit is due to lycopene, a straight chain carotenoid, whereas that of blood orange is caused by anthocyanis, the water-soluble pigments. In addition to imparting attractive color to citrus fruit and juice, some carotenoids are also sources of vitamin A. β-Carotene can be converted to retinol in animal metabolism. α- and γ-Carotene and β-cryptoxanthin are also precursors of vitamin A but have only about 50% of the activity of an equal quantity of β-carotene.

5. Lipids

The amound of lipids in citrus is relatively low, but they are important due to their potentials in producing off-flavor through their oxidation (Swift, 1951; Huskins et al., 1952). The production of unsaturated fatty acids due to elevated storage temperature has been suggested to cause commercial oranges to develop off-flavor (Kenny, 1962).

6. Volatile Compounds

The most characteristic properties of citrus are their unique aroma. Differnet citrus cultivars are distinguished by their essential oils which impart the pleasant characteristic to each citrus fruit and its product. The volatile compounds of the essential oils are produced by the ductless oil glands located in the flavedo layer of the peel.

The essential oils of all citrus fruit are complex mixtures of many compounds. At least 112 compounds have been reported from cold-pressed orange oil, 66 from grapefruit oil, 73 from tangerine oil, and 75 from lemon oil. The studies on lime oil have only identified 46 compounds (Shaw, 1977). Table 6 lists the number of constituents in each classification of compounds that have been reported in the literature.

Approximately 90 to 95% of all citrus essential oil is d-limonene, a hydrocarbon terpene. The remaining 5 to 10% are other hydrocarbon terpenes or oxygenated terpenes which contain the constituents that give citrus fruit their characteristic and typical aromas.

Cold-pressed oils can be obtained directly from the fruit peel either before, during, or after the juice extraction process, depending upon the system and the type of equipment used. During juice evaporation in the manufacturing of concentrated citrus juices, oil is also recovered from the condensate, as essence oil, which is different from the cold-pressed oil in character and composition (Shaw, 1977).

The process to recover the volatiles from the condensate produces both essence oil and an aqueous essence. The oil layer separates from

Table 6 Number of Volatile Compounds Reported in Different
Components of Citrus Oils

	Orange	Grapefruit	Tangerine	Lemon	Lime
Acids	5	—	7	4	—
Alcohols	26	20	24	18	11
Aldehydes	25	14	11	16	7
Esters	16	13	4	11	3
Hydrocarbons	32	14	24	22	22
Ketones	6	3	2	3	1
Miscellaneous	2	2	1	1	2
Total	112	66	73	75	46

Source: Shaw (1977).

the aqueous phase which contains the more fruity bouquet of the
juice and can be added to the concentrated citrus juice. After concentration, the product pumped out from the evaporator has very
little aroma. The addition of fresh juice gives the final product the
fresh orange juice flavor. The aqueous essence can also be added
to enhance the aromas that are removed during the evaporation process. However, the addition of essence to orange juice does not
completely restore the flavor. Occasionally the essence produced may
contain undesirable flavor. Usually the characteristic aroma of a
citrus fruit is due to one or two specific compounds. Nookatone is
a primary compound of grapefruit (MacLeod and Buigues, 1964).
Kugler and Kovats (1963) believed that thymol was responsible for
the tangerine flavor. Methyl-methyl anthranilate has also been suggested (Braverman, 1949) as a characteristic tangerine aroma. Nerol
and geraniol have been reported as the flavoring constituents of
cold-pressed lemon and lime oil (Ikeda et al., 1961; Slater and
Watkins, 1964). In distilled lime oil, Slater and Watkins (1964) identified the presence of 1,8-cineole which was shown to be a major component of that oil. Several compounds in orange essence have been
evaluated singly or in combination to determine their importance in
flavor contribution. Dougherty and Ahmed (1973) found that acetal-
dehyde, ethyl butyrate, and methyl butyrate, when added to the
evaporator pumpout (concentrate with little aroma), caused the flavor
of the product to increase in the direction of frozen concentrated
orange juice produced with added fresh juice.
    Cold-pressed citrus oil, essence oil, and the aqueous phase of the
essence are all used in the flavor-enhancing of citrus concentrate today. These volatile materials are also widely used in flavoring the
juice drinks contain various mixtures of natural juices and in citrus-
flavored soft drinks or carbonated drinks containing no natural juice.

7. Enzymes

Vandercook (1977b) cataloged 50 different enzymes that have been reported to occur in citrus. Whereas all these enzymes are important in the metabolizm of the fruit, only a few are of importance in citrus technology. The loss of citrus juice cloud was first studied by Mac-Donnell et al. (1945) and was found to be due to pectinesterase (PE). Atkins and Rouse (1953,1954) studied the time-temperature relationship in the heat-inactivation of this enzyme during citrus processing. Temperatures of 96 to 99°C for 3 sec are generally necessary for complete inactivation of pectinesterase in orange juice with a pH from 3.8 to 4.1. Citrus juices with low pH can have their PE activity completely inhibited at much lower temperatures and shorter times than those with high pH. Grapefruit juice at pH 3.4 would require only 0.8 sec at 96°C, and lemon and lime require only 85 to 88°C for the same time duration since the pH of these juices is around 2.5. Fresh citrus juices have also been observed to form coagulates. This phenomenon has been suggested to be caused by the enzyme rennin and is often observed in juices with lower pH during storage (Braverman, 1949). It can also be inactivated by pasteurization.

VI. NUTRIENT COMPOSITION OF CITRUS

Citrus fruits and their products are the best food source for vitamin C. In most developed and some developing countries they are stapel food items. It has also become known that citrus fruits also contain a myraid of other vitamins and mineral nutrients (Ting et al., 1974). In addition, several constituents in citrus are found to be beneficial to health, for example, the bioflavonoids (Robbins, 1976), synepherine (Stewart et al., 1964), and inositol (Krehl and Cowgill, 1950). The last compound mentioned is known to be a growth factor for some animals. Its importance in human nutrition has not been substantiated.

A. Macronutrients

As a food, citrus products provide a source of energy in the form of soluble sugars; and they also contain complex carbohydrates, namely pectin, hemicellulose, and cellulose, which are essential as dietary fibers. The benefit of dietary fiber to health has not been fully elucidated, but it has been proposed that fiber assists in decreasing the transit time of food material through the gastrointestinal tract (Scala, 1975). Pectin, a main component of the complex carbohydrates of citrus, have been associated with the property of lowering the cholesterol in mammals (McCready, 1977).

The organic acids of citrus fruit are also metabolized and may be considered with the sugars as energy-supplying nutrients. Citrus have very little protein, and the major portion of the approximately 100 mg of nitrogen in 100 ml of orange juice (Ting, 1967) is from free amino acids. The lipid content of citrus is maily in the seeds. The amound of lipid in the juice is negligible, only in the range of 0.06 to 0.09% (Swift and Veldhuis, 1951; Huskin and Swift, 1953). The suspended solids were considered by Curl (1946), Curl and Veldhuis (1947), and Swift (1951) to be the principal contributor to off-flavor in aged orange juice. The fine suspended material (the cloud) in commercially extracted orange juice was found by Scott et al. (1965) to consist of 25% lipids and 75% alcohol-insoluble solids, and half of the latter was found to be protein (Baker and Bruemmer, 1969). Although the juice lipid content is not high, its effect on quality of stored juice is an important consideration. Dried citrus seeds contain between 30 to 45% lipid (Hendrickson and Kesterson, 1963; Braddock and Kesterson, 1973). The oils made from citrus seeds have a mixture of glycerides of various fatty acids, a large percentage of which is unsaturated. The fact makes the citrus seed oil a desirable dietetic substitute for other unsaturated food fats.

B. Vitamins and Minerals

Listed in Table 7 are the vitamins and the approximate amounts that have been reported in different citrus fruit. Besides vitamin C, orange juice can be considered as significant sources for thiamine and folic acid since it can supply 10% or more of the U.S. RDA of these nutrients in a serving (6 fl oz) (Ting et al., 1974).

Table 7 Vitamins in Citrus Juices

	Unit	Oranges	Grapefruit	Tangerines	Lemon	Lime
Vitamin C	mg/100 ml	25-80	25-70	10-50	30-60	20-40
Vitamin A	IU	80-200	1500[a]	1000-3200	0-2	—
Thiamine	µg/100 ml	90-100	40	60	30	—
Riboflavin	µg/100 ml	20-40	—	—	12	—
Niacin	µg/100 ml	300-400	200	—	70	—
Vitamin B_6	µg/100 ml	50-56	8-18	—	50	—
Folic acid	µg/100 ml	26-40	3-24	17-24	6	—
Pantothenic acid	µg/100 ml	130-250	—	—	100-150	—
Biotin	µg/100 ml	0-8	trace	—	0-3	—

[a]In red and pink grapefruit only.
Source: Atkin et al. (1943), Birdsall et al. (1961), Burger et al. (1956), Lime et al. (1954), Rakieten et al. (1951,1952), Stewart (1977), Streiff (1971), Ting et al. (1974), and Ting and Deszyck (1958).

Although some carotenoids are known to be precursors for vitamin A, the major portion of citrus carotenoid is not a vitamin A precursor. As a matter of fact, the carotenes are only a small percentage of total citrus carotenoids. β-Cryptoxanthin, a major carotenoid of tangerine juice and Valencia orange juice was found to be a major contributor of vitamin A in these products (Stewart, 1977). White grapefruit is devoid of vatiman A, but pink and red grapefruit are significant sources (Ting and Deszyck, 1958; Lime et al., 1954) of this vitamin.

Like most food derived from plant sources, citrus contains most of the inorganic elements of the periodic table. McHard et a., (1979), using plasma spectroscopy, reported the presence of 32 mineral elements. Earlier reports by Roberts and Gaddum (1937) and Birdsall et al. (1961) showed the presence of 29 to 32 elements, including the nonmetal elements (i.e., the halogens, sulfurs, etc.). Only 10 to 11 elements have been found to be necessary for the growth of citrus (Hume, 1957). The inorganic nutrients of which the RDA were established by the Food and Nutrition Board, National Academy of Science are calcium, magnesium, phosphorus, iron, zinc, and iodine. The U.S. Food and Drug Administration (1973) listed 2 mg as the U.S. RDA for copper. Although copper is toxic to lower forms of life, it is relatively nontoxic to mammals, including humans (Food and Nutrition Board, 1978). The Food and Agriculture Organization/World Health Organization (FAO/WHO) (1971) has stated that a copper intake of 0.5 mg/kg body weight per day would cause no injurious effect. Other minerals that are considered to be essential in humans, although in trace amounts, are maganese, fluoride, chromium, selenium, and molybdenum. Selenium is highly toxic, but a daily intake of not more than 200 µg is considered to be adequate. Selenium is not one of the elements reported by McHard et al. (1979). The major mineral elements of different citrus are shown in Table 8. The trace metals listed as essential

Table 8   Mineral Content of Citrus Juices

Mineral (mg/100 ml)		Citrus fruit			
		Grapefruit	Mandarin	Lime	Lemon
Total ash	270-590	218-440	300-410	150-350	250-400
K	89-284	78-208	177-178	94-208	104
Na	0.2-2.4	0.3-2.6	1-6	0.5-5.0	1.1
Ca	1.3-20	1.7-12	14.18	3.1-27-9	4.5-10.4
Mg	3-19	5-15	7	1-11.3	—
Fe	0.02-0.5	0.06-1.9	0.20-0.28	0.14-1.0	0.19-0.92
P	7-24.9	7-30	14-15	3.2-16.6	9.3-11.2

Source: Compiled from Nagy (1977).

in human nutrition by the FDA were found in citrus to be all below 2%
U.S. RDA for the respective minerals, except copper (Ting et al.,
1974, Ting, 1980).

Although potassium is an essential element for human nutrition, it
is seldom thought to be deficient in a normal diet because of its wide
distribution in foods. Potassium deficiency usually occurs when one
has a restricted diet or where excess loss occurs. Citrus fruits are
high in potassium (Krehl, 1976) and can supply as much as 10 meq/
177 ml (6 fl oz) of the approximately 50 to 100 meq suggested for a
healthy adult (Food and Nutrition Board, 1978).

C. Factors Affecting Nutrient Content

The most important contribution of citrus fruits to human nutrition is
the high ascorbic acid content in their juices. Yet, the ascorbic acid
in the juice of an orange only represents about 25% of the total ascorbic
acid that a fruit contains. In grapefruit, the juice contains only about
one-sixth of the total ascorbic acid of the fruit. The major portions are
in the peel and the rag (Atkins et al., 1945). The rag is the residue
after juice extraction which contains the membrane and pulp.

Considerable variations in ascorbic acid content are found in different citrus fruits, and it also follows a seasonal change with fruit
maturity. Harding and his co-workers (1940,1943,1945) reported that
(a) the ascorbic acid content in all citrus fruits decreased as fruit
mature; (b) the decrease was more pronounced in late-season oranges
as they matured, when the ambient temperatures were relatively high;
(c) grapefruit also lost more ascorbic acid when the fruit was picked in
late April or May; and (d) the rootstocks greatly affect the ascorbic
acid content of the fruit. Lesser amounts of ascorbic acid were found
in fruit from trees on rough lemon rootstocks than those on sour
oranges.

From a single tree, Sites and Reitz (1951) found that there is a
positive correlation between vitamin C content in fruit and the height
at which the fruit is located and also that the vitamin C content is
higher in fruit on the periphery of the tree than that in the interior
of the tree. Vitamin C content was also found to be lowest on the outer
layer of a fruit and highest toward the central core (Ting, 1968).

Although ascorbic acid is easily oxidized to dehydroascorbic acid
and may proceed to di-ketogulonic acid, it is relatively stable to heat
during processing. Orange juice heated to boiling for 15 min only lost
about 5% of the total l-ascorbic acid (Krehl, 1976). The dehydroascorbic acid has nearly as much antiscorbutic activity as the reduced form,
but the di-ketogulonic acid is devoid of physiological activity (Krehl,
1976).

Freshly extracted orange juice and grapefruit juice can retain between 96 to 99% ascorbic acid for several days, that is, 3 to 7 days at

4.4°C (Moore et al., 1945). Atmospheric oxygen is by far the most important factor responsible for loss of ascorbic acid in juice. Bissett and Berry (1975) found that containers in which the citrus juices are packed have significant effect on the rate of loss of ascorbic acid. Squires and Hanna (1979) found that pasteurized orange juice may lose 1 to 2% vitamin C per day in cardboard cartons. In canned juices, the ascorbic acid content decreased at first and remained relatively constant thereafter. Usually 70 to 85% of the ascorbic acid is retained after the head space oxygen is exhausted (Moschette et al., 1947). Nagy and Smoot (1980) found that at a higher storage temperature the ascorbic acid content loss continued with the storage duration. A comparison of the vitamin C content of freshly extracted orange juice and reconstituted frozen concentrated orange juice (FCOJ) showed no marked differences both in the amount and rate of loss during storage in a household refrigerator for up to 1 week (Rakieten et al., 1951). Fresh orange fruit had no significant loss of its vitamin C during a marketing period of up to 3 weeks (Harding, 1954).

The vitamin B_1 (thiamine) content increased with fruit maturity in oranges. When compared at similar degree of maturity, the early-season fruit, Hamlin, has the lowest vitamin B_1 content and Valencia, the late-season orange, the highest (Hsu, 1974). Thiamine is also stable in canned orange juice. After 18 months at 27°C, Moschette et al. (1947) reported more than 80% retention.

The mineral content of the citrus juice remains unchanged if the juice is stored in glass or other nonmetal containers. Rouseff and Ting (1980) reported that grapefruit juice in soldered cans may increase in their lead content from 0.06 to 0.2 ppm, due to the lead in the solder. Nagy et al. (1981) found that orange juice in cans also dissolves some tin and iron from the containers.

VII. CITRUS PROCESSING

In most citrus-producing nations in the world, citrus fruit is still mainly consumed as fresh fruit. In the United States and Brazil, frozen concentrated orange juice (FCOJ) utilized most of the crop production. In the United States more than 92% of the more than 9 million tonnes of oranges and 62% of the approximately 3 million tonnes of grapefruit in the 1978 and 1979 season in Florida were used in processing (Florida Department of Agriculture, 1979). Orange concentrate accounted for over 84% of the 1978 and 1979 Florida orange crop, with pasteurized juice in cans, cartons, or glass bottles nearly accounting for all the remainder with a small percentage for citrus sections. Fresh-fruit sales continue to be about 7 to 8% of the Florida orange crop and one-third of the Florida grapefruit. In other citrus-producing areas in the United States, for example, California and Texas, fresh fruit is still their main outlet.

The utilization of citrus juices in cans, especially for orange juice, has dramatically declined in recent years, both because of the cost of the containers and the comparatively inferior quality of the canned product as compared with the FCOJ. Canned grapefruit juice sales, although also showing a decline, still hold their position in the market. The introduction of pasteurized juice and 100% citrus juice from concentrate in cartons or plastic containers in recent years has increased citrus juice consumption in noncitrus-producing nations, especially in Europe. Aseptic processing in inexpensive containers with reduction in low temperature storage requirements could further increase citrus juice demands.

A. Canned Citrus Juices

Despite their low quality and high cost of production and transportation, canned citrus juices are still in good demand. Under many curcumstances where strong and durable containers are required or where refrigeration is not available, hermetically sealed metal cans are the containers of choice.

1. Harvesting and Testing Maturity Index

The production of citrus juice for canning begins with the harvesting of mature fruit. The soluble-solids content and the Brix-to-acid ratio are important factors to be considered. Methods of testing these internal qualities are the same as described previously. Only fruit that meet a preestablished maturity index should be used if high-quality juice is to be produced.

2. Preparing Fruit for Juice Extraction

When fruit are delivered to the canning plant, they are transported across a conveyer belt made of a row of rollers in order that leaves, trash, twigs, and other extraneous matter can drop through the spaces between the rollers. Damaged and spoiled fruit are manually removed. The fruit are then conveyed to a washer in which they are cleaned with a food-grade detergent and rotating brushes, as with the packing-house process. After rinsing, excess water is removed and fruit are mechanically sized for the juice extractors which are designed for fruit of various sizes.

3. Juice Extraction and Finishing

The juice is generally removed from the fruit with commerical automated juice extractors. Several of these mechanical juice extractors are on the market. The two major manufactures of juice extractors for citrus fruit in the United States are the FMC Corporation and the Automatic Machinery Corporation (AMC). The FMC Inline extractor (Fig. 3) extracts the juice from a whole fruit whereas the AMC extractor (Fig. 4) cuts the fruit into two halves before removing the juice.

Figure 3 FMC inline citrus juice extractor. (Courtesy of the FMC Corporation, Lakeland, Fla.)

Unless the operation is very small, that is, less than 400 or 500 liter/day production, an automatic extractor is definitely needed. A simple automated machine can extract 40 to 75 fruit per minute or approximately 200 to 250 liters of juice per hour. More recently developed extractors are capable of producing 10 times that amount. Of course, several extractors are needed for fruit of different sizes to give the most efficient juice recovery from the fruit.

The extracted juice contains different amounts of pulp. A machine used to remove the pulp is the finisher. The finisher is a cylindrical screen through which the product is pushed by a rotary screw auger inside the screen (Fig. 5). Another type of finisher utilizes the principle of the paddling action. The pulp from the finisher is composed of the juice vesicle residue, the segment membrane, the central core, seeds, and some peel. The pressure used in the finishing can alter the amount of juice retained by the pulp and the amount of incorporation of soluble pulp constituents in the juice, thus affecting its flavor. This is especially important in the preparation of grapefruit juice. The two known bitter principles in grapefruit, naringin, and limonin, occur mostly in the peel and the rag (Kesterson and Hendrickson, 1957; Maier and Dryer, 1968). Excessive finishing pressure will increase these two constituents in the juice, thus rendering the juice, sometimes, a very bitter taste.

Figure 4 A Brown Model 400 rotary citrus juice extractor. (Courtesy of The Automatic Machinery Corporation, Winter Haven, Fla.)

Figure 5 A screwtype juice finisher. (Courtesy of The Automatic Machinery Corporation, Winter Haven, Fla.)

4. Deoiling and Deaeration

During the extraction, much of the peel oil may be incorporated into the product. Although a certain amount of citrus oil in the juice is necessary to give the product its characteristic aroma, an excessive amount of oil is objectionable. For most commercial juices, the oil content is limited to 0.035% by volume (USDA, 1976a). A limit of 0.015 to 0.025% oil for these juices is optimum. The oil content of the juice can be estimated by a standard chemical method (AOAC, 1980).

The deoiler is a tank under vacuum. The juice is flashed into the tank at about 52°C and about 5% of the juice is evaporated. The oil accumulates as the upper layer of the condensate and is removed while the aqueous layer is returned to the juice. The deoiling operation also removes the air that has been incorporated in the juice during extraction. The removal of air eliminates foaming of the juice during filling. It has been assumed that dissolved oxygen has an adverse effect on ascorbic acid retention (Pulley and Von Loesecke, 1939). Passy and Manneheim (1979) failed to detect the benefit of deaeration in the ascorbic acid retention in concentrated grapefruit juice.

5. Heat Stabilization and Pasteurization

For aseptic canning, it is essential that microbial organisms be totally destroyed. Kew et al. (1957) found a processing temperature of 71°C could prevent the growth of yeast and other microorganisms in orange juice. In citrus juices with a lower pH, such as grapefruit, lemon, and lime, a lower temperature of around 60 to 65°C could accomplish this purpose. Juice thus preserved, although it does not spoil due to microbial action, would not maintain its cloud. This clarification phenomenon was found to be due to the presence of pectinesterase (MacDonnell et al., 1945). Temperatures as high as 88 to 99°C may be needed to prevent this cloud loss in orange juice and grapefruit juice. Juice with a low pH may be stabilized at lower processing temperatures or with shorter heating time at higher temperture than juices with high pHs. Recommended temperatures and retention time to stabilize different citrus juices are shown in Table 9.

Because flavor of citrus juices is imparied by heat, the judicial use of temperature and retention time in stabilization of juice cloud is very important. Generally, the least time with corresponding higher temperature is preferred. The heat stabilization and pasteurization is effected

Table 9 Temperature, pH, and Retention Time Relationship for the Inactivation of Pectinesterase in Citrus Juices

Citrus juice	pH	Temperature	Time (sec)
Valencia orange	3.5	93.5	3
	4.1	99	0.8
Pineapple orange	3.5	93.5	3
	4.1	99	0.8
Dancy tangerine	3.8	96	3
	3.8	99	0.8
Seedy grapefruit	3.3	93.5	3
	3.8	96	0.8
Marsh seedless	3.4	96	0.8
grapefruit	3.8	96	0.8
Lemon	2.4	80	3
	2.4	85	0.8
Lime	2.5	85	3
	2.5	88	0.8

Source: Atkins and Rouse (1953,1954).

either in a plate-type or tubular pasteurizer. The juice is pumped through the pasteurizer at the desired temperature. The rate of pumping is adjusted to conform to the total time the juice is to be in contact with the heat exchanger.

6. Filling

The heated juice is pumped into a filler which has a holding bowl. The hot juice is then filled into the empty cans or glass jars. The filler is adjusted so that each container holds the proper amount of the juice. The container is sealed either manually or by an automatic sealing machine. For cans, they are inverted so that the hot juice will sterilize the can lid. For glass containers, the lid should be pasteurized before capping. Manual inversion of glass containers can also be an effective means of sterilizing the lids.

7. Cooling

The filled containers should be cooled as rapidly as possible. Glass bottles will break if cold water is directed to them. The cooling of glass bottles must be done in several stages with the bottle and cooling water temperature differing not more than 10 to 16°C at each stage. The cans can be cooled directly with the water spray without regard to the temperature. After cooling, the containers are allowed to dry by their residual heat.

8. Storage

Glass bottles are stored in cardboard boxes after proper labeling. The boxes are stacked in the storage room. The cans are stored either as they are in a bin or in cases after the labels are attached. Storage temperatures for canned juice can vary from refrigerated to ambient, but a lower storage temperature can delay the development of off-flavors. Generally, temperatures no higher than 21°C are suitable. When a low storage temperature is used, the product should be allowed to come to room temperature slowly in order to avoid condensation on the container which can spoil the labels. In the case of unlabeled tin cans, the condensate will cause rust on the can exterior.

B. Chilled and Pasteurized Juices

In most developed countries where refrigerators are generally available, chilled orange and grapefruit juices are becoming increasingly popular because of their freshlike flavor. The preparation of chilled and pasteurized juice is similar to that for canned juice as for the extraction and finishing. The nonpasteurized juice can be filled into paper or plastic cartons directly from the finisher and sold at the local markets. The shelf life of these products is extremely short, probably less than

48 to 72 hr. The pectic enzyme will cause a rapid cloud loss, probably within 24 hr in a refrigerator. The loss of fresh flavor is also rapid. The degree of microbial spoilage will depend on the temperature of the product and the original microorganism count. Even at temperatures near the freezing point of the juice, flavor loss and cloud loss make this practice commercially unfeasible.

Proper sterilization of the juice is necessary to prolong the shelf life of chilled juice. In this respect, the juice is passed through a plate or tubular pasteurizer for a short time for stabilization and the destruction of microorganisms, as with the canned juice. The temperature required for stabilization far exceeds that necessary to destroy the microorganisms. Unlike the process for canning, the juice is pumped through a cooling portion of the heat exchanger to be cooled in part by the incoming juice and finally by a cooling liquid in the heat exchanger to about 0 to 4°C. It is then filled into paper or plastic cartons of various sizes and kept cold at all times. Chilled juice should not be kept at a temperature higher than 10°C and preferably at 4°C, or below. Since the product is not sterile, it will eventually spoil, especially if higher temperatures are used.

The products can be aseptically packed either into cartons or glass bottles. Aseptic packaging practices must be strictly followed. Tetra Pak* of Tetra-Brik* packagings use a laminated foil-lined paper container formed at the time of filling under asceptic conditions. The containers are presently chemically sterilized with H_2O_2. With class containers, the bottles and caps are cold-sterilized with a solution of iodophor or chlorine (Bonnell, 1968), and the filling and sealing are done under aseptic conditions. Properly prepared and carefully handled, chilled juices have very freshlike flavor of the respective products.

C. Citrus Juice Concentrates

The development of full-flavored concentrated orange juice was the beginning of the modern processed citrus industry. Today citrus juices are staples in most developed countries, and they can become the natural food source of vitamin C for the entire world. The advantages of concentrated citrus juice over the chilled juice are as follows: the reduction of transportation cost, year-round availability of the product, utilization of entire crops, better preservation of nutrients, and a product which is within the economic reach of a large segment of the world population.

In the production of concentrated orange juice, the steps described for chilled juice are followed up to deaeration and deoiling. The juice is pumped into the evaporator as it comes out the blending tank. The most popular evaporator used today is the temperature acceleraged short time evaporator (TASTE) described by Cook (1963). The evaporation takes place in seven stages, and the juice can be concentrated from single strength of about 12° Brix to 65 to 68° Brix in a few minutes.

---

*
Trademark.

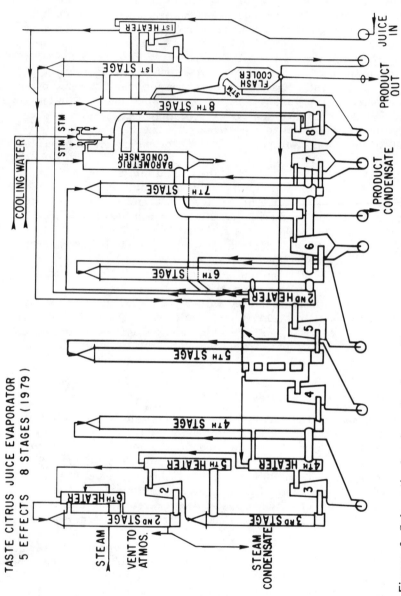

Figure 6   Schematic drawing of a four-effect, seven-stage TASTE evaporator.   (From Chen et al., 1979).

For production of a concentrate with a higher degree of concentration, it may be necessary to centrifuge the juice before it enters into the evaporator. A diagram of the evaporator is shown in Fig. 6.

The juice is heated to a temperature of 96 to 105°C in the first-stage preheater for a few seconds to destroy microorganisms and to stabilize the juice by inactivating the pectic enzymes. As the heated juice enters the different stages, vaporization and concentration take place, and the product heat is used both in the vaporization process of the other stages and in preheating the incoming juice. With a properly constructed evaporator, a theoretical efficiency of stem is 1 kg of steam for the removal of 4 kg of water (Chen et al., 1979). Practically a 3:1 ratio, or 3 kg of water removal per 1 kg of steam, is a general rule. The concentration, rate of water removal, and the temperature at each stage are shown in Table 10.

Prior to the adoption of the TASTE evaporator, various low-temperature evaporators were in use. Whereas the low temperatures did not seriously affect the flavor of the product, the juice had to be pasteurized first to inactivate pectic enzymes. The resident time of the juice in the low-temperature evaporator posed a microbial problem in the evaporator (Patrick and Hill, 1959). These low-temperature evaporators are still being used for the concentration of lemon and lime juice, especially the latter because of its heat sensitiveness. Both low- and high-temperature evaporators are used for lemon juice. Commercially available lemonade and limeade concentrate are actually made by adding sugar to single-strength juice to a high Brix. When diluted with the proper amount of water, the product is a refreshing juice drink with a sugar-to-acid ratio of nearly 14:1.

Table 10 Degree of Concentration and Temperature at Different Stages of a TASTE Evaporator

Stage	Temperature (°C)	Volume of % of incoming juice	Concentrations of product (° Brix)
Feed	21	100	12
1	40	94	13
2	96	74	16
3	88	46	33
4	77	27	40
5	63	21	48
6	46	18	56
7	40	16	63
Flash	16	15	66

Source: Berry and Veldhuis (1977).

1. Essence Recovery

When discussing juice concentration, it is not uncommon to discuss the essence recovery process which is an integral part of some commercial evaporators. The essence recovery unit is generally incorporated in the TASTE evaporation at the first effect. Citrus essence is the condensate of the volatile comopunds from the fresh juice, together with water. The concentrated essence, generally 100- to 200-fold, can be added back to the finished juice concentrate to fortify its aroma. The recovered essence solution is easily oxidized to form undesirable odors. It should be stored with as little head space as possible in containers blanketed with an inert gas at temperatures near freezing.

2. Packaging and Storage of Concentrated Citrus Juices

The concentrated juice product pumped out from the evaporator is usually over 60% soluble solids and is relatively low in aroma. In order to restore a fresh citrus flavor, freshly extracted juice is added as a "cutback" juice to reduce the product concentration to desired range, either for a 3 + 1 or 4 + 1 concentrate. Cold-pressed peel oil is added also as a flavor agent. With the development of essence recovery systems (Wolford and Attaway, 1967), the restoration of aroma can also be accomplished by the addition of essence supplemented by cold-pressed oil. The blending of concentrate with cutback juices, essence, and oil should be done in a cold-wall tank.

The concentrate can be stored in polyethylene-bag-lined 55-gallon drums. Since 1970, storage of concentrate in large tank-farms is becoming increasingly popular with citrus juice concentrate manufacturers (Ratcliff, 1974). The tanks ranging from about 0.25 to 1 million liters are enclosed in well-insulated and refrigerated rooms. Concentrates of various batches of fruit can be pumped into different tanks in the room by a series of valves operated by remote controls. Either in barrels or in tanks, a storage temperature in the range of -4 to -18°C is used. For the concentrate in the tank to be fluid enough to be removed by pumps, temperatures should not be lower than -10°C. Concentrates of different color, soluble-solids-to-acid ratio, flavor, and pulp content, either stored in different barrels or tanks, may be blended to get the desired specifications. For such blending, cold-wall tanks or low-temperature rooms are desirable. The blended concentrates are then ready for consumer packages of different sizes. Because the product is not aseptic, the concentrate in these containers must be kept at low temperatures to prevent spoilage. If aseptic packaging techniques are used, the blended concentrate is pasteurized again at 75 to 85°C for 5 sec, cooled to 5°C, filled into sterile containers, and sealed aseptically. Concentrates thus packed can be stored unfrozen and kept without refrigeration. However, high temperatures have deleterious effects on the flavor, color, and nutritional values of the concentrates. Hence low-temperature storage, even though not essential to keep the product from microbial spoilage, is nevertheless desirable. Temperatures between 2 to 7°C should be sufficient for short storage periods. The most important advantages of these unfrozen concentrates are their savings in refrigeration and transportation costs and in their conveniences.

D. Other Processed Citrus Products

1. Orange Juice Reconstituted from Concentrate

During the past two decades, the utilization of 100% pure orange and grapefruit juice from concentrate has increased markedly. The concentrate produced in regions where the fruit are grown is shipped in large drums or tank cars to other areas where it is reconstituted to single-strength juice by the addition of an appropriate amount of water. The concentrates used in this manner are designated as concentrates for manufacturing and are generally 60 to 65° Brix. When reconstituted, the juice should be 11.8° Brix for orange juice and 10° Brix for grapefruit juice.

After reconstitution, the juice should not be agitated excessively to avoid the incorporation of air which not only has a deleterious effect on the flavor but can also cause excess loss of ascorbic acid since oxygen is one of the main factors in ascorbic acid oxidation. The water used for reconstitution should be pure, preferably filtered through a carbon filter and deionized. High inorganic salt content in the water, such as calcium and iron, may cause off-flavor and possibly calcium salt flocculation. Organic contaminates in the water or chlorine are removed by the carbon filter.

Since the concentrates are usually shipped with the necessary amount of cold-pressed oil or essence oil added, it is ready for reconstitution without further oil fortification. An oil concentraton of 0.015 to 0.020% by volume of the reconstituted juice is optimum. Oil concentration should not exceed 0.035% or the juice may be too oily. Oil content is determined by the Scott-Veldhuis method (AOAC, 1980), which is also used as the official methods of the USDA Standards for Grades for processed orange products (1976a).

Although the concentrate used in the reconstituted products has been pasteurized, repasteurization of the finished products is definitely desirable to avoid spoilage. Either the plate-type or the tubular-type pasteurizer can be used. The juice should be heated to 72 to 75°C for 15 sec or to 85°C for 1 sec. Samples of the product should be examined to ensure complete destruction of yeast and mold. The juice is cooled immediately, either in the cooling phase of the pasteurizer or by any other means, and then packed into containers which are usually cartons and which may have a shelf life at 4 to 6°C of 3 weeks. When an aseptic packaging process is used, the juice can be packed in sterilized cans, glass jars, or the recently developed Tetra Brik containers or

Scholle bags. Even when the juice is aseptically packed, storage at temperatures below 10°C is necessary. Temperatures just above 0°C are more desirable.

2. Citrus Sections

Citrus segments are processed sucessfully in glass jars or tin cans. The peel of the fruit is removed either manually or mechanically. Machines that will automatically remove the peel (flavedo and albedo) of grapefruit are on the market and successfully used commercially in the United States, as described by Berry and Veldhuis (1977). Other machines that will peel oranges and grapefruit are also available. In the manual peeling process, the operator slices the peel longitudinally from the stem end to the stylar end after first cutting off a slice about 1/2 in. thick from each end of the fruit. In the peeling process a part of the segment membrane of the sections underneath is also removed exposing the juice vesicle. Each section is then separated out by hand.

In the mechanical peeling operation for grapefruit, the segment membrane is not cut and must be removed by a hot alkali treatment. The peeled fruit are placed in a lye bath made of a mixture of 0.5 to 2.0% sodium hydroxide-sodium carbonate solution, at 95 to 100°C for 10 to 15 sec. A water spray and a water bath completely remove the alkali on the fruit. Sometimes a small amount of calcium chloride is put in the rinsing water to firm the sections. Too long a duration in the alkali bath must be avoided. If the treatment is not long enough, the membrane is not completely removed. Sections are then removed manually.

Mechanically operated sectionizers have also been available and are used commercially in the United States. The loss due to broken sections by machine sectionizing is not significantly more than the manual operation. Where labor cost is excessive or labor supply inadequate, machine sectionizing can be economical. Generally, where citrus sections are packed, sectionizing is done by manual labor except in the United States.

The orange or grapefruit segments prepared by machine or by manual sectionizing are hand-packed or machine-filled in cans or glass jars with a sugar syrup ranging from 12 to 18° Brix. The net contents of the can are based on the drained weight of the fruit. The cans or jars should be sealed with as little air space as possible. Huggart et al. (1955) reported that the color of grapefruit segments was affected by the conditions under which the fruit was packed, especially if the acidity was high and a low vacuum existed in the can. The packed segments are processed at 75 to 85°C or 15 min and cooled to about 40°C. The residual heat helps to evaporate the excess water remaining on the container. After labeling, the cans can be stored in cartons. Storage temperature as near 20°C as possible can minimize the loss of quality and nutrients. Orange and grapefruit segments can also be cold-packed. Such a product has a very short shelf life and

must be kept refrigerated. Preservatives, such as sodium benzonate
or potassium sorbate, are usually added to prolong its shelf life.

Mandarin sections are extensively packed in Japan and other manda-
rin-producing regions. They are produced by hand-peeling the fruit
and separating the segments. The peeling is made easier if the fruit
is first treated with hot water (85 to 90°C) for 1 min and cooled with a
water spray. The separated segments are placed in a tray and immersed
in a 2.5% hydrochloric acid solution at 20 to 25°C for about 2 hr, rinsed
with water to remove the acid reimmersed in a 1% sodium hydroxide solution at 45°C for 20 to 30 min, and again rinsed in a stream of running
water. This process as described by Boswell (1946) completely removes

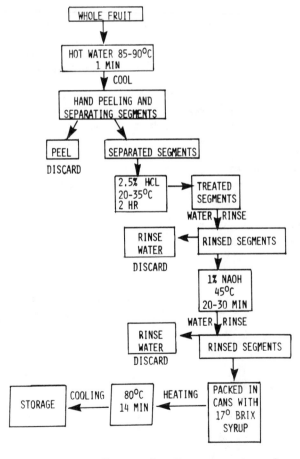

Figure 7 Flow diagram for the processing of mandarin segments.

the segment membrane and other cellulosic substances from the juice vesicles. These sections are packed in canns filled with a 16 to 18°C Brix hot syrup and sealed and processed at 80°C for 14 to 16 min. The entire operation is shown in Fig. 7.

3. Citrus-Base Drinks

Citrus beverages are very popular in many areas of the world. Orange juice drinks have proved to be most popular, but lemon and lime are also used extensively. Beverage bases for these drinks are manufactured by the addition of sugar or syrup, citric acid, color, flavoring agent, salts, vitamin C, and sodium benzoate to concentrated citrus juices at 65° Brix. The flavoring agents are generally the commerically available oil emulsions of the different flavors. The ratios of Brix to acid should be between 15 and 25:1. Lemonade and limeade have been found to be preferred when the Brix-to-acid ratios are between 14 and 16:1 (Bissett et al., 1954). Comminuted lime purée, when added to the concentrated lime juice, increases its oil content for the prepared limeade. An oil concentration of 0.003 to 0.004% in the finished products was found to be desirable.

Formulations of orangeade bases for various percentages of orange juice are shown in Table 11. Most citrus-base drinks contain between 3 to 30% juice although 10% is the most commonly used amount. The table can be used for other citrus juices by varying the amount of citric acid and sugar required. The base can also be prepared without the syrup. Such formulations can be prepared so that 1 liter of the amount can be diluted to 20 to 100 liters of drink with the addition of

Table 11 Formulation of Orange Base for 1000 Liters of 11.9° Brix Orange Drinks with Varying Percentage of Natural Juice

	Juice in finished drink (%)		
	10	20	30
Orange concentrate[a] 65° Brix (gal)	14.58	29.17	43.68
Sugar (kg)	49.11	36.68	24.33
Citric acid (kg)	3.97	2.87	1.82
Salt (g)	132	132	132
Vitamin C (g)	400	400	400
Oil emulsion (ml)	265	265	265
Sodium benzoate (g)	100	100	100
Water to make (liter)	83.35	83.35	83.35

[a]Adapted from Kesterson and Braddock (1976).

sweeteners. Whether with or without syrup, the base is pasteurized and packed into containers of appropriate sizes, either in 3.8 liter (1 gal) or 19-liter (5 gal) pails, polyethylene-lined steel drums, or polyethylene drums, and hermetically sealed. For short storage durations, they can be kept at 10°C. Drums should be kept frozen at -18°C to prevent browning.

4. Comminuted Citrus Drinks

Comminuted fruit is similar to the purée. When diluted with water, with the addition of sugar and food acids, a quite acceptable drink can be made. Because of the strong peel flavoring, fruit content of 2 to 5% is generally used. Charley (1963) made a detailed study of the comminuted citrus beverage and emphasized that the oil content could be as high as 0.8% (v/v) but the concentrated base should not exceed 0.08% oil. Generally an oil content of 0.010% should be acceptable.

Comminuted citrus beverage base is also produced by mixing the finished juice with various peel fractions from the juice extractors which have been ground through a hammer mill. The mixture is then passed through a collodial mill with a clearance of about 12.5 μm. The collodidal mill not only reduces the particle size but also tends to produce a fine emulsion of the peel oil throughout the mixture. The purée with 1800 ppm of sodium benzoate is pasteurized for 40 to 90 sec through a tubular pasteurizer at 85 to 95°C and packed in an appropriate container and sealed. Such a product when stored at 5°C or lower does not develop a canned off-flavor for 12 months (Charley and Swindells, 1962). A 10% comminuted citrus drink is made by using 10% purée, 12.5% sucrose, 0.75% citric acid, and 76.75% water (Lime and Cruse, 1972). Grapefruit purée, because of its high naringin content, was first treated with 0.05% naringinase for 3 hr before the preparation of the drink (Cruse and Lime, 1973). The addition of ascorbic acid in the comminuted base is desirable since the natural ascorbic acid contribution by the fruit component is limited due to the low content of fruit. Charley (1963) found that the comminuted orange base was remarkably stable and attributed this phenomenon to the presence of α-tocopherol. Ascorbic acid retention in the comminuted drink is satisfactory when stored at temperatures not higher than 20°C (Bender, 1958).

VIII. CITRUS BYPRODUCTS AND SPECIALITY PRODUCTS

Citrus, when utilized as fresh produce, does not have a waste disposal problem. However, when processing citrus products, more than 50% of the fruit results in the peel, rag, pulp, and seed which are not generally used as human food. Specialized products, such as candied peel, marmalades, and citrus essential oil are made and used in food preparation.

With the tremendous increase in the utilization of citrus fruit in frozen concentrated juices, the disposal of citrus-processing waste materials as byproducts became of paramount importance. Today, the main outlet of the citrus-porcessing residue is in the manufacture of dried citrus pulp as cattle feed. Many other specialty products can also be prepared from citrus waste (Keterson and Braddock, 1976).

A. Dried Citrus Pulp

The peel, membrane, pulp, and seeds that are left after the juice extraction has been used as animal feed directly. However, when the quantity is too large to be consumed by the livestock, it must be dried and stored. Because of the high moisture and high sugar content of ths material, it should be pressed to remove excess liquid before drying. Hydrated lime at a rate of 0.9 to 2.1 kg/455 kg (2 to 5#/1000#) is added to the peel residue which has been first chopped in a hammer mill to pass a 6.1-mm (1/4 in.) screen. The addition of lime is to degrade the pectic substance which would prevent efficient pressing. After the lime has been thoroughly mixed, the material becomes less slimy and more fluid. By pressing in a hydraulic press, nearly 50% of the liquor can be removed, and the water content can be changed from around 80 to 70%. The pressed residue then is dried in a rotating dryer to about 8 to 10% moisture. The proximate composition of the dried citrus pulp is shown in Table 12. Dried citrus pulp is highly concentrated in nutrients and can be used to substitute other animal feedstuff.

B. Citrus Molasses

The pressed liquor, together with the soluble lime and small peel particles, is first passed through a 40- to 80-mesh vibrating screen to

Table 12 Proximate Composition of Dried Citrus Pulp

Fraction	Composition (%)
Water	8-10
Dry matter	90-92
Crude protein	5.3-6.2
Crude fiber	9.3-12.0
Nitrogen-free extract	62.7-66.6
Crude lipid	2.8-4.9
Ash	4.9-8.0

Source: Kesterson and Braddock (1976).

remove solids. It is heated to prevent spoilage and to distill off the
peel oil, which is recovered as d-limonene. The calcium salts tend to
precipitate at high temperatures. The liquor is concentrated either by
boiling or by vacuum evaporation to about 72° Brix as citrus molasses.

Molasses can be incorporated to the dried pulp to increase its nutrient value. One of the major use of citrus molasses is in the production
of vinegar (McNary and Dougherty, 1960), bland syrup (Breslau et al.,
1976), or alcohol (Kesterson and Braddock, 1976).

C. Essential Oil

The essential oils of the citrus are located in the oil glands in the
flavedo, and are used both in the pharmaceutical and food industries
as aromatic and flavoring agents. The general methods in collecting
the oil can be either before, during, or after the juice has been extracted from the fruit. Large quantities of the various citrus oils are
also used by the beverage manufacturers. While the manual method of
oil recovery by pressing has been practiced in the past and may still
be used in some operations, the trend is toward continuous extraction
using modern technology and machinery. In order to remove the oil
from the oil sacs, the latter must be ruptured and the oil rinsed off
with a stream of water. The mixture, usually in an emulsion, is separated by several steps of centrifugation.

Machines that remove the oil from whole fruit either rasp the flavedo
(the Fraizer brace excoriator) or pierce the oil sacs (Automatic Machinery Scarifier) as the fruit pass through a conveyor. Water is used to
carry the oil to a collector. The FMC Inline extractor has a special
device to collect the oil emulsion during the juice extraction. Water is
also used to carry the oil to a collecting vessel. The Automatic Machinery peel shaver removes the flavedo from the half-peel of freshly
extracted citrus fruit, and the oil sac of the flavedo is ruptured by
passing through rough pressing rollers. Again the oil is collected with
a stream of water.

Regardless of the methods of getting the oil from the peel, the
emulsion is first passed through a finisher to remove large particles
before being fed into a desludger to remove the finer particles and some
water. Additional clarification or deemulsifying can be accomplished by
the use of more efficient centrifuges, such as the Sharples, DeLaval,
and Westfalia.

The refined oil is stored in drums or tanks either of stainless steel
or coated with oil-resistant resins at -4 to -23°C for 4 to 6 weeks to
precipitate the waxes. The dewaxed oil is then transferred to another
container by decantation. Care is taken to leave little head space since
the oil is easily oxidized. The head space can be flushed with inert
gasses (i.e., nitrogen or carbon dioxide). Antioxidants such as
butylated hydrosyanisole (BHA) or butylated hydroxytoluene (BHT)

can be added at 100 to 200 ppm. The oil should be stored at a cool place around 18 to 20°C.

To concentrate the citrus oil to produce what the trade terms folded oil, the hydrocarbons, which are about 90% of the oil, are removed by vacuum or steam distillation, alcohol extraction, or by a chromatographic process. The folded oils are in great demand by the perfume and cosmetic industry.

D. Pectin

Citrus peel, lemon, grapefruit, and orange are sources for commerical pectin production. The general procedure for the extraction of these pectins from the peel is the same. A procedure for the extraction of pectin from grapefruit is reported by Sinclair (1972).

One of the main uses of pectin is in the manufacturing of jelly. The degree of capability of the pectins to form jelly is termed the jelly grade. Most commercial pectin is standardized at a jelly grade of 150. It means that 1 kg of that pectin when cooked with 150 kg of sugar to 65° Brix will give a satisfactory jelly under standard conditions. Pectin is also used in the manufacturing of fruit jam and marmalades. Lemon peel generally produces the highest jelly grade. Grapefruit peel is superior to orange peel in that aspect (Crandall and Rouse, 1977). Several methods of pectin production are reported by Swisher and Swisher (1977).

E. Other Citrus Specialty Products

Many other products can be recovered from citrus waste. Among these are the bioflavonoids and citrus seed oil. By further processing, several products can be made with the peel, such as the candied peel, citrus marmalades, brined citrus peel, and peel grits for flavoring (Braddock and Kesterson, 1973).

The juice sacs from the finisher can be frozen and used in beverage manufacturing. Alternately, the soluble solids can be removed from the pulp by water extraction and the diluted extract concentrated to produce a pulpwash-solids concentrate which is most suitable for citrus beverage manufacturing because it imparts a turbid appearance to the drink. An edible oil can be produced from citrus seeds. Braddock and Kesterson (1973) studies the seed oil production and composition and reported that citrus seed oil can be utilized as oils of soybean and cotton seeds. The residue after seed oil extraction is useful as animal feed.

IX. CONCLUSION

Both from a world economic and nutritional point of view, citrus fruits are the single largest group of fruit important for the human diet. The world production of these fruits will continue to expand as the demand for them is increasing each year. The rapid expansion of citrus fruit production is the result of improvements in the processing technology, better transportation, and the increasing knowledge of nutrition. The pleasant taste and aroma and the appealing color of all citrus fruits and their products are also important factors in the rapid growth of the world citrus industry.

With better virus control and cultivars, the areas of the world in which citrus can be planted will continue to increase to meet the demand. More efficient cultural practices, better cold protection, and better methods of harvesting and handling, as well as continuous advancements in processing and packaging technology, will all contribute to more economic utilization. The byproducts from citrus processing are also becoming important both as human food and animal food. Everything from a citrus fruit is utilized. From the seed to the aroma recovered as essence.

REFERENCES

Araujo, P. E. (1977). Role of citrus fruit in human nutrition. In *Citrus Science and Technology, Vol. 1* (S. Nagy, P. E. Shaw, and M. K. Veldhuis, eds.). Westport, Conn., Avi Publishing Co., pp. 1-32.

Association of Analytical Chemists (1980). *Methods of Analysis,* 14th ed., Washington, D.C., Association of Analytical Chemists.

Atkin, L., Shultz, A. S., Williams, W. L., and Frey, C. N. (1943). Yeast microbiological methods for determination of vitamins. *Ind. Eng. Chem. Anal. Ed.* 15:141-144.

Atkins, C. D., and Rouse, A. H. (1953). Time-temperature relationship for heat inactivation for pectinesterase in citrus juices. *Food Technol.* 7:489-491.

Atkins, C. D., and Rouse, A. H. (1954). Time-temperature relationship for heat inactivation for pectinesterase in citrus juices. *Food Technol.* 8:498-500.

Atkins, C. D., Wiederhold, E., and Moore, E. L. (1945). Vitamin C content of processing residue from Florida citrus fruits. *Fruit Prod. J. Am. Food Manuf.* 24(9):260-262,281.

Attaway, J. A., Barron, R. W., Blair, J. G., Buslig, B. S., Carter, R. D., Dougherty, M. H., Fellers, P. J., Fisher, J. F., Hill, E. C., Huggart, R. L., Maraulja, M. D., Petrus, D. R., and Ting, S. V. (1973). Some new analytical indicators of processed orange juice quality, 1971-72. *Proc. Fla. State Hortic. Soc.* 85:192-203.

Baker, R. A., and Buemmer, J. H. (1969). Cloud stability in the absence of various orange juice soluble constituents. *Proc. Fla. State Hortic. Soc.* 82:217-220.

Bender, A. E. (1958). Stability of vitamin C in a commerical fruit squash. *J. Sci. Food Agric.* 9:754-760.

Berry, R. E., and Veldhuis, M. K. (1977). Processing of oranges, grapefruit and tangerines. In *Citrus Science and Technology, Vol. 2* (S. Nagy, P. E. Shaw, and M. K. Veldhuis, eds.). Westport, Conn., Avi Publishing Co.

Birdsall, J. J., Derse, P. H., and Teply, L. J. (1961). Nutrients in California lemons and oranges. II. Vitamin, mineral and proximate composition. *J. Am. Diet. Assoc.* 38:555-559

Bissett, O. W., and Berry, R. E. (1975). Ascorbic acid retention in orange juice as related to container type. *J. Food Sci.* 40:178-180.

Bissett, O. W., Veldhuis, M. K., and Scott, W. C. (1954). Lime juice super-concentrates. *Food Eng.* 26(6):56-58, 190-195.

Bonnell, J. M. (1968). Production of asceptically packed orange juice by the Tropicana method. *Report. Int. Fed. Fruit Juice Prod. Congress* 7:201-207.

Boswell, V. P. (1946). New canning process for oranges in Japan. U.S. Off. Foreign Agric. Relation. *Foreign Crop and Market* 52(19): 285-286.

Braddock, R. J., and Kesterson, J. W. (1973). Citrus seed oils. *U. of Fla. Agric. Exp. Sta. Bull.* 756.

Braverman, J. B. S. (1949). *Citrus Products.* New York and London, Interscience, p. 58.

Brenoe, C. (1971). Research studies of the distribution of free amino acid and other compounds in orange fruits picked in Greece during the period January to March, 1968 and collected during this period January to March, 1969. *Husholdingsradets Tekniske Meddelesen* 9:15-59.

Breslau, B. R., Pensenstadler, D. F., and Mitchell, W. G. (1976). The recovery of the sugar from citrus press liquor by ultrafiltration. *Trans. The Citrus Eng. Conf. Fla. Sec. A.S.M.E., Lakeland. Fla., March 1976.*

Burger, M., Hein, L. W., Teply, L. J., Derse, P. H., and Kreiger, C. H. (1956). Vitamin, mineral and proximate composition of frozen fruits, juices and vegetables. *J. Agric. Food Chem.* 4:418-425.

Chandler, B., and Kefford, J. (1970). The chemical constituents of citrus fruits. In *Advances in Food Research Supplement 2.* New York, Academic Press.

Charley, V. L. S. (1963). Some technical aspects of British communited drink production. *Food Technol.* 17:987-994.

Charley, V. L. S., and Swindells, R. (1962). Effect of storage temperatures on quality of comminuted fruit juice raw materials. *Proc. First Int. Cong. Food Sci. Technol.* 3:623-625.

Chen, C. S., Carter, R. D., and Buslig, B. S. (1979). Energy requirements for the TASTE citrus juice evaporator. In *Changing Energy Use Futures, Vol. IV* (R. D. Fazzolare and C. B. Smith, eds.). New York, Pergamon Press.

Clements, R. L. (1966). Disc electrophoresis of citrus fruit proteins. *Phytochemistry* 5: 243-249.

Cook, R. W. (1963). High temperature short time evaporator. *Proc. Citrus Eng. Conf. Lakeland Fa, March 1963.* 9:1-7.

Cooper, W. C., and Chapot, H. (1977). Fruit production with special emphasis on fruit for processing. In *Citrus Science and Technology Vol. 2* (S. Nagy, P. E. Shaw, and M. K. Veldhuis, eds.). Westport, Conn., Avi Publishing Co., Inc.

Cooper, W. C., and Henry, W. H. (1973). Chemical control of fruit abscission. In *Shedding of Plant Parts* (T. T. Koslaski, ed.). New York, Academic Press.

Cooper, W. C., Peynado, A., Furr, J. R., Hilgeman, R. H., Cahoon, G. A., and Boswell, S. B. (1963). Tree growth and fruit quality of Valencia oranges in relation to climate. *Proc. Am. Soc. Hortic. Sci.* 82:180-192.

Coppock, G. E. (1978). Mechanical harvesting and handling of citrus fruits. *Proc. Int. Soc. Citriculture.* pp. 87-91.

Crandall, G. E., and Rouse, A. H. (1977). Pectin quality and quantity differences between whole peel and shaved albedo from 'Ducan' grapefruit and 'Pineapple' and 'Valencia' oranges. *Proc. Int. Soc. Criticulture* Orlando, Fla. May 1977, Vol. 3, pp. 810-813.

Cruse, R. R., and Lime, B. J. (1973). Citrus puree. U.S. Pat. 3,747,585, July 31.

Curl, A. L. (1946). Off-flavor development in processed tangerine juice. *Fruit Product J.* 25:356-357.

Curl, A. L. (1965). The occurence of B-citraurin and B-apocarotenal in the peels of California tangerines and oranges. *J. Food Sci.* 30:13-18.

Curl, A. L., and Veldhuis, M. K. (1947). The origin of the off-flavor which develops in processed oranges. *Fruit Product J.* 26:329-330.

Dougherty, R. H., and Ahmed, E. M. (1973). Flavor enhancing potential of selected orange oil and essence components and their relationship to product quality. Gainesville, Fla., University of Florida, U. S. Dept. Agric. Contract 12-14-100-10337(72).

Florida Department of Agriculture (1979). *1978-79 Annual Report.* Winter Haven, Fla., State of Florida, Department of Agriculture Fruit Inspection Service.

Florida Department of Citrus (1974). State of Florida citrus fruit laws (rev.), January 1974, Lakeland, Fla.

Food and Agriculture Organization/World Health Organization (1971). Evaluation of food additives report of a FAO/WHO expert committee on food additives. *WHO Tech. Rept. Ser. No. 463,* Geneva, WHO.

Food and Nutrition Board (1978). *Recommended Dietary Allowances,* 9th ed. Washington, D.C., Printing and Publishing Office, National Academy of Sciences.

Ford, H. W., and W. A. Feder (1964). Three citrus rootstocks recommended for trial in spreading decline area. *University of Fla. Agr. Expt. Sta. Circ. S-151.* University of Florida.

Friend, B., and Clark, F. (1959). *Food, The Yearbook of Agriculture.* Washington D.C. U.S. Dept of Agriculture, p. 606.

Grierson, W., and Ting. S. V. (1978). Quality standards for citrus fruits, juices and beverages. *Proc. Int. Soc. Citruculture,* Sydney, Austrialia, pp. 21-27.

Harding, P. L. (1940). Seasonal changes in the principal varieties of Florida oranges. *Proc. Fla. State Hortic. Soc.* 53:78-86.

Harding, P. L. (1954). Effects of simulated transit and marketing periods on quality of Florida oranges. *Food Technol.* 8:311-312.

Harding, P. L., and Fisher, D. F. (1945). Seasonal changes of Florida grapefruit. *U.S. Dept. Agr. Tech. Bull. 886.*

Harding, P. L., and Sunday, M. B. (1953). Seasonal changes of Florida oranges. *U.S. Dept. Agr. Tech. Bull. 1072.*

Harding, P. L., Winston, J. R., and Fisher, D. F. (1940). Seasonal changes in Florida oranges. *U.S. Dept. Agr. Tech. Bull.* 735:1-89.

Hendrickson, R., and Kesterson, J. W. (1963). Seed oils from Citrus sinensis. *J. Am. Oil. Chem. Soc.* 40:746-747.

Hensz, R. A. (1971). 'Star Ruby,' a new deep-red fleshed grapefruit variety with distinct tree characteristics. *J. Rio Grande Hortic. Soc.* 25:54-58.

Horowitz, R. M. (1977). Flavonoid constituents of citrus. In *Citrus Science and Technology,* Vol. 1 (S. Nagy, P. W. Shaw, and M. K. Veldhuis, eds.). Westport, Conn., Avi Publishing Co.

Huggart, R. L., Wenzel, R. W., and Moore, E. L. (1955). Effect of storage temperature on quality of canned grapefruit sections. *Food Technol.* 9:268-270.

Hume, H. H. (1957). *Citrus Fruits.* New York, Macmillan.

Hsu, J. N. (1974). Seasonal variations of thiamine in citrus juices. Unpublished, Lake Alfred, Fla., Florida Department of Citrus.

Huskins, C. W., and Swift, L. J. (1953). Changes in the lipid fraction of Valencia orange juice during pasteurization. *Food Res.* 18:305-307.

Huskins, C. W., Swift, L. J., and Veldhuis, M. K. (1952). Constitution of the lipid from stored Florida Valencia orange juice. *Food Res.* 17:109-116.

Institute of Food Technology Committee (1959). Pectin standardization: final report of the IFT Committee. *Food Technol.* 13:496-500.

Ikeda, R. M., Stanley, W. L., Vannier, S. H., and Rolle, L. A. (1961). Monoterpene hydrocarbon composition of citrus oils. *J. Food Sci.* 27:593-596.

Keeny, M. (1962). Secondary degradation products. In *Lipids and their oxidation* (H. W. Schultz, E. A. Day, and R. H. Sinnhuber, eds.). Westport, Conn., Avi Publishing Co.

Kesterson, J. W., and Braddock, R. J. (1976). By-products and specialty products of Florida citrus. Gainesville, Fla., *University of Fla. Agri. Exp. Sta. Bull.* 784.

Kesterson, J. W., and Hendrickson, R. (1957). Naringin, a bitter principle of grapefruit. Gainesville, Fla., *University of Fla. Agr. Exp. Sta. Bull.* 511A.

Kew, T. J., Veldhuis, M. K., Bissett, O. W., and Patric, R. (1957). The effect of time and temperature of pasteurization on the quality of canned citrus juices. Winter Haven, Fla., *U.S. Dept. Agric. ARS-72-6.*

Krehl, W. (1976). *Citrus in Health and Disease.* University Press of Fla. Gainseville, Fla.

Krehl, W. A., and Cowgill, G. R. (1950). Vitamin content of citrus products. *Food Res.* 15:179-191.

Kugler, E., and Kovats, E. (1963). Information on mandarin peel oil. *Helv. Chim. Acta.* 46:1480-1513.

Lime, B. J., and Cruse, R. R. (1972). Beverage from whole citrus fruit puree. *J. Food Sci.* 37:250-252.

Lime, B. J., Stephens, T. S., and Griffith, F. P. (1954). Processing characteristics of colored Texas grapefruit. I. Color and maturity studies of Ruby Red grapefruit. *Food Technol.* 8:566-569.

MacDonnell, L. R., Jansen, F. F., and Lineweaver, H. (1945). The properties of orange pectinesterase. *Arch. Biochem.* 6:389-401.

MacLeod, W. D., and Buigues, N. M. (1964). Sesquiterpenes. I. Nootkatone, a new grapefruit flavor constituent. *J. Food Sci.* 29:565-568.

Maier, V. P., and Dreyer, D. L. (1965). Citrus bitter principles IV. Occurrence of limonin in grapefruit juice. *J. Food Sci.* 30:874-875.

McCornack, A. A., and Wardowski, W. F. (1972). Postharvest decay control recommentations for fresh citrus fruit. *University of Fla. Agr. Exp. Sta. Circ. No. 359.*

McCready, R. M. (1977). Carbohydrates: composition, distribution, significance. In *Citrus Science and Technology* (S. Nagy, P. E. Shaw, and M. K. Veldhuis, eds.). Westport, Conn., Avi Publishing Co.

McHard, J. A., Foulk, S. J., and Winfordner, J. D. (1979). A comparison of trace element contents of Florida nad Brazil orange juice. *J. Agric. Food Chem.* 27:1326-1328.

McNary, R. R., and Dougherty, M. H. (1960). Citrus vinegar. *University of Fla Agric. Exp. Sta. Bull. 622.*

Miller, E. V., Winston, J. R., and Schomer, H. A. (1940). Physiological studies of plastid pigment in rind of maturing oranges. *J. Agric. Res.* 60:259-267.

Moore, E. L., Atkins, C. D., Wiendenhold, E., and MacDowell, L. G. (1945). Flavor and ascorbic acid retention in fresh Florida citrus juices. *J. Home Econ.* 37:290-293.

Moschette, D. S., Hinman, W. F., and Halliday, E. G. (1947). Nutritive values of canned foods. XXII. Effect of time and temperature of storage on vitamin content of certain commercially canned fruits and fruit juices. *Ind. Eng. Chem.* 39:994-999.

Moshanas, M. G., Shaw, P. E., and Seins, D. A. (1976). Abscission agent effects on orange juice flavor. *J. Food Sci.* 41:809-811.

Nagy, S. (1977). Inorganic elements. In *Citrus Science and Technology*, *Vol. 1* (S. Nagy, P. E. Shaw, and M. K. Veldhuis, eds.). Westport, Conn., Avi Publishing Co.

Nagy, S., and Smoot, J. M. (1980). Effects of storage temperature and deaeration on total vitamin C content of canned single-strength grapefruit juice. *J. Agric. Food Chem.* 28:417-421.

Nagy, S., Rouseff, R. L., and Ting, S. V. (1980). The effects of temperature and storage on the iron and tin contents of commercially canned single-strength orange juice. *J. Ag. Food. Chem.* 28:1166-1169.

Newhall, W. F., and Grierson, W. (1955). A low cost self polishing fungicidal wax for citrus fruits. *J. Am. Soc. Hort. Sci.* 66: 146-154.

Passy, N., and Mannheim, C. H. (1979). The effect of deaeration on quality of concentrated grapefruit juice. In *Tropical Foods: Chemistry and Nutrition, Vol. 1)* (G. E. Inglett and G. Charalmbous, eds.). New York, Academic Press.

Patrick, R., and Hill, E. C. (1959). Microbiology of citrus processing. Gainesville, Fla., *Fla. Agr. Exp. Sta. Bull.* 618.

Pulley, G. N., and Von Loesecke, H. W. (1939). Gases in the commercial handling of citrus juices. *Ind. Eng. Chem.* 31:1275-1278.

Rakieten, M. L., Newman, B., Falk, K. B., and Miller, I. (1951). Comparison of some constituents in fresh frozen and freshly squeezed orange juice. *J. Am. Diet. Assoc.* 27:864-868.

Rakieten, M. L., Newman, B., Falk, K. B., and Miller, I. (1952). Comparison of some constituents in fresh frozen and freshly squeezed orange juice. *J. Am. Diet. Assoc.* 28:1050-1053.

Ratcliff, M. (1974). Bulk storage of citrus juice concentrate. *Proc. Citrus Eng. Con.* 20:1-6. *Fla. Sec. Am. Soc. Mech. Eng.*, Lakeland, Fla. March 1974.

Robbins, R. C. (1976). Regulatory action of phenylbenzopyrone (PBP) derivatives on blood constituents affect rheology in patients with coronary heart disease. *Int. J. Vit. Nutr. Res.* 46:338.

Roberts, J. A., and Gaddum, L. W. (1937). Composition of citrus fruit juices. *Ind. Eng. Chem.* 29:574.

Rouse, A. H. (1967). Evaluation of pectin from Florida citrus peels and cores. *Citrus Industry* 48(6):9-10.

Rouseff, R. L., and Ting, S. V. (1980). Lead uptake in canned grapefruit juice. *J. Food Sci.* 45:965-968.

Scala, J. (1975). Dietary Fiber. In *Physiological Effects of Food Carbohydrate* (A. Jeans and J. Hodge, eds.). Washington, D.C., American Chemical Society.

Scott, W. C., Kew, T. J., and Veldhuis, M. K. (1965). Composition of orange juice cloud. *J. Food Sci.* 30:833-837.

Shaw, P. E., (1977). Essential oils. In *Citrus Science and Technology Vol. 1* (S. Nagy, P. E. Shaw, and M. K. Veldhuis, eds.). Westport, Conn., Avi Publishing Co.

Sinclair, W. B. (1961). *The Orange, Its Biochemistry and Physiology,* Berkley, Calif., University of California Press.

Sinclair, W. B. (1972). Grapefruit by-product. In *The Grapefruit, its Composition, Physiology and Products.* Riverside, Calif., University of California Division Agricultural Science.

Sites, J. W., and Reitz, H. J. (1951). The variation in individual Valencia ornages from different locations of the tree as a guide to sampling methods and spot picking for quality. III. Vitamin C and juice content of the fruit. *Proc. Am. Soc. Hortic. Sci.* 56-103-110.

Slater, S. A., and Watkins, W. T. (1964). Citrus essential oils. IV. Chemical transformation of lime oil. *J. Sci. Food Agric.* 15:657-664.

Squires, S. R., and Hanna, J. G. (1979). Concentration and stability of ascorbic acid in marketed reconstituted orange juice. *J. Agric. Food. Chem.* 27:639-641.

Stevens, J. W., and Baier, W. E. (1939). Refractometric determination of soluble solids in citrus juices. *Ind. Eng. Chem. Anal. Ed.* 11:447.

Stewart, I. (1977). Pro-vitamin A carotenoids in citrus juices. *J. Agric. Food Chem.* 25:1132-1137.

Stewart, I., and Wheaton, T. A. (1964). Phenolic amines in citrus juices. *Proc. Fla. State Hortic. Soc.* 77:318-20.

Stewart, I., and Wheaton, T. A. (1973). Conversion of B-citraurin to reticulataxanthin and B-apo-carotenal to citranaxanthin during the isolation of carotenoids from citrus. *Phytochemistry* 12:2947-1951.

Stewart, I., Newhall, W. F., and Edwards, G. J. (1964). The isolation and identification of l-synephrine in the leaves and fruit of citrus. *J. Biol. Chem.* 239:930-932.

Streiff, R. R. (1971). Folate levels in citrus and other juices. *Am. J. Clin. Nutr.* 24:1390-1392.

Swift, L. J. (1951). Flavor changes in stored canned orange juice. *Proc. Fla. State Hortic. Soc.* 64:181-185.

Swift, L. J., and Veldhuis, M. K. (1951). Constitution of the juice lipids of the Florida Valencia oranges (*C. sinensis*). *Food Res.* 16:142-146.

Swisher, H. E., and Swisher, L. H. (1977). Specialty citrus products. In *Citrus Science and Technology* (S. Nagy, P. E. Shaw, and M. K. Veldhuis, eds.). Westport, Conn., Avi Publishing Co.

Szent-Gyorgyi, A. (1928). Observations on the function of peroxidase systems and the chemistry of the adrenal cortex. Description of a new carbohydrate derivative. *Biochem. J.* 22:1387-1409.

Tatum, J. H., Hearn, H. J., and Berry, R. E. (1978). Characterization of citrus cultivars by chemical differentition. *J. Am. Soc. Hort. Sci.* 104:492-496.

Ting, S. V. (1967). Total nitrogen in Florida orange juice. *Proc. Fla. State Hortic. Soc.* 80:257.

Ting, S. V. (1969). Distribution of soluble components and quality factors in the edible portion of citrus fruits. *J. Am. Soc. Hortic. Sci.* 94:515-519.

Ting, S. V. (1970). Alcohol-insoluble constituents of juice vesicles of citrus fruits. *J. Food Sci.* 35:757-761.

Ting, S. V. (1980). Nutrients and nutrition of citrus fruit and products. In *Nutrition and Quality of Citrus Fruit and Products* (S. Nagy and J. A. Attaway, eds.). Washington, D.C., American Chemical Society.

Ting, S. V., and Attaway, J. A. (1971). Citrus. In *Biochemistry of Fruits and Their Products* (A. C. Hulme, ed.). New York and London, Academic Press.

Ting, S. V., and Deszyck, E. J. (1958). The internal color and carotenoid pigments of Florida red and pink grapefruit. *Proc. Am. Soc. Hortic. Sci.* 71:271-277.

Ting, S. V., and Deszyck, E. J. (1961). The carbohydrates in the peel of oranges and grapefruit. *J. Food Sci.* 26:146-152.

Ting, S. V., Huggart, R. L., and Ismail, M. A. (1980). Processing characteristics of 'Star Ruby' grapefruit. *Proc. Fla. State Hortic. Soc.* 93:293-295.

Ting, S. V., and Vines, H. M. (1966). Organic acids in the juice vesicles of Florida 'Hamlin' oranges and 'Marsh' seedless grapefruit. *Proc. Am. Soc. Hortic. Sci.* 88:291-297.

Ting, S. V., Moore, E. L., McAllister, J. W., Streiff, R. R., Hsu, J. N. C., and Hill, E. C. (1974). Nutrient assay of Florida frozen concentrated orange juice for nutrition labeling. *Proc. Fla. State Hortic. Soc.* 87:206-209.

University of Florida (1980). *Spray Schedule for Citrus.* Lake Alfred, Fla., Argicultural Research and Education Center, Institute of Food and Agricultural Sciences. University of Florida.

U.S. Department of Agriculture (1956). Chemistry and technology of citrus, citrus products and byproducts. *Agriculture Handbook No. 98.* Washington D.C., U.S. Department of Agriculture.

U.S. Department of Agriculture (1976a). *Standards for Grades in Orange Juice.* Agric. Marketing Service, Fruit and Vegetable Division, Processed Products, Standardization and Inspection Branch. U.S. Department of Agriculture, Washington D.C.

U.S. Department of Agriculture (1976b). *World Citrus Fruit Production and Trade Statistic Summary 1968/69 to 1973/74 Seasons.* Washington, D.C., Foreign Agriculture Service.

U.S. Food and Drug Administration (1973). Food: nutrition labeling. *Federal Register* 38(49):6959-6961. Washington, D.C., U.S. Government Printing Office.

Vandercook, C. E. (1977a). Organic acids. In *Citrus Science and Technology* (S. Nagy, P. E. Shaw, and M. K. Veldhuis, eds.). Westport, Conn., Avi Publishing Co.

Vandercook, C. E. (1976b). Nitrogenous compounds. In *Citrus Science and Technology*, *Vol. 1* (S. Nagy, P. E. Shaw, and M. K. Veldhuis, eds.). Westport, Conn., Avi Publishing Co.

Veldhuis, M. K., and Gordon, W. O. (1947). Experiments on production of feed yeast from citrus press juice. *Proc. Fla. State Hortic. Soc.* 60:32-36.

Wallace, J. M. (1978). Virus and virus-like diseases. In *The Citrus Industry*, *Vol. 4* (W. Reuther, E. Calava, and G. Carman, eds.). Berkeley, Calf., Division of Agricultural Sciences, University of Calif.

Wardowski, W., Soule, J., Grierson, W., and Westbrook, G. (1979). Florida citrus quality tests. Gainesville, Fla., *University of Florida Ext. Bull. 188.*

Wheaton, T. A., and Stewart, I. (1973). Optimum temperature and ethylene concentrations for postharvest development of carotenoid pigments in citrus. *J. Am. Soc. Hortic. Sci.* 98:337-348.

Wilson, W. C., Holm, R. E., and Clark, R. K. (1977). Abscission chemicals—aid to citrus fruit removal. *Proc. Int. Soc. Citriculture* 2:404-406.

Wolford, R. W., and Attaway, J. A. (1967). Analysis of recovered natural flavor enhancement materials using gas chromatrography. *J. Agric. Food Chem.* 15:369-377.

Young, L. B., and Erickson, L. C. (1961). Influence of temperature on color changes in Valencia oranges. *Proc. Am. Soc. Hortic. Sci.* 78:197-200.

6

Fermented Fish Products

Florian Magno-Orejana College of Fisheries, University of the
Philippines in the Visayas, Diliman, Quezon City, Philippines

I. INTRODUCTION

Uyenco (1953) noted with chagrin that some early foreign workers of the Philippine Bureau of Science, for lack of understanding the true nature of certain products, described "bagoong," a Philippine fish paste, as "wholly or in part, a filthy decomposed or putrid animal substance and in many cases dangerous to health." Another described it as an evil-smelling substance greatly relished by many Filipinos.

Later investigators, however, proved these statements to be ill-founded. In fact, well-processed fermented fish products have come to be regarded by some Americans as highly desirable condiments.

A. Summary of Fermentation Methods

Fermentation methods may be grouped into four categories. Group 1 includes those containing high concentrations of salt, with 15 to 20% in the final product. The traditionally fermented fish products of Southeast Asia—for example, nampla (Thailand), budu (Malaysia), patis (Philippines), and nuoc-nam (Vietnam)—belong to this group. These products are used mainly as condiments and the protein intake is limited by the high salt content.

Group 2 comprises those methods employing a process of fermentation by the generation of organic acids or other processing materials (such as carbohydrate sources) to conserve the product. Included in this category are traditional products fermented by the combined effects of fish enzymes and microbial enzymes added with salt as starters. This group includes funazushi (Japan), burong-dalag (Philippines).

Group 3 methods are those employing preservatives or mineral acids to eliminate the microflora. The addition of strong acids (e.g., sulfuric and hydrochloric acids) to forage crops was developed by Virtanen in 1929 (Wirahadikusumah, 1968). However, the use of these corrosive chemicals requires care in handling, a distinct disadvantage.

Group 4 methods are those employing an initial dosage of organic acids or other preservative agents instead of mineral acids. Addition of organic acids, such as formic acid to fish, can be applied to produce chemical silage (Tatterson and Windsor, 1974). Additional processing costs and lack of expertise at the village level in handling strong acids are a few disadvantages of these methods.

The first two groups mentioned above will be given emphasis in this chapter. Fish silage methods (groups 3 and 4) have been developed recently—mainly for animal feeds—and will be discussed briefly.

B. Species of Fish and Shellfish Used Mainly for Fermentation

The by-catch of commercial shrimp trawlers is a potential source of raw material (Gonzales, 1977) for fermented fish and fish silage production and includes the following families: Ariidae (catfish), Leiognathidae (slipmouth), Mullidae (goatfish), Nemipteridae (butterfly bream), Platycephalidae (flatheads), Pomadasidae (grunts), Synodontidae and Scianidae (croakers and drums), Theraponidae (tiger fish), and Trichiuridae (cutlass fish).

Marine as well as freshwater fish, and shellfish such as oysters, shrimp, and mussels, have been used for fermentation processes (Table 1).

Table 1 Marine and Freshwater Fish and Shellfish Mainly Used in Fermentation Processes in Southeast Asia

Fish	Common name
Marine fish	
Rastrelliger sp.	Mackerel
Stolephorus indicus	Anchovy
Engraulis spp.	Anchovy
Stolephorus commersonii	Anchovy
Sardinella longiceps	Herring
Sardinella perforata	Deep-bodied herring
Sardinella fimbriata	Fimbriated herring
Leiognathus equulus	Slipmouth
Decapterus macrosoma	Round scad
Freshwater fish	
Opicephalus striatus	Mudfish
Trichogaster	Gourami
Anabas testudineus	Climbing perch
Clarias sp.	Catfish
Cirrhinus	Carp
Shellfish	
Ostrea/Crassostrea	Oysters
Atya sp.	Shrimp
Mytilus	Mussel
Omnastrephes sp.	Squid

C. Economic and Nutritional Significance of Fermented Fish Products in Southeast Asia

In Southeast Asia (excluding Japan) fish pastes and sauces are of greater importance than fish preserved by other methods, such as salting and drying, which are common to all parts of the world (Mackie et al., 1971).

Fermenting of fish or fish parts produces highly flavored products, and is one of the major food processing industries in many countries of the Indo-Pacific area. Practically all countries produce some type of fermented fish products; in some of these countries, the per capita consumption is quite high and is, in the case of poorer sections of the populace, the main source of animal protein in an otherwise predominantly rice diet (Subba Rao, 1967).

Periodic surpluses of fish and fish by-products may be used for fermentation, making these products available for human consumption, especially in developing countries. A reduction in wastage of fish through spoilage may be attained by conversion to fermented fish products with good shelf life.

The world consumption of protein and limiting amino acids is generally lower for the countries of Far East (55.3 g protein per day) than in North American (95.5 g/day) countries (Jansen and Howe, 1964). Expressed as the percentage of calories supplied by protein, the North American consumes 12.2% compared to 10.3% in the Far East, with 66.2% calories supplied by grain.

Nutritionally, fish sauce is an important protein supplement, supplying as much as 7.5% of an individual's nitrogen intake (Amano, 1962), and the high value of lysine in fish sauce can compensate for the low levels of lysine in rice (Jansen and Howe, 1964).

The fermented fish sauce of the nuoc-nam type, constitutes a good source of essential amino acids. The Vietnamese have a daily intake of 1.2 to 2.4 g of nitrogen from this source (Geiger and Borgstrom, 1962).

Reports of quantitative distribution of amino acids in fermented fish (Orejana, 1978; Beddows et al., 1976; and Amano, 1962), show that the essential amino acids are usually fairly well preserved. Generally speaking, fish tend to have a higher lysine and lower tryptophan content than meat, but have a relatively high methionine content (Mackie et al., 1971). Amino acid retention in both ngapi and nuoc-nam was reported to be good, but there was no sufficient information given (Amano, 1962). Free amino acid composition of salted internal organs of some Korean fish were reported by Shin and Kim (1968).

The protein efficiency ratio (PER) and digestibility coefficients of anchovy fish paste preparations in rats were found to compare well with that of standard casein (Tan et al., 1967). Amano (1962) noted that 2.5% of the total nitrogen is obtainable during fermentation and that the nitrogen of raw fish can be made better available with fish sauce

Table 2 Concentration of Metals in
Laboratory and Commercial
Roundscad Patis

Element	Commercial Sample (μg/g)	Laboratory Sample (μg/g)
Calcium	1.044	1.5400
Iron	0.0574	0.0825
Potassium	6.0870	9.5910
Magnesium	2.2670	2.8370
Sodium	146.6000	200.9000
Phosphorus	0.447	0.3690
Strontium	0.0636	0.0010
Zinc	0.0086	0.1287
Cobalt	0.0010	—
Manganese	0.0033	—

Source: Orejana (1978).

than with other types of fermentation, provided there is no loss of
nitrogen due to bacterial breakdown.

It would appear that fermentation does not improve the nutritive
values of the protein, although the digestibility for humans of some
fermented products is improved over that of the original ingredients
(van Veen and Steinkraus, 1970).

Fish sauces may be good sources of calcium and other inorganic
nutrients (Table 2). Certain fish species serve as important sources
of polyunsaturated fatty acids (Lovern, 1962). Amano (1962) and
Taarland et al. (1958) reported a high retention of the B-group of
vitamins in fermented fish products.

II. BIOCHEMICAL AND NUTRITIONAL COMPOSITION AND CHANGES OCCURRING DURING FERMENTATION

Several reviews on fish fermentation (Amano, 1962; van Veen, 1965;
Batra and Millner, 1976; and Mackie et al. 1971) have discussed many
aspects of the chemistry, biochemistry, and microbiology of fermented
fish products.

A. Proximate Analysis of Fish and Shellfish: Proteins and Lipids

The moisture, ash, protein, and oil content in some types of shellfish
used in fermented fish manufacture in Southeast Asia as listed in

Table 3 Moisture, Ash, and Protein Content and Oil in Various
Types of Fish and Shrimp Used in Fish Sauce

Species	Moisture (%)	Protein (%)	Oil (%)	Ash (%)
Mackerel, Herring, or Sardine	52.5-67.5	11.3-18.0	13.0-36.0	8.5-11.5
Anchovies (*Stolephorus* sp.)	52.5-73.7	11.3-13.4	13.0-36.0	8.5-11.5
Small whole herring (*Clupea*)	76.1	16.9	4.8	2.4
Shrimp	81.5	17.9	0.6	1.6
Slipmouth (*Leiognathus*)	79.5	17.32	1.82	—
Roundscad (*Decapterus*)	74.19	21.90	3.95	—

Source: Orejana (1978).

Table 3, shows a wide variation in protein and oil content. These
differences in proximate composition of the raw materials may account
for the variation in nutritive and organoleptic qualities in various
fish sauces. Proteolysis and lipolysis, whether microbial or non-
microbial will yield soluble compounds that contribute to the flavor
and aroma of the products.
      A study of the chemical composition of several shrimp by-catch
fish in the Gulf of Mexico (Meinke, 1974) shows that the protein content ranges from 14.4 to 20.8%, oil from 1.2 to 14.5%, ash from 3.2 to
8.8%, and moisture from 67.3 to 81.5%.
      A survey of the oil content of by-catch fish in Southeast Asia
(Raa and Gildberg, 1980) shows that the by-catch contains oily, intermediate, fat and lean fish, and that the composition is variable,
probably due to seasonal variations and fluctuations during growth
and maturation.
      Jebsen (1962) divided fish proteins into three groups. The first
group includes tropomyosin, actin, myosin, and actomyosin, which are
present at about 65% of the total proteins, and are soluble in neutral
salt of high ionic strength (higher than 0.50). The second group,
consists of globulin-x, myosin, and myoglobin, which are present at
about 25 to 30% of the total proteins and are extractable with neutral
salt of low ionic strength (lower than 0.15). The third group, consists

of stroma proteins and accounts for only about 3% of fish proteins. The proteins in this group are not soluble in neutral salt, dilute acid, or alkali.

B. Significant Role of Salt

Salt is used as a means of extracting liquid from fish and as a means of controlling fermentation. It is desirable from a nutritional stand-point to keep the concentration of NaCl as low as possible, and the amount used is determined by the processing requirements. The growth of spoilage bacteria likely to be present in fish is inhibited by high concentrations of salt. Prescott and Dunn (1959) reported that spoilage bacteria are generally inhibited by a salt level of 7% or more, hence, the level of salt in fish sauce preparation is more than adequate to arrest spoilage by nonhalophiles. The bacteriostatic effect of salt is due mainly to the reduction in water activity (a_W), which disrupts the osmotic balance in bacterial cells (Christian and Waltho, 1962).

Among the bacteria of fresh fish, the genus *Micrococcus* seems to offer the greatest resistance to NaCl in low concentrations of from 4 to 5.5% (Dussault, 1957).

The difference in the salt requirements of the enzymes might explain in part, at least, some of the variations in biochemical reactions observed at different salt concentrations.

The slow rate of fermentation is undoubtedly due to the high concentration of salt (Amano, 1962). Cathepsins which induce protein hydrolysis of muscle tissues of salted herring were inhibited by salt concentrations exceeding 15%.

According to Voskresensky (1965), the digestive enzymes from the visceral organs of fish are also affected by high salt concentrations, but to a lesser degree than the cathepsins.

C. Changes During Fermentation of Fish Sauce

Physical, chemical, and sensory changes occur in fish during fermentation. Fish sauce is prepared by mixing fish with salt in containers which are then tightly closed. The containers are filled to reduce the surface area in contact with air and to encourage rapid achievement of anaerobic conditions. A brine quickly forms due to osmotic action of salt. The proportion of salt to fish is set at a level which prevents bacterial spoilage processes and even leads to a rapid reduction in bacterial count. The solid material is progressively digested, the protein being solubilized gradually by enzyme action, leading to the increase in peptides and amino acids in the liquid component. In addition, free fatty acids appear in the supernatant, and browning, which contributes to the desirable color in patis, increases with prolonged periods of fermentation.

Table 4 Some Chemical and Bacterial Changes in Anchovy Patis Samples at Various Stages of Fermentation

	Days of fermentation					Commercial market sample
	0	15	40	70	140	
Amino nitrogen (mg/g)	1.23	6.23	10.18	13.30	12.92	10.34
Total volatile base (mg%)	34.22	33.22	63.87	130.60	163.00	246.00
Free fatty acid (%FFA)	4.77	3.51	1.21	8.06	8.32	—
Browning index E_{1cm}^{375nm}	—	0.35	0.39	0.54	0.68	0.70
Optical density $_{280nm}$ (protein)	—	0.41	0.44	0.50	0.49	—
Optical density $_{254nm}$	—	0.69	0.72	0.76	0.73	0.75
pH	6.00	5.60	5.47	5.35	5.30	5.40
$\log_{10}$ bacterial count	7.23	2.95	1.30	1.30	1.30	2.25
NaCl (%)	22.67	28.56	27.50	27.40	27.40	31.60

Source: Orejana (1978).

1. Proteolytic Changes in Fish Sauce

Most of the primary changes in protein during fish sauce fermentation take place during the first 2 months as evidenced by changes in amino nitrogen and soluble protein (Rose, 1918; Uyenco et al., 1953; and Orejana and Liston, 1979). The soluble protein/polypeptides ratio was relatively constant after 1 month, suggesting that most of the proteolytic activity occurred in the early period. Proteolysis in patis (Philippine fish sauce), resulting in the production of peptides and amino acids, was monitored by fractionation in Sephadex G-25 gel filtration and absorbance measurements of eluates from gel filtration chromatography (Orejana and Liston, 1979). Amino nitrogen and total volatile bases (TVB) increased steadily from 0 until the seventienth day of fermentation in patis (Table 4).

Changes in nitrogen-containing compounds in nuoc-nam fermented up to 180 days were analyzed by Rose (1918). Total nitrogen increased from 5.3 g in the 1-day samples, to 22.6 g/liter in the 3-month-old nuoc-nam. Uyenco et al. (1953) reported an increase in amino nitrogen from 2.9 to 20.7 g/liter, respectively, in 10-day- and 100-day-old patis from anchovies. Guevarra et al. (1972) reported an increase in crude protein (Kjeldahl N × 6.25) from 4.2 g/liter after 1 day to 12.2 g/liter after 35 days of fermentation of patis from anchovies. Beddows et al. (1979) have described the biochemical changes occurring during the manufacturing of "budu," a Malaysian fish sauce.

The chemical composition of various commercial brands of patis (Bersamin, 1964, Guevarra et al., 1978) nuoc-nam, and nampla (Boury, 1952; and Velankar, 1957) are shown in Table 5. The variations in the nitrogen content of fish sauces are due to the dilution of the residue in the fermented fish sauce after the removal of the fish pickle.

Table 5 Chemical Composition of Fermented Fish and Fermented Fish Pastes

Percent	Makassar fish from anchovy	Ngapi from shrimp	Trassi	Belachan	Shiokara from squid
Moisture	65.80	43.0	38.20	27-40	74.20
NaCl	—	22.0	—	13-18	7.82
Protein	15.0	20.0	38.70	30-40	11.60
Fat	0.40	2.0	3.4	1.4-2.6	2.83
Ash	16.90	27.0	12.4	20-24	8.68
Ammonia	—	0.6	—	—	—

Source: Subba Rao (1961); Amano (1962).

The amount of nitrogen before and after fermentation is difficult to observe, however, since there is little information involving the change from the raw material to the finished product (Amano, 1962). Orejana (1978), comparing the amino acid content of herring before and after fermentation, showed that nitrogen loss occurs by the formation of ammonia during fermentation.

2. Lipolysis and Browning

According to Dougan and Howard (1975) and Saisithi (1967), lipids in fish may be broken down during fermentation to yield fatty acids which may act as precursors for flavor and aroma compounds and may also participate in the browning reactions that take place progressively during fermentation. Beddows et al. (1980), however, reported that in their study of the origin and mechanisms of formation of the volatile fatty acids (VFA) present in budu (Malaysia), the acids did not appear to derive from the breakdown of the fish lipid. Instead, the amino acids from a ^{14}C-protein hydrolysate were shown to be the precursors of the n-butanoic and n-pentanoic acids and also to be contributing factors in the formation of other acids.

Browning reaction in fish sauce is considered desirable. Non-enaymic browning may include two types: sugar-amino acid or Maillard and lipid-amino reactions (Jones, 1962). In the lipid-amino reaction which most likely exists in fish sauce, there are three main types of browning reactions: (a) oxypolymerization; (b) oxidation of unsaturated oils; and (c) reaction between the carbonyl groups and the basic nitrogenous constituents. Defatting of anchovy fish samples before fermentation reduced browning in fish, indicating a major role of lipids in color development (Orejana, 1978).

D. Sources of Flavor and Aroma

Consumers often judge the quality of fish sauce by its aroma and flavor. Dougan and Howard (1975) described three major factors contributing to aroma of Thai fish sauce: (a) ammoniacal aroma due to ammonia and trimethylamine; (b) cheesy aroma due to low molecular weight VFA; and (c) meaty aroma caused by a large number of factors.

The aroma and flavor of nuoc-nam and nampla have been studied by several workers (Saisithi et al., 1966; Dougan and Howard, 1975; and Boez and Guillerm, 1930).

Substances such as N-aminopiperidines, aminovaleraldehyde, isovaleraldehyde, isovaleric acid, and pyridine have been isolated from fresh fish, as have free amino acids that can develop substances forming the basis for the development of flavors and odors (Bramstedt, 1957). Organic acids and sulfur compounds are generally found to be responsible for the flavor and aroma of fermented fish products. Yanagihara et al. (1963) found acetic acid and L-isovaleric acid to be responsible for the flavor of dried fish, fish soy (Japanese fish sauce), and fermented soybeans. Isovaleric acid may be derived from leucine. Truong-van-Chom (1963) reported that the characteristic aroma of nuoc-nam may be due to the formation of formic acid, acetic acid, and butyric acid. Fermented herring contained methyl mercaptan (Alm, 1965), and van Veen (1965) also reported that methyl mercaptan may contribute largely to the flavor of pedah-siam. A steady increase of methyl ketones in some fermented fish products was detected and was believed to be a component of flavor (van Veen, 1965), together with other substances such as carbonyl compounds and amines.

The presence of large amounts of 5'mononucleotides in salted yellowtail pickle was detected (Lee, 1968a) and high nucleotide levels were detected in patis (Orejana and Liston, 1981).

1. Amino Acids

Bound and free amino acids may contribute to the flavor of fermented fish products as well as to their nutritive quality.

Lee (1968b) analyzed the free amino acids in Korean fish sauce by paper partition chromatography and detected sixteen amino acids by ninhydrin color reaction. The content of some amino acids such as glutamic acid, lysine, leucine, and isoleucine was higher than others.

The sodium salt of glutamic acid has been detected in large amounts in fish paste (Bagoong), and the compounds and other salts of amino acids produced in the fermentation may be responsible for the characteristic odor and flavor of the finished products (Harrow and Apfelbaum, 1947).

The free amino acid composition of salted internal organs of several fishes were also determined. Seven essential amino acids—leucine, isoleucine, phenylalanine, tryptophan, threonine, lysine, and methionine (but not valine)—were detected in the organs. The content of tyrosine and hydroxyproline were relatively high, whereas tryptophan was in trace amounts.

Analyses of the free amino acids in salted clam pickle revealed the presence of high amounts of glutamic acid and aspartic acid (Lee, 1968b). Lee considered the abundance of these amino acids as contributing significantly to the specific flavor of the food. Large amounts of histidine and arginine were detected in salted yellowtail pickle. In salted oyster pickle, a high content of some essential amino acids such as lysine, threonine, isoleucine, and leucine was demonstrated, and the specific flavor was attributed to those sweet amino acids. Contents of alanine and glycine in the salted oyster pickle were four times as much as the other amino acids measured.

The amino acid profiles of artifically produced hydrolysates were compared with some commercial sources of Thai and Malay fish sauces, and arginine was shown to be present in some of the artificially produced sauce and absent in the commercial samples. Glutamic acid and

Table 6 Amino Acid Profiles of Commercial Fish Sauces from Thailand, Malaysia, Philippines, Vietnam, and Burma

Amino acid (in mg/ml)	Thai fish sauce	Malaysian (Budu)	Philippines (Patis)	Vietnam (nuoc-nam; ordinary quality)	Burma (ngapi)[a]
Glutamic acid	5.82	1.78	14.48	4.0	8.8
Alanine	2.82	1.52	6.74	4.2	9.3
Aspartic acid	2.76	1.10	6.59	2.4	5.6
Lysine	0.72	0.40	6.02	4.0	8.4
Valine	1.82	1.00	5.87	3.0	4.3
Leucine	2.02	1.64	5.72	4.0	5.9
Glycine	1.10	0.44	5.61	2.4	8.5
Threonine	1.61	0.70	4.90	2.0	2.7
Proline	6.88	0.26	4.37	0.5	3.0
Isoleucine	1.82	0.98	4.01	4.0	3.8
Phenylalanine	–	–	3.02	1.5	2.3
Serine	0.74	0.16	2.97	0.8	–
Methionine	0.74	0.48	2.98	0.8	1.3
Histidine	3.06	1.66	2.82	0.3	2.1
Cystine	0.24	0.42	0.90	0.25	–
Tyrosine	0.14	0.32	0.53	0.8	1.4
Arginine	–	–	0.16	2.0	5.8

[a]As grams of amino acid nitrogen per 100 g of dialysable nitrogen.
Source: Beddows et al. (1979); Orejana (1978); and Subba Rao (1967).

proline occurred at relatively higher levels in Thai sauce (Beddows et al., 1976). Table 6 shows the amino acid profiles of commercial fish sauce from Thailand, Malaysia, Philippines, Vietnam, and Burma.

The quantitative distribution of amino acids in commercial samples at various stages of fermentation of round scad patis indicated the decrease in arginine, histidine, and tyrosine with longer periods of incubation. Amino acids detected in anchovy, herring, and round scad patis samples by ion-exchange chromatography include the following: glutamic acid, glycine, aspartic acid, lysine, alanine, arginine, threonine, valine, serine, proline, histidine, leucine, isoleucine, phenylalanine, methionine, tyrosine, and half-cystine (Orejana, 1978).

2. Volatile Fatty Acids

VFA contribute to the cheesy aroma of fish sauces (Dougan and Howard, 1975, and Nieto, 1979). The mechanism of formation of VFA have been attributed either to amino acid breakdown or to lipolysis (Dougan and Howard, 1975; and Beddows et al. 1980).

Nguyen-An-Cu and Vialard-Goudou (1953), identified ethanoic acid and n-butanoic acid, and suggested that lactic-acid-digesting bacteria could be involved in VFA formation.

Truong-van-Chom (1963) found formic, acetic, propionic, and n-butyric acids, and Saisithi et al. (1966) obtained isobutyric acid instead of n-butyric acid in addition to the other volatile fatty acids.

The quantitative proportion of VFA in Malaysian and Thai fish sauces was studied by Dougan and Howard (1975) and Beddows et al. (1976) and is given in Table 7. Beddows (1980), using a $U-^{14}C$-protein

Table 7 Concentrations of Volatile Acids Present in Some Fish Sauce Samples (mg/ml)

Acid	Thai Fish Sauce Sample[a]				Malaysian[b]
	A	B	C	D	
Acetic	2.10	5.30	3.66	4.70	2.30
Propionic	0.11	0.47	0.33	0.33	0.11
Iso-butyric	—	0.01	0.04	—	0.08
n-Butyric	0.06	0.31	0.15	0.16	0.16
Iso-valeric	0.30	0.06	0.46	0.03	0.07
n-Valeric	—	—	—	—	0.04

[a]Samples were obtained form different factories. Sample A is a 12-month-old sample of fish sauce using *Stolephorus* sp., B is a 48-month-old sample; C is a 6-month-old sample whose values are an average of three samples reported; and D is a 15-month-old sample.
[b]Sample prepared by Beddows et al. (1976).
Source: Howard and Dougan (1976); and Beddows et al. (1976).

hydrolysate, attributed the formation of acids to some bacteria acting as precursors on the amino acids. The appropriate VFA were produced when spoilage was allowed to occur prior to salting under normal conditions in Malaysia. The change in VFA with time in budu fermentation is shown in Table 8.

Kasemsarn (1963) believes that reductive deamination, rather than oxidative deamination, of amino acids occurs more often in fish sauce produced under virtually anaerobic conditions.

III. ROLE OF MICROORGANISMS

A. Fermented Fish Sauces with 20 to 25% Salt

By the time seafood has been prepared for fermentation and the process is about to start, large numbers of bacteria and yeasts from diverse origins are likely to be present. There are four possible sources of fermented inoculum: (a) organisms occurring naturally in marine animals; (b) organisms associated with the marine environment and seawater; (c) terrestial organisms not normally associated with the marine environment; and (d) organisms associated with natural microflora of marine salt and other additives in preparing seafoods.

The production of flavors and aroma in fermented fish products has been related to the growth of different types of bacteria. Fifty-two bacterial strains representing fifteen species of microorganisms and two species of yeast were isolated from fermented Korean seafoods, including cuttlefish, clams, oysters, pollack, and anchovy (Sands and Crisan, 1974). *Bacillus* sp. comprised 36 of the 52 strains and occurred in each fermented food. *Micrococcus* and *Pediococcus* were the second and the third most commonly isolated genera. *Pseudomonas, Serratia,* and *Clostridium* were isolated only from a single species. *Debaryomyces* and *Hansenula anomala* were the only yeasts isolated, and they were found exclusively in the two samples of fermented roe. Eleven of the microorganisms, representing 60% of the isolated cultures, have been reported from the marine environment or from fermented seafoods by other authors.

Nagao and Kimura (1951) isolated halo-tolerant bacteria from Ikashiokara containing 20% NaCl and found *Micrococcus* sp., *Lactobacillus* spp., and *Bacillus* sp., but in addition found *Achromobacter, Flavobacterium,* and *Vibrios.*

Saisithi (1967) isolated a homofermentative organism, *Pediococcus halophilus,* from Thai fish sauce and attributed the typical fish aroma to this organism.

Avery (1952) and Orejana and Liston (1979) showed that in patis manufacture, the initial bacterial count decreased rapidly as the fermentation proceeded (Table 9). Similar studies by Velankar (1957) showed that nampla obtained at the end of the first month has a count

Table 8 The Change in Volatile Fatty Acid Concentration with Time in a Budu Fermentation Tank at Kuala Trenganna, Malaysia

Time (days)	Ethanoic (mg/ml)	Propionic (mg/ml)	iso-Butanoic (mg/ml)	n-Butanoic (mg/ml)	iso-Pentanoic (mg/ml)
1	1.29	0.14	0	0.20	0.04
2	1.23	0.10	0	0.17	0.07
3	1.36	0.11	0	0.17	0.07
5	1.15	0.07	0	0.18	0.04
7	1.19	0.12	0	0.24	0.04
14	1.21	0.14	0	0.21	0.10
28	1.70	0.12	0	0.20	0.08
60	1.70	0.13	0	0.22	0.07
91	1.81	0.12	0	0.23	0.06
156	2.15	0.12	0	0.23	0.07

Source: Beddows et al (1979).

Table 9 Log_{10} Bacterial Count of Anchovies at Various Stages of Fermentation

No. of days	PC Agar	
	without NaCl	with 10% NaCl
0	7.23	2.41
15	2.95	2.00
40	1.30	—
70	1.30	—
140	1.30	—

Source: Orejana (1979).

of about 500 colonies per ml, and strains of *Micrococcus* and *Bacillus* were found to be the dominant organisms.

B. Fermented Fish Products with Cooked Rice and Salt

In another type of fermented fish product, a fermentable carbohydrate source such as cooked rice is added. This combination favors the growth of lactic acid bacteria. The carbohydrate is first hydrolyzed by amylases from the rice mixture, and the simpler sugars are then acted upon by lactic acid bacteria which may be added as a starter culture, if necessary.

Lactic acid bacteria may be either homofermentative or heterofermentative. The former is more desirable in fermented products because it produces 2 mols of lactic acid per mol of glucose, while the heterofermentative variety may produce other undesirable end products in addition to 1 mol each of lactic acid, ethyl alcohol, and carbon dioxide per mol of glucose.

Burong-dalag (*Ophicephalus* sp.) with rice and salt was observed to become acidic due to the metabolism of lactic acid bacteria. The lactics—*Leuconostoc mesenteroides*, *Pediococcus cerevisiae*, and *Lactobacillus plantarum*—were the dominant species isolated. A change in the dominant species with time was noted, indicating fermentation by a sequence of bacteria (Orillo and Pederson, 1968).

In balao-balao (Solidum, 1979), a fermented rice-shrimp mixture generally prepared by mixing cooked rice, whole raw shrimp, and solar salt (20% of shrimp weight), a sequence of microorganisms similar to that of burong-dalag (Orillo and Pederson, 1968) and sauerkraut were also observed. A decrease in pH, due to the formation of lactic acid from hydrolyzed sugars added to the fish-salt mixutre by microbial action, contributed to preservative action in the fermented fish-rice mixture.

IV. PROTEOLYTIC ENZYMES

A. Fish Muscle and Viscera

Proteolytic enzymes from the fish may be classified into: (a) acid proteases (pepsin); (b) serine proteases (trypsin and chymotrypsin); (c) cathepsins and thiol proteinases; and (d) carboxypeptidases and aminopeptidases.

At neutral pH, the enzymes of the viscera and the digestive system are the most active. Croston (1960) noted that extracts of pyloric caeca from chinook salmon are inactivated in acid conditions (pH 2 to 3, in contrast to mammalian trypsin). In Japanese fermented fish products (Shiokara-type) using viscera, the digestive enzymes hydrolyze the fish proteins during fermentation. A seasonal variation in the activity of trypsin and pepsin of some freshwater fish has been shown (Ananichev, 1959).

The catheptic enzymes in fish muscle have maximum activity in both acid and alkaline conditions. However, proteolytic activity varies with species (Groninger, 1964; and Takahashi, 1961).

Siebert (1962), in his studies on the enzymes of marine fish muscle and their role in fish spoilage at 37°C, revealed that freshly caught fish display a penetration from the gut through the abdominal cavity into the muscular tissue if the digestive tract is not carefully removed within a short time after capture. Trypsin from the intestines increases eightfold in the abdominal cavity and the abdominal part of the muscles within 4 hr aboard the trawler.

Using cod muscle, Siebert and Schmitt (1965) detected cathepsins, peptidases, transaminases, amidases, amino acid decarboxylases, glutamic dehydrogenases, and related enzymes.

Decarboxylases, transaminases, and deaminases have also been isolated from fish muscle (Tarr, 1972). Muscle of mackerel or yellowtail, homogenized and partially purified, was able to catalyze the enzymatic decarboxylation of histidine, giving rise to histamine (Simidu et al., 1953). There is now good evidence that fish muscle enzymes exist in the particle-bound state, presumably attached to lysosomes (Siebert and Schmitt, 1965).

Trypsin activity at various stages of anchovy fermentation was high up to 1 month in patis (Table 10; Orejana, 1978). Cathepsins from fish muscle also contribute to the proteolytic breakdown during fermentation, although high salt concentration reduces enzyme activity in patis.

B. Bacteria, Molds, and Yeasts

Bacterial, mold, and yeast proteases are predominantly extracellular, and are isolated in active form from the culture filtrates of the appropriate organisms (Matsubara and Feder, 1971): (a) acid proteases,

Table 10 Trypsinlike Activity at Various Stages of Fermentation of Commercial and Laboratory Roundscad Patis

Preparation	Days fermented	Trypsin units[a]	$\Delta E/min$ [b]	Activity as % maximum
Laboratory	0	44.36	.013 ± .0010	22.04
roundscad	1	146.75	.043 ± .009	72.88
patis	6	201.24	.059 ± .002	100.00
	30	109.21	.032 ± .001	52.24
	60	95.56	.028 ± .002	47.45
	77	58.01	.017 ± .002	28.81
Commercial	1	262.80	.077 ± .0010	100.00
roundscad	5	10.20	.003 ± .0014	
patis	7	9.20	.009 ± .004	11.68
	8	6.80	.002 ± .001	2.50
	12	13.60	.004 ± .001	5.17
	24	27.30	.008 ± .004	10.39

[a] Trypsin units per liter $= \dfrac{E/min}{2.93} \times$ dilution factor $\times$ 100 .

[b] $\Delta E/min$ = Change in extinction at 410 nm per min (slope of E vs. time).

Source: Orejana (1981).

characterized by their low pH requirement reminiscent of animal pepsins and rennins (e.g., *Aspergillus saitori*, acid protease; *Rhizopus*, acid protease); (b) DFP-sensitive alkaline proteases, represented by the subtilisin which appear to be serine proteases similar to trypsin and chymotrypsin (e.g., trypsinlike enzymes from *Streptomyces griseus*; enzymes in this group are active at neutral or alkaline pH); (c) Neutral proteases, exhibiting pH optimum near neutrality (including *Bacillus subtilis* neutral protease, thermolysins, and neutral proteases from *Streptomyces griseus* and *Aspergillus oryzae*); and (d) thiol proteases, which are microbial enzymes found to be sensitive to sulfhydryl reagents (e.g., *Streptococcal* proteinase and clostripain).

Nonirradiated and radiation-sterilized anchovies were fermented and proteolysis compared to ascertain the role of microbial proteases during fermentation. Proteolytic activity of untreated patis was similar to that of radiation-sterilized anchovies, indicating that protein breakdown due to microbial enzymes are insignificant compared to the endogenous enzymes in the fish (Orejana and Liston, 1981). Similarly, Alm (1965) tried to establish the true significance of bacteria in the maturing process of anchovies by gamma radiation or antibiotics. Maturing was faster in ungutted Isclandic herring than in eviscerated fish. Alm (1965) attributed this to either the microbial enzymes in the intestine or proteolytic enzymes of the digestive tract.

C. Plants

The plant enzymes bromelain, ficin, and papain may be added to fish-salt mixtures to accelerate the rate of fermentation. The products of hydrolysis may differ, depending on the substrate specificity of the enzyme. If the cleavage site of the protein occurs at the aromatic ring, the formation of bitter peptides may affect the flavor of the fermented product.

V. PRESERVATION METHODS

A. Traditional Methods

Cheap and reliable methods of preservation of fish and shellfish must be employed to improve shelf life in developing countries where refrigeration and canning are expensive. Salting is the most important means of preserving fish in Southeast Asia (Hamm and Clague, 1950, and Sulit and Martin, 1955).

Fermentation is an ancient procedure for processing fish, once widespread in application, but now used principally in Southeast Asia (Kreuzer, 1973).

Traditional products will be grouped into two categories: (a) those mainly fermented in the presence of salt by the action of enzymes in fish flesh and entrails; and (b) those fermented by combined effects of fish and microbial enzymes which may be added as starters in addition to salt. In Southeast Asia, cooked or boiled rice or another carbohydrate source is usually added to the fish-salt mixture.

1. Fermented Fish Sauces with 20 to 25% Salt

Fish pastes and sauces are fermented as a result of the action of proteolytic enzymes in the presence of high concentrations of salt. This highly salted type is of greater importance in Southeast Asia (excluding Japan) than fish preserved by other methods (such as salting and drying) which are common to all parts of the world (Mackie et al. 1971).

Southeast Asia. Fish sauce is a clear, brown liquid with a characteristic flavor and aroma, and is rich in amino acids and soluble proteins. The procedure for manufacture of fish sauces has been described by a number of authors (van Veen, 1965; Pederson, 1971; Subba Rao, 1961). Nuoc-nam from Vietnam, shottsuru from Japan, nampla from Thailand, patis from the Philippines, and budu from Malaysia are among the best

known of the fish sauces. A glossary of some fermented fish products appear at the end of this chapter.

Generally, the process involves washing and packing of eviscerated
fish with high concentrations of salt (usually 4 to 5 parts salt to 6 parts
of fish) in large earthenware or wooden containers. The fish are then
allowed to hydrolyze by the action of enzymes. After several months,
a clear amber liquid rises and is decanted or separated by pressing it
from the sediments. The clear liquid is highly priced, while the sedi-
ment is frequently eaten with freshly cooked fish. Species commonly
used for this purpose is shown in Table 1.

The methods of manufacturing nuoc-nam may vary somewhat in
other parts of Indochina. The basic principle, however, is the same.
They involve the careful regulation of enzymic degradation and extraction of fish proteins under mild pressure and anaerobic conditions
(van Veen, 1965). Essentially, the method of manufacture consists of
mixing uneviscerated fish and salt in earthenware pots which are then
tightly sealed and buried in the ground. The pots are dug up after
several months, opened, and the supernatant liquid, nuoc-nam, is desalted.

On a commercial scale, nuoc-nam is manufactured using large vats
fitted with bamboo taps near the bottom (Rose, 1918; Subba Rao, 1967).
Fish and salt are layered alternately from bottom to top in the vats, with
a final layer of salt being placed on top. Generally, 4 to 5 parts of
salt to 6 parts of fish are used. The bloody liquor (nuoc-boi) is drained
off over the next 3 days and kept separate. The fish are pressed to
pack thoroughly and flattened the upper surface. Some of the nuoc-
boi is poured back over the fish until they are fully immersed. The
vat is then covered with bamboo trays and heavily weighted. Depending on the size and the species of fish, the vats are tapped after
varying periods of time, and the fermented liquor is drawn off. For
small fish, only a few months are required to produce nuoc-nam, but
for larger fish, a year or more may be required (Westenberg, 1951).

Lower qualities of nuoc-nam are obtained by leaching the residue
in vats with fresh brine or seawater. During the leaching process
in some cases, caramelized honey, toasted rice, or maize are added to
the vats. These additives may lower the pH due to the production of
lactic acid and butyric acids (Vialard-Goudou, 1941), and improve the
keeping quality of the sauce. The nuoc-nam is sometimes further
matured or aged in the sun in glass bottles or earthenware.

Standards and regulations as to the quality of nuoc-nam were introduced in Vietnam in 1933 to safeguard the consumer against adulteration
of the product. A minimum of 15.0 g nitrogen per liter of nuoc-nam in
the south and 5.0 g per liter of nuoc-nam in the north were required
(Westenberg, 1951).

Present regulations (Subba Rao, 1967) require at least 16 g nitrogen
per liter of first-class nuoc-nam, with the bound titratable nitrogen
being at least 50% of this figure. Ammoniacal nitrogen should not
exceed 50% of the bound nitrogen.

Nguyen Thi Lau and Richard (1959) state that a measure of the
degree of spoilage is given by the ratio of ammoniacal nitrogen to
bound nitrogen, which should never exceed 1:2. Insufficient salt
results in the increase of ammonia nitrogen over amino acid nitrogen,
while excessive salting retards the digestion of the protein but reduces the ammonia-to-amino-acid ratio to a minimum. Chemical analysis
of nuoc-nam showed the presence of 12.4% total nitrogen; amino acid
nitrogen, 5.7 g/liter; NaCl, 28%; and salts of phosphorus, calcium,
magnesium, and sulfur and 18 amino acids (Nguyen Thi Lau and
Richard, 1959).

In the Philippines the counterpart of nuoc-nam is called "patis."
The method of manufacture of patis is somewhat similar to that of
nuoc-nam, although less complicated, and it requires considerable time
(van Veen, 1965). The first extract with a characteristic flavor is
known as class A or high-grade patis. After the first extraction,
saturated brine is added to extract the fish flavor repeatedly. This
accounts for the various grades of patis in the local markets. Some
factories sell the fish residue after two extractions as canned or bottled products known as "bagoong" (Arcega, 1969; Bersamin, 1964).
The species of fish used and the manner of processing are similar to
that used in nuoc-nam. Patis is usually prepared from small fish of
the genera *Stolephorus, Engraulis, Clupeides, Dorosoma,* and *Decap-*
terus (Bersamin and Napugan, 1962; Hamm and Clague, 1950; Uyenco
et al., 1953; Orejana and Liston, 1979). Small shrimp (*Atya* spp.) or
alamang, goby fry (*Ostrea* spp.), herring fry (*Clupea* spp.) and
anchovy (*Stolephorus* spp.) yield the best quality sauces.

Sufficient salt to saturate the water content of the fish must be
added. A ratio of 1 part salt to 3.5 to 4 parts of fish yields a product
with 20 to 25% salt. Hamm and Clague (1950) and Orejana (1978) showed
that temperatures up to 45°C at the initial stage of 1 to 2 weeks of
fermentation increases the rate of protein degradation.

Subba Rao (1967) reported considerable variation in the nitrogen
contents of various grades of commercially produced patis. The metal
content of patis (Orejana, 1978) as shown in Table 2 includes a high
level of Ca (1.04 to 1.54 μg/g) and Mg (2.2 to 2.4 μg/g). The amino
acid profile of patis is shown in Table 6.

Shellfish sauce can be prepared from small shellfish such as oysters
and clams (Namisato, 1974). To process, the shellfish is first washed
in clean water. The shells are crushed and the meat is removed. The
meat is washed in clean water and 3 to 5% salt is added. Shellfish sauce
contains seasoning and flavoring compounds which are different from
those of fish sauce. High levels of succinic acid were found in shellfish, for example, in short-neck clams, 0.03%; in common freshwater
clams, 0.41%; in white clams, 0.15%; and in earshells and hen clams,
less than 0.03%.

In Thailand, the local name for the sauce is "nampla" (Saisithi,
1967; Subba Rao, 1967; van Veen, 1965; Velankar, 1957). The

production of fish sauce in 1961 was 40,000 tons (Saisithi, 1967).
Species mainly used for nampla production include, *Stolephorus* spp.,
Scomber, *Rastrelliger*, *Cirrhinus*, and *Clupeidae*. After fermentation,
ripening in the sun may be required, lasting from several months to
2 years.

Budu, a Malaysian fish sauce, is a brown liquid having a pH of 5.6,
saturated with salt, and containing 1.77% organic nitrogen (with some
66% being in the form of amino acids) and 0.12% being volatile nitrogen.
Beddows et al. (1979) have found 75% of this volatile nitrogen to be
ammonia. Tamarind and palm sugar may be added to the fish-salt
mixture in earthenware jars.

In Indonesia, the liquors obtained from salting fish in different
ways are boiled and concentrated. The product is called "patis" in the
Philippines and "tuk-trey" in Cambodia (van Veen, 1965). In a process
analogous to that for nuoc-nam, fish sauce called "ketjapakan" is produced in Borneo from *Clupea*, *Stolephorus*, *Leiognathus* spp., and from
freshwater species of *Osteochilus* and *Puntius* (Saanin, 1954).

Japan. The Japanese equivalent of the nuoc-nam of the Southeast
Asia is soy sauce ("shoyu"), produced from soybeans. However, a
sauce (shottsuru) is also produced in Japan from sand fish (hata-hata,
Arctoscopus japonicus; Subba Rao, 1967). Sardines, anchovies, and
molluscs are also used as raw materials. The liquid is filtered, boiled,
and stored after fermentation, sometimes for years. Soybean lees or
"koji" (wheat fermented with yeast) may be added to shottsuru to
process it into "shoyu." Squid viscera yields "ika-shoyu," hata-hata
yields "uwo-shoyu."

Europe and the Mediterranean. Fish sauces in the Mediterranean
region have been produced since classical times (Mackie et al. 1971),
although they are not of much significance in Europe. In Greece,
"garos," a liquefied fish product, is still made from the liver of
Scomber colias (Kelaiditis, 1949). Larvae or small fish of *Aphya pel-*
luerda, *Gobius*, *Atherina*, *Melleta*, and *Engraulis* spp. have been used
to prepare fish sauce called "pissala" in southern France (Creac'h,
1952). The liquid is filtered after fermenting the fish with salt for
10 to 12 days. In the Sudan, small, fatty fish from the Nile have been
converted to a fermented product called "fessikh" (Cutting, 1962).

2. Fish Pastes and Whole Fish

Southeast Asia. A considerable proportion of the protein intake of
many Southeast Asians is obtained through consumption of fish pastes,
which are more important nutritionally than the fish sauces. There are
two types of fish pastes in Southeast Asia: (a) fish-salt mixtures, and
(b) products fermented in the presence of cooked, boiled, or roasted
rice mollasses containing yeasts and molds.

In the Philippines, bagoong is one of the staple protein foods of an ordinary household. In 1977, production amounted to 272,000 kg valued at 1.7 million pesos. Hamm and Clague (1950) defined bagoong as "a clear, sound product obtained by the fermentation of properly prepared whole or ground fish, shrimp, fish roe, shrimp roe, in the presence of not less than 20% nor more than 25% by weight of salt." Fish of genera *Stolephorus, Sardinella, Decapterus,* and *Atya* are used. As a by-product from fish sauce manufacture, the product has a pasty consistency and is sometimes colored by adding "angkak," a rice treated with a red yeastlike organism *Monascus purpureus* (Miller et al., 1946). Factors that affect the degree of proteolysis include: temperature, time, species, and size of fish, purity, and concentration of salt used (Uyenco, 1953; Avery, 1950; Hamm and Clague, 1950; Orejana, 1978).

Balao-balao (Philippines) is a fermented rice-shrimp mixture gengerally prepared by mixing cooked rice, whole raw shrimp, and solar salt (20% of the shrimp weight), and then allowing the mixture to ferment for several days (Solidum, 1979; Arroyo et al., 1977). The mixture becomes acidic during fermentation, the shell of the shrimp reddens and softens, and the mixture acquires a flowing consistency indicative of starch hydrolysis. It is commonly prepared by sautéing with garlic and onions, and is eaten either as a sauce or main dish. The changes in acidity of balao-balao during fermentation are shown in Table 11.

Table 11 Changes in Acidity of Balao-Balao During Fermentation at Room Temperature (28 ± 1°C)

Fermentation (days)	pH	Titratable acid as lactic acid (%)	Volatile acid as acetic acid (%)	Fixed acid as lactic acid (%)
0	7.52	0.12	—	—
1	6.15	0.42	—	—
2	5.34	0.53	0.03	0.49
3	4.63	0.96	0.08	0.83
4	4.37	1.38	0.13	1.19
5	4.07	1.81	0.16	1.57
6	3.97	1.62	0.12	1.45
7	3.83	1.77	0.11	1.61
8	3.83	2.16	0.13	1.97
9	3.77	1.96	0.17	1.70
10	3.80	2.00	0.10	1.84

Source: Solidum (1979).

In Khmer republic, the fish paste corresponding to bagoong (Philippines) is called "prahoc." Fish are beheaded, scaled, gutted, thoroughly washed, then drained for 24 hr. Fish are salted, dried in the sun, then pounded into a paste, which is placed in open jars in the sun. The pickle which forms on top is removed and consumed when no further pickle forms (Mackie et al., 1971). It contains 37.8 g of nitrogen per liter, 22.4 g of which is soluble (van Veen, 1965).

In Cambodia, Vietnam, and Laos, addition of grains such as rice, glutinous or roasted, and molasses to the paste is very common. To prepare "mam-cho," the fermented fish is mixed with glutinous rice and "angkak;" the mixture is well kneaded and allowed to ferment for 3 more months. In "mam-ca-sat," unripe papaya or pineapple is added to accelerate ripening (van Veen, 1965). A mixture of salted fish and rice bran is used to prepare "padec" in Laos. Similar to prahoc, padec is called "kapi" in Thailand (Subba Rao, 1967) and mam-tom in Vietnam (Westenberg, 1951). Table 12 shows the chemical composition of various Vietnamese pastes or mams.

In Burma, the most important fishery product is "ngapi" (Subba Rao, 1967), which includes not only wet, salted, fermented fish, but also shrimp paste, which is a comminuted product. The fresh fish is immersed in brine for 2 days, then drained in a basket overnight. It is then packed in dry salt in baskets and allowed to stand for 3 days until all the salt has drained off. The product is then packed in dry salt in earthenware jars ready for sale.

In Malaysia, a product related to ngapi is produced. "Belachan" is a paste prepared from small shrimp, with only a relatively small amount of salt added (4 to 5 kg per 100 kg of shrimp). Due to the low salt content, bacterial decomposition may occur after a few days.

"Trassi" is a fish paste manufactured in Indonesia (van Veen, 1965). The paste is dried in the sun in thin layers. Three parts of shrimp yield 2 to 2.5 parts of trassi. In a similar product, "trassi-ikan," the fish are powdered and dried until a paste is formed. Starch, rice bran, potato peel, and dyestuffs are sometimes added. A fermented product, "makassar" fish (red fish), consists of small, salted fish in a spicy red sauce and is used as a condiment in Indonesia. Anchovies (*Engraulis* and *Stolephorus*) are used in this process. The products contain 65 to 80% moisture, 15% protein, 0.4% fat, and 16.9% ash. To prepare makassar fish, the fish are beheaded and placed in earthenware jars with large amounts of salt. After a few days, the fish and salt mixture is mixed with angkak and ragi (a Japanese preparation made from yeast and rice) and spices. After a few days, the fish and pickle develop a deep red color.

A similar product of eastern India and Pakistan is prepared from small fish, mostly *Barbus* spp. The product, called "sida," is dried in the sun, damped, and packed with crude fish oil in earthenware jars. The jars are sealed with clay and buried for 3 to 4 months.

Table 12 Chemical Composition of Various Vietnamese Fish Pastes

	Mam-ca-loc (*Ophicephalus*)	Mam-ca-sat (*Trichogaster*)	Mam-ca-tre (*Clarias*)	Mam-ca-ro (*Anabas*)	Mam-ca-linh (*Dangila* sp.)
Water	45.55	56.60	50.35	51.27	58.22
Protein	22.57	20.10	26.25	21.87	21.87
Lipid	1.08	0.93	0.69	2.02	4.00
Carbohydrate	20.31	14.87	7.14	15.61	1.30
Ash	10.75	11.50	15.57	9.43	14.61
Chloride	5.82	6.15	6.03	6.07	6.50
Sodium	3.62	3.60	4.00	3.00	4.40
Potassium	0.28	0.30	0.30	0.26	0.28

Source: Nguyen Thi Lau and Richard (1959) as cited by Mackie et al. (1971).

In addition to fish sauces and fish pastes, fermented whole fish are also prepared in Southeast Asia. The best known of this group is a product in Indonesia called "pedah-Siam" (van Veen, 1965). It is made from salted *Rastrelliger* spp., *Scomber neglectus*, and *Scomber kanagurta*. The entrails are removed through the throat during the pretreatment, then salted in a ratio of 3 parts fish to 1 part salt, and stored for 24 hr. Ripening takes place in vitrually anaerobic conditions. Partial dehydration of the fermented fish occurs since the liquid or pickle which forms is drained off. A fresh red color and a pasty consistency are obtained after maturation. The brown color is due to fat oxidation products, and a peculiar odor may arise from methyl ketones. Pedah-Siam contains 44 to 47% moisture, 21 to 22% protein, 7 to 15% fat, and 15 to 17% NaCl. In hot tropical climates, the fish deteriorates rapidly.

Indonesia produces an important product called "pindang" (van Veen, 1965). Salt varying from 5 to 15% by weight of the fish is added to the water in which the fish is boiled. The fish is then packed in earthenware pots or petrol cans and kept for days or months.

In India, mackerel (*Rastrelliger* spp.) is gutted and gilled and salted in a salt-to-fish ratio of 1:5 or more. These are then wrapped in mats and buried in pits (Subba Rao, 1961). The process yields a product similar to pedah-Siam.

Dried pulp of tamarind (*Garcinia camboges*) is added to gutted fish mixed with salt (3:1) in a pickle cure or the "Colombo cure" method used in southern India. The lowering of pH to about 6 improves the process (Ventkataraman and Sreenivasan, 1955). Five percent acetic acid may be used to replace the tamarind (Vasavan and Varma, 1959).

Japan. Although Japan produces diverse types of marine foods, these can be grouped into three categories: (a) fermented fish products called "shiokara," prepared by fermenting fish meat or visceral mass (roe or milt and other parts of visceral mass), with spoilage being prevented by the addition of salt; (b) cured marine foods prepared by fermenting fish roe or meat in boiled rice ("i-zushi"), in "koji" (Koji-zuke"), in rice bran ("nuka-zuke"), in sake lees ("kasu-zuke"), or in vinegar ("su-zuke"), referred to as "tsukemono"; and (c) shiokara-type products prepared from fermented squid meat, bonito visceral mass, sea urchin, sea cucumber, crab roe, or visceral mass of abalone (Tanikawa, 1971). Shiokara is a dark brown viscous-liquid-containing solid tissue. In squid shiokara, slices of squid flesh are mixed with the paste. Salt is added to these mixtures to retard spoilage.

Visceral proteolytic enzymes of pyloric caeca, pancreas, intestines, and stomach act on the proteins, as observed in the fermentation of nuoc-nam. Zenitani (1955) attributed the ripening of shiokara to the action of halotolerant and halophilic bacteria such as *Micrococcus* sp. The role of bacteria in the ripening of shiokara has also been studied by Nagao (1951a and b) and Nagao and Kimura (1951). A variety of cured fermented fish products are produced in Japan. Addition of boiled rice to fermented fish and salt yield products called "sushi." The low pH produced by the lactic acid bacteria growing in the cereal contribute to the preservative action (Matsushita, 1937). The products are prepared from "ayu" (*Plocoglossus altivelis*), and a sand fish (*Astroscospus japonicus*) (Tanikawa, 1971). The general procedure usually involves the gutting of fish and curing with 20 to 30% by weight of salt. The fish bodies are stored for 1 to 2 months, then desalted and the liquor drained off. Boiled rice and koji are sprinkled at the bottom of a barrel, and the desalted fish bodies are mixed in alternate layers of boiled rice and koji. The amount of boiled rice added is about 40 to 50% by weight of fish, and that of koji is half that of boiled rice. Fermentation is allowed to proceed for about 10 days.

The special flavor and taste of fish sushi is due to the formation of basic substances such as ammonia, cadaverine, piperidine, trimethylamine, and volatile acids such as lactic, valerianic, butyric, propionic acid, and acetic acid, as well as alcohol (Matsushita, 1937). The chemical composition of the fermented cooked rice removed from "funa-zushi" after 80 days of fermentation is shown in Table 13.

The product "katsuobushi," which is prepared from skipjack tuna (*Katsuwomus pelamis*) is unique to Japan. The multistep process involves deboning, boiling, drying, and storage under conditions which allow mold growth which is believed to improve the flavor of the finished product.

Table 13 Chemical Composition of the Fermented Cooked Rice Removed from Funazushi after 80 Days of Fermentation

Component	Percent
Moisture	67.31
Total solid	33.69
Soluble solid	13.38
Ash	4.02
Volatile acids	0.18
Nonvolatile acids	1.68
Alcohol	3.80
Sugar	2.46
Dextrin	3.77
Starch	7.65
Total nitrogen	1.82

Source: Amano (1962).

Europe and the Mediterranean. Surstrømming (fermented herring) and rakørret (fermented trout) are prepared in Scandinavia as delicacies (Schmidt-Nielsen and Bohmer, 1937). These products are made from whole herring and trout of relatively low fat content. The fish are immersed in saturated brine for 30 to 40 hr, eviscerated, retaining the roe of milt, and packed in barrels with freshly made brine of 17° Baumé. The fish are repacked in cans after the fermentation period (Mackie et al., 1971).

Another fermented product which is sealed in cans without sterilizing treatment is Scandinavian anchovies. The sprats are packed whole, either in barrels or in retail cans. Salt, sugar, and spices are mixed with the sprats and packed in barrels. Other preservatives, such as sodium nitrate and benzoic acid, are also added. Brine forms after 1 to 2 days and the barrels are stored at low temperature (12 to 15°C). Fish are filleted after the maturation process and packed into cans with sauce containing salt, sugar, and spices.

"Tidbits," another Scandiavian product, makes use of herring instead of sprats. These are canned or bottled with vinegar, sugar, and spices after maturation and filleting.

In France, anchovies are prepared by salting *Engraulis encrasicholus.* For long shelf life, these are canned or bottled in oil. The product is prepared from beheaded and gutted fish layered with salt in barrels. The fish-salt mixture is weighted down to keep the fish well pressed and to squeeze out the "pickle." The fish mature at ambient temperature for 6 to 7 months. They are desalted before being eaten, and kept in oil overnight if meant for immediate use (Le Pierre and Mercier-Marquez, 1951).

Salted or pickled herring is of considerable economic importance in Europe (Voskresensky, 1965). The salt content of the fish after pickling varies from 16 to 23%, depending on the method employed.

B. Nontraditional Methods

The long period of fermentation of the fish and shellfish products as traditionally prepared offers is a big disadvantage, hence, more recent studies have investigated means of accelerating the process by (a) addition of proteolytic enzymes; (b) addition of inorganic and organic acids; (c) use of proteolytic fungi and yeasts and lactic-acid-producing bacteria.

1. Addition of Proteolytic Enzymes

Studies have been conducted on the application of proteolytic enzymes for fermented fish products for human consumption (Freeman and Hoogland, 1956; Guevarra et al., 1972; Beddows et al., 1976). The effect of adding plant proteases, bromelain, papain, or ficin on the rate of hydrolysis and the extent of conversion of insoluble fish protein

Table 14 Distribution of Nitrogenous Compounds Formed in Supernatant Obtained after 21 Days from Incubation of Proteolytic Enzymes with Mixtures of Minced *Stolephorus* sp. and Salt (3:2) at 33°C

Supernatant liquor	Amino nitrogen (%)	Volatile nitrogen (%)	Protein nitrogen (%)	Polypeptide nitrogen (%)
Bromelain	68.3	7.1	4.1	20.5
Papain	63.1	6.6	5.7	24.6
Ficin	68.6	7.6	4.2	19.6
Budu[a]	66.3	6.6	0.56	26.5

[a]Malaysian fish sauce.
Source: Beddows and Ardisher (1979).

to soluble nitrogen was recently investigated by Beddows and Ardisher (1979). Bromelain tended to give higher conversions of insoluble proteins to soluble ones (Table 14) in *Stolephorus* spp.

Proteolytic enzymes from plant, animal, and microbial sources are commercially available. Due to the high cost, however, crude preparations of enzymes are employed. The digestion rate of freeze-dried fish using pepsin, papain, pancreatic acid, and ficin as compared by Hale (1969), increased to a greater extent than by the use of microbial proteases.

Optimum conditions for the proteolysis by papain (Sen et al., 1962; Sripathy et al., 1962), and proteolytic enzymes from *Bacillus subtilis* and *Streptomyces* sp. (Higashi et al., 1965) have been studied using mixtures of salt and fish. The rate of hydrolysis increased in enzyme treated mixtures as compared to the traditional fermentation process.

2. Addition of Organic and Inorganic Acids or Alkali

In this type of process, bacterial growth is inhibited by reducing the pH of the fish to between 2.5 and 4.0 by the addition of strong mineral or organic acids such as sulfuric acid, hydrochloric acid, and formic acid. The proteolytic enzymes of the fish tissues and pepsin of the stomach are activated by the acid pH and then liquefaction takes place. The acidity of the digest makes it necessary to neutralize the product before being used as food.

Beddows and Ardisher (1979) studied the production of soluble protein solution for use in fish sauce manufacture by acidification with hydrochloric acid up to pH 2.0 to 3.5 at 30°C. Solutions from *Stolephorus* spp. produced by acid ensilation had very little aroma or taste but did have a high soluble nitrogen content (Table 15) and could be used

Table 15 Comparison of Distribution of Soluble Nitrogen Compounds of Some Supernatant Liquors Produced by Acid-Ensiling Ikanbilis

	Salt added initially (%)	Protein nitrogen	Amino nitrogen	Volatile nitrogen (total)	Polypeptide nitrogen
pH 2	10	5.2	64.7	7.2	22.8
	15	4.7	65.4	7.0	23.9
pH 3	10	3.9	63.1	5.3	27.9
	15	3.8	66.5	6.9	22.3
Budu	—	0.6	66.3	6.6	26.5

Source: Beddows and Ardisher (1979).

to add to traditionally prepared fish sauce in order to increase both the net volume and the rate of production.

Acid hydrolysis using higher temperatures and higher concentrations of mineral acids solubilizes the protein by breaking up the peptide bonds (Ryan and Wilson, 1952).

Fish and marine products have also been treated with alkali to hydrolyze the proteins and extract the fish oil more efficiently from fish waste (Lovern, 1951; Mohanty and Roy, 1955).

Products prepared with the use of acid or alkali, however, have been mainly used as animal feedstuff (Bramnaes, 1952; March, et al., 1961; Disney et al., 1977).

3. Fermentation with the Use of Microorganisms

Biological Ensilage of Fish by Lactic-Acid-Producing Bacteria.
Traditional products involving lactic acid bacteria include burong-dalag (Orillo and Pederson, 1968) and balao-balao (Solidum, 1979) and paak of Cambodia (Westenberg, 1951).

The traditional Asian fish sauce used for human consumption may be categorized as a type of fish silage where salt is used as a preservative agent. Raa and Gildberg (1980), who recently prepared an exhaustive review on fish silage, state that ideally, fish silage or fish meal for animal food should be made only from fish not suitable for human consumption. However, affluent countries convert a high percentage of fish catch to animal feeds.

The preservation of minced fish for animal feed by fermentation with the addition of carbohydrate-source starter cultures have received renewed interest (Disney et al., 1978; James et al., 1977; Herborg and Johansen, 1977; Stanton and Yeoh, 1977).

Minced herring (*Sardinella aurita*), horse mackerel (*Caranx* sp.), and trigger fish (*Balistes carolensis*) were mixed with cassava powder and a variety of acid mixtures. Chemical and microbiological tests were conducted to monitor changes (Disney et al., 1978).

In biological silage preparations, bacteria ferment sugars to lactic acid, and this process lowers the pH and preserves the product (Disney et al., 1977). Carbohydrate sources are added to the fish protein to serve as energy sources for bacterial growth and to act as natural sources of lactobacilli. Lactic-acid-forming bacteria are added in the form of starter cultures in other similar preparations. The reduction of pH to approximately 4.5 by production of enough lactic acid must be achieved in the process. At this pH level, the toxin of *Clostridium botulinum* type E cannot develop (Wirahadikusumah, 1968). Scandinavian workers (Nilsson and Rydin, 1963; Nilsson, 1970) have recommended the use of 2% malted barley and 18% cereal meal or molasses and cereal meal, malt and tapioca meal, or molasses, for the fermentation of fish in tropical areas. Roa (1965) has ensiled minced herring with 10% molasses after inoculation with *Lactobacillus plantarum* and a similar process has been used in Tasmania as a means of using abalone waste (Olley and James, 1972). A similar product, using molasses as the carbohydrate and starter cultures of homofermentative lactobacilli, has been reported earlier (Kreuzer, 1952; Prolux, 1961).

Temperatures of 25 to 30°C accelerate the pH reduction, but an acceptable silage can be produced at 20°C (Kreuzer, 1952). A review of the feasibility of producing fish silage in the Indo-Pacific region was made recently by Sumner (1978).

Fermentation by Proteolytic Fungi and Yeasts. Some traditional products of Japan, particularly the shiokara-type product, are prepared with the use of the proteolytic fungi of *Aspergillus* sp. Koji, which is a preparation of steamed rice with the mold, *Aspergillus* sp., is often added to the fermented fish-salt mixture. One part wheat bran, previously inoculated with *Aspergillus oryzae,* is added to three parts crushed fish meat. Ripening by the enzymes of the fish and the proteolytic enzymes of the mold is allowed to occur for about 2 weeks at 25 to 30°C. The mixture is smoked after 2 weeks to inactivate the enzymes (Higashi et al., 1951; Tanikawa et al., 1950).

A proteolytic yeast, *Saccharomyces* sp., has been added to minced fish and fermentable sugar and kept for 8 days, and spray-dried after centrifugation and concentration (Bertullo and Hettich, 1959).

VI. QUALITY CONTROL AND SPOILAGE PROBLEMS

In Southeast Asia, the traditional products prepared from fermented fish are diverse, and it is impossible to control all the establishments engaged in producing them (Subba Rao, 1967). In small communities, fermented fish are often prepared under unhygienic conditions and with water from open sources such as rivers. In these cases, thorough education and a better price for products of good quality may help achieve improvements.

The uncontrolled nature of the processes involved in fermented fish manufacture makes it important that the nutritional value of the products be standardized. Such standards should include minimum requirements for both the essential amino acids and total nitrogen (Mackie et al., 1971).

Although heavily salted products have limited consumption, slightly salted ones, such as fermented shrimp pastes, are perishable without refrigeration. At present, regulations for the quality control and standardization of these products such as patis and nuoc-nam have been introduced, although the implementation of such standards still has to be made more effective.

The lack of quality control measures for the production may occasionally result in food poisoning. Botulism has been reported from a variety of fermented and cured fish products, particularly, involving the consumption of "izushi" in Japan (Yamamoto, 1960; Nakamura et al., 1956).

The high salt concentration and low pH of some fermented fish products may reduce the possibility of food poisoning from $Clostridium$ $botulinum$ and $Staphylococcus$ $aureus$. All types of $C.$ $botulinum$ are inhibited by 10 to 20% salt and generally by a pH less than 4.5. $S.$ $aureus$ is inhibited by 15 to 20% salt and by a pH between 4.5 and 5.0.

For fermented products with lower salt content and higher pH, the potential hazards that exist for the food poisoning organisms would be about the same as in other types of food.

GLOSSARY

Angkak Rice treated with the red yeastlike organism, $Monascus$ $purpureus$.

Ayu $Plocogossus$ $altivelis$.

Bagoong A paste from the Philippines. Fish used: $Sardinella$ spp., $Stolephorus$ sp., $Ostrea$ spp., $Acetes$ sp., and $Atya$ spp. Fermented 3 months.

Balao-balao A product of Philippines. Fish used: $Ophicephalus$ spp. Preparation of fish: whole; salting method: after salting, cooked rice added, but not angkak; fermentation: 1 week.

Belachan A product of Malaysia. Fish used: $Acetes$ shrimp, $Misydacea$. Preparation of fish: whole; salting method: 100:4-5; fermented and dried; duration of fermentation: 1 month.

Budu A product of Malaysia. Fish used: $Stolephorus$ spp. Salting method: 5:1; tamarind and palm sugar added; fermented: 40 days. Keeps for 2 years.

Buro A product of the Philippines. Fish used: *Ophicephalus* spp., *Chanos chanos*, dwarf gouramy, (freshwater fish). Preparation of fish: dressed; salting method: after salting and fermenting rice, salted cooked rice, and angkak mixed; fermentation: 1 week.

Fessikh A product of Sudan. Fish used: small fatty fish from the Nile. Preparation of fish: whole; salting method: salted and packed in used oil cans; duration of fermentation: several months.

Funa Prussian carp.

Funazushi A product of Japan. Fish used: Crucian carp (*Carassius auratus*); preparation of fish: gutted, but gonads retained; salting method: 1:1; fermented: 2 months.

Gyomiso Fermented fish paste from Japan.

Hata-hata Sand fish, *Arctoscopus japonicus*.

Izushi Cured fermented Japanese marine foods in boiled rice.

Kasu-zuke Cured fermented products in sake lees.

Koji Wheat fermented with yeast.

Koji-zuke Cured herring in koji.

Makassar A product of Indonesia. Fish used: *Engraulis* spp., *Stolephorus* spp. Preparation of fish: beheaded; salting method: large amount. After few days angkak, ragi, and spices are added (deep red color).

Mam-ca-loc A product of Khmer Republic. Fish used: *Ophicephalus striatus*. Preparation of fish: beheaded, gutted, scaled, and boned; salting method: salted 10-30 days mixed with roasted rice, ginger, sugar, and pineapple; fermentation: 5 days after adding rice.

Mam-ca-sat A product of Khmer Republic. Fish used: *Pangasius* sp. Preparation of fish: beheaded and gutted; salting method: 7:1 for 6-10 days; roasted rice added; fermented 10 days, but can be stored for years.

Mam-chao A product of Khmer Republic. Fish used: *Cirrhinus micropeltes*. Preparation of fish: beheaded and gutted; salting method: 5.1-30:1, salted 30 days; added glutinous rice, angkak, palm sugar, and yeast; duration of fermentation: 1-3 months after adding rice.

Nampla A sauce from Thailand. Fish used: *Stolephorus* spp., *Rastrelliger* spp., and *Cirrhinus* spp. Salting method: 5:1-1:1; fermented 5 months-1 year.

Ngapi A product of Burma. Fish used: anchovy (*Engraulis commersonii*), shrimp (including planktonic shrimp). Preparation of fish: whole; salting method: not specified; fermented: several weeks after salting, pounding, and drying.

Nuka-zuke A Japanese cured fish product in rice bran.

Nuoc-boi A bloody liquor drained from the fish-salt mixture in the preparation of nuoc-nam.

Nuoc-nam A sauce from Vietnam. Fish used: *Stolephorus* spp., *Engraulis* spp., *Decapterus, Dorosoma, Clupea lile*; salting method: 3:2; fermented: 3 months-1 year. Will keep indefinitely.

Patis A sauce from Philippines. Fish used: *Stolephorus* spp.,
Clupea spp., *Decapterus* spp., *Leiognathus* spp. Salting method:
3:1, 4:1; fermentation: 3 months-1 year.

Pedah-Siam A product of Thailand. Fish used: *Rastrelliger* spp.
Preparation of fish: guts and gills removed through throat;
salting method: 3:1; packed in crates; fermented: 2-3 months.

Pissala A fish sauce of southern France prepared from small fish
Engraulis, Aphya, Gobius.

Pra-hoc A product of Khmer Republic. Fish used: *Ophicephalus,
Labeo, Clarias, Cirrhinus microlepsis.*

Rakørret A product of Norway. Fish used: *Salmo salar* var. *trutta,*
Perch, and gwyniad. Preparation of fish: gutted, but gonads retained; salting method: brine 17° Bé; fermented 2 weeks.

Ragi A Javanese preparation made from yeast and rice.

Shiokara A paste from Japan. Fish used: squid. Preparation of
fish: entrails; salting method: 3-5:1; malted rice added; fermented: a few weeks-1 year.

Shottsuru (uwo-shoyu, ika-shoyu) A sauce from Japan. Fish used:
sand fish, *Astroscopus japonicus*, sardine, squid *Omnastrephes sloani,
Omnastrephes pacificus.* Preparation of fish: whole; salting method:
salt and malted rice 3:1; koji added: 3:1; fermented: 6 months.

Surstrømming A product of Sweden. Fish used: *Clupea harengus*
var. *membras.* Preparation of fish: gutted, but gonads retained;
salting method: brine 17° Bé; fermented: 2 weeks.

Tai Sea bream.

Trassi-ikan A product of Indonesia. Fish used: small fish. Preparation of fish: whole; salting method: drying, pounding, and salting.

Tsukemono Cured-fermented marine foods from Japan.

REFERENCES

Alm, F. (1965). Scandinavian anchovies and herring tidbits. In *Fish
as Food* (G. Borgstrom, ed.). New York Academic Press.

Amano, K. (1962). The influence of fermentation in the nutritive value
of fish with special reference to fermented fish products of South East
Asia. In *Fish in Nutrition* (E. Heen and R. Kreuzer, eds.) London,
Fishing News (Books) Ltd., pp. 180-200.

Ananichev, A. V. (1959). Digestive enzymes of fish and seasonal
changes in their activity. *Biochemistry (U.S.S.R.)* 24:952.

Arcega, L. B. (1969). The manufacture of sauce. In *N.I.S.T.
Technical Bulletin, 9,* Manila, Philippines, National Institute of
Science and Technology.

Arroyo, P. T. (1975). *The Science of Philippine Foods.* Manila,
Abaniko Enterprises, 300 pp.

Arroyo, P. T., Ludovico-Pelayo, L., Solidum, H. T., Chiu, Y. N.,
Lero, M., and Alcantara, E. (1977). Studies on rice-shrimp fermentation: balao-balao. *Phil. J. Food Sci. and Tech.* 2:106-125.

Avery, A. C. (1950). Preservation of small fish in the Philippine islands. *Food Technol.* 6:4-5.

Batra, L. R. and Millner, P. D. (1976). Asian fermented foods and beverages. In *Developments in Industries Microbiology.* Washington, D.C., Am Inst. of Biol. Sciences, pp. 117-124.

Beddows, C. G. and Ardisher, A. G. (1979). The production of soluble fish protein solution for use in fish sauce manufacture. II. The use of acids at ambient temperature. *J. Food Technol.* 14:613-623.

Beddows, C. G., Ardisher, A. G., and bin Daud, W. J. (1979). Biochemical changes occurring during the manufacture of 'budu.' *J. Sci. Food Agric.* 30:1097-1103.

Beddows, C. G., Ardisher, A. G., and bin Daud, W. J. (1980). Development and origin of the volatile fatty acids in 'budu.' *J. Sci. Food Agric.* 31:86-92.

Beddows, C. G., Ismail, M., and Steinkraus, K. H. (1976). The use of bromelain in the hydrolysis of mackerel and the investigation of fermented fish aroma. *J. Food Technol.* 14:613-623.

Bersamin, S. V. (1964). Technological advances in the manufacture of fermented fish products, 'bagoong' and 'patis.' *Proc. Indo-Pacif. Fish. Coun.* 9:105.

Bersamin, S. V. and Napugan, R. S. J. (1962). Preliminary studies on the comparative chemical composition of the different commercial brands of 'patis' in the Philippines. *Phil. Fishing J.* 2:11-14.

Bertullo, V. H. and Hettich, F. P. (1959). Protein hydrolysis by yeast. U.S. Patent 3,000,789.

Boez, L. and Guillerm, J. (1930). Le facteur microbien dans la fabrication de la samure indochinoise ('nuoc-mam'). *Compt. Rend.* 190:533-535.

Boury, M. (1952). Les hydrolysats du poisson. *Revue Trav. Off. (scient. tech.) Pech. Marit.* 17:27.

Bramnaes, F. (1952). Salt and salt-sugar curing of Fladen Ground herring. In *Meddelelse fra Fiskeriministeriets Forsøgslaboratorium* Copenhagen.

Bramstedt, F. (1957). Geschmacks und geruchsstoffe in fischfleisch. *Arch. Fisch. Wiss.* 8:94.

Christian, J. H. B and Waltho, J. (1962). The water relations of staphylococci and micrococci. *J. Appl. Bact.* 25:369-377.

Cole, R. C. (1963). Fish preservation in the tropics. *Fishing News Int.* 2:385.

Creac'h, P. V. (1952). Un actuel 'Garum' francais: 'Le pissala.' La peche du Nonnat et de la Poutine. *Revue Trav. Off. (sceint. tech.) Pech. Marit.* 17:57.

Croston, C. B. (1960). Tryptic enzymes in chinook salmon. *Arch. Biochem. Biophys.* 89:202.

Cutting, C. L. (1962). The influence of drying, salting and smoking on the nutritive value of fish. In *Fish in Nutrition* (E. Heen and R. Kruzer, eds.). London, Fishing News (Books) Ltd.

Disney, J. G., Tatterson, I. N., and Olley, I. (1977). Recent developments in fish silage. In *Proc. Conf. Handl. Proc. Mark. Trop. Fish* London, Tropical Products Institute, pp. 231-240.

Disney, J. G. Hoffman, J. Olley, I. J., Clucas, A. B., and Francis, B. J. (1978). Developemnt of a fish silage/carbohydrate animal feed for use in the tropics. *Trop. Sci.* 20:129-144.

Dougan, J. and Howard, G. E. (1975). Some flavoring constituents of fermented fish sauces. *J. Sci. Food Agric.* 26:887-894.

Dussault, H. P. (1957). The salt tolerance of bacteria from lightly salted fish. In *Proc. 2nd. Intern. Symp. on Food Microbiol.* (B. P. Eddy, ed.), London, Dept. of Ind. Research, p. 61.

Freeman, H. C. and Hoogland, P. L. (1956). Processing of cod and haddock viscera. Pt. 1. Laboratory experiments. *J. Fish Res. Bd. Can.* 13:869.

Geiger, E. and Borgstrom, G. (1962). Fish protein, nutritive aspects. In *Fish as Food* (G. Borgstrom, ed.), New York, Academic Press, pp. 30-114.

Gonzales, F. R. (1977). Traditional processing in the Philippines. In *Proc. Conf. Handl. Proc. Mark. Trop. Fish* London, Tropical Products Institute, pp. 315-317.

Groninger, H. (1964). Partial purification and some properties of a proteinase for albacore (*Germo alalunga*) muscle. *Arch. Biochem. Biophys.* 108:175.

Guevarra, G., Matias, V. C., and de la Peña, P. O. (1972). Fish fermentation with the use of papain. *The Phil. J. Fish* 10:30-38.

Guevarra, G., Marfori, E., Matias, V., de la Peña, P. O., Sanchez, and de Guzman, M. (1978). Drying, smoking, fermentation and pickling of milkfish. In *Milkfish (Bangos) as Food*. Manila, National Science Development Board, pp. 94-131.

Hale, M. B. (1969). Relative activities of commercially available enzymes in the hydrolysis of fish protein. *Fd. Technol.* 23:107.

Hamm, W. S., and Clague, J. A. (1950). Temperature and salt purity effects on the manufacture of fish paste and sauce. In *Res. Rep. No. 24*, Washington, D. C., Fish and Widelife Service, U.S. Dept. of Interior.

Harrow, B. and Apfelbaum, P. M. (1947). Quoted by Sulit, J. I. and Martin, C. (1955). Studies on the preparation of salted fish paste (bagoong) from dried dilis. *The Phil. J. Fisheries* 3:39-45.

Herborg, L., and Johansen, S. (1977). Fish cheese: the preservation of minced fish by fermentation. In *Proc. Conf. Handl. Proc. Mark. Trop. Fish.* London, Tropical Products Institute, pp. 253-255.

Higashi, H., Murayama, S., and Onishi, T. (1965). Nutritive value of 'liquefied fish protein.' *Bull. Tokai reg. Fish. Res. Lab.* 43:77.

Higashi, H., Nitta, T., Nagakura, K., and Umento, S. (1951). Studies on the utilization of fish meal for food. *Bull. Jap. Soc. Scient. Fish* 17:147.

James, M. A., Iyer, K. M., and Nair, M. R. (1977). Comparative study of fish ensilage prepared by microbial fermentation and formic acid ensilage. In *Proc. Conf. Handl. Proc. Mark. Trop. Fish.* London, Tropical Products Institute, pp. 273-275.

Jansen, G. R. and Howe, E. E. (1964). World problems in protein nutrition. *The Amer. J. Clinical Nutrition* 15:262-274.

Jebsen, J. W. (1962). Proteins in fish muscle. In *Intern. Symp. on Fish in Nutrition* (E. Heen and R. Kreuzer, eds.). London, Fishing News (Books) Ltd., pp. 68-72.

Jones, N. R. (1962). Browning reactions in dried fish products. *Rec. Advanc. Food Sci.* 2:74-80.

Kasemsarn, B. (1963). Studies on fish sauce fermentation. M.S. thesis, Univ. of Washington, Seattle, Washington.

Kelaiditis, G. C. (1949). The enzymatic condition during the maturing of the Greek salted and pressed small fish. *Praktika of the Hellenic Hydrobiological Institute* 3:5.

Kreuzer, R. (1952). Untersuchungen zur Durchfuhrung der Fischgarungssilage. I. Teil. Die Saure-und pH-Wertbildung und ihre Beziehung zur Haltbarkeit und Qualitat der Fischsilagen, *Arch. f. Fisch* 4:57.

Kreuzer, R. (1973). *Fishery Products,* London, Food and Agricultural Organization, U.N. Fishing News (Books) Ltd., 462 pp.

Lee, K. H. (1968a). Microbiological and enzymological studies on the flavor compounds of sea food pickles. *J. of Korean Agr. Chem. Soc.* 11:1-27.

Lee, K. H. (1968b). Studies on the digestion of fish protein. *J. of Korean Agr. Chem. Soc.* 8:51-57.

Le Pierre, C., and Mercier-Marquez, J. (1951). Studies on the production of anchovies at the Portugese Institute for Fish Preservation. In *Proc. 2nd. Intern. Congr. Canned Foods,* Paris.

Lovern, J. L. (1951). The production of herring oil. *The Fishing News* 14:1985.

Lovern, J. L. (1962). The lipids of fish and changes occurring in them during processing and storage. In *Fish in Nutrition* (E. Heen and R. Kreuzer, eds.), London, Fishing News (Books) Ltd.

Mackie, I. M., Hardy, R., and Hobbs, G. (1971). Fermented fish products. In F. A. O. Fish. Rep. No. 100. Rome, U.N. Food and Agricultural Organization.

March, B. E., Biely, J., McBride, J. R., Idler, D. R., and MacLeod, R. A. (1961). The protein nutritive value of 'liquid herring' preparations. *J. Fish. Res. Bd. Can.* 18:113.

Matsubara, H., and Feder, J. (1971). Other bacterial, mold and yeast proteases. In *The Enzymes* (P. D. Boyer, ed.). New York, Academic Press, pp. 721-839.

Matsushita, K. (1937). Studies on 'funa-sushi', a fermented Crucian carp. *Bull. Agric. Chem. Soc. Japan* 13:629.

Meinke, W. W. (1974). The potential of the by-catch from shrimp trawlers. In *Fishery Products* (R. Kreuzer, ed). Food and Agricultural Organization, U.N. Fishing News (Books) Ltd., London, pp. 233-237.

Miller, C. D., Louis, L., and Yonazawa, K. (1946). Foods used by Filipinos in Hawaii. *Hawaii Agr. Exp. Sta. Bull.* No. 98.

Mohanty, G. B. and Roy, A. B. (1955). Hydrolyzed fish protein from the flesh of waste fish. *Science* 121:41.

Nagao, K. (1951a). Bacteriological studies on 'shiokara' or 'soused squid'. 2. Studies on the chemical changes in the ripening process. *Bull. Fac. Fish. Hokkaido Univ.* 1:81.

Nagao, K. (1951b). Bacteriological studies on 'shiokara' or 'soused squid'. III. On the variation of the number of bacilli in 'shiokara' during its ripening. *Bull. Fac. Fish Hokkaido Univ.* 2:145.

Nagao, K., and Kimura, T. (1951). Bacteriological studies on 'shiokara.' *Bull. Fac. Fish. Hokkaido Univ.* 1:21.

Nakamura, Y., Iida, H., Saeki, K., and Karashimada, T. (1956). Type E botulism in Hokkaido, Japan. *Japan. J. Med. Sci. Biol.* 9:45.

Namisato, T. (1974). *The Chemistry and Technology of Marine Products Processing*, Manila, Philippines, Japan Overseas Cooperation Volunteers, 196 pp.

Nguyen-An-Cu and Vialard-Goudou. (1953). Sur la nature de l'acidite volatile et de la saumure vietnamienne 'nuoc-mam'. *C. R. Acad. Sci.* (ii) 236:2128.

Nguyen Thi Lau and Richard, C. (1959). Le poisson dans l'alimentation du Vietnamien. *Rev. elevage Med. Vet. Pays Trop.* 12:313.

Nieto, M. (1979). Chemical and microbiological processes in the fermentation of fishery products of South East Asia. Special Problem, Manila, Philippines, Univ. of the Phil. College of Fisheries.

Nilsson, R. (1970). Evaluation of novel protein products. In *Proc. Int. Biol. Programme and Wenner-Gren Centre Symp. Stockholm* (A. E. Bender, R. Kihlberg, B. Loftqvist, and L. Munck, eds.) Oxford, Pergamon Press.

Nilsson, R. and Rydin, C. (1963). Fermentation as a means of preserving organic materials. *Acta Chem. Scand.* 17:174-179.

Olley, J. and James, D. (1972). Rural Research. CSRIO *Rep.* No. 77.

Orejana, F. M. (1978). Proteolysis and control mechanisms in fish sauce fermentation. Ph.D. thesis, Univ. of Washington, Washington, D.C.

Orejana, F. M. and Liston, J. (1979). Protein and lipid hydrolysis in Philippine fish sauce (patis) prepared from irradiated and non-irradiated anchovies. *Phil. J. Food Sci. and Tech.* 3:17-30.

Orejana, F. M. and Liston, J. (1981). Agents of proteolysis and its inhibition in patis (fish sauce) fermentation. *J. Food Sci.* 47:198-209.

Orillo, C and Pederson, C. (1968). Lactic and bacterial fermentation of 'burong-dalag.' *Applied microbiology.* 16:1669-1671.

Pederson, C. S. (1971). *Microbiology of Food Fermentation* Connecticut, AVI Publishing Company, p. 245.

Prescott, S. C. and Dunn, C. G. (1959). *Industrial Microbiology,* New York, McGraw-Hill, pp. 335-343.

Prolux, S. A. (1961). Fish protein hydrolysate. Israeli Patent 13,812.

Raa, J. and Gildberg, A. (1980). A Review on Fish Silage. University of Trφmso, Trφmso, Norway.

Roa, D. P. (1965). Ensilage of fish by microbial fermentation. *Fish News Int.* 4:283-286.

Rose, F. (1918). Recherches sur la fabrication et la composition chimique du 'nuoc-mam'. *Bull. Econ. Indochina N.S.* 20:955.

Ryan, J and Wilson, W. C. (1952). Liquid fish process. U.S. Patent 2,588,287.

Saanin, H. (1954). 'Ketjap ikan.' *Berita Perik.* 6:831.

Saisithi, P. (1967). Studies on the origin and development of the typical flavor and aroma of Thai fish sauce. Ph.D. thesis, Univ. of Washington, Washington, D.C.

Saisithi, P., Kasemsarn, B. O., Liston, J., and Dollar, A. M. (1966). Microbiology and chemistry of fermented fish. *J. Fd. Sci.* 31:105.

Sands, A. and Crisan, E. V. (1974). Microflora of fermented Korean foods. *J. Food Sci.* 39:1002.

Schmidt-Nielsen, S. and Bohmer, T. (1937). Small salted herrings, 'Surstromming.' *K. Norske Vidensk. Selsk. Fork.* 10:20.

Sen, D. C., Sripathy, N. V., Lahiry, N. L., Sreenivasan, A., and Subrahmanyan, V. (1962). Fish hydrolysates. I. Rate of hydrolysis of fish flesh with papain. *Food Tech.* p. 138.

Shin, D. W., and Kim. G. S. (1968). Studies on the free amino acid compositions of salted internal organs of several fishes. *J. Korean Agr. Chem. Soc.* 9:83-93.

Simidu, W. S., Ikeda, S., and Kurokawa, Y. (1953). Quoted by Tarr, H. L. A. (1972). Enzymes and intermediary metabolism. In *Fish in Nutrition* (J. E. Halves, ed.). New York, Academic Press, pp. 256-321.

Siebert, G. (1962). Enzymes of marine fish muscle and their role in fish spoilage. In *F.A.O. Fish in Nutrition* (E. Heen and R. Kreuzer, eds.), London, Fishing News (Books) Ltd., pp. 80-82.

Siebert, G. and Schmitt, A. (1965). Fish tissue enzymes and their role in the deteriorative changes in fish. In *F.A.O. Intern. Symp. on the Technology of Fish Utilization* (R. Kreuzer, ed.). Fishing News (Books) Ltd., London, pp. 47-52.

Solidum, H. T. (1979). Chemical and microbiological changes during the fermentation of *balao-balao. J. Food Sci. and Tech.* 3:1-16.

Sripathy, N. V., Sen, D. P., Lahiry, N. L., Sreenivasan, A., and Subrahmanyan, V. (1962). II. Standardization of digestion conditions for the preparation of hydrolysate rich in peptones and proteins. *Food Tech.* p. 140

Stanton, W. R. and Yeoh, Q. L. (1977). Low salt fermentation method for conserving trash fish waste under Southeast Asian conditions. In *Proc. Conf. Handl. Proc. Mark. Trop. Fish.* London, Tropical Products Institute, pp. 277-282.

Subba Rao, G. N. (1961). *Fisheries Product Manual,* Bangkok, Thailand Food and Agricultural Organization Regional Office for Asia and Far East, p. 233.

Subba Rao, G. N. (1967). Fish processing in the Indo-Pacific area. In *Indo-Pacific Fisheries Council Regional Studies* No. 4, Bangkok, Thailand, Food and Agricultural Organization, pp. 231.

Sulit, J. I. and Martin, C. (1955). Studies on the preparation of salted fish paste (bagoong) from dried dilis (*Stolephorus indicus*). *The Phil. J. Fisheries* 3:39-45.

Sumner, J. (1978). Fish silage production in the Indo-Pacific region — a feasibility study. In *I.P.F.C. Occasional Papers,* Bangkok, Thailand, Regional Office for Asia and the Far East, 29 pp.

Taarland, T., Mathisen, E., Ovsthus, O., and Braekken, O. R. (1958). Nutritional values and vitamins of Norwegian fish and fish products. *Tissskr. Hermetikind.* 44:405.

Takahashi, T. (1961). Biochemical studies on the viscera of cuttle fish (*Omnastrephes sloani pacificus*). *Bull. Jap. Soc. Scient. Fish.* 27:85.

Tan, T. H., van Veen, A. G., Graham, D. C. W., and Steinkraus, K. H. (1967). The manufacture of low salt fish paste. *The Phil. Agriculturist.* 51:625-635.

Tanikawa, E. (1971). Marine products in Japan. Tokyo, Koseisha-koseikaku Co. 507 pp.

Tanikawa, E., Akiba, M., and Akiba, S. (1950). Studies on the manufacture of 'gyomiso.' Parts I and II. *Bull. Jap. Soc. Scient. Fish.* 15:689.

Tarr, H. L. A. (1972). Enzymes and intermediary metabolism. In *Fish in Nutrition* (J. E. Halver, ed.). New York, Academic Press, pp. 256-321.

Tatterson, I. N. and Windsor, M. L. (1974). Fish silage. *J. Sci. Food Agric.* 25:369-379.

Truong-van-Chom. (1963). The volatile fatty acids of 'nuoc-mam.' *Proc. Ninth Pacific Sci. Congr.* 5:135.

Uyenco, V., Lawas, I., Briones, P. R., and Taruc, R. S. (1953). Mechanism of 'bagoong' (fish paste) and 'patis' (fish sauce) processing. *Proc. Indo-Pacif. Fish Coun.* 4:210.

van Veen, A. G. (1965). Fermented and dried seafood. In *Fish as Food* (G. Borgstrom, ed.). New York, Academic Press, p. 107.

van Veen, A. G., and Steinkraus, K. H. (1970). Nutritive value and wholesomeness of fermented foods. *J. Agr. Food Chem.* 18:576-578.

Vasavan, A. G. and Varma, K. G. (1959). Experiments on pickling fish with vinegar and Malabar tamarind. *Curr. Sci.* 28:153.

Velankar, N. K. (1957). Protein hydrolysate from fish. *J. Sci. Ind. Res.* (India). 16A:141-142.

Ventkataraman, R. and Sreenivasan, A. (1955). A preliminary investigation of the mackerels of the West Coast. *Ind. J. Med. Res.* 40:529.

Vialard-Goudou, A. (1941). Teneur en bases volatiles et en acides volatiles de la saumure indo-chinoise 'nuoc-mam.' *Revue Med. fr. Extr.-Orient* (Hanoi). 19:1061.

Voskresensky, N. A. (1965). Salting and herring. In *Fish as Food* (G. Borgstrom, ed.). New York, Academic Press, p. 107

Wirahadikusumah, S. (1968). Preventing *Clostridium botulinum* type E poisoning and fat rancidity by silage fermentation. *Lanbrukshoegsk. Ann.* 34:551-689.

Westernberg, J. (1951). Fishery products of Indo-China, a compilation of literature up to the Japanese invasion. *Proc. Indo-Pacific. Fish. Coun.* 2:125.

Yamamoto, K. (1960). Quoted by Dolman, C. E. (1960). Type E botulism: a hazard in the north. *Artic.* 13:230.

Yanagihara, T., Komoda, H., Yoneyama, H., and Yamada, M. (1963). The oriental flavor of food. *Shiokuhu Eeseigaku Zasshi.* 4:348-358.

Zenitani, B. (1955). Studies on fermented fish products. I. On the aerobic bacteria in 'shiokara.' *Bull. Jap. Soc. Scient. Fish* 21:200.

7

Ginger

Rowland E. Leverington Horticulture Branch, State Department of Primary Industries, Brisbane, Queensland, Australia

I. INTRODUCTION

A. Origin and Distribution

Ginger is one of the oldest spices and is reported by Bailey (1947) to be supposedly native to India and China, but, like many other tropical plants of economic importance, its exact origin is uncertain. It is mentioned in the early literature of China and India (Gildemeister and Hoffman, 1913a,b; Sills, 1961; Akamine, 1962). The adventurer Marco Polo, in recording his travels during the thirteenth and fourteenth centuries noted that ginger was being cultivated in south China and the Malabar Coast of India.

Parry (1953) reports that the earliest recorded use of ginger in southern Europe was in ancient Greece and that the spices from the east passed through the hands of traders via the Red Sea. The Romans likewise obtained ginger and other spices through the Red Sea trading posts of Coptus, Memphis, and Alexandria. While serving in the Roman army under Nero, the Greek military surgeon, Dioscorides (A.D. 40 to A.D. 90), ascribed certain beneficial effects to ginger in his celebrated *Materia Medica*. It is interesting to note that the modern *British Pharmaceutical Codex* (1963) lists ginger as a carminative. Apparently ginger was introduced into Germany and France during the ninth century and England during the tenth century (Gildemeister and Hoffman, 1913a. Sills (1961) and Guenther (1952) report that in the age of exploration that followed, the Spaniards took ginger to Mexico and the West Indies early in the sixteenth century, and by 1547 the spice was being exported from these areas to Europe. In more recent times, ginger has been cultivated in many places, perhaps the most important of these being Australia, China, Fiji, Hawaii, Hong Kong, India, Jamaica, Japan, Mauritius, Nigeria, Pakistan, Sierra Leone, and Taiwan.

B. Botanical Description and Varieties

The *Encylopaedia Brittanica* (1974) has suggested that as the spice was known by the Sanskritic name of *singabera* in India, the Greek word for ginger, *zingiberi*, arose which, with further modifications, led to the botanical and common names which are used today. Nearly all the ginger in commerce comes from one species of the ginger plant, *Zingiber officinale Roscoe,* which is the species commercially cultivated throughout the producing countries of the world. The only exception is *Z. mioga Roscoe* which is grown in Japan (Tropical Products Institute, 1964), but it has not the characteristic pungent flavor of the other species (Guenther, 1952). Throughout the world there are about 70 other *Zingiber* species, a few of which are used as decorative plants, particularly for their spectacular blooms. *Z. officinale Roscoe* is unknown in a wild state, having been cultivated since ancient times.

The plant is a perennial monocotyledon producing buff-colored fibrous underground branching rhizomes in a palmate pattern (Figs. 1 and 2). Morphologically, it is a modified stem and consists of nodes which carry buds. Each portion of the rhizome develops from one of these buds and in turn carries as many as 10 buds of which several, but not all, develop into further portions of rhizome. The ginger of

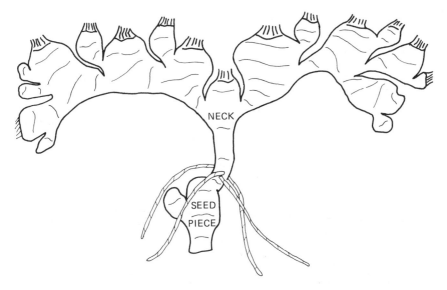

Figure 1 Hand of ginger rhizome showing branching development.

Figure 2 Early-harvest ginger rhizome. (Courtesy of Buderim Ginger Growers Co-operative Association Ltd. and Queensland Department of Primary Industries.)

commerce is derived from the rhizome. Each rhizome portion or knob gives rise to a leafy aerial shoot that is slender and grasslike, consisting mainly of tightly sheathed leaf bases, and may reach a height of 1.5 m. The laminae are carried alternately along the pseudostem and are generally linear lanceolate in shape, pointed, and reach a length of 15 cm. The midrib is pronounced while the laminae are well supplied with parallel veins. The conelike inflorescence or flower is carried terminally on a leafless stem up to 30 cm long (Fig. 3). In some areas the plant seldom flowers, but in other places flowering is regular although seed is rarely produced. The roots arise predominately from the neck region (i.e., the first formed part of the rhizome) though adventitious roots may develop later from more terminal areas. The roots are fibrous and develop mainly in the surface regions.

Whiley and Saranah (1978) grew and studied the basic agronomic features of 41 lines of ginger imported from 15 countries, and noted that four distinct groups existed. Their studies revealed that considerable natural diversity within the species exists and that they appear to be genetically fixed. They named the groups generally according to the origin of the material imported and described then as follows.

Figure 3 Early-harvest ginger showing drumsticks (flower stems). (Courtesy of Buderim Ginger Growers Co-operative Association Ltd. and Queensland Department of Primary Industries.)

The *Canton* group includes cultivars with rhizomes having the largest knob size; these tend to be blocky in shape having both depth and width. The rhizome is attractive in general appearance, projecting an impression of size. This feature is desirable for fresh marketing. At maturity, the internal flesh color is a pale yellow with some blue pigment discoloration believed to be anthocyanin in the oldest portions of the rhizome. The cellular material tends to be less dense than in cultivars of the other groups. When cut, there is a citruslike aroma consequential of citral content. The fiber tends to be thicker or ropy when compared with other groups. Countries where this type is known include China, Taiwan, Philippines, India, Thailand, Hawaii, and Fiji.

The *Chinese* group includes the cultivar known in Australia as Queensland ginger, which is thought to have its origin somewhere in mainland China, and a line imported into Queensland from Fiji that has been termed Fijian ginger. Cultivars in this group produce medium-sized knobs which tend to be more elongated and flattened than the Canton group. In general this group has the highest-yielding clones. Fiber development tends to be earlier and less ropy than the Canton group whereas anthocyanin pigmentation develops a greater intensity. When cut, rhizomes have a strong citruslike aroma. Countries where this group is known include Australia, Fiji, Malaysia, and the Philippines.

The *Malay* group includes cultivars with a smaller knob size than either the Canton or Chinese groups. The anthocyanin pigmentation in the rhizome is more intense at maturity than either of the former groups, and the rhizome scales are generally a darker brown. When cut, a mild citruslike aroma is present in the rhizome. Fiber is similar to the Chinese group. There are considerable variations in growth habit within this group with most cultivars developing rhizomes at ground level, but some rhizomes form at a depth of 10 cm. Others produce dense adventitious root systems from the main body of the rhizome. Countries where this group are known include India, Malaysia, the Philippines, and Sri Lanka.

The *Jamaican* group takes its name from rhizomes obtained from Jamaica. Cultivars in this group have the smallest knob size and when mature develop an intense blue color from the anthocyanin pigmentation. Fiber development in the rhizome is similar to the Chinese group whereas, when cut, there is greater pungency than with other groups, with only a faint trace of the citruslike aroma. The rhizome scales are similar in color to the Malay group. For the most part, cultivars in this group are low yielding and not suitable for processing into confectionery. Planting material of this group was obtained from India, Jamaica, and Mauritius.

C. Forms of Ginger and Marketing

Leverington (1975) reported that ginger rhizomes are substantially utilized as follows.

Fresh ginger or green ginger is used for culinary purposes.
Preserved ginger or confectionery ginger in the form of ginger in
  syrup or crystallized ginger is preserved by virtue of the very high
  sugar concentration—more than 70% total soluble solids (TSS).
Dried ginger (the dehydrated rhizome) is used as a spice in its own
  right or as a source of flavorings.
Seed ginger is used for propagation of the next crop.

Whereas varieties grown in most countries for dried ginger usually
have smaller, denser hands than the succulent bulbous varieties used
for confectionery ginger, Australia utilizes only one variety for the
whole range of products. Harvest time is varied to suit the market
(Bendall and Daly, 1966).

Figure 4 illustrates how ginger is utilized. This calls for a highly
integrated and mechanized industry and perhaps partly accounts for
the increasing dominance that Australia now has on the preserved
ginger market.

Because ginger is cultivated as an annual crop and propagated
vegetatively, it is possible to adjust relatively quickly the supply of
raw material to changes in demand. The most recent review of international marketing entitled *"The Market for Dried, Preserved and
Fresh Ginger"* has been compiled by Edwards (1975) of the Tropical
Products Institute (TPI) and updates the TPI *Report G. 8* of 1964 and
notes the significant changes during the subsequent decade. Relevant
sections of this update as well as a TPI monograph (n.d.) are summarized next.

1. Fresh or Green Ginger

Fresh ginger or green ginger is the untreated rhizome usually sold
through the fresh fruit and vegetable markets. It is grown largely
for consumption in the countries of production and little enters international trade. Exceptions are western Malaysia and Singapore both of
which import fresh ginger from China, Taiwan, and Thailand while the
United Kingdom imports from Mauritius, Fiji, and west Africa.

2. Preserved Ginger or Confectionery Ginger

The products traded as preserved ginger on the international market
are made from the peeled rhizome preserved in sugar syrup. This ginger is harvested earlier than that destined for dried ginger and, hence,
it is more succulent, less pungent, and less fibrous. The main industrial uses for perserved ginger are in the manufacture of fancy choco-
lates, other confectionery, crystallized ginger, jams, sauces , and
pickles, as well as being used in the bakery industry. Ginger in syrup
is also sold in jars through the retail trade. During the past 15 years,
the main development on the world market has been the firm establishment of the Australian industry. Of the other two major exporting

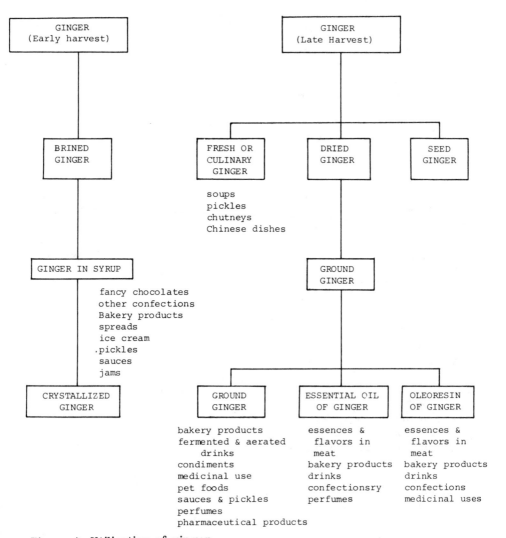

Figure 4 Utilization of ginger.

areas, Hong Kong processes green ginger imported from Thailand, the Philippines, Taiwan, and the Canton region, whereas China utilizes domestic production.

The sole Australian marketing organization, the Buderim Ginger Growers' Co-operative Association Limited, conducted an extensive market survey, which indicated that the major customers, both domestic and overseas, were interested in a mild ginger flavor and not the heat previously associated with ginger products. A vigorous development

program, including major investments in capital equipment and government technological research support, enabled the industry to produce a
milder-flavored product from an early-harvested crop which contained
a lower ginger oil content. Coupled with improved quality control, it
was possible to meet the specific requirements of the industrial customers throughout the world and to provide a guaranteed supply of
standardized high-quality ginger. The Australian product is sold at a
premium price, the advantages of consistency, milder flavor, and freedom from fiber being in its flavor. The standardization of production
has also facilitated a reduction in the ratio of syrup to ginger which
has led to the reduced costs of transport, handling, and storage.

For some decades preserved ginger was categorized on the basis of
a number of qualities, namely, stem (the finest ginger made from the
youngest sections of rhizomes), and cargo, made from the remainder
and divided into the four subgrades of bold, medium, small-medium as
well as tails and pieces. A quality known as shavings, for which there
is only a limited demand, is made from the trimmings. These categories
have lost much of their significance with a greater proportion of the
preserved ginger in syrup now being made to the specific requirements
of the large industrial users.

3. Dried Ginger

The product traded as dried ginger consists of the ginger rhizome
after it has been dried in the country of production and marketed
either in the peeled whole rhizome, unpeeled whole rhizome, or unpeeled sliced (split) form. It is usually packed in bulk and shipped in
jute or Hessian sacks (Fig. 5). The better-quality dried ginger, usually in the whole peeled form, commands the highest price.

The consensus of opinion in the trade is that the Jamaican dried
ginger containing about 4.4% oleoresin and 1 to 1.3% volatile oil marketed in the whole peeled form is of superior quality and attracts a
premium price by virtue of its light color, a good aroma, and mellow
flavor. The dried ginger of India is of two types originating in either
the Cochin or Calicut districts. It contains about 4.3% oleoresin and
1.9 to 2.2% volatile oil and is usually exported in the rough peeled or
scraped form, although sometimes it is unpeeled. The ginger of Cochin
is more widely available and has a lemonlike flavor and odor. The dried
ginger of Nigeria is derived from plants originating in Jamica, although
the environment has influenced significantly the properties of the spice
obtained. It has about 6.5% oleoresin and 1.9 to 2.2% volatile oil and is
normally split longitudinally to speed drying. The dried ginger of
Sierra Leone was for many years referred to in the trade as African
and considered a good all-purpose product. It is exported in the unpeeled form and contains about 4.3% oleoresin and about 1.6 volatile oil.
The flavor is described as being somewhat camphoraceous. The dried,
washed, and bleached ginger produced in China has gained in

Figure 5 Bulk package dried ginger. (Courtesy of Buderim Ginger Growers Co-operative Association Ltd. and Queensland Department of Primary Industries.)

popularity in some European markets, particularly France. The sulfur dioxide present prohibits importation into some markets, such as the United Kindom. Other sources of dried ginger are Mauritius, Uganda, Australia, Bangladesh, Chile, Taiwan, and the eastern Carribean.

Traditionally, ground ginger is retailed through the grocery trade. It is primarily used as a source of flavoring material in the manufacture of bakery products, confectionery, sauces, and pickles, as well as a condiment in human and pet foods. Several aerated and fermented drinks use ginger as their principal flavoring component. Ginger ale is manufactured by adding ginger essence, sugar, permitted coloring, and a frothing agent to carbonated water. Ginger beer is a pale, frothy aerated drink made by the fermentation of sugar, ginger, cream of tartar, and yeast with water, and is bottled before it has finished fermenting. Ginger wine is manufactured by fermenting ginger, yeast, sugar, lemon rind, raisins, and water, and sometimes fortifying with spirits and ginger essence. Ginger is also an ingredient in some perfume and pharmaceutical products.

Food manufacturers are using increased amounts of the essential oil and oleoresin extracted from dried ginger (see Sec. IV). Oleoresin has the advantage of being more economical in use than the powdered spice. In addition, uniformity of flavor is much easier to achieve. Perhaps even more importantly, the oleoresins are sterile and free from any bacteriological contamination. Oleoresin, having an essential oil content of 15 to 30%, contains all the flavor principles including pungency. It is used to a limited extent in the pharmaceutical trade in throat lozenges. Ginger volatile oil contains the aroma principles, but not the pungency. There is a small outlet in the perfume industry, particularly in cosmetics for men. Small amounts of ginger oil may be added to the oleoresin to restore balance between aroma and pungency.

II. HORTICULTURAL ASPECTS

A. Cultivation Practices

Many aspects of ginger crop production were reported by Whiley (1974).

1. Climatalogical and Soil Requirements

High humidity brought about by high temperatures and moderate rainfall during the growing season are essential for the successful cultivation of ginger. For the late harvest, it is also beneficial to have a cooler, dry season while the rhizome matures and is being harvested. Meterological data for the Nambour district where the Australian crop is produced are shown in Table 1.

It is not unusual to record temperatures below freezing during winter. This induces an apparent rhizome dormancy and growth does not resume until the soil temperature at a depth of 150 mm exceeds 20°C. Most favorable growth is obtained at a soil temperature between 25 and 30°C. Sunburning of the newly emerged shoots can be a serious problem during early summer when screen temperatures exceed 32°C. Leaf burn and chlorophyll destruction also occur under conditions of excessive temperature and high light intensity, but the effects on yields are not as serious. To produce high yields, ginger requires a well-drained, loose, and friable soil, offering minimum resistance to rhizome development. Waterlogging retards growth and promotes the development of fungal diseases. The depth of topsoil is ideally 200 to 250 mm, although where bedding and/or surface mulching is practiced a shallower soil is utilized satisfactorily. To build up organic matter in soil, cover crops are grown and ploughed in during the 12 months before the crop is planted.

Table 1 Meterological Data, Major Australian
Ginger-Growing Area: 11-Year Average

Month	Season	Temperature Maximum °C	Minimum °C	Rainfall (mm)	Relative humidity (%)
January	Summer	28.4	18.8	208	70
February		28.1	19.2	293	71
March		27.0	17.6	297	70
April	Autumn	25.7	15.1	145	72
May		23.0	11.1	119	68
June		21.3	8.9	86	72
July	Winter	20.5	6.9	82	62
August		22.0	7.6	41	60
September		24.1	10.1	54	60
October	Spring	26.1	13.7	116	59
November		27.3	15.9	125	58
December	Summer	28.2	17.5	153	63
Total				1719	

Source: Whiley (1974).

2. Planting Material

Ginger flowers are generally sterile and rarely set seed. The plant
is therefore vegetatively propagated from portions of rhizome referred
to as seed pieces, each weighing 45 to 50 g. Growers obtain their
seed either by retaining a portion of the previous late-harvest crop
or more preferably utilizing rhizomes specially grown for seed purposes. Extra precautions for a seed crop include soil fumigation with
ethylene dibromide or methyl bromide, hot water treatment of the
seed at 48°C for 20 min, and sawdust mulching to a depth of 50 to
75 mm to provide nematode control.

Seed ginger is harvested when the rhizomes are mature, approximately 6 weeks before they are to be used for planting. It is stored
in Hessian bags in a shaded, dry, and well-ventilated situation. The
seed is prepared for planting by cutting or breaking the rhizome into
pieces. To prevent infection, the cut seed is treated with fungicides
such as benomyl to prevent entry of fungal diseases.

3. Planting

Although ginger is a perennial plant, it is generally cultivated as an
annual crop because ratoon ginger is usually of a much lower quality

than a plant crop, and has a high-fiber content and smaller knob size. In Australia, the best time to plant is in September which permits the young plants to become established before the onset of hot sunburning weather in late October, November, and December. The seed pieces are normally planted in three rows on beds 1.5 m wide. Whiley (1980b) has reported that within reasonable limits, seed piece size and plant and row spacing have no significant influence on yield when a given mass of seed is planted per unit area. Seeding rates of up to 10 tonnes/ha are preferred for early harvesting of confectionery-grade ginger since rhizomes do not reach full development before harvest. The ginger plant has a low light saturation point and prefers a semi-shaded environment. Whiley (unpublished departmental report, 1980) has shown that optimum growth is obtained at 75% of full sunlight, and under these close planting conditions earlier interplant shading is promoted which results in stimulated growth rates, reduced weed competition, and more efficient utilization of applied fertilizers. Although it has been known for many years that a larger knob size results in a high recovery of confectionery-grade ginger and a more attractive fresh market product, close planting was not accepted as a commercial practice because it was thought that knob size would be depressed.

Whiley (1980b) has shown that close planting of ginger (up to 11.2-cm intrarow spacing) increased the yield of rhizomes at both early and late harvest and advanced time of maturity for early harvest without a deleterious effect on knob size. However, increased seed piece mass increased rhizome knob size. In addition, it was concluded that the mass of seed per unit area is one of the most relevant planting factors influencing ultimate yield.

A uniform, large knob size obtained by grading seed to within 70 to 80 g is important in the production of confectionery-grade ginger to give uniformity of maturity between sets at harvest. Planting that is normally undertaken in the September to mid-October period is a mechanized operation using potato planters adapted to suit the irregular shape of ginger seed. Four persons with one machine can plant about 0.1 ha/hr. A fully automatic planter has been recently developed in Australia requiring only a tractor operator, and this unit is capable of planting 0.2 ha/hr.

4. Fertilization

In its natural environment ginger derives its nutritional requirements from decaying organic matter that gives a slow but continuous supply of essential minerals. Many production areas rely substantially on animal manures and other organic residues for fertilizing ginger. However, for high productivity these must be supplemented with inorganic nitrogen, phosphorus, and potassium fertilizers.

Whiley (1974) found under Queensland conditions that a ginger crop required 275 kg/ha of phosphorus, and 140 kg/ha of potassium on most local soils. Asher and Lee (1975, personal communication) reported from glass house experiments that ginger grows best at a pH of 5.6 but that they could not measure any differences over the range of 5.3 to 6.5 in the field.

On some soil types, trace element toxicities or deficiencies can occur, but once the problem is recognized low-cost corrective measures are generally easily carried out. In Queensland, maganese toxicity occurs on some soil types whereas copper and zinc are commonly deficient.

5. Irrigation

Irrigation serves a dual purpose in the production of ginger (Fig. 6). As well as supplementing rainfall to maintain soil moisture, it is used to protect young emerging shoots from sunburning. In Australia, irrigation is applied to provide approximately 10 mm of water every second day from mid-January until early March when the most rapid growth occurs. During sunburning weather, low-precipitation irrigation water at 2.5 mm/hr is usually applied from 10:00 a.m. to 3:00 p.m. daily, thereby establishing a high humidity below 33°C microclimate over the

Figure 6 Ginger crop under irrigation. (Courtesy of Buderim Ginger Growers Co-operative Association Ltd. and Queensland Department of Primary Industries.)

crop by evaporative cooling. Growth rate is accelerated by cloudy conditions. When both rainfall and sunburning conditions are experienced within a short period, overwatering may lead to excessive leaching of plant nutrients, stimulate development of diseases, and reduce soil temperatures below the optimum for growth.

6. Weed Control

Weed control is essential to produce maximum yields. For many years, a 50- to 75-mm-thick sawdust mulch was used for weed control in Australia. However, with the availability of suitable herbicides, mulching for this purpose has generally been discontinued. Sawdust was considered to have the added benefit of maintaining soil moisture, avoiding sunburn, providing better-shaped, cleaner ginger, and simplifying hand-harvesting (Bureau of Agricultural Economics, Canberra, Australia, 1971. Hilling or ridging and clipping are standard weed control techniques in most other ginger-growing countries.

7. Pest and Disease Control

There are several serious diseases known to infest ginger, causing severe economic losses in various world production centers. The most serious have been described by Pegg et al. (1969, 1974).

Bacterial wilt is caused by *Pseudomonas solanecearum* biotype IV. It was first recorded in Queensland in 1965 (Pegg and Moffett, 1971). It was thought to have been introduced with a shipment of seed from Taiwan in 1954 which was contaminated with *Fusarium* sp. (Simmonds, 1955) and which caused a major wilt problem. The disease is also reported from Hawaii, Malaysia, and Mauritius. The only effective method of control of this organism in Australia has been the quarantining of farms where outbreaks have occurred.

Fusarium rhizome rot is caused by *Fusarium oxysporum* f. sp. *zingiberi*. This was first recorded in Queensland in 1930 and thought to be introduced with early planting material. It is also known to occur in Hawaii and is possibly present throughout Southeast Asia. Control measures include selection of disease-free seed material, preplant dipping of seed in fungicides, and crop rotation.

Other diseases of generally minor significance are rhizome, root, and basal stem rot, caused by an unidentified white fungus; armillaria rhizome rot, caused by *Armillariella mellea;* rhizome and stem rot, caused by *Sclerotium rolfsii;* big bud, caused by the tomato *Mycoplasma* organism; and a bacterial soft spot caused by *Erwinia carotovora* which is associated with seed storage.

Pegg et al. (1969, 1974) have also described the root-knot nematode *Meloidogyne javanica* and *M. incognita,* which may cause a reduction of yield of more than 50%. The Fijian crop is reported to be infested by an additional species, the burrowing nematode *Radopholus similis* (Vilsoni et al., 1976).

B. Harvesting

As previously pointed out, the time of harvest depends on the product for which the rhizomes are to be used. This was recognized as long ago as 1886 by the District Agricultural Board of Trinidad (1892).

1. Early Harvest (Confectionery or Brined Ginger)

Plants are pulled from the damp ground to avoid damage to the tender rhizomes. Mechanical harvesters are being developed (Fig. 7). On the smaller farms, the early-harvest ginger is pulled from the ground by hand and stacked ready for the pickers (Fig. 8). Pickers remove the roots, seed piece, stalks, and excess soil, and place the rhizome into cans (Fig. 9). Timing is critical with this crop which must arrive at the factory as soon as possible after it is pulled from the ground. The cans are emptied into bulk bins which hold about 500 kg of ginger (Fig. 10). Careful handling of this early-harvest ginger is essential to avoid damage to the tender, fine-skinned rhizomes.

The first recorded attempt to determine the optimum harvesting time for ginger to be used for confectionery was made by Leverington (1969c) during the 1956 and 1957 season while assisting in the revival of the Australian ginger industry (which collapsed after World War II) following the resumption of world trade of ginger in syrup. During the postwar decade, it was customary to harvest ginger from mid-April onwards when it was mature and it had reached its maximum green

Figure 7 Experimental mechanical harvester. (Courtesy of Buderim Ginger Growers Co-operative Association Ltd. and Queensland Department of Primary Industries.)

Figure 8 Hand-harvesting of early-harvest ginger. (Courtesy of Buderim Ginger Growers Co-operative Association Ltd. and Queensland Department of Primary Industries.)

weight (Groszman, 1954) and the crop was ready for ratooning (Grosz-mann, private communication). The rate of harvest was often governed by the speed at which the crop could be processed. The fibers in the ginger at this stage were like sewing cotton, it was no longer succulent and the final product was unpalatable. Because of this, Australian confectionery ginger had a reputation of being hot, hard, and fibrous.

As shown in Fig. 11, Leverington (1969c) demonstrated the percentage of succulent stringless material or choice-grade ginger, as it became known, was at its peak of about 80% in midsummer (January and early February) and gradually fell until mid-March, when flowering usually commenced. It then fell more sharply, until by the end of March the stringless portion had dropped to 50% and then to 40% within another week. During the period under study, the rhizomes were undergoing vigorous growth as shown in Fig. 12, but the total recovery of choice reached a peak towards the end of March. Experience over five seasons showed that recovery and percentage stringless ginger per rhizome were dependent not only on time of planting, mulching, and soil condition, but also on the weather, which appeared to be capable of causing a variation of ±2 weeks in optimum harvest time.

Figure 9 Hand-topping of early-harvest ginger. (Courtesy of Buderim Ginger Growers Co-operative Association Ltd. and Queensland Department of Primary Industries.)

Figure 10 Bulk-bin handling of ginger. (Courtesy of Buderim Ginger Growers Co-operative Association Ltd. and Queensland Department of Primary Industries.)

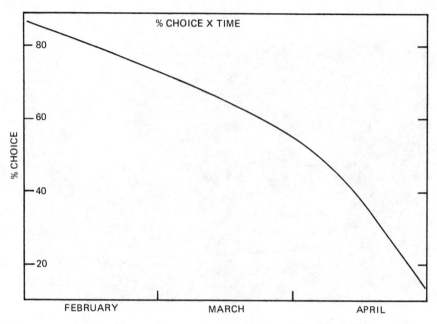

Figure 11 Approximate changes in percentage of stringless ginger with time.

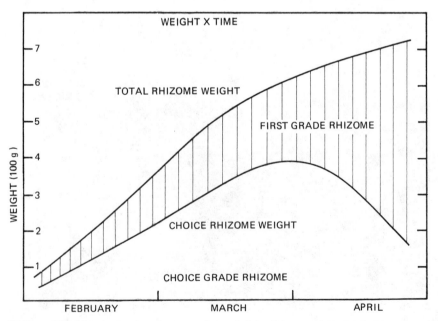

Figure 12 Approximate changes in weight of stringless ginger and total rhizome with time.

These findings led to the development of an incentive payment scheme based on ginger quality. Growers were paid a very high price for fiber-free ginger and a very low price for fibrous ginger. This scheme, which was an important factor in the development of the Australian industry, has subsequently been reported by Bendall and Daly (1966) and the Bureau of Ag. Economics, Canberra, Australia (1971). It ensures relatively fiber-free (string-free) ginger, at the sacrifice of yields as compared with late harvest.

In later years Page and Cornwall (1969, private communication) and Whiley (1980a) made detailed plant growth studies of ginger grown under varying conditions and times. These studies confirmed the extremely rapid changes that occur in the composition and size of ginger rhizomes. The time of harvest for confectionery ginger is most critical and necessitates the almost daily examination of developing rhizomes to determine optimum harvest date. Within the industry, this harvest is known as early harvest and commences in late February and continues until late March. The appearance of flower stems (Fig. 3) is usually an indication of more rapid fiber development. The terms fiber, commercial fiber, visible fiber, and others used have no direct relationship to the percentage of chemical fiber (Leverington, 1969c). Whiley (1980a,b) reports that although flowering appears to be a major contributor in reducing choice-grade rhizome production, other factors have been observed that slow growth rates and influence choice-grade recovery, the most important being temperature, moisture stress, and planting density.

2. Late Harvest (Dried or Green Ginger)

Dried ginger is produced from the mature rhizome gathered during the late harvest, but the timing of harvesting is not as critical as with confectionery-grade ginger. Whiley (1974) reported that the maximum fresh weight of the rhizome is reached in June, 9 months after planting. From then on there is a gradual loss in rhizome weight. On the other hand, Whiley (1980a) has reported that the rhizome dry weight peaked 32 weeks after planting (early May). This point indicates the optimum period of harvest to maximize recovery of dehydrated ginger. Jogi et al. (1972) selected a different criterion for harvesting ginger in India, based on fat (oleoresin) and protein content in the rhizome, suggesting harvesting 26 weeks after planting when the concentration of components is at an optimum.

Methods of harvesting late ginger vary, but most growers remove the stalks by slashing and then use adapted diggers to lift the rhizomes. These lift a complete bed of three rows at a time. After surplus soil and roots as well as the original seed piece are removed, the ginger is bulk handled to the factory (Fig. 10). In experimental plots, yields in the vicinity of 120 tonnes/ha have been recorded, but the industry average for late-harvest ginger is 37 tonnes/ha.

Late-harvest ginger, provided it is maintained dry, can be kept for some weeks at ambient temperature. It is marketed as green ginger through the wholesale and retail markets. Alternatively, it is dried. The Tropical Products Institute in a monograph (n.d.) reported that adhering soil on the rhizome should be removed as soon as possible after harvesting if a pale-color dried product is required.

III. BIOCHEMICAL AND NUTRITIONAL COMPOSITION

A. General Composition

Although ginger has been an important commodity in world trade for centuries and has some medicinal carminative properties, it cannot be considered to have any significant nutritional value, particulary when the normal daily intake is considered. Its value as a food is limited to its flavoring properties or its ability to be converted into confectionery, in which form it has a high calorific value due to the presence of at least 70% carbohydrates (usually invert sugars and sucrose). Table 2 sets out the composition per 100 g of edible portion. Figures for green ginger and crystallized ginger were reported by Watt and Merrill (1975) and dried ground ginger by Thomas and Corden (1970). Green ginger in the fresh raw state is rather unpalatable and is not consumed in that form.

Changes in composition during processing are quite drastic as would be expected. During dehydration, solids are increased generally in proportion to the dehydration ratios except in the case of some vitamins which are lost. When brined ginger is cooked in water for a prolonged period prior to syruping, solids are leached out and sulfur dioxide volatilized. The water is displaced with carbohydrates, usually sugars, during syruping. The development of strings or visible fiber is discussed in the section on harvesting. Natarajan et al. (1972) have demonstrated a wide variation in chemical composition in 26 varieties of ginger grown in India.

B. Flavoring Components

The two distinct flavoring components discussed in Sect. I. C are: (a) an aromatic essential oil which contains all the characteristic flavor and aroma compounds but is nonpungent and can be steam-distilled from the comminuted green or ground dried rhizome; and (b) a pungent oleoresin that contains the essential oil and is extracted from the ground dried spice with solvents, mainly acetone or ethanol. Both products are marketed for use in further manufacture but are not available to the consumer through the retail trade. The chemistry of ginger essential oil and oleoresin has been reviewed by Connell (1970). A summary of his and more recent work is detailed next.

Table 2 Composition of Ginger per 100 g of Edible Portion

Component or value	Unit measured	Green ginger[a]	Dry ground ginger[b]	Crystallized ginger[a]
Water	(g)	87.0	—	12.0
Food Energy	(cal)	49.0	259.0	340.0
Proteins	(g)	1.4	7.4	0.3
Fat	(g)	1.0	3.3	0.2
Carbohydrates				
Total	(g)	9.5	60.0	87.1
Fiber	(g)	1.1	—	0.7
Ash	(mg)	1.1	—	0.4
Calcium	(mg)	23.0	97.0	—
Phosphorus	(mg)	36.0	136.0	—
Iron	(mg)	2.1	17.2	—
Sodium	(mg)	6.0	34.0	—
Potassium	(mg)	264.0	910.0	—
Vitamin A value	(IU)	10.0	—	—
Thiamine	(mg)	0.02	—	—
Riboflavin	(mg)	0.04	—	—
Niacin	(mg)	0.7	—	—
Ascorbic acid	(mg)	4.0	—	—

[a]Data from Watt and Merrill (1975).
[b]Data from Thomas and Corden (1970).
Source: Australian Government Printing Service, Canberra, p. 12.

1. Essential Oil

Essential oil of ginger is usually light yellow in color with a specific gravity less than 1.00. It does not contain any pungent principle, but it contains the volatile flavoring principles that give ginger its distinctive flavor and aroma. Guenther (1952) reported that the cell sacs containing the oil are located in the epidermal tissues of the rhizome and that peelings and shavings of the rhizomes constitute an ideal raw material for distillation of the essential oil.

The recovery of essential oil from ginger grown in various countries ranges from 0.8 to 4.4%. In Queensland ginger, the recovery has been shown to increase from 1.8 to 4.4% on a dry wt basis over the commercial growing season, but when this is expressed on a green wt basis the recovery is approximately constant at 0.4% (Winterton and Richardson, 1965). A study in India (Natarajan et al., 1972) using eight ginger varieties showed that over a 4-month period the essential oil content rose from 1.79% (mean of eight varieties) to 2.28%, on a dry wt. basis.

Ginger essential oil is a complex mixture of chemical compounds of which about 60 have been identified (Heath, 1973; Gildemeister and Hoffman, 1956; Connell and Jordan, 1971; Bednarczyk and Kramer, 1971; Kami et al., 1972). The largest class of compounds present, the sesquiterpene hydrocarbons, although accounting for between 70 and 90% of the total oil, are only weakly odorous and contribute little to the distinctive aroma. This aroma is believed to be due to the relatively volatile monoterpene hydrocarbons and other compounds with similar volatility, with oxygenated monoterpenes exerting a modifying influence under some circumstances. The monoterpene hydrocarbons, camphene, di-β-phellandrene, β-pinene, mycrine, p-cymene, α-pinene, d-limonene, and cumene, have been identified as well as the oxygenated compounds n-nonanal, n-decanal, methyheptanone, 1,8-cineole, d-borneol, linalool, geranial, citral, 2-heptanol, 2-nonanol, and bornyl acetate. Each of these compounds has a relatively strong distinctive odor but not one alone is characteristic of ginger.

Connell and Jordan (1971) reported that the compounds geranial and neral (citral a and citral b) produce a lemonlike aroma in Queensland ginger, the concentration in the oil ranging from 8 to 27%. A variety of ginger from Fiji grown under identical conditions with Queensland ginger has also been shown to produce essential oil with a lemonlike aroma and the same concentration of citrals (Jordan, 1972, personal communication). It is interesting to note that Fijian ginger was reported in Royal Gardens Kew (1892) by the District Agricultural Board of Trinidad in 1892 to be remarkable for its exceedingly fine aroma and peculiar pleasant taste recalling that of lemon.

The major sequiterpene constituents of the essential oil, ar-curcumene, zingiberene, βbisabolene, β-sesquiphellandrene, and trans-β-farnesene (Connell, 1970), although contributing little to the aroma of ginger volatile oil, are significant indicators of the quality of the oil. Salzer (1975) has shown that on storage in light and air the ar-curcumene in the oil increases while both zingiberene and β-sesquiphellandrene decrease. This change occurs relatively rapidly. Over a 4-week period, Salzer (1975) observed zingiberene and β-sequiphellandrene decreasing from 34.8 and 19.6% to 0 and 2.4%, respectively, while the ar-curcumene increased from 35.7 to 87.1%. Based on this, he suggested that ar-curcumene is absent from fresh oil and only forms during the isolation process. An increase in viscosity has also been observed during storage (Connell and Jordan, 1971), indicating that a significant amount of polymerization is taking place.

2. Oleoresin

The recovery and quality of oleoresin can also be dependent on the source of material and the solvent used. Connell (1970) reported that recovery of oleoresin extracted with acetone from Queensland dry, ground ginger, varies from 5 to 11%. Winterton and Richardson (1965) reported significant increases in recovery when using ethanol. When ethanol is used as a solvent, significant amounts of nonpungent material, particularly starch and lipids, are extracted (Jordan, 1972, private communication). However, corresponding analysis carried out on Jamacian African and Indian ginger showed only a small difference in concentration between solvents (Winterton and Richardson, 1965). The Tropical Products Institute (1979b) has reported that the presence of water in the system can greatly vary the amount of material extracted. The average composition (Salzer, 1975) is essential oil 20 to 30%, fatty acids 10%, pungent substances 50 to 70%, water 0.5 to 1%, and some nitrogenous substances.

The constituent of the oleoresin responsible for the pungency was first isolated by Thresh (1879) and named gingerol. Later, Nomura (1917a,1917b,1918) isolated two pungent compounds from the oleoresin that he named zingerone and shogaol. Subsequently, it was shown that zingerone formed when gingerol was treated with hot alkali (Varier, 1945). More recently Connell and Sutherland (1966,1969) have re-examined ginger oleoresin and have shown that gingerol, is in fact, a mixture as shown in Fig. 13. A partial separation allowed the calculation of the ratios of the components (6):(8):(10) as 56:13:31. Later Raghuveer and Govindarajan (1978), using a gas chromatographic method, showed that the ratio of the homologues was 65:16:19. Gingerols, shogaols, and zingerone are related by the reactions shown in Fig. 14. An understanding of the reaction I→II and I→III is central to the appreciation of the changes which can occur in the oleoresin during extraction and handling.

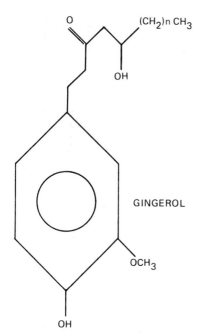

GINGEROL

Figure 13 Structure of gingerol.

Connell and Sutherland (1966,1969) suggested that shogaol and zingerone are artifacts or at most very minor constituents of ginger rhizomes and that their presence in ginger oleoresin in easily detectable quantities indicates exposure of the oleoresins (pH 3.5 to 5.0) to excessive heat treatment in the course of preparation. Connell (1969) also demonstrated that the gingerol content of oleoresin decreases rapidly, forming shogaols as the pH is lowered and the temperatures are raised. The shogaol concentration increased and then decreased as these compounds underwent further decomposition to nonpungent residues. More recently, work by Narasimhan and Govindarajan (1978) has shown that the pungent fraction of shogaols is twice as pungent as the pungent fraction of gingerols. This clearly indicates that oleoresin with relatively high-shogaol content and low-gingerol content could have a pungency level as high as oleoresin containing mostly gingerol and almost no shogaol.

The pungency of ginger is a primary-quality attribute, and its objective determination has been a major goal of researchers. The early methods of Parry (1948) and Garnett and Grier (1909) proved difficult and unreliable because they failed to discriminate between pungent and nonpungent compounds. Connell and Sutherland (1969) developed thin layer and column chromatographic (TLC) techniques for resolving gingerol and shogaol, and they were able to achieve semi-quantitative results. The method was improved by Ananthakrishna and Govindarajan (1974) when they demonstrated that the method of Connell and Sutherland failed to resolve some nonpungent material from both the gingerol and shogaol. The method was extended by removing the pungent compounds from the TLC and applying colorometric determinations. Nambudiri et al. (1975) have reported on a similar method. Gas chromatography has been used as a means of determining oleoresin constituents by Connell and McLauchlan (1972) and Raghuveer and Govindarajan (1978). The nonpungent substances have not been thoroughly investigated, but Jordan (1972, private communication) has reported the extraction of starch and lipids. Singh et al. (1975) have extracted the lipids from dried ginger and identified some of the components of the mixture including linolenic, capric, lauric, palmitic, stearic, oleic, and linoleic acids.

C. Biochemical Aspects

Ichikawa et al. (1973) reported the isolation of a protease from green ginger. Two fractions were detected with a molecular weight of 22,500 but with different electrophoretic mobility. Both fractions had an optimum pH of 6.5 to 7.0 and were activated by thiol-type compounds.

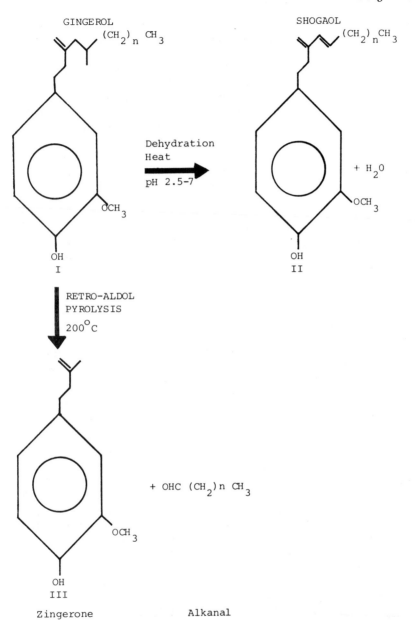

Figure 14 Decomposition of gingerol.

At about the same time, Thompson et al. (1973) reported the isolation of ginger protease, for which the name Zingibain was proposed. This work was mainly concerned with a study of the properties of the enzyme such as optimum pH (5.0 to 5.6) and optimum temperature (60°C). It was also reported that the enzyme was an effective meat tenderizer, being most effective during the cooking process. More recently, Ohtsuki et al. (1978) have shown that the enzyme is very unstable, losing its activity rapidly in the absence of moisture and air at low temperatures.

IV. THE TECHNOLOGY OF GINGER STORAGE AND PROCESSING

A. Confectionery Ginger

Although the preservation of succulent fruits and ginger by boiling in sugar solutions seems to have been practiced for a century or so, few technical data on syruping techniques (U.S. Dept. of Commerce, 1908; U.S. Consular Report, 1923; *Bulletin of the Imperial Institute,* 1926; Kurmara Das, 1929) were available at the time the Australian ginger-processing industry developed during the early 1940s.

1. Raw Material

While investigating and developing the concept of an optimum time of harvest for ginger in 1955 and 1956 (see Sect. II. A), Leverington (1969c) designed a ginger fibrometer to objectively measure ginger quality based on texture. This was used to develop and standardize a commercial-quality hand-grading method that industry has adapted and refined over the years to the point at which reproducibility is of a very high order.

Ginger quality is determined by cutting the nonhomogeneous ginger rhizome cross sectionally with a knife, beginning at the growing point and cutting into approximately 4-mm slices. As fibrous strings are encountered, greater resistance to the knife is felt by the operator and the fiber strands drag across the cut surface and are easily seen. Fiber-free succulent ginger is denoted choice grade. When a small quantity of soft fiber is encountered, it is classified first grade. Both grades are used for confectionery ginger. The stringy portion of the rhizome is used for other ginger products, including dry ginger, whereas the neck is used for drying only.

Commercially, the proportion of choice-grade tissue is expressed as a percentage of the total rhizome, and the first harvest is made when the proportion of choice grade is between 35 and 42% of the whole rhizome. The rate of change is about 1%/day, thus harvest date is critical.

Attempts to establish a single, objective method of grading ginger with the aim of eliminating operator fatigue and other subjective factors have not been successful (Jordan, 1972, unpublished departmental report, 1972). Flotation methods tested were affected by air occluded under the skin of the diced ginger even after vacuum treatment. Green pea Maturometer techniques were impracticle because of the need to orientate each ginger piece. Total solids and alcohol-insoluble solids determinations were too variable. Chemical degradation of the tissue and separaton of the fibers proved unsuitable for the early harvest due to inaccuracies and difficulties of separation in the very-low-fiber samples.

2. Factory Receival

A typical flow diagram for the modern manufacture of ginger products is shown in Fig. 15. Unwashed hands of ginger are transferred in bulk bins from the field to the factory where they are dumped into water and then cleaned by high-pressure sprays in a rotary reel washer (Shrapnel, 1967) and then scrubbed. The gnarled shape of the rhizome makes hand-washing a very inefficient and time-consuming job for a grower. At this point, the ginger is continually sampled for grading, weighed for payment purposes, and then transferred to waxed 300-mm ferroconcrete vats for storage in continuously circulated brine until ready for processing during the ensuing 12 months. The intake period for the crop (about 3 weeks) is so short that sufficient storage capacity is necessary to take the whole crop, and syruping and crystallizing facilities are so sized to process the crop over a 10- to 12-month period.

3. Brining

Ginger is similar to other horticultural produce in its requirements for storage brines. Figure 16 shows brined ginger in storage vats. Acidified sulfur dioxide brines, sodium chloride brines, and mixtures of the two have been researched by Brown (1972,1975), Brown and Lloyd (1972), and Lloyd (1975a). The best recovery of sound ginger was obtained using sulfur dioxide/citric acid brines while maintaining not less than 0.1% SO_2 and pH not greater than 4.0. On the other hand, ginger stored for up to 9 months in sulfur dioxide/sulfuric acid brines suffered rapid and relatively severe tip-tissue deterioration at concentrations as low as 0.1% sulfuric acid, with damage increasing with higher acid concentrations. The sulfur dioxide had a very desirable bleaching effect that permitted a golden ginger to be produced due to slight caramelization of the sugar during subsequent processing. Brining also appeared to leach some of the undesirable components present in raw ginger.

　Because sulfur dioxide brines require frequent adjustments to maintain the critical levels and some countries do not permit this preservative, Brown and Lloyd also undertook investigations on the use of sodium chloride brines, some of which utilized a lactic acid fermentation. These studies showed that ginger stored in an equilibrated 16% salt brine with 0.1% citric acid with or without 0.5% sulfur dioxide and subsequently syruped had a much higher recovery and had a crisper texture than ginger stored in sulfur dioxide/acid brines. However,

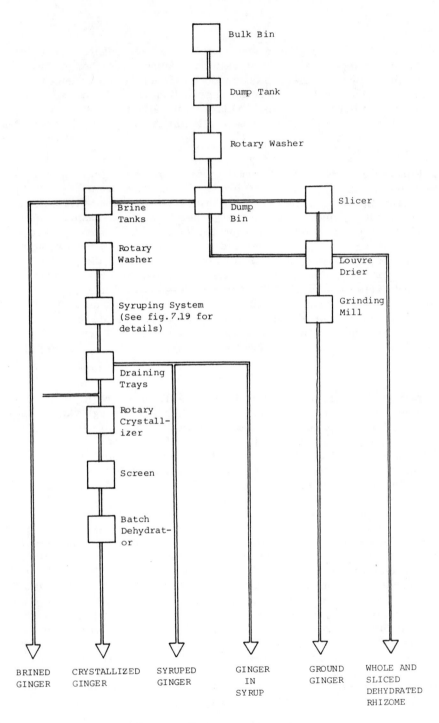

Figure 15 Flow diagram of ginger processing.

Figure 16 Brined ginger in storage vats. (Courtesy of Buderim Ginger Growers Co-operative Association Ltd. and Queensland Department of Primary Industries.)

they found that there was no merit in attempting natural or controlled lactic acid fermentation because of the lack of natural nutrients. Ginger produced from acidified salt brines was a darker color than that produced with sulfur dioxide brines, though taste panels found it difficult to detect a significant difference in flavor and texture. The cost of citric acid and salt brines was much higher than that of sulfur dioxide/sulfuric acid brines. A commercial appraisal of costs versus recovery and quality would be necessary in individual cases. It has been noted that if adequate hygiene standards are not maintained during production and brining is not carefully controlled, rots which have been attributed to a *Clostridia* species may ret the whole rhizome during storage, leaving only a few fibers.

4. Peeling

Shrapnel (1967) reported that by using young succulent rhizomes rapid brine penetration was achieved through the fine skin, thereby avoiding time-consuming peeling and dicing upon receival. *Food Science* (1960) suggested that the skin of ginger, presumably mature, can only be scraped off as rotary potato peelers cannot cope with the irregular shapes and, in addition, injure the surface of the ginger.

Care is taken to ensure that the rhizomes are always covered with brine. Failure to do so will set up pressures on the lower levels, causing compression and shrinkage with consequent loss in product recovery.

5. Dicing

It is simpler and faster to syrup diced ginger than whole hands. All of the early-harvest crop for confectionery ginger is cut and graded by hand (Shrapnel, 1967) (Fig. 17) to ensure uniform quality in terms of freedom from fiber and to prepare the maximum quantity of regular-sized pieces. This is a prime requirement for chocolate enrobing. To meet requirements, standards have been laid down based on the number of pieces per pound, giving a choice of cubes averaging approximately 16 mm, 19 mm, and 22 mm and, in addition, a special cut of much higher uniformity where a very high standard of accuracy is required for luxury box packs. Confectionery ginger for other purposes is also required to be in discrete pieces or blocks (approximately 12.5 to 19.0 mm). Dicing by hand is obviously a very labor-intensive operation. Costs could be cut by machine-dicing, but only about 10% of the end product would be

Figure 17 Hand-grading of brined ginger. (Courtesy of Buderim Ginger Growers Co-operative Association Ltd. and Queensland Department of Primary Industries.)

in perfect cubes, another 10% in reasonably acceptable cubes (for chocolate enrobing), and 40 to 45% in pieces suitable for crystallizing. This
would leave 35 to 40% of the usable rhizome in a small chip form.

Only about 6% of young stem tips are produced by hand-cutting.
These are required by cake and chocolate manufacturers, either in that
form or small dices (5 mm × 8 mm × 8 mm), that are used in dried fruit
packs, fruit cakes, curries, fruit salad, cheese and cheesecakes, health
food bars, ice cream, and yogurt.

Shrapnel (1967) reported a problem that he aptly called hard center
which became apparent only after dicing. He noted that it occured when
a ginger crop suffered from a severe setback such as drought. There
was a tendency for the rhizome to develop a hard, dry center. This was
surrounded by a normal-quality young material when good growing conditions later prevailed. This was also observed in Chinese ginger, but
was overcome in Australia by irrigating the crops as necessary.

6. Cooking

After brine storage, ginger should be cooked in several changes of
boiling water in order to:

Soften the texture to permit rapid impregnation of sugar syrup.
Remove some of the heat by leaching out pungent and volatile components.
Remove excess sulfur dioxide.

When cooking ginger in boiling water care is taken to overflow rinse when
adding fresh water. Exposure of the hot ginger to the air will not only
cause rapid shrinkage due to evaporation from the surface, but pressure
on the lower levels will also cause shrinkage. With each batch of ginger,
process conditions are adjusted to ensure a balance between these objectives and the maintenance of a crisp ginger texture. Citric acid may
be used to maintain pH 4.0 during this process which may proceed for
about 1 hr. Failure to maintain an appropriate acid medium during this
stage can cause blue anthocyanin pigments to appear that can persist
into the syruping stages and cause undesirably dark colorations.

Shrapnel (1967) reported that market research showed that the high
level of heat in Chinese ginger was not required by the great majority
of consumers. Fortunately, the ginger oil content, and hence heat, of
the early-harvest ginger was comparatively low and yielded a mild ginger
with a good crisp texture without prolonging the cooking process. Permitted firming additives such as calcium and aluminum salts gave a
noticeable improvement in crispness of texture in young stem tips that
had the tendency to break down during protracted storage in brine.

7. Syruping

Brown (1969a) reported that traditional methods of preserving ginger
by immersion in sugar syrups have been practiced in China and India

for centuries. The art of processing these products for confection-
eries remained basically unchanged and very little was published about
production until the early 1900s. These classic methods of syruping
ginger (U.S. Dept. of Commerce, 1908; U.S. Consular Report, 1923;
Bulletin of the Imperial Institute, 1926; Kurmara Das, 1929) used commercially up until the 1940s required the steeping of batches of cooked
ginger in syrups of increasing concentration, usually accompanied by
boiling or at least some heating. Apparently cognizance was not taken
of the shrinkage and incidental loss of recovery or the spoilage of caramelization. Authors appear to have overlooked this economic aspect
(Brown, 1969a). There seems little doubt that these methods are still
used in cottage industries in developing countries and certainly by the
cooking enthusiast even in the most highly developed countries.

When these methods were adopted commercially in Australia in 1945,
it became obvious to the author that they were extremely wasteful of
sugar because of the rapidly accumulating volumes of syrup which,
when concentrated by open-pan evaporation, had an increasing concentration of heat and continued to carmelize and darken the product.
This led to the development and commercial adoption of the chain batch
process in 1945 but this process was not published until 1969 at the
specific request of industry (Leverington, 1969a).

The procedure is best described by reference to Fig. 18. The diagram represents the process at any one day. Tank A was a complete
batch that was discharged for packing in syrup or crystallizing. Its
syrup was placed on tank C, thereby making its equilibrium Brix about
58° on the following day. Tank B was at the third stage, and received
a high-Brix syrup to lift its equibibrium Brix to 72° on the following
day. The 58° Brix syrup on tank B was fed onto tank D so that its
equilibrium Brix was lifted to 44° on the following day. Tanks C and D
syrups were combined, evaporated, and divided so that by the addition
of the requisite amount of sugar, the required volumes of syrups of
85° Brix and 72° Brix were prepared for adding to tanks B and E,
respectively. The process worked very well until caramelization of the
syrups in continuous use rendered them too dark. The problem was
largely overcome by using a vacuum evaporator operated at 43.5°C
to remove sufficient water to balance the fresh water being added in
the new batch. In this way, excessive volumes of syrup were not accumulated. However, the circulating syrup continuously extracted the
hot ginger flavor, increasing pungency to a point at which the syrup
was no longer suitable for impregnating fresh ginger. A sandwich or
biscuit spread was developed to utilize this syrup by blending it with
candied honey and comminuted sugar-impregnated ginger. The recovery of drained ginger having an equilibrium Brix of 72° was approximately 80% of the brined ginger weight.

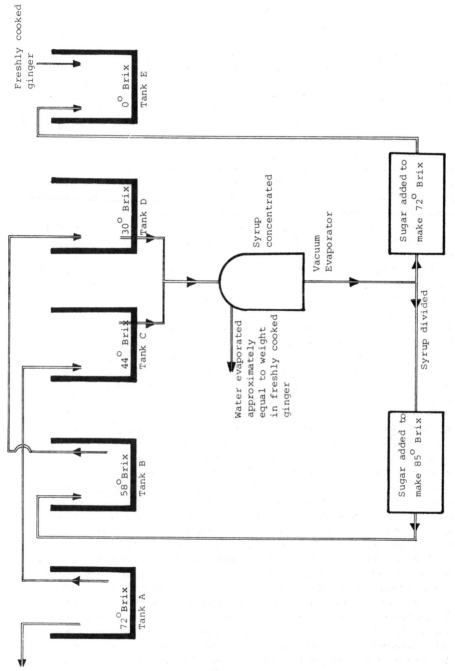

Figure 18 Flow diagram of four-stage chain-batch process (1945).

   At intervals during the following 24 years the basic principles of this technique were developed and improved first by Leverington (1969a,b,c) and then by Brown (1969a,b,c). The ginger industry progressively adopted these improved methods thereby producing a consistently high-quality, mild-flavored, golden-colored ginger with a succulent texture. These techniques prevent shrinkage while replacing most of the original moisture by an equivalent amount of sugar with a net drained weight gain as high as 22%. Sudden changes of the osmotic pressure environment of the ginger being syruped (Leverington, 1969b; Brown, 1969b,c) must be avoided, particularly at the higher Brix levels. This is best achieved by the use of a multivat system so that the rise in Brix gradually decreases to 1 to 2° Brix/day in the final stages. Utilization of close to the theoretical amount of sugar for impregnation can be achieved. One tonne of sugar should be used for each tonne of green ginger. It has been noted that under commercial conditions the losses of sugar due to spillage and other causes, during processing can reach significant proportions unless strict control is enforced.

   The optimal processing conditions which are represented in the flow diagram in Fig. 19 are as follows. Ginger is impregnated with sugar syrup by immersion in syrup for up to 15 days while syrup strength is gradually raised from 0 to 75° Brix by means of a vacuum evaporator and the addition of sugar. This is achieved by having about 12 stainless steel tanks, one for each processing day, connected in series so that the syrup is moved from the base of one vat to the top of the next one in such a way that the sugar concentration in the ginger gradually rises while it steadily drops in the syrup. On leaving the end of the chain of tanks, the syrup is vacuum-concentrated and adjusted with fresh sugar to 76° Brix ready for the final syruping stage. A small bleed of syrup at the end of the chain prevents excessive buildup of heat components in the body of the circulating syrup. Another four tanks are needed for the cooking and final equilibrium stages. To minimize compression effects on ginger in the lower levels of the tanks, the vessels are usually squat, the diameter being greater than the height. The ginger is always kept covered with syrup to avoid compression and loss of drained weight. Vats are fitted with rotating syrup sprinklers above the product to ensure adequate mixing of viscous syrups from about the 60° Brix stage upwards (Fig. 20).

   Process control involves the following tests. Ginger texture must be checked regularly during the boiling stages to ensure that the finished product will meet market requirements. Regular checks of total soluble solids are necessary to ensure that the concentration within the ginger gradually increases without a drastic osmotic pressure effect causing loss in drained weight (Leverington, 1969b; Brown, 1969b,c). Daily monitoring of sucrose:reducing sugar ratios are necessary to ensure that the final product has between 25 and 30% reducing sugars. Brown (1969b) has reported that severe syneresis occurred in crystal-

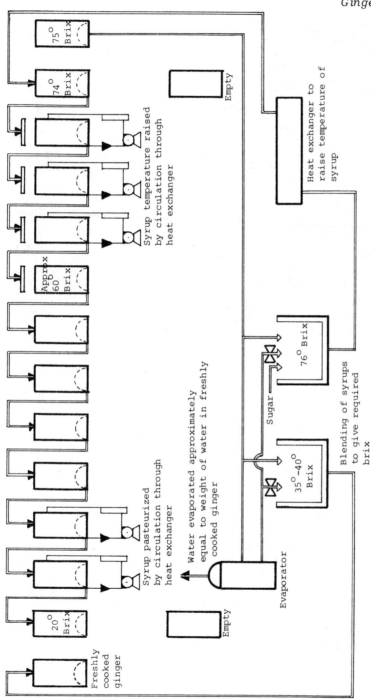

Figure 19 Flow diagran of modern 12-stage ginger syrup vat system.

Figure 20 Ginger-syruping tanks with sprinklers. (Courtesy of
Buderim Ginger Growers Co-operative Association Ltd. and Queensland
Department of Primary Industries.)

lized ginger when it contained more than 39% reducing sugars and that
it hardened during storage when it contained less than 25% reducing
sugars. Some confectionery manufacturers require a proportion of
liquid glucose (corn syrup) to be used in syruped ginger. pH requires regular monitoring to control to 4 ± 0.2 (Shrapnel, 1967). Not
only does this permit the development of a golden ginger, it is also
critical in maintaining the required sucrose:reducing sugar ratio. Too
low a pH will rapidly invert all sucrose to reducing sugars. Temperature control during syruping is also vital to maintain the required
sucrose:invert sugar ratio. Brown (1969c) has shown that the raising
of syrup temperatures to 71°C increases drained weight but that 54.5°C
is the highest temperature at which sugar inversion control is achieved.
As shown in Fig. 19, these results have been adapted to use heat during the later stages of syruping for limited periods.

The type of vacuum evaporator used to concentrate the ginger
syrups is not critical provided it can handle the 76° Brix syrup at
fairly low temperatures. Multiple-effect units provide economy in operation, but turbulent thin-film evaporators are more compact and probably cause less caramelization.

8. Storage

After reaching equilibrium with the 76° Brix syrup, which normally takes 24 hrs, the ginger is packed into 200-liter polyethylene-lined steel drums containing 220 to 270 kg (Figs. 21 and 22). Depending on whether the ginger is to be used for further manufacture or sold in the syruped form, an appropriate amount of 75° Brix syrup is added. Naturally the more syrup that can be sold at this stage, the less the load on the evaporator. It is important that ginger in syrup be stored at comparatively low temperatures to avoid slow continuous inversion of the sucrose.

9. Consumer Packaging

Choice crisp tips and other very succulent pieces are packed off into clear glass jars or stone jars (Chinese style) for sale as ginger in syrup.

Figure 21 Bulk package of ginger in syrup. (Courtesy of Buderim Ginger Growers Co-operative Association Ltd. and Queensland Department of Primary Industries.)

Figure 22 Weighing bulk package of ginger in syrup. (Courtesy of Buderim Ginger Growers Co-operative Association Ltd. and Queensland Department of Primary Industries.)

10. Crystallizing

Crystallized ginger consists of discrete pieces of 75° Brix ginger that have been enrobed in a hot supersaturated sucrose solution, which acts as an adhesive, and then coated with a layer of dry crystalline sucrose. In contrast to the classic methods of crystallizing fruits (Campbell, 1945; Morris, 1945), it has been shown that ginger needs to be coated with pure commercial sucrose crystals, preferably 300 to 600 μm, whereas castor sugar tends to adhere in lumps (Leverington, 1969c). As the coating cools, it forms a matrix of commercial sugar crystals held in place by a mass of fine sucrose crystals from the super-saturated syrup. It is important to note that the term crystallized re-fers to the sharp crystal coating on the ginger and not the consistency of the ginger pieces. If the whole piece is crystallized throughout, as can occur with incorrect sucrose:reducing sugar ratios, the ginger loses its tender succulent texture and becomes hard.

When ginger in syrup is required for crystallizing, it is drained on a wire mesh screen preferably in a layer not exceeding 150 mm to avoid compression effects. Draining for 10 min will remove 90 to 95% of the syrup, but centrifuging in a basket will leave the pieces with a more even film of syrup. The ginger pieces are then dipped into an 80° Brix hot (93 ± 1°C) sucrose solution and rolled in the sucrose crystals. The product is screened to remove excess adhering sucrose crystals and then air-dried to remove the moisture remaining in the matrix. This basic treatment and earlier work conducted by Nguyen (unpublished departmental report, 1970) were utilized by Scudamore-Smith (unpublished departmental report, 1980) in developing a continuous mechanized method to crystallize ginger. This was undertaken to eliminate the highly labor-intensive manual operation which is inevitable due to the intrinsic nature of the product. He has recently completed his investigation and has reported in the following terms.

Adhesive Syrup Coating. The drained ginger pieces were readily coated with 80° Brix syrup held at 93 ± 1°C by passage through a trough on a stainless steel mesh conveyor so that the product was heated for a minimum of 2-1/2 min. Fresh syrup was prepared daily or more frequently if the invert syrup concentration exceeded 20%. In a commercial operation, discarded syrup may be transferred to the ginger-syruping system for utilization, the ginger pieces discharged with a doctor blade, and the belt cleaned with live steam before ginger pieces are fed onto it again. In arriving at these conditions consideration was given to:

Minimizing syrup evaporation to maintain Brix
Balancing the dilution effect of the film of syrup (75° Brix) on the
 ginger pieces
Minimizing viscosity to increase convection currents and general mixing
 of syrup
Producing a tacky coating within a realistic temperature range
Sterilizing the ginger pieces, particularly the destruction of osmophilic
 yeasts (Lloyd, 1975b)

Cooling of Syrup Coating. A cooling stage was introduced to adjust the adhesive syrup to the optimum tackiness. Although maximum tackiness was attained at 49 ± 4°C, the resultant crystal sugar coating was excessively thick and lacked sales appeal. The optimum temperature to give an attractive even coating of sugar crystals was 60 ± 4°C. This temperature was achieved by cooling the product in air at +24°C with sufficient air circulation to drop the temperature in approximately 7 min. Faster cooling caused clumping of syrup and uneven sugar coatings. This process was achieved by passing the product through a temperature-controlled tunnel.

Sugar Coating. The sugar was applied by passing the tacky pieces of ginger through a curtain of 300 to 600 μm sugar at 24°C as they passed into an inclined rotating cylinder with a peripheral speed of 35 m/min, angled so that the pieces took 1 min to pass through it. In the first half of the cylinder the sugar crystals were mixed intimately with the tacky syruped pieces, while in the second half which was perforated the excess sugar crystals were removed. Excess sugar crystals may be transferred to the syruping system. A commercial sugar coater and the finished products are shown in Figs. 23 and 24, respectively. At this stage the average moisture in the product should be 22 to 23%.

Product Drying. This stage was necessary to reduce the average moisture content to 19%, at which level the ginger was shelf-stable and had a succulent texture inside the crystal coating. Moisture concentra-

Figure 23 Ginger sugar coater (Rumbler). (Courtesy of Buderim Ginger Growers Co-operative Association Ltd. and Queensland Department of Primary Industries.)

Figure 24 Crystallized ginger. (Courtesy of Buderim Ginger Growers Co-operative Association Ltd. and Queensland Department of Primary Industries.)

tions above 19% caused the lower layer of 5-kg packs of crystallized ginger to exude syrup after a storage period of 3 months at ambient temperature. Various conventional belt dehydrators can be used for this operation, provided the speed is adjusted to give the desired moisture level by heating for 30 min at 49°C air temperature. Air flow of at least 2.3 m/sec is desirable. During this stage further crystallization of very fine crystals from the supersaturated sucrose syrup occurs.

Product Cooling. It was essential to cool the product with air at 10°C to the temperature of the packing room, which was held at about 22°C with a relative humidity of 70%. By this time the final product consisted of two phases: firstly, the succulent piece 75° Brix ginger with its original physical dimensions; second an enveloping matrix of very fine sucrose crystals binding an even layer of commercial sucrose crystals. The weight gain during the crystallizing process from the drained ginger to the packed crystallized product varied according to the size of pieces and other variables previously discussed, but should be about 20%. Too high a recovery was indicative of an uneven heavy sucrose coating which caused consumer resistance.

Packaging of Crystallized Ginger. Nguyen (unpublished departmental report, 1969) made a study of several packaging materials. He reported that unless packaged in the appropriate puncture-resistant films, crystallized ginger may become hard and dry, or conversely soggy, depending on the climatic conditions of the environment. In general, ginger marketed in hot, moist tropical areas and temperate coastal areas should be packaged in water-vapor-impermeable films such as polyethylene or one of the laminated cellulose films. For marketing in the cooler, drier areas, it may be packaged in less permeable films. To avoid syrup exudation, crystallized ginger in bulk should not be packed to a depth greater than about 250 mm.

11. Microbiological Aspects of Preserved Ginger

Leverington (1969c) reported the presence of osmophilic yeasts in Chinese ginger syrups that gave the product a characteristic ginger beer flavor. This flavor was developed in experimental batches of ginger to demonstrate that such a product could be satisfactorily produced with strict microbiological controls. However, because of an accidental fermentation of export ginger in syrup which caused the drums to burst in transit, investigations to develop a fermented-flavor ginger were discontinued.

Problems also arose with yeast fermentation in the crystallized product that were traced to contamination in the open syruping vats. Lloyd (1975b), in an intensive microbiological study of syruped and crystallized ginger, showed that osmophilic fermentation is able to proceed actively in stored syruped ginger. Also, the osmophilic yeasts belonging to the species *Saccharomyces rouxii* could be destroyed by dipping the drained, diced pieces of syruped ginger in the 80° Brix sucrose syrup, at $93 \pm 1°C$ for a period of 2 min by which time the center of each piece of ginger has reached minimum temperature of approximately 60°C.

B. Dried Ginger

1. Raw Material

Because dried ginger is a raw material for flavorings as pointed out previously, the texture is not a significant quality characteristic, whereas concentrations of oleoresin and volatile oil are of major importance. Sills (1961) has reported that ginger grown in Fiji has a drying ratio of 8:1 compared with 4:1 for Jamaican ginger. The latter does not develop the shriveled appearance of many other gingers. In Australia, mature ginger is used for drying and is harvested over a 3-month period from May to July during which time the total solids increase and drying ratio falls gradually from about 9:1 to 6:1 (Winterton and Richardson, 1965). This is of commercial significance and is reflected in the type of dried product produced from the particular crop (Shrapnel, 1967). Up until the end of June, dried, peeled whole ginger is produced and is used mainly for the extraction of oleoresin or volatile oil. For the balance of the season, the ginger rhizomes, because of the hard, impervious-to-moisture skin that has developed, have to be cut into 3-mm slices before dehydration and are used primarily for ground ginger. A Tropical Products Institute monograph (n.d.) reports that very large bulbous rhizomes usually have a high moisture content that may cause difficulty in drying. Material handling of whole green ginger as well as whole dried ginger can be difficult, but robust screen conveyors coupled with antibridging devices are usually satisfactory.

2. Preparation for Drying

Food Science (1960), Sills (1961), Shrapnel (1967), and a Tropical Products Institute monograph (n.d.) have reported preparation methods which generally involve carefully scraping the rhizomes with a special knife (sometimes made from a conch shell or bamboo), preceded by and followed by washings and soakings, preferably in hot water. These procedures are labor-intensive and are only possible where cheap labor is available. Potato and other abrasive peelers have been tested for this operation, but the gnarled nature of the whole rhizomes render them impractical. Sills (1961) stressed that only a thin outer layer of skin should be removed because the oil-bearing cells are located close to the surface and the value of the ginger is reduced if these cells are removed. He also reported that "ginger is sometimes par boiled in water or in water containing lime juice before peeling" giving rise to the "black" ginger of commerce.

3. Sun-Drying

Sun-drying on a clean surface has been the classical method for centuries and takes 6 to 8 days under optimum drying conditions. Regular turning of the rhizomes is essential to ensure even drying and to prevent the growth of molds on the moist underside. If the produce is not sufficiently light in color, it is bleached further in the sun. To make dried ginger less susceptible to insect attack, some countries lime the rhizomes with strictly limited amounts of calcium sulfate or calcium carbonate, giving it a whitish appearance. A Tropical Products Institute monograph (n.d.) reported that traditional drying methods may cause losses up to 20% in the volatile oil content.

4. Artificial Drying

Carefully controlled artificial drying methods can produce a superior product (Tropical Products Institute, n.d.) which is of considerable value to essence houses. In Australia, sun-drying is not practicable since ginger matures during the wet season and handling costs are too high also.

Shrapnel (1967) reported that washed ginger may be dehydrated in a propane-gas-fired rotary louvre dryer operating at 54°C (product temperature 49°C). Myklestad (1965) described the design, construction, and performance of a rotary louvre dryer suitable for this purpose (Fig. 25.). Cross draft shelf dehydrators may also be used but require considerable labor for handling trays.

Natarajan et al. (1972) have made a study of hand-and abrasive-peeling methods, and sun-drying and artifical drying as well as tempertures of drying. Peeling for 60 sec in an abrasive peeler was conducive to the production of high-grade ginger, but the hand-peeled product was found superior to mechanically peeled ginger with regard to uniform size and color. The optimum temperature for dehydration was found to be 60°C. It is presumed that they used nobs of ginger and not hands.

Richardson (1966) investigated the effect of artificial drying temperatures on 3-mm slices of ginger and reported a preference by soft drink manufacturers for ginger dried in the range of 38 to 65°C and suggested that 57°C would be an optimum temperature. Ginger dried at higher temperatures up to 82°C was distinctly darker and less acceptable.

5. Grinding

Hammer mills, both fixed and swinging arms, are normally used for grinding ginger. Shrapnel (1967) described how a fully mechanized dehydration plant can be integrated with a 0.3-mm mesh grinder so that it can operate 20 hr/day, 7 days/week, with one person per shift. This person can operate the entire plant, from handling the bulk-bin supply through to stacking the bagged, ground ginger onto pallets ready for dispatch (Fig. 26).

Figure 25 Rotary louvre dryer. (Courtesy of Buderim Ginger Growers Co-operative Association Ltd, and Queensland Department of Primary Industries.)

6. Packaging of Ground Ginger

Richardson (1967) while investigating the packaging of dried, sliced and ground ginger showed that ground ginger, which has about three times the bulk density of dry, sliced ginger, should not be stored in Hessian or certain kinds of plastic bags. During a 6-month storage, the concentration of ginger volatiles decreased by about 50%, whereas in the dried, sliced material the concentration did not change significantly. Jordan (1972, private communication) explains this apparent loss by the observation that the volatile oil components are readily decomposed to nonvolatile products. If ginger must be stored in a ground form, it should be sealed in metal drums or in metal foil bags.

C. Volatile Oil

Guenther (1952) briefly described a typical distillation technique for ginger oil. The Tropical Products Institute (1979a) has detailed the technology of ginger oil extraction. It is summarized as follows.

1. Selection and Preparation of the Raw Material

The type of dried ginger used, the stage of maturation at harvest, the method of drying, and conditions and duration of storage prior to distillation greatly affect the recovery and aroma/flavor character of the essential oil obtained on distillation. Selection of raw material, therefore, influences both production economics and product acceptability. The optimum grinding screen for the spice is about 5-mm mesh since material which has been finely ground may cake during the distillation stage.

2. Equipment

The distillation equipment includes a steam generator, a still pot, condenser, and collection flasks. The condenser and flasks are preferably constructed from stainless steel, but the still pot itself may be made from mild steel. The steam generator is matched to the size of the still pot which is fitted with a sparge ring in its base to ensure even distribution of the steam. A number of perforated trays are fitted above the sparge ring at intervals of about 30 cm to hold the ground ginger. They must fit closely to the still body to prevent steam bypassing the charge.

3. Distillation

The charge of ground ginger should be packed evenly on perforated trays to avoid the formation of channels through which the steam will pass without volatilizing the oil, resulting in a low recovery. Distilla-

Figure 26 Ginger grinder and bag filler. (Courtesy of Buderim Ginger Growers Co-operative Association Ltd. and Queensland Department of Primary Industries.)

tion is carried out with direct (live) steam, which should not be too wet since this can result in caking by swelling of the ginger starch. The condensed oil and water discharging from the condenser are collected, the oil accumulating on the surface. To minimize losses of some of the more water-soluble components of the oil, the condensed water is fed back to the base of the still where it is reboiled. Distillation may take up to 20 hr because of the high proportion of low-vapor pressure sesquiterpenes, but will also depend upon the size of the charge and the steam pressure.

Alternatively, investigations in Australia (Connell and Jordan, 1971; Winterton and Richardson, 1965) have shown that comminuted green ginger or fresh peelings and trimmings may be boiled in a still and the oil removed by steam distillation. This method has been used on a laboratory scale and found to produce oil of very high quality. However, the use of green ginger for the commercial production of essential oil has disadvantages principally associated with the storage of green ginger.

4. Storage and Packaging

Freshly distilled ginger oil is a light green or yellow mobile liquid, possessing the characteristic aromatic odor of the spice. The oil deteriorates in quality on aging, especially when exposed to the air, becoming more viscous through the formation of nonvolatile, polymeric residues. This change is accompanied by a decrease in its optical rotation value. The minimum contact with air is, therefore, desirable during any storage prior to eventual packing and shipment. The oil may be stored for a short period in a tank after distillation to permit separation of occluded water. It should then be transferred to airtight containers that are filled to exclude as much air as possible. Small batches of ginger oil may be shipped in glass containers whereas tin plate or aluminium containers may be used for batches up to about 50 kg. Internally lacquered steel drums are preferred for large consignments. Ginger oil should never be stored or shipped in any form of plastic container since plasticizers may become dissolved in the oil and collapse the container.

D. Oleoresin

Guenther (1952) has also briefly described the extraction of oleoresin by percolating ground, dried ginger with volatile solvents such as acetone or ethanol. Concentration of the solution by careful distillation of the solvent under vacuum is a particularly critical stage to avoid excessive heating and degradation of pungent compounds. For the same reason, Connell (1969,1970) reported that hot solvent extraction of ginger was undesirable. The Tropical Products Institute (1979b) has detailed the technology of oleoresin extraction. It is summarized as follows.

1. Selection and Preparation of Raw Material

The type of dried ginger used, the stage of maturation at harvest, the method of drying, and the conditions and duration of storage prior to extraction greatly affect the yield and the aroma/flavor character of the oleoresin extracted. Selection of the raw material is, therefore, of significance both to the production economics and product acceptability. The grind size is of importance to ensure efficient extraction and 30 to 40 mesh (nominal aperture size, 400 to 500 µm) is probably optimal.

Finely ground ginger tends to cause caking and very slow rates of extraction. Optimum conditions have to be determined for particle size, density of packing, bed height, and area for the particular type of equipment used.

2. Equipment

The extractor is constructed of stainless steel or glass and consists of a column, packed with a series of trays containing ground ginger. A recirculating pump is installed at the base so that cold solvent can be introduced as a spray at the top of the column and then percolated through the ginger to the base where it is recirculated. An alternative system employs a number of extractors in series and countercurrent flow pumping technique. The capacity of commercial extractors varies considerably as does the time required for efficient extraction. The solvent stripper is also constructed of glass or stainless steel and consists of a heated pot to hold the extract, a fractionating column, solvent collector, and vacuum pump.

3. Extraction

Several purified solvents such as ethylene dichloride, ethylene trichloride, acetone, and ethanol are used commercially for ginger extraction. The choice of solvent has an influence on the recovery, chemical constitution, and aroma/flavor properties of the oleoresin product. Care is necessary with hydrophilic solvents, such as acetone or ethanol, to ensure that dry ginger is sufficiently dry, otherwise the extraction is effectively carried out in an aqueous solvent medium. This results in the extraction of undesirable, water-soluble components and difficulties in final concentration of the product.

Portions of the solvent extract are drawn off when they contain at least 10% soluble solids. Solvent is distilled off under reduced pressure taking care to prevent foaming and, particularly, to avoid overheating which can cause the destruction of some of the pungent principles and formation of off-flavors. Quality deterioration becomes noticeable at a temperature of 90°C, and much lower temperatures are advisable. Tall fractionation columns and carefully controlled distillation rates are also important to minimize loss of the volatile oil. Determination of residual solvent levels is particularly important to ensure that the product complies with the appropriate health and safety regulations.

4. Storage and Packaging

Ginger oleoresin is a dark brown viscous liquid that can deteriorate in quality during prolonged storage. Freshly prepared batches of oleoresin should be placed in clean, dry, airtight canisters as soon as possible, and storage conditions should be cool. Glass bottles are frequently used for small quantities, whereas for larger batches, internally lacquered, stainless steel drums are used.

E. Fresh or Green Ginger

Green ginger is harvested after the plant has reached maturity and has a fairly impervious hard skin. The rhizomes are normally washed to remove adhering soil, surface-dried in a blast of air, and held at room temperature in well-ventilated containers such as crates or open-mesh sacks. Some weight loss occurs, but this is not of great significance. Sprouting may occur, but every effort is made to sell the produce before this develops. Watkins and Brown (unpublished departmental report, 1967) have attempted to store ginger for longer periods using various waxes, fungicides, nitrogen gas flushes, and temperatures from 1 to 21°C. Slime and mold problems were encounted in polyethylene pouches packed with ginger, and no firm conclusion was reached. Akamine (1962) closely examined techniques for storing green ginger and came to the conclusion that the following techniques should be applied.

Wash thoroughly to remove adhering soil.
Air-dry for 1 to 2 days.
Store in a cool room at 13°C with a relative humidity of 65% until required for sale or shipment.
Remove from store, allow to stand at atmospheric temperature to equilibrate and evaporate excess moisture, and then pack into cardboard cartons for sale or export without refrigeration.

He claims that ginger can be stored in a marketable condition for about 6 months by this method. However, moisture loss may be as high as 16.5%, and surface shriveling and discoloration may be apparent. Strict hygiene standards are essential because the high relative humidity induces mold development. Retail packs of green ginger sealed in airtight bags may constitute a health hazard because of the anaerobic conditions in the package.

To cater for those wishing to use green ginger in gourmet cooking through the year, a sterile canned pack is processed in Australia. Green ginger (from late harvest) is sliced across the fibers at 2-mm intervals, placed in small lacquered cans, covered with a salt brine, and then processed by standard canning methods for nonacid packs. This pack can be sorted for several years.

ACKNOWLEDGMENTS

The author wishes to thank the officers of the Horticulture Branch of the Queensland Department of Primary Industries, in particular Brian Brown, Rodney Jordan, Tony Whiley, and Peter Scudamore-Smith for assisting in the preparation of the manuscript within their particular fields of expertise; Eric Gall for overall assistance in the assembly of information and preparation and editing of the manuscript; and Leigh

Barker for preparation of line drawings. The preparation of photographs by the Departmental Photographic Section is appreciated. Thanks are also due to the management of the Buderim Ginger Growers' Co-operative Association Limited for making time, facilities, information, and photographs available for the preparation of this chapter.

REFERENCES

Akamine, E. K. (1962). Storage of fresh ginger rhizomes. *Bull. Hawaii Agric. Exp. Stn. No. 130.*

Ananthakrishna, S. M., and Govindarajan, V. S. (1974). Evaluation of spices and oleoresins. IV. Estimation of pungent principles of ginger oleoresin. *Lebensm-Wiss, u. Technol.* 7(4):220-222.

Asher, C. J., and Lee, M. T. (1975). *Diagnosis and Correction of Nutritional Disorders in Ginger.* Brisbane, Dept. Agric., Univ. of Queensland.

Australian Government Bureau of Ag. Econ. (1971). *The Australian Ginger Industry, A Continuous Farm Study 1965-66 to 1967-68.* Canberra, Aust. Govt. Publ. Service.

Bailey, L. H. (1947). Zingiber. In *The Standard Cyclopedia of Horticulture, Vol. 3.* New York, Macmillan, pp. 3543-3544.

Bednarczyk, A. A., and Kramer, A. (1971). Practical approach to flavor development, statistical pre-selection of significant flavor constituents, speeds development of synthetic ginger flavor and flavor fortified ginger oil. *Food Technol.* 25(2):1098-1107.

Bendall, R. L., and Daly, R. A. (1966). Ginger growing in the Nambour area, Queensland. *Q. Rev. Agric. Econ.* 19(2):83-96.

British Pharmaceutical Codex. (1963). Ginger. London, Council of the Pharmaceutical Soc. of Gr. Britain, p. 337.

Brown, B. I. (1969a). Processing and preservation of ginger by syruping under atmospheric conditions 1. Preliminary investigations of vat systems. *Fd. Technol.* 23(1):87-91.

Brown, B. I. (1969b). Processing and preserving of ginger by syruping under atmospheric conditions 2. Effects of syrup temperature, flow rate and sucrose: Reducing sugar ratios on the processing of ginger in invert sugar. *Fd. Technol.* 23(7):93-96.

Brown, B. I. (1969c). Processing and preserving ginger by syruping under atmospheric conditions 3. Processing techniques and syrup concentration for maximum drained weight recovery of syruped ginger. *Fd. Technol.* 23(7):109-112.

Brown, B. I. (1972). Ginger storage in acidified sodium metabisulphite solutions. *J. Fd. Technol.* 7(2):153-162.

Brown, B. I. (1975). Further studies on ginger storage in salt brine. *J. Fd. Technol.* 10(4):393-405.

Brown, B. I., and Lloyd, A. C. (1972). Investigation of ginger storage in salt brine. *J. Fd. Technol.* 7(3):309-321.

Bull. Imp. Inst. (1926). Ginger: Its cultivation, preparation and trade, 24:667-682.

Campbell, C. H. (1945). *Campbells Book, Canning, Preserving, and Pickling.* Chicago, Vance Publishing Corp.

Connell, D. W. (1969). The pungent principles of ginger and their importance in certain ginger products. *Fd. Technol. Aust.* 21(11): 570-575.

Connell, D. W. (1970). The chemistry of the essential oil and oleoresin of ginger (*Zingiber officinale* Roscoe). *Flav. Ind.* 1(10):677-693.

Connell, D. W., and Jordan, R. A. (1971). Composition and distinctive volatile flavor characteristics of the essential oil from Australian grown ginger (*Zingiber officinale*). *J. Sci. Fd. Agric.* 22(1):93-95.

Connell, D. W., and McLauchlan, R. L. (1972). Natural pungent compounds. IV. Examination of the gingerols, shogaols, paradols and related compounds by thin layer and gas chromatography. *J. Chromat.* 67(1):29-35.

Connell, D. W., and Sutherland, M. D. (1966). Terpenoid chemistry. XI. (-)β Sesquiphellandrene. *Aust. J. Chem.* 19(1):283-288.

Connell, D. W., and Sutherland, M. D. (1969). A re-examination of gingerol, shogaol, and zingerone, the pungent principles of ginger (*Zingiber officinale,* Roscoe). *Aust. J. Chem.* 22(5):1033-1043.

District Agricultural Board of Trinidad (1892). *Bull. Misc. Inf. Royal Gardens Kew* 64:77-81.

Edwards, D. (1975). The market for dried, preserved and fresh ginger. *Tropical Products Institute Report No. G95.* London, Tropical Products Institute.

Encyclopaedia Brittanica (1974). Vol. IV, 15th ed. Micropaedia Publ. H. H. Benson, Chicago, Univ. of Chicago, p. 547.

Food Science (1960). Removal of skin in ginger. March:99.

Garnett, H., and Grier, J. (1909). Determination of ginger oil in ginger. *Pharm. J.* 83:159-160.

Gildemeister, E., and Hoffman, F. R. (1913a). Oil of ginger. In *The Volatile Oils, Vol. 1.* London, Longman's, Green and Co., p. 109.

Guildemeister, E., and Hoffman, F. R. (1913b). *The Volatile Oils. Vol. 2.* London, Longman's, Green and Co., p. 280.

Gildemeister, E., and Hoffman, F. R. (1956). *Die aetherischen Oele* 4 (Academie Verlag). Berlin, pp. 489-495.

Groszman, H. M. (1954). Ginger production. *Qld. Agric. J.* 78: 259-262.

Groszman, H. M. (1956). Private communication.

Guenther, E. (1952). Oil of ginger. In *The Essential Oils, Vol. 5.* New York, D. Van Nostrand Co. Inc., pp. 106-120.

Heath, H. (1973). Herbs and spices, a bibliography. Part I. *Flavour Ind.* 4:24, 65, 169, 217, 346, 394.

Ichikawa, Y. Sasa, H., and Michi, K. (1973). Purification of ginger protease. *EIYO To Shokuryo* 26(6):377-383.

Jogi, B. S., Singh, I. P., Dua, H. S., and Sukhija, P. S. (1972). Changes in crude fibre, fat and protein content in ginger (*Zingiber officinale* Rosc.) at different stages of ripening. *Indian J. Agric. Sci.* 42(11):1011-1015.

Jordan, R. A. (1972). Private communication.

Jordan, R. A. (1972). Unpublished departmental report.

Kami, T. Narkayama, M., and Hayashi, S. (1972). Volatile constituents of *Zingiber officinale*. *Phytochem.* 11:3377-3381.

Kurmara, D. (1929). Preservation of ginger in syrup. *Bull. Dept. Ind. Travancore* 29:

Leverington, R. E. (1969a). Ginger processing investigations. 1.Batch methods for sugar impregnation. *Qd. J. Agric. Anim. Sci.* 26(2): 243-251.

Leverington, R. E. (1969b). Ginger processing investigations. 2. An improved method for the sugar impregnation of ginger by continuous evaporation. *Qd. J. Agric. Anim. Sci.* 26(2):253-261.

Leverington, R. E. (1969c). Ginger processing investigations. 3. Improving the quality of processed ginger. *Qd. J. Agric. Anim. Sci.* 26(2):263-270.

Leverington, R. E. (1975). Ginger technology. *Fd. Technol. Aust.* 27(8):309-313.

Lloyd, A. C. (1975a). Yeasts in ginger storage brines. *J. Fd. Technol.* 10(4):407-413.

Lloyd, A. C. (1975b). Osmophilic yeasts in preserved ginger products. *J. Fd. Technol.* 10(5):575-581.

Morris, T. N. (1945). *Principles of Fruit Preservation.* Chapman and Hall, London.

Myklestad, O. (1965). Design, construction and performance of a roto-louvre dryer for ginger. Sidney, *CSIRO Div. of Food Preservation Research, Research Report No. 32.* CSIRO.

Nambudiri, E. S., Mathew, A. G., Krishnamurthy, N., and Lewis, Y. S. (1975). Quantative determination of the pungent principle in ginger. *Int. Flavours Food Addit.* 6(2):135-137.

Narasimhan, S., and Govindarajan, V. S. (1978). Evaluation of spices and oleoresin. VI. Pungency of ginger components, gingerols and shogaols and quality. *J. Food Technol.* 13(1):31-36.

Natarajan, C. P., Padma Bai, R., Krishnamurthy, M. N., Raghavan, B., Shankaracharya, N. B., Kuppuswamy, S., Govindarajan, V. S., and Lewis, Y. S. (1972). Chemical composition of ginger varieties and dehydration studies on ginger. *J. Fd. Sci. Technol.* 9(3):120-124.

Nguyen, M. H. (1969). Unpublished departmental report.

Nomura, H. (1917a). Pungent principles of ginger. I. A new ketone zingiberone occurring in ginger. *Sci Rep. Tohoku Imp. Univ.* 6(1):41-53.

Nomura, H. (1917b). The pungent principles of ginger. Part I. A new ketone, zingerone (4-hydroxy-3-methyloxy-phenylethyl-methyl ketone), Occurring in ginger. *J. Chem. Soc.* CXI paper LXIV:769-776.

Nomura, H. (1918). Pungent principles of ginger. I. Zingiberone, a correction. *Sci. Rep. Tohoku Imp. Univ.* 6(1):375.

Ohtsuki, K., Kawabata, M., and Taguchi, K. (1978). Purification and stabilization of ginger protease. *Kyoto-furitsu Daigaku Gakujutsu Hokoku, Rigaku, Seikatsu Kagaku* 29:33-40.

Page, P. E. and Cornwall, N. A. (1969). Private communication.

Parry, E. J. (1948). *Allen's Commercial Organic Analysis, Vol. 4,* 5th ed. Philadelphia, Blackiston, p. 340.

Parry, J. W. (1953). *The History of the Spices.* New York, Chemical Publishing Co., p. 51.

Pegg, K. G., and Moffett, M. L. (1971). Host range of the ginger strain of *Pseudomonas solanacearum* in Queensland. *Aust. J. Exp. Agric. Anim. Husb.* 11(53):696-698.

Pegg, K. G., Moffett, M. L., and Colbran, R. C. (1969). *Diseases of Ginger in Queensland.* Buderim, The Buderim Ginger Growers' Co-operative Assn. Ltd.

Pegg, K. G., Moffett, M. L., and Colbran, R. C. (1974). Diseases of ginger in Queensland. Brisbane, *Qld. Agric. J.* 100(12):611.

Raghuveer, K. G., and Govindarajan, V. S. (1978). Evaluation of spices and oleoresins. VII. Gas chromatograph examination of gingerol, shogaol and related compounds in ginger. *J. Food Quality* 2(1):41-54.

Richardson, K. C. (1966). Effect of dehydration temperature on the quality of dried ginger. *Fd. Technol. Aust.* 18(1):93-95.

Richardson, K. C. (1967). Investigations into the packaging and storage of dried ginger. *Fd. Technol Aust.* 19(4):165-166.

Salzer, U. (1975). Analytical evaluation of seasoning extracts (oleoresins) and essential oils from seasonings. II. *Int. Flavours Food Addit.* 6(4):206-210.

Scudamore-Smith, P. D. (1980). Unpublished departmental report.

Shrapnel, G. S. (1967). The technological development of the green ginger industry in Australia. *Fd. Technol. Aust.* 19(13):604-607.

Sills, V. E. (1961). Processing and marketing ginger products. *South Pacific Bull.* South Pacific Commission Noumea. 11(3):58-61.

Simmonds, J. H. (1955). Report of the plant pathology section. In *Dept. of Ag. and Stock, Brisbane, Qld., Annual Report, 1954-55.* p. 52.

Singh. I. P., Jogi, B. S., Dua, H. S., and Gupta, M. L. (1975). Tentative identification of various components and fatty acids of ginger lipids. *Indian Fd. Agric. Sci.* 45(11-12):545-549.

Thomas, S., and Corden, M. (1970). *Tables of Composition of Australian Foods.* Canberra Department of Health.

Thompson, E. H., Wolf, I. D., and Allen, C. E. (1973). Ginger rhizome: A new source of proteolytic enzyme. *J. Fd. Sci.* 38(4):652-655.

Thresh, J. C. (1879). Proximate analysis of the rhizome of *Zingiber officinalis*, and comparative analysis of typical specimens of commercial gingers. *Pharm. J.* 10(3):171.

Tropical Products Institute (1964). The market for dried, preserved and fresh ginger. *Report No. G8.* London.

Tropical Products Institute (1979a). A note on ginger oil distillation. London.

Tropical Products Institute (1979b). A note on ginger oleoresin, London.

Tropical Products Institute (n.d.) *The Preparation of Dried Ginger, Tropical Products Institute Monograph.* London.

U.S. Dept. of Commerce (1908). *Monthly Consular and Trade Reports* 339:151.

U.S. Consular Report (1923). *Commerce Reports* 37:693.

Varier, N. S. (1945). Essential oil from ginger scrapings. *Curr. Sci.* 14:322.

Vilsoni, F., McClure, M. A., and Butler, L. D. (1976). Occurrence, host range and histopathology of *Radopholus similis* in ginger *(Zingiber officinale).* *Plant Disease Reporter* 60:417-420.

Watkins, J. B. and Brown, B. I. (1967). Unpublished departmental report.

Watt, B. K., and Merrill, A. L. (1975). Composition of foods. In *Agriculture Handbook No. 8.* Washington, D. C. Agriculture Research Service, U.S. Department of Agriculture.

Whiley, A. W. (1974). Ginger growing in Queensland. *Qld. Agric. J.* 100(11):551.

Whiley, A. W. and Saranah, J. (1978). The classification of ginger varieties. In *M.H.R.S. Biennial research Report No. 1.* (K. R. Chapman, compiler). Brisbane, pp. 69-70.

Whiley, A. W. (1980). Unpublished departmental report.

Whiley, A. W. (1980). Growth and fibre development of ginger *(Zingiber officinale* Roscoe*)* in south-east Queensland. *Aust. J. Exp. Agric. Anim. Husb.* 20(10):608-612.

Whiley, A. W. (1981). Effect of plant density on time to first harvest, maturity, knob size, and yield in two cultivars of ginger *(Zingiber officinale* Roscoe*)* grown in south-east Queensland. *Tropic. Agric.* 58(3):245-251.

Winterton, D., and Richardson, K. S. (1965). An investigation into the chemical constituents of Queensland grown ginger. *Qd. J. Agric. Anim. Sci.* 22(2):205-214.

8

Guava

Harvey T. Chan, Jr. Tropical Fruit and Vegetable Research
Laboratory, U.S. Department of Agriculture, Hilo, Hawaii

I. INTRODUCTION

Guava (*Psidium guajaba*), native to tropical America, is widely distributed throughout the tropics (Kennard and Winters, 1960). The guava
is the most widely known and important fruit plant in the Myrtaceae
family. Introduced to Hawaii in about 1790, it flourishes in nearly all
parts of the islands at elevations below 3000 ft. Under favorable growing conditions in Hawaii, the guava plant develops into a small tree
often attaining heights of 30 ft or more. As described by Hamilton and
Seagrave-Smith (1959), the bisexual or perfect flowers are white in
color and from 1 in. to about 1-1/2 in. in diameter. The stamens are
numerous and pollen plentiful. Cross-pollination is frequently aided
by pollen-carrying insects. Self-pollination is possible, and isolated
trees often set satisfactory crops of fruit without cross-pollination.

The fruits, which are round, ovate, or pea-shaped, vary from 1 to 4 in. in diameter and from 2 oz to 1 lb in weight. The skin color of the ripe fruit is yellow, and the flesh color may be white, pink, yellow, salmon, or carmine. The fruits range in flavor from quite sweet to sour.

II. HORTICULTURAL ASPECTS

The main guava crop usually ripens from May through August. A smaller distinct crop is produced during the winter season. New and novel techniques for crop cycling of guavas have been recently developed by University of Hawaii and Australian horticulturists (Shigeura et al., 1979). The techniques employ defoliation, pruning, fertilization, irrigation, and various combinations of these methods. A mixture of 1500 ppm ethaphon with 0.5 lb/gal of urea was found to be the most effective defoliant (Shigeura and Bullock, 1979). The concept of crop cycling promises to ensure a continous yearly supply of fruit for the processors in addition to increased yields of 60%/year. Another advantage of crop cycling is the shortening of the harvest period which reduces labor costs, allows better economic control of fruit flies, and provides more precise scheduling for the fruit processor. Trees which have been propagated by budding or air layering usually begin to bear within 2 years after transplanting. Seedlings usually begin to bear the second or third year after transplanting.

The guava is adaptable over a wide range of soil and climatic conditions. It often grows wild in places where other fruit trees would fail. Annual rainfall between 40 and 150 in. is sufficient to permit satisfactory growth (Hamilton and Seagrave-Smith, 1959). The predominant cultivar grown commercially in Hawaii is the Beaumont which produces 45,000 lb of fruit per acre annually (Nakasone et al., 1976). The Beaumont is considered superior to the wild types for processing because of its higher yield which averages about 80 to 85% compared with 70 to 75% for the wild types (Gerakas and Lee, 1974).

In 1978 Hawaii produced 5.5 million lb of guava purée. About half of the tonnage was cultivated guavas with the remainder being harvested from the wild. Currently there are about 700 acres of guavas planted in Hawaii which will produce about 26 million lb of fruit when the plantings reach full productivity (Hawaii Agric. Rep. Serv., 1979).

III. BIOCHEMICAL AND NUTRITIONAL COMPOSITION

The composition of guava is shown in table 1. Nutritionally guava is an excellent source of ascorbic acid, ranging well over 100 mg/100 g; it is a good source of niacin, the edible portion containing more than 1 mg/100 g (Wenkam and Miller, 1965). As shown in Table 1, the

Table 1 Composition of Guava,
Per 100 g of Edible Portion

Moisture	84.35 %
Calories	55 cal
Protein	0.28 g
Fat	0.1 g
Carbohydrate	14.79 g
Fiber	2.38 g
Ash	0.48 g
Calcium	14.6 m
Phosphorus	15.5 m
Iron	0.29 m
Vitamin A	0.09 µg
Thiamine	0.056 m
Riboflavin	0.060 m
Niacin	1.28 m
Ascorbic Acid	100 m

Source: Data from Wenkam
and Miller (1965).

carbohydrates are the principal nonaqueous constituents of guava.
Of the 14.8 g/100 g fruit of total carbohydrate 5.82 g are the sugars,
fructose, glucose, and sucrose. In guava, fructose is the predominant sugar, constituting 58.9% of the sugars, followed by glucose
at 35.7% and sucrose at 5.3% (Chan and Kwok, 1975). Differences in
acid content between the cultivated (Beaumont) variety versus the
wild types were determined by Chan et al. (1971). The total acidity
of cultivated and wild guavas was 18.4 and 14.08 mg/100 g, respectively. The Beaumont fruit had 128 mg/100 g of ascorbic acid. In
the wild guava, we measured 56 mg/100 g of ascorbic acid. The
polybasic organic acids were separated and quantitatively determined
by gas liquid chromatography; the results are shown in Table 2.
Malic and citric acids were found in Beaumont guavas in approximately equal amounts, 0.47 and 0.53% by weight, respectively. These
acids are about 20 times greater in abundance than lactic acid, present in the amount of only 0.025%. In wild guava extract we measured 0.18% malic, 0.54% citric, and 0.12% lactic acid. The pH of
guava purées ranges from 3.0 to 3.5 depending upon the seasonality
and varieties processed.

The pink coloration in the Beaumont variety has been attributed to
the presence of lycopene (Brekke and Yamamoto, 1970). The lycopene
content in Beaumont was found to be 5.87 %mg/100 g fruit. In nine
newly developed cultivars with pink-to-red coloration, the lycopene
content was found to range from 4.78 to 6.90 mg/100 g fruit (Nakasone
et al., 1976).

Table 2 Quatitative Determination
of Organic Acids in Wild and
Beaumont Guavas by Gas Liquid
Chromatography

Acid (g /100 g)	Beaumont	Wild
Malic	0.469	0.182
Citric	0.532	0.541
Lactic	0.025	0.012

Source: Data from Chan et al.
(1971).

The volatile flavor constituents of guava have been isolated and separated by gas liquid chromatography (Stevens et al., 1970; Torline and
Ballschmieter, 1973; Smith and Siwatibau, 1975). Stevens et al. (1970).
identified 22 compounds in Hawaiian guavas of which methyl benzoate,
hexanol, p-phenyl ethyl acetate, methyl cinnamyl acetate are believed
to play predominant roles in the flavor and odor of guavas (Table 3).
Wilson and Shaw (1978) reported the presence of cinnamyl alcohol,
cinnamaldehyde, neolidol, and 2-hexanol. They also stated that the
cinnamic acid derivatives played an important role in guava aroma
(Wilson, 1980). Using South African guavas, Torline and Ballschmieter
(1973) identified 16 additional new compounds. A flavor evaluation of
each of the newly identified compounds was not given. The results
of both Stevens et al. (1970) and Torline and Ballshmieter's (1973)
results are summarized in Table 3. Smith and Siwatibau (1975) classified wild guava trees in Fiji on the basis of the relative amounts of
sesquiterpenes present in leaf essential oils. The principal components
include caryophyliene, β-bisabolene, aromadendrene, β-selinene, nero-
lidiol, carophyllene oxide, and sel-11-en-4α-ol.

IV. PRESERVATION METHODS

The processing of guava into purée or juice is a relatively simple matter. Commonly available fruit processing equipment is used and little
labor is required. In processing purée or juice the first step involves
a thorough washing of the fruit to remove any adhering soil or contamination and a sorting procedure to remove unsound or immature fruit.
From this stage on the processes differ.

Table 3 Volatile Compounds in Guava

Compound	Data from Torline and Ballschmieter (1973)	Data from Stevens et al. (1970)
Alcohols		
Methanol	X	
Ethanol	X	
2-Methyl-1-Propanol		X
1-Penten-3-ol		X
1-Pentanol		X
1-Hexanol		X
3-Hexen-ol		X
1-Octanol	X	X
1-Nonanol		X
a-Terpeneol		X
β-Phenyl ethyl alcohol		X
Ketones		
Acetone	X	
Methyl isopopyl ketone	X	
β-Ionone		X
Aldehydes		
n-Butanal	X	
2-Butenal	X	
n-Pentanal		X
2-Methyl-2-pentenal	X	
n-Hexenal	X	X
2-Hexenal	X	
Benzaldehyde		X
Citral		X
Esters		
Methyl acetate	X	
Ethyl acetate	X	X
Methyl propanoate	X	
Methyl butanoate	X	
Ethyl butanoate	X	
3-Hexen-1-yl acetate	X	X
Methyl benzoate		X
β-Phenyl ethyl acetate		X
Methyl cinnamate		X
Cinnamyl acetate		X
Hydrocarbons		
n-Pentane	X	
n-Hexane	X	
Benzene	X	
3,5-Dimethyl heptane	X	
Limonene	X	X
Caryophyllene		X

A. Guava Purée

Guava purée is used in the manufacture of guava nectar, various juice drink blends, and in the preparation of guava jam. Ideally it would be a bright pink color that will not require the addition of artifical color in the manufacture of the finished products. The washed, sound fruit is first passed through a chopper or slicer to break up the fruit, and this material is fed into a pulper. The pulper will remove the seed and fibrous pieces of tissue and force the remainder of the product through a perforated stainless steel screen. The holes in the screen should be between 0.033 and 0.045 in. The machine should be fed at a constant rate to ensure efficient operation. The puréed material coming from. the pulper is next passed through a finisher. The finisher is equipped with a screen containing holes of approximately 0.020 in. The finisher will remove the stone cells from the fruit and provide the optimum consistency to the product. Yield data computed on the basis of a 0.033-in. screen for the pulper and a 0.020-in. screen in the finisher showed 12.0% is waste as seed and 5.5% waste was stone cells (Seagrave-Smith and Sherman, 1954).

Perhaps the best way to preserve the guava purée is by freezing, and the material passing through the finisher can be packaged and frozen with no further treatment. It is not necessary to heat the product to inactivate enzymes or for other purposes. The material can be frozen in a number of types of cartons or cans; however, a fiber box with a plastic bag inside is commonly used and is probably the least expensive. Care should be taken to see that the boxes are frozen quickly to protect the quality of the product. The purée should be frozen in a blast freezer at approximately -20°F and stored at 0°F. It is also possible to can and heat process the guava purée, and this can be accomplished by heating the purée to 195°F in an open kettle, filling into cans, inverting the cans and holding them for a few seconds, followed by cooling. Cans should be cooled rapidly to approximately 100°F before they are cased and stacked in warehouses.

B. Guava Juice

Guava juice can be used in the manufacture of a clear guava jelly or in various drinks. It will have a light amber or slight pink coloration since most of the pink pigments in the guava remain with the solid material.

A clear juice is prepared from guava purée that has been depectinized enzymatically. About 0.1% by weight of Pectinol 10-M (or an equivalent amount of any pectin-degrading enzyme) is mixed into the purée at room temperature. Heating of the product to approximately 120°F will greatly speed the action of the enzyme. After 1 hr, clear juice is separated from the red pulp by centrifuging or by pressing in a hydraulic juice press. A batch-type or continuous-flow centrifuge can be used on the depectinized purée with no further treatment.

If a hydraulic press is used, diatomaceous earth must be mixed into the depectinized purée to facilitate the pressing operation. About 0.5% to 1.0% of a coarse grade of filter aid (Celite 545 or equivalent) is mixed in the purée with a power stirrer. The purée is filled into the nylon press cloths or bags, and juice is expressed by applying hydraulic pressure. This press juice usually contains some suspended solids and must be further clarified in a filter press. The clear juice effluent from the filter press can be preserved by freezing or by pasteurization in hermetically sealed cans. The clear juice can be used in preparation of a beverage, or as the fruit ingredient in guava jelly.

Following pressing, the clear guava juice should be heated sufficiently to destroy the pectic enzyme. This is best done in a plate heat exchanger and, while a few seconds at a temperature of 165° or more is usually sufficient, the actual time-temperature relation will depend on the pectic enzyme used. Following the destruction of the enzyme, the juice may be further clarified by passing through a filter press with the addition of a suitable pressing aid such as diatomaceous earth. After clarification, the juice may be frozen in a suitable container, or it may be canned and heat processed.

C. Guava Concentrate

For shipment to overseas markets it may be advantageous to concentrate either the purée or the juice. Much of the work on guava processing and products at our laboratories has placed emphasis on concentration of purée and juice. A new type of vacuum concentrator, the Centritherm, is part of the equipment in our pilot plant, and this was used in experimental production of guava concentrates. The purée is treated with a pectin-degrading enzyme (Pectinol 10-M), 0.1%, before concentration. This decreases the consistency (thickness), thus a higher degree of concentration can be achieved. The enzyme-treated purée is kept at ambient temperature for 1 hr and then concentrated in a Model CT1B Centritherm evaporator. Evaporation was conducted at reduced pressures (62–72 mmHg) and at a vapor temperature of 108 to 113°F. Guava purée has been concentrated to 3.5-fold; clear guava juice from which all the pulp has been removed can be concentrated to eight-fold or higher. Means of stabilizing these concentrates at refrigerated temperatures (35 to 45°F) have been devised making it possible to transport the concentrates overseas at above-freezing temperatures. The method involves the addition of potassium sorbate to a level of 1000 ppm to a 2.5-fold concentrate, 22.5° Brix. After 5 months of storage at 45°F, no gross signs of spoilage were present. Flavor and aroma quality were good and did not deteriorate appreciably until the fourth month in storage (Brekke et al., 1970).

Guava formulations for syrups (Brekke, 1968), beverage bases (Brekke, 1973), and nectars, jams, and jellies (Boyle et al., 1957) have been devised and in use for many years. A method for the vacuum-puff freeze-drying of guava purée to yield dry powder has been reported (Moy, 1971). Powders of goods have attracted much interest for special uses by the military and for campers' rations.

Current work in progress is the aseptic processing of guava purée. The purée is heat-sterilized in a scraped-surface heat exchanger and packaged aseptically into sterile plastic containers. An aseptically processed purée promises the economic advantages of bulk handling and the elimination of the need for refrigerated warehousing and shipping. For overseas markets aseptic processing of guava appears to have great potential.

REFERENCES

Boyle, F. P,, Seagrave-Smith, H., Sakata, S., and Sherman, G. D. (1957). Commercial guava processing in Hawaii. *Bull. 111, Hawaii Agric. Exp. Sta.* Univ. of Hawaii.

Brekke, J. (1968). Tropical fruit syrups. *Circular 70, Hawaii Agric. Exp. Sta.* Honolulu, Univ. of Hawaii.

Brekke, J. (1973). Tropical fruit beverage bases. *Research Report 198. Hawaii Agric. Exp. Sta.* Honolulu, Univ. of Hawaii.

Brekke, J. E., Tonaki, K. I., Cavaletto, C. G., and Frank, H. A. (1970). Stability of guava puree concentrate during refrigerated storage. *J. Food Sci.* 35:469-471.

Brekke, J., and Yamamoto, H. Y. (1970). Guava carotenoids. Unpublished data.

Chan, H. T., Jr., and Kwok, S. C. M. (1975). Identification and determination of sugars in some tropical fruit products. *J. Food Sci.* 40:419.

Chan, G. T., Jr., Breeke, J. E., and Chang, T. (1971). Nonvolatile organic acids in guava. *J. Food Sci.* 36:237-239.

Chapman, K. R., Saranah, J., and Paxton, B., (1979). Induction of early cropping of guava seedlings in a closely planted orchard using urea as defoliant. *Aust. J. Exp. Agric. Anim. Husb.* 19:382-284.

Gerakas, A., and Lee, C. (1974). *Profit Potentials in Hawaii's Guava* Honolulu, Hawaii, Dept. of Plan. and Econ. Dev., State of Hawaii.

Hamilton, R. A., and Seagrave-Smith, H. (1959). Growing guava for processing. *Hawaii Agric. Exp. Sta. Bull. 63.* Honolulu, Univ. of Hawaii.

Hawaii Agric. Rep. Serv. (1979). *Statistics of Hawaiian Agric. 1978.* Honolulu, Hawaii, Hawaii Dept. of Agric., State of Hawaii.

Kennard, W. C. and Winters, H. F. (1960). Some fruits and nuts for the tropics. *USDA Misc. Publ. 801.* Washington, D.C., U.S. Department of Agriculture.

Moy, J, H. (1971). Vacuum-puff freeze drying of tropical fruit juices. *J. Food Sci.* 36:906-910.

Nakasone, H. Y., Brekke, J. E., and Cavaletto, C. G. (1976). Fruit and yield evaluation of ten clones of guava (Psidium guajava L.). *Hawaii Agric. Exp. Sta. Res. Rep. 218.* Honolulu, Univ. of Hawaii.

Seagrave-Smith, H., and Sherman, G. D. (1954). *Removal of stone cells in common guavas (Psidum guajava). Hawaii Agric. Exp. Sta. Progress Notes No. 101.* Honolulu, Hawaii, Univ. of Hawaii.

Shigeura, G. T., Bullock, R. M., and Silva, J. A. (1979). Defoliation and fruit set in guava. *Hort. Sci.* 10:509.

Smith, R. M., and Siwatibau, S. (1975). Sesquiterprene hydrocarbons of Fijian guavas. *Phytochemistry* 14:2013.

Stevens, K. L., Brekke, J. E., and Sterns, D. J. (1970). Volatile constituents in guava. *J. Agric. Food Chem.* 18:(4)598-599.

Torline, P., and Ballschmieter, H. M. B. (1973). Volatile constituents from guava I. A comparison of extraction methods. *Lebensm.-Wiss u. Technol.* 6:32.

Wenkam, N. S., and Miller, C. D. (1965). Composition of Hawaii Fruits. *Hawaii Agric. Exp. Sta. Bull. 135.* Honolulu, Univ. of Hawaii.

Wilson, C. W., III. (1980). Guava. In *Tropical and Subtropical Fruits: Composition, Nutritive Values, Properties and Uses* (S. Nagy, and P. E. Shaw, eds.). Westport, Conn., Avi Publishing Co., pp. 316-340.

Wilson, C. W., III, and Shaw, P. E. (1978). Terpene hydrocarbons from *Psidium gaujava. Phytochemistry* 17:1435-1436.

9
Macadamia Nuts

Catherine G. Cavaletto   University of Hawaii, Honolulu, Hawaii

I. INTRODUCTION

It is only in the last 20 years that the macadamia nut has risen from relative obscurity to its present position among the most treasured of

salted and confectionery nuts. Whether consumed as roasted salted
nuts, chocolate-coated, or as an ingredient in a variety of other products, macadamia nuts have come to be recognized as a gourmet item.
A unique flavor and texture combine to provide one of the world's most
pleasant sensory experiences.

A. Botanical Description and Cultivars

The botanical family Proteaceae includes about 10 species of the genus
Macadamia, two of which produce edible nuts: *M. tetraphylla*, known
as the rough-shell macadamia nut, and *M. integrifolia*, known as the
smooth-shell macadamia nut. Characteristics of the two species are
given in Table 1. A third species, *M. ternifolia*, called the Gympie
nut or Maroochie nut produces small nuts that are bitter and considered inedible. Hybrids between the two edible species are also found.
Although the nut is most commonly referred to as the macadamia nut,
it has also been known as the Queensland nut, Australian nut, Bauple

Table 1 Contrasting Characteristics of *M. integrifolia* and
M. tetraphylla

	M. tetraphylla (rough-shell type)	*M. integrifolia* (smooth-shell type)
Nuts	Usually slightly elliptical or spindle-shaped; surface pebbled	Round or very nearly round; surface smooth or nearly so
Mature leaves	Commonly four leaves at at node, but rarely three or five; young seedlings have two; leaves usually larger and longer than *M. integrifolia*; leaf sessile or stems with very short petioles, leaf margins serrate with many spines along the edges; leaves up to 20 in. in length	Three leaves at a node (except for young seedlings which have two), leaves usually shorter than *M. tetraphylla*, ranging from 4 to 12 in. in length. Leaf stems usually about 1/2 in. long; leaf margins on mature trees are much less spiny than *M. tetraphylla* and often without spines
Young leaves	Purple or reddish in color	Pale green or bronze
Flower	Pink	Creamy white

Source: Hamilton and Fukunaga (1959).

nut, bopple nut, popple nut, and kindal-kindal (the Australian aboriginal name). Numerous cultivars have been described in Hawaii, California, Australia, and South Africa. Presently, production in Hawaii is in seven cultivars of *M. integrifolia*, Keauhou (HAES 246), Ikaika (Hawaiian Agricultural Experiment Station no. 333), Kakea (HAES 508), Keaau (HAES 660), Ka'u (HAES 344), Mauka (HAES 741), and Makai (HAES 800). Two additional cultivars, Purvis (HAES 294) and Pahala (HAES 788) were named in 1981 (Hamilton, 1981). Major plantings in other areas rely heavily but not exclusively on the Hawaii cultivars. In California, where the climate is generally cooler than in Hawaii, two cultivars of *M. tetraphylla*, Elimbah and Cate, and one of *M. integrifolia*, Keauhou, are recommended (James, 1978). In addition to the Hawaii cultivars, Australia is producing Own Choice and Hinde. In South Africa, the Hawaii cultivars are grown along with Beaumont, Nelmac-1, and Nelmac-2, all interspecific hybrids. Production in Kenya consists primarily of *M. tetraphylla* seedlings.

The most successful plantings of macadamia nuts are entirely of selected cultivars of *M. integrifolia*. This situation may be attributed to the fact that commercialization of macadamia nuts first occurred in Hawaii where *M. tetraphylla* was rejected early in the development of the industry. The extensive selection program there has not included *M. tetraphylla* and, therefore, improved cultivars of this species have not been developed.

This evergreen tree with its hollylike leaves grows to a height of about 10 m (Fig. 1). Once the tree begins producing nuts at an age

Figure 1 Mature *M. integrigolia* tree.

of 5 to 7 years, it continues to produce for many years if provided
adequate cultural and environmental conditions. The limits of commercial production are not known, but Hamilton and Fukunaga (1959)
estimate a capability of 40 to 60 years of production. Some of the
earliest plantings in Hawaii, planted in the late nineteenth century,
are still alive and bearing.

Flowering occurs on racemes over a period of several months
(Fig. 2). Only a few nuts set on each raceme (Fig. 3), and their
development requires about 215 days to maturity (Jones and Shaw,
1943). The fully mature nut consists of a nearly spherical white embryo in a hard spherical brown shell (testa) about 25 mm in diameter
and 2 to 3 mm thick (Fig. 4). Surrounding this shell or seed coat is
a fibrous green pericarp or husk that is 2 to 4 mm thick (Fig. 5). Occasionally, both ovules contained in the pistil will develop, resulting
in two hemispherical nuts within one husk. These nuts are referred to
as *twin* nuts.

The fruit of the macadamia is a follicle, not a drupe, and the "nut"
is not truly a nut but is the seed contained in the follicle (Hartung
and Storey, 1939). However, since the seed is commonly referred to
as a nut, common usage will be followed in this chapter. Detailed
studies on the anatomy of the nut are reported by Francis (1928),
Hartung and Storey (1939), and Strauss (1970).

Figure 2 *M. integrifolia* flowering.

Figure 3 Cluster of
M. integrifolia nuts.

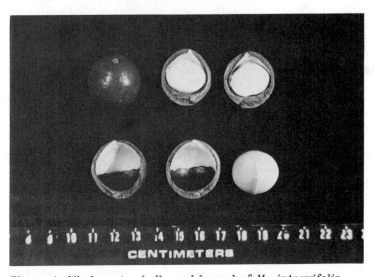

Figure 4 Whole nut, shell, and kernel of *M. integrifolia*.

Figure 5 *M. integrifolia* nuts in husk.

B. Origin and Distribution

Australia is the home of the macadamia nut, having been discovered there in 1843 by Ludwig Leichardt (McConachie, 1980). In 1857, specimens were collected by Walter Hill, director of the Brisbane Botanical Gardens, and Ferdinand von Mueller, a botanist for the Government of Victoria. They subsequently named that nut for Dr. John Macadam, secretary of the Philosophical Institute of Victoria (McConachie, 1980).

Introduction into Hawaii in 1881 by William H. Purvis and in 1892 by Edward W. and Robert A. Jordan (Storey, 1956) led eventually to the development of commercial plantings which in 1981 totaled more than 5400 ha (Hawaiian Agricultural Reporting Service, 1981). Commercialization of the crop in Australia lagged behind Hawaii, but has now become significant with large areas planted. Plantings in South Africa, Malawi, and Kenya are also producing commercial quantities of nuts as are small plantings in Southern California. Other plantings are in Costa Rica, Brazil, Guatemala, Fiji, and Zimbabwe.

C. Economic and Nutritional Significance

At the present time, greatest economic significance is recognized in Hawaii, where producers realized $24.2 million for the 1980 crop (Hawaii Agricultural Reporting Service, 1981). Significant growth is also being seen in Australia, Africa, and Central America. Macadamia nuts are one of those foods consumed for the pleasure derived rather than for any significant nutritional contribution to the diet. Because of their high cost ($15 to $25 per kilogram to the U.S. consumer), they are considered a luxury food and, normally, too few are consumed to be of significance nutritionally. Second, they are a high-calorie food, providing 727 calories/100 g, and have a relatively low nutrient density (Wenkam and Miller, 1965). One-half cup of roasted kernels contributes nearly 500 cal to the diet.

II. HORTICULTURAL ASPECTS

A. Cultivation Practices

1. Climatological and Soil Requirements

The macadamia is best adapted to frost-free subtropical climates with at least 127 cm of annual rainfall distributed throughout the year (Hamilton and Ito, 1980). It grows in the approximate range of 0° to 34° latitude, but not in all locations within that range. In some areas, the tree may grow, but produce no crop. Although the tree can tolerate a range of temperatures, optimum production occurs in areas where temperature does not exceed 32°C or fall below about 13°C. Elevation is also a factor in a given growing area. For example, elevations between 213 and 549 m have proven best for macadamia in Hawaii (Hamilton and Ito, 1980), but at other latitudes, optimum elevation may differ considerably. *M. tetraphylla* is able to tolerate cooler temperatures and, in fact, grows better at cooler temperatures than *M. integrifolia*. For that reason, it is sometimes selected for cooler climates.

Macadamias in Hawaii are grown in soil ranging from loose, volcanic lava soils to well-drained lateritic clays. In California, sandy loam and decomposed granite soils are preferred (Storey, 1969). In general, macadamias require good drainage and soil depth sufficient for root system penetration (Storey, 1969).

2. Propagation and Planting Characteristics

The macadamia tree is usually started in the nursery from the seed of either *M. integrifolia* or *M. tetraphylla*, and at about 10 to 12 months of age, the seedlings are grafted to the desired cultivar. These young plants are then transplanted in orchards about 1 year after grafting. In South Africa, some plantings have been propagated from cuttings. However, this system is not widely used elsewhere because it can result in weak-rooted trees that can be easily toppled by strong winds. Orchards are usually planted with several cultivars because it is thought that pollination is improved by this mixture. The time from transplanting to the first significant nut production is about 5 to 7 years.

3. Productivity

Seedling orchards have never proven satisfactory because of low productivity, extreme nut variability, and poor nut quality. Furthermore, seedling trees usually take longer to begin producing and produce less kernel per kilogram of in-shell nuts. Hamilton and Fukunaga (1959) found that grafted trees of *M. integrifolia* produced three to four times as many nuts on the average as seedling trees of similar size and age.

Yield of in-shell nuts per tree can vary widely depending on environment and cultural practices. A reasonable goal for production of *M. integrifolia* in Hawaii is 45 to 50 kg per tree. However, in some areas, production may exceed 90 kg per tree. Another important aspect of yield is kernel percentage which is calculated as grams kernel per 100 g dry in-shell nuts × 100. For cultivars currently produced in Hawaii, kernel yields range from 34 to 44% (Hamilton and Ito, 1976).

B. Harvesting

Because flowering extends over a period of several months, maturation of the crop likewise extends over a long period. The normal harvest period is about 7 months, from August through February in the northern hemisphere and from about March through September in the southern hemisphere, during which time essentially the entire crop is harvested. Length of the harvest season varies between cultivars, with some cultivars having a peak season but some production throughout the year.

Traditionally nuts are harvested from the ground by hand after falling naturally from the tree. A large portion of the crop continues to be harvested in this fashion, but mechanical harvesting of naturally fallen nuts by a combination of sweepers and collectors is also used. Still a third method to harvest naturally fallen nuts is the use of nets suspended beneath the trees (Liang and Lopez-Madrazo, 1973). To date, this system has not proven staisfactory due to high costs and collection of large amounts of leaf material in the nets. Harvest intervals for naturally fallen nuts range from approximately 2 weeks to 2 months, depending on weather and availability of labor. Long harvest intervals may result in mold growth, germination, and development of rancidity. Therefore, it is recommended that the harvest interval not exceed 1 month and that it be shorter, especially during rainy weather.

In recent years, shake harvesting has also been employed in areas where labor costs are unusually high or where there is insufficient labor for ground harvesting. Trees are shaken after most of the nuts on the tree have matured. Monroe et al. (1972) showed that one cultivar (Keauhou) could be harvested from the tree early in the season with resulting kernel quality and yield comparable to that from a series of ground harvest over a 3-1/2-month period. Nonetheless, several obstacles remain in shake-harvesting systems. A simple field test for maturity remains to be developed. Beyond this, seasonal variations in

Figure 6 Mature nuts with simultaneous flowering.

flowering may necessitate harvesting at a time before optimum maturity has been reached. In such a situation, large numbers of immature nuts may be harvested representing an economic loss to the grower. This loss must be weighed against any labor cost savings that has been achieved. If flowering begins while nuts remain on the tree (Fig. 6), shake harvesting will reduce the subsequent year's crop.

C. Postharvest Handling

Nuts are husked on the farm or at a nearby facility. It is necessary to husk nuts within 24 hr of harvest to reduce the opportunity for heat buildup due to respiration. Removal of the husk facilitates the drying process. After the nuts have been husked, they are normally transported to the processing plant to be dried.

III. BIOCHEMICAL AND NUTRITIONAL COMPOSITION

A. Nutritional Composition

Nutrient composition of *M. integrifolia* is given in Table 2. The nutrient composition of macadamia nuts has also recently been reviewed by this author in an earlier work (Cavaletto, 1980).

Table 2 Nutrient Composition of
Roasted Macadamia Nuts

Per 100 g edible portion	
Food energy (cal)	727
Moisture (g)	1.19
Protein (g)	9.23
Fat (g)	78.21
Total carbohydrate (g)	9.97
Fiber (g)	1.84
Ash (g)	1.40
Ca (mg)	53.4
P (mg)	240.8
Fe (mg)	1.99
Vitamin A value (μg)	0
Thiamin (mg)	0.216
Riboflavin (mg)	0.119
Niacin (mg)	1.60

Source: Wenkam and Miller (1965).

B. Chemical and Biochemical Composition

1. Moisture

Kernels of freshly harvested mature macadamia nuts normally contain
23 to 25% moisture. After falling from the tree and awaiting harvesting, the nuts begin a drying process during which the husk
usually splits open. However, under rainy conditions or exceedingly
high relative humidities, kernel moisture may not be reduced at all.
Thus, kernel moisture at the time of harvest ranges from as low as
10% to as high as 25% in mature nuts. At these high moistures, shell
moisture content is about the same as that of the whole nut, but
when the nuts have been dried to a low moisture level, the shell
contains most of the water (Hansen and Gough, 1977). When kernel
moisture is reduced to 1.5%, shell moisture is about 4 to 5%. The
macadamia husk may contain as much as 45% moisture at the time of
harvest (Chu et al., 1953).

2. Oil

The macadamia kernel is characterized by a high oil content which
is a major quality factor. High-quality kernels of *M. integrifolia*
contain 75 to 79% oil whereas those of *M. tetraphylla* are generally
thought to contain slightly less. Winterton (1968) found 5% less oil
in *M. tetraphylla* than in *M. integrifolia*. However, Saleeb et al.
(1973) reported the same oil content for samples of both species.

In the early days of the macadamia industry in Hawaii, Ripperton et al. (1938) recognized the importance of oil content as a quality factor and developed an indirect method for its determination. Specific gravity was found to be highly correlated with oil content in both the smooth-shell and rough-shell types (Fig. 7). The degree of correlation was sufficiently high ($r = 0.979$ for the smooth-shell type and 0.985 for the rough-shell type) to permit the use of specific gravity as a measure of oil content. Kernels separated into groups according to specific gravity exhibited the roasting characteristics shown in Table 3. Those kernels having a specific gravity less than 1.000 (72% or more oil) exhibit desirable roasting characteristics. Those with a specific gravity 1.000 or greater (less than 72% oil) show varying degrees of objectionable characteristics. Based on this knowledge, a simple grading system was devised where kernels are separated into three grades using two solutions having specific gravity of 1.00 (tap water) and

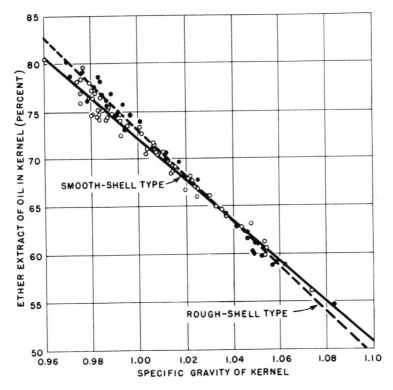

Figure 7   Relation of specific gravity of macadamia kernels to ether extract. (*Source:* Ripperton et al., 1938.)

Table 3   Relation of Specific Gravity of Smooth-Shell-Type Kernels in Roasting Qualities

Specific gravity	Proportion of oil in kernel (%)	Appearance of raw kernel	Roasting qualities
>1.100	<50	Small size, shriveled base, hard or tough texture, off-color	Very dark color, unpleasant burnt flavor, hard texture
1.100-1.050	50-61.5	Small size, shriveled base, hard or tough texture, off-color	Very dark color, unpleasant burnt flavor, hard texture
1.050-1.025	61.5-67	Small size, shriveled base, hard or tough texture, off-color	Very dark color, unpleasant burnt flavor, hard texture
1.025-1.000	67-72	Slight shriveling of base; variable in size and color	Somewhat dark in color, tendency to off-flavors and spongy texture; saleable, but distinctly inferior to lighter nuts
1.000-0.985	72-75	Smooth base, plump, well filled, light color	Light golden color, mild nutty flavor, crisp texture, excellent
0.985-0.970	75-78.5	Smooth base, plump, well filled, light color	Light golden color, mild nutty flavor, crisp texture, excellent
<0.970	>78.5	Smooth base, plump, well filled, light color	Light golden color, mild nutty flavor, crisp texture, excellent

Source: Ripperton et al. (1938).

1.025 (salt brine) (Fig. 8). This method, or variations of it, is still
in use to grade macadamia samples.

The oil is rich in monounsaturated fatty acids, predominantly oleic
and palmitoleic (Table 4). This relatively high concentration of palmitoleic acid (about 20%) appears to be unique to oil seeds of Proteaceae.

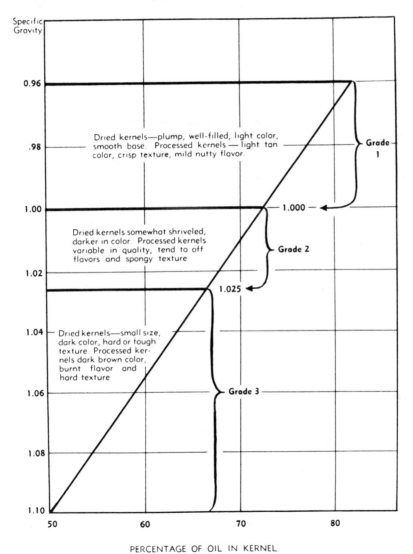

Figure 8 Relation of kernel quality to specific gravity and percentage
of oil. (*Source:* Ripperton et al., 1938.)

Table 4   Fatty Acid Composition of Macadamia Nut Kernels

	Composition (%)				
	M. integrifolia			M. tetraphylla	
Fatty acids	Cavaletto et al. (1966)	Saleeb et al. (1973)	Bridge and Hilditch (1950)	Saleeb et al. (1973)	Beuchat and Worthington (1978)
Lauric	Trace	—	—	—	
Myristic	0.8	0.7	1.6	0.6	
Palmitic	7.4	9.1	8.0	8.8	8.3
Palmitoleic	18.5	21.9	20.4	23.6	21.8
Stearic	2.8	2.2	3.3	5.2	2.1
Oleic	65.0	59.9	59.3	56.3	56.4
Linoleic	1.5	1.9	2.2	1.7	2.8
Arachidonic	1.9	1.8	2.2	2.7	
Eicosenoic	2.3	2.0	2.2	1.0	

Palmitoleic acid rarely exceeds 10% in most oil seeds and animal fats (Vickery, 1971). The two species show only minor differences in fatty acid composition, but Saleeb et al. (1973) found the ratio of unsaturated to saturated fatty acids to be slightly higher in M. integrifolia (6.2:1) than in M. tetraphylla (4.8:1).

Small amounts of oil are also found in macadamia husk and shell. Chu et al. (1953) report 1.2% in the husk and Saleeb et al. (1975) found 1 to 1.5% in the shell (species unspecified). Fatty acid composition of that shell oil is given in Table 5; it is similar to that of kernel oil.

Table 5   Fatty Acid Composition of Macadamia Nut Shell Oil

Fatty acids	Composition (%)
Myristic	0.49
Palmitic	9.44
Palmitoleic	20.81
Stearic	1.50
Oleic	55.40
Linoleic	4.38
Arachidic	1.57
Linolenic	4.50

Source: Saleeb et al. (1975).

3. Sugars

The fresh kernel of *M. integrifolia* contains 4.57% total sugar, most of which is nonreducing sugar. Reducing sugar constitutes 0.06% of the total weight (Prichavudhi and Yamamoto, 1965). This level is further reduced upon drying to 0.03 to 0.04% reducing sugar (Prichavudhi and Yamamoto, 1965; Cavaletto et al., 1966). Total sugar is usually 2 to 4% higher in *M. tetraphylla* than in *M. integrifolia*. For this reason, *M. tetraphylla* usually, but not always, browns more rapidly than *M. integrifolia* during roasting. This difference appears to depend on the cultivar, but as a general rule, nuts from the two species should not be mixed for processing.

The relationship between total sugar content and specific gravity is slightly different from that between oil content and specific gravity. Ripperton et al. (1938) found that total sugars in normal, mature *M. integrifolia* kernels ranged from about 3 to 5%. In this range, there was little correlation between total sugar content and specific gravity (Fig. 9). However, when the kernels were obviously immature and total sugar content was high, the correlation was high. These kernels with high sugar content tend to overbrown during roasting. The macadamia husk at the time of harvest contains 9.2% glucose (Chu et al., 1953).

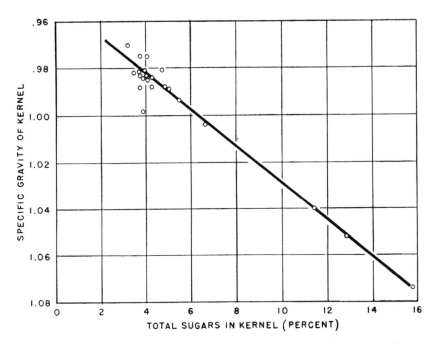

Figure 9 Relation of total sugars in macadamia kernels to specific gravity. (*Source:* Ripperton et al., 1938.)

4. Protein

Dry *M. integrifolia* kernels contain about 9.2% protein (Wenkam and
Miller, 1965), but just as in many oil seeds, the protein is low in
methionine. Table 6 gives the amino acid composition of *M. integrifolia* and *M. tetraphylla* as determined by Saleeb et al. (1973).
Almost no difference is found between the two species. A small
amount of protein, 2%, is found in the shell (Saleeb et al., 1975)
and in the husk, 3.4%, (Chu et al., 1953).

5. Antioxidants

Although tocopherols occur in significant amounts and appear to be
responsible for flavor stability in some nuts such as filberts and
almonds (Lambertsen et al., 1962), such does not seem to be the
case with macadamia. Wang (1972) found only small amounts of
tocopherols (6.4 to 18.0 μg/g dry matter), and these probably do
not account for the stability of macadamia kernels. In *M. integrifolia*, Wang found α-tocotrienol and trace amounts of α-tocopherol.
When kernels were analyzed following grading based on oil content,
Wang found that kernels with the highest oil content (i.e., highest
quality), also had the greatest amount of tocopherols on a per kernel basis. However, these high-oil kernels had the lowest amount
of tocopherols on a microgram per gram lipid or microgram per gram
dry matter basis. Although it is generally thought that kernel
stability is reduced if nuts remain on the ground for long periods
prior to harvest, Wang (1972) was able to show only a slight decrease in tocopherols in nuts after periods of up to 3 months on the
ground.

6. Bitter Substances

Bitter kernels occur occasionally in seedling orchards, but have not
been found in orchards consisting of grafted trees of known cultivars.
The bitter substance was identified as a cyanogenic glucoside, composed of two molecules of glucose and one molecule of p-hydroxy-
mandelonitrile (Young and Hamilton, 1966). The compound, named
proteacin for the family of plants in which it occurs, is also found
in small amounts in nonbitter kernels. Young and Hamilton suggest
that proteacin may be a normal constituent of macadamia nuts, but
one that occurs at subthreshold levels in nonbitter kernels.

The bitter principle can be transmitted through seed or by grafting scions from a tree known to produce bitter kernels (Hamilton and
Young, 1966). Since there is no visible difference between bitter
and nonbitter kernels, it is not possible to segregate them. Therefore, the only practical solution is to eliminate trees known to produce bitter kernels.

Table 6 Amino Acid Composition of Macadamia Nut Oilfree Meal of *M. tetraphylla* and *M. integrifolia*

Amino acid	Free amino acids (mg/100 g)		Total amino acids (mg/100 g)	
	M. tetraphylla	*M. integrifolia*	*M. tetraphylla*	*M. integrifolia*
Lysine	73	54	1153 (4.2)[a]	1313 (4.3)
Histidine	24	22	599 (2.2)	679 (2.2)
Ammonia	—	—	453 (1.6)	475 (1.6)
Arginine	18	22	3259 (11.8)	3571 (11.7)
Tryptophan	13	15	—	—
Aspartic acid	232	198	3020 (10.9)	3278 (10.7)
Threonine	106	94	943 (3.4)	1058 (3.5)
Serine	275	261	1257 (4.5)	1444 (4.7)
Glutamic acid	255	149	6586 (23.8)	6974 (22.8)
Proline	211	144	1263 (4.6)	1803 (5.8)
Glycine	33	30	1308 (4.7)	1529 (5.0)
Alanine	226	130	1246 (4.5)	1247 (4.1)
Cystine	5	1	378 (1.3)	371 (1.2)
Valine	65	60	1177 (4.2)	1282 (4.2)
Methionine	16	10	337 (1.2)	356 (1.2)
Isoleucine	40	28	861 (3.1)	1016 (3.3)
Leucine	28	19	1662 (6.0)	1887 (6.1)
Tyrosine	48	49	1238 (4.5)	1315 (4.3)
Phenylalanine	48	48	971 (3.5)	1002 (3.3)
Total	1716	1334	27,711	30,600

[a] Amino acids expressed as percent of total amino acids recovered, in parenthesis.
Source: Saleeb et al. (1973).

Table 7 Compounds Identified from Roasted Macadamia Nuts Essence Extract Analysis

Compound	Retention index	Size of peak[a]	Present in peanuts[b]	Present in filberts[c]	Present in pecans[d]
Neutral					
2,3-Pentadione	4.1	S	X	X	X
n-Hexanal	4.5	M	X	X	X
p-Xylene	5.0	S	X	X	
n-Heptanal	5.5	M	X	X	X
2-Heptanone[e]	5.5	S	X	X	
n-Pentanol	6.0	S	X	X	X
2-Pentylfuran[e]	6.0	S	X	X	
p-Cymene[e]	6.3	S	X	X	
2-Methyltetrahydro-furan-3-one[e]	6.4	S		X	
n-Octanal	6.6	M	X	X	X
n-Hexanol	7.0	M	X	X	X
n-Nonanal	7.7	L	X	X	
n-Heptanol	8.1	M	X	X	X
2-Furfural	8.2	S	X	X	X
3-Methylthiopro-pionaldehyde	8.2	S	X	X	
Benzaldehyde	9.0	S	X	X	
n-Octanol	9.1	M		X	X
3,5,5-trimethyl-2-cyclohexen-1-one[e]	9.6	S		X	
Phenylacetaldehyde	10.1	L	X	X	
1-Phenyl-2-propanone	10.9	M	X	X	
2-Phenylethanol	12.7	S	X	X	
2-Phenyl-2-butanal	13.0	S		X	
phenol	13.3	M		X	
Basic					
2-Methylpyrazine	6.4	S	X	X	X
2,5-Dimethyl-pyrazine	7.0	L	X	X	X
2,3-Dimethyl-pyrazine	7.2	S	X	X	X
2-Ethyl-5-methyl-pyrazine	7.7	S	X	X	X
2,3,5-Trimethyl-pyrazine	7.8	M	X	X	X

Table 7 (Continued)

Compound	Retention index	Size of peak[a]	Present in peanuts[b]	Present in filberts[c]	Present in pecans[d]
Basic (continued)					
2-Ethyl-3,6-dimethyl-pyrazine	8.2	L	X	X	X
2,5-Diethyl-3-methyl-pyrazine[e]	8.7	S		X	

[a]Estimate of peak size relative to size of other peaks in the same group. The symbols L, M, S indicate large, medium, and small, respectively.
[b]Walradt et al. (1971).
[c]Kinlin et al. (1972).
[d]Wang and Odell (1972).
[e]Tentative identification.
Source: Crain and Tang (1975).

7. Volatile Components

The volatiles found in roasted macadamia kernels are similar to those found in other roasted nuts. Crain and Tang (1975) identified the compounds found in the basic portion of an essence extract (Table 7) as well as those found in the neutral portion and by headspace analysis (Table 8). Most of the pyrazines found in the basic portion of the essence extract were the same as those found in peanuts, filberts, and pecans although not necessarily in the same amounts. Neutral and headspace compounds consisted mostly of alcohols, aldehydes, and ketones also found in other nuts. A major component, methyl sulfide, was unique to macadamia nuts. Crain and Tang (1975) suggested that this highly volatile compound might play a role in the characteristic macadamia flavor. It has been observed that overroasted macadamia kernels do not possess the characteristic macadamia flavor but more closely resemble other roasted nuts. The volatilization of methyl sulfide during roasting might explain this observation.

8. Tannins

Kawano et al. (1961) examined the husks of *M. integrifolia* and found 6 to 12% tannin. However, no commercial use has been made of tannin from macadamia husks. Currently, husks are used for mulching material or are discarded.

Table 8 Compounds Identified from Roasted Macadamia Nuts Head-Space Analysis

Compound	Retention index	Size of peak[a]	Present in peanuts [b]	Present in filberts[c]
n-Hexane	0.3	S		X
n-Heptane	0.5	M		X
Methyl sulfide	0.6	L		
n-Octane	0.8	M		X
2-Methylpropanal	1.0	L	X	X
Methylfuran	1.9	S		X
2-Methylbutanal	2.4	L	X	X
3-Methylbutanal	2.5	L		X
Benzene [e]	2.8	S	X	X
Toluene[e]	4.0	S	X	X
Methyl disulfide	4.4	S	X	X

[a]Estimate of peak size relative to size of other peaks in the same group. The symbols L, M, S indicate large, medium, and small, respectively.
[b]Walradt et al. (1971).
[c]Kinlin et al. (1972).
[e]Tentative identification.
Source: Crain and Tang (1975).

9. Fiber

Only 1.84% fiber is found in the macadamia kernel (Wenkam and Miller, 1965), but the shell contains 60% fiber (Saleeb et al., 1975).

C. Changes in Composition

1. During Physiological Development

Macadamia nuts are characterized by a high oil content that can be traced through physiological development of the nut (Jones and Shaw, 1943). During the first 90 days after flowering, the fruit structures are laid down and growth of the husk, shell, and endosperm occurs. After 90 days, the embryo enlarges rapidly and begins to form and accumulate oil (Tables 9-11). At the same time, protein and sucrose are being accumulated. Reducing sugars increase until about 111 days following flowering and then decrease until maturity is reached. Sucrose shows the same pattern, but it increases in weight per embryo until about 136 days before declining. Total nitrogen increases in

Table 9 Changes in the Macadamia Fruit During Development

Time after flowering (days)	Fresh weight per embryo (g)	Dry weight per embryo (g)	Percent dry weight	Condition of shell
90	1.138	0.067	5.0	Soft and white
111	2.806	0.491	17.5	Hard and white
136	3.410	0.992	29.1	Hard and light brown
185	2.877	1.382	48.0	Hard and brown
215	2.781	1.882	67.7	Hard and dark brown

Source: Jones and Shaw (1943).

Table 10 Carbohydrates, Nitrogen, and Oil Changes in the Macadamia Embryo, Expressed as Percentage of Dry Weight, in Relation to Age

Constituent (%)	Days after flowering				
	90	111	136	185	215
Reducing sugar	1.47	3.21	1.07	0.41	0.30
Sucrose	6.07	24.07	21.91	9.19	5.50
Total sugar	7.54	27.28	22.98	9.60	5.80
Soluble nitrogen	2.92	1.13	0.61	0.33	0.27
Insoluble nitrogen	1.96	1.91	1.58	1.39	1.43
Total nitrogen	4.88	3.04	2.19	1.72	1.70
Acid-hydrolyzable matter	4.54	4.88	3.85	2.56	2.16
Soluble solids in 80% alcohol	60.10	39.92	28.36	14.82	9.88
Ether and alcohol-insoluble material	36.43	28.88	23.69	17.89	16.68
Petroleum ether extract	3.46	31.19	47.94	67.28	73.44

Source: Jones and Shaw (1943).

Table 11 Carbohydrate, Nitrogen, and Oil Changes in the Macadamia Embryo, Expressed As Milligrams per Embryo, in Relation to Age

Constituent (mg)	Days after flowering				
	90	111	136	185	215
Reducing sugar	0.85	13.69	8.39	5.41	3.97
Sucrose	3.93	115.03	196.65	128.25	100.87
Total sugar	4.78	128.72	205.04	133.66	104.84
Soluble nitrogen	1.94	5.26	5.33	4.33	4.75
Insoluble nitrogen	1.33	8.28	14.35	19.08	26.12
Total nitrogen	3.27	13.54	19.68	23.41	30.87
Acid-hydrolyzable matter	3.00	23.27	34.34	33.43	39.41
Soluble solids in 80% alcohol	40.02	187.25	251.65	201.20	177.72
Ether and alcohol-insoluble material	24.92	139.29	213.54	245.12	304.22
Petroleum ether extract	2.40	164.95	456.81	936.02	1339.39

Source: Jones and Shaw (1943).

amount throughout development, but as percentage of dry weight, it declines after 90 days. In the period from 90 to 111 days after flowering, the most marked change in oil characteristics takes place (Table 12). Acid value, saponification number, and soluble acids decrease sharply and the iodine number increases. Early investigators (Jones and Shaw, 1943) believed that hexose sugar was the starting point for oil synthesis in macadamia nuts. More recent accounts of fatty acid biosynthesis in plants have been reviewed by Stumpf (1980).

2. Changes During Postharvest Storage

At the time of harvest, macadamia husks contain as much as 45% moisture (Chu et al., 1953), and the mature embryo normally contains up to about 25% moisture. If the nuts are stored in bulk at these moisture levels, either husked or unhusked, respiratory activity will result in increasing temperature and deterioration of kernel quality. Chu et al. (1953) attributed these changes to action of respiratory, lipolytic, and proteolytic enzymes. The resulting oxidation and lipolysis are the chief factors in deterioration.

When high-moisture in-shell nuts are stored at high temperature and high relative humidity, mold growth as well as lipolysis occurs (Higaki and Dedolph, 1963). However, lipolysis does not appear to be directly related to mold growth.

During peak harvest, it is sometimes necessary to hold nuts in-shell because processing capacity is insufficient to accommodate surges in production. In-shell nuts can be successfully stored provided that the nuts are thoroughly dried and that low moisture content is maintained during storage. Cavaletto et al. (1968) found that flavor stability of roasted kernels prepared from in-shell nuts that had been dried to 1.2% kernel moisture and stored for 12 months was equal to that of roasted kernels prepared from freshly harvested nuts. However, roasted kernels prepared from in-shell nuts that had been only air-dried (3.8% kernel moisture) and stored for 12 months maintaining that moisture content had reduced shelf life. It is clear that kernel stability is related to kernel moisture content and that storage of high-moisture nuts is not desirable.

3. Changes During Processing and Storage

The objective of processing and storage methods is to produce kernels that are crisp, light brown in color, and free of blemishes and to prevent rancidity and other off-flavors. The removal of moisture from kernels is required for desired texture and for flavor stability. Following harvesting and husking, nuts must be dried to reduce kernel moisture to 1.5% or lower before roasting. Drying temperatures are critical in this process. Initial drying of freshly harvested nuts should be at 38°C or lower (Prichavudhi and Yamamoto, 1965) to lower kernel moisture to at least 15% before drying temperature is increased.

Table 12 Changes in the Characteristics of Macadamia Oil in Relation to Age

Characteristics	Days after flowering				
	90	111	136	185	215
Acid number	163.90	6.56	2.26	0.73	0.57
Saponification number	380.6	204.2	199.7	197.7	197.3
Soluble acids (%)	23.65	1.67	0.46	0.23	0.26
Insoluble acids (%)	48.14	81.49	86.42	94.09	94.21
Iodine number	64.4	75.4	74.4	75.7	75.2
Unsaponifiable matter (%)	a	0.75	0.58	0.42	0.34
Hydroxyl number	—	11.1	9.0	6.0	4.8
Index of refraction, 25°C	—	1.4681	1.4669	1.4658	1.4657

[a]insufficient material for analysis.
Source: Jones and Shaw (1943).

Under such conditions, reducing sugar content is reduced by about one-half. High-moisture nuts dried at higher temperatures develop dark brown centers when the kernels are roasted. These dark brown areas contain higher reducing sugar levels, nearly double that found in the outer portion of the kernel. Minimum reducing sugar levels can be obtained if kernel moisture content is reduced to 8% before increasing the drying temperature to 52°C and to 6% before increasing the temperature to 60°C (Prichavudhi and Yamamoto, 1965). The drying temperature should never exceed 60°C. It appears that total sugar content is also reduced by initial low-temperature drying. However, drying temperature does not affect kernel oil content; no oil synthesis occurs during the drying process.

Raw kernels with moisture content exceeding 2% have been shown to have poor storage stability (Cavaletto et al., 1966). In that study, marked flavor deterioration occured in kernels with 2.3% moisture after 4 months at ambient temperature. At higher moisture levels and at higher storage temperature, the deterioration progressed more rapidly. Corresponding to the flavor changes were reductions in total sugar and increases in reducing sugar and free fatty acids. It was suggested that naturally occurring enzymes were responsible for these changes.

Upon roasting, kernels with more than 2% moisture do not possess the desired crisp texture, brown too rapidly, and have reduced shelf life. Dela Cruz et al. (1966) roasted kernels with 1.4, 2.3, and 4.3% moisture. The time required to achieve the same roasted color was 15, 13 and 8 min, respectively. The decrease in roasting time is presumably due to higher reducing sugar content in higher-moisture nuts (Cavaletto et al., 1966). The two higher moisture levels both resulted in a soft, not crisp, texture and reduced flavor quality and were considered unacceptable. Those kernels roasted at 1.4% moisture showed a slight increase in free fatty acids after storage under vacuum at ambient temperature for 16 months. This increase corresponded with a slight decrease in flavor quality. Clearly, low kernel moisture content is required for the desired quality and stability.

Since a large share of the nuts are oil-roasted, the influence of roasting oil on kernel composition and stability is of some interest. Less than 1% increase in oil occurs in the kernels during roasting (Dela Cruz et al., 1966). Thus, roasting oil is used up slowly and may be in continuous use for an extended period of time. Cavaletto and Yamamoto (1970) showed that coconut oil used for 13 weeks with only small additions of fresh oil became thicker, darker, less saturated, and higher in free fatty acids. Despite these changes, shelf life of kernels roasted in it was not lessened. Winterton (1962) likewise found no difference in rancidity development or thiobarbituric acid (TBA) value between kernels roasted in fresh and used oil. Analysis of the fatty acid composition of the roasting oil in the 1971 study showed that after 13 weeks the roasting oil was more similar to macadamia oil than to coconut oil, suggesting that an exchange of oil had taken place during roasting. The percentage of macadamia oil in the roasting oil was based on the content of lauric and palmitoleic acids which are characteristic of coconut and macadamia, respectively. After 2, 4, and 13 weeks, the estimated macadamia oil content of the roasting oil was 21, 56, and 77%, respectively. Furthermore, the iodine number of the roasting oil showed an increase from an initial 9.74, typical for coconut oil, to 57.4 approaching that reported by Cavaletto et al. (1966) for macadamia (80.9). This exchange of oil may be responsible, in part, for the slow deterioration of the roasting oil.

Shelf life of roasted macadamia kernels varies considerably, but is normally at least 1 year. Dela Cruz et al. (1966) found that roasted kernels that had been vacuum packed showed a slight gradual decline in quality over a period of 16 months. When the kernels were rated by a sensory panel, no difference in quality was attributed to differences in storage temperatures ranging from 2 to 38°C.

Packaging plays an important role in storage of the processed product, in large part because of its function as a moisture barrier. Cans and jars that are properly sealed are ideal in this respect. Flexible packaging materials seldom have sufficient moisture barrier capability to protect the nuts over a long period. However, shelf life of 6 to 7 months can be expected when kernels are packed in flexible materials with a water vapor transmission rate of 0.02 g/100 sq in./24 hr at 90% relative humidity and 38°C (Cavaletto and Yamamoto, 1968). Macadamia nuts that are sold in cans or jars are vacuum sealed to exclude oxygen, reducing the possibility of oxidative rancidity. Those kernels that are bulk packed are also sometimes vacuum packed in foil-laminated bags.

IV. PRESERVATION METHODS

A. Processing Technology

Processing methods are essentially the same for small and large operations, but equipment varies according to size of the operation. Initial steps are carried out at the farm level where growers harvest and husk the nuts and may partially dry them by air-drying prior to delivery to the processor. There are two general types of processors. The first type processes the nuts only to the dry raw kernel stage for sale to a manufacturer for further processing. The second type of processor receives wet in-shell nuts and processes them to roasted kernels and other finished products. Roasting is usually limited to large-scale operations, but a few small roasters are in existence also.

1. Husking

Shake-harvested or freshly fallen fruit is composed of 40 to 45% husk and 55 to 60% nut. If the fruit remains on the ground for a long period, the husk dries and turns brown. By that time, the nut may account for up to 70% of the total wieght (Cavaletto, 1981).

Husks should be removed from macadamia nuts within 24 hr of harvest to prevent quality deterioration. Several huskers have been developed to fit the needs of small, as well as large processors. Hamilton and Fukunaga (1959) described a simple rubber tire husker in which the nuts pass between a spinning tire of a vehicle and a wooden chute. A later version differed in that it had beads welded across a metal chute (Kinch et al., 1961). These huskers were particularly useful for small farmers because of low cost, but their husking efficiency was low.

A plate-type husker and cylinder-type husker were later developed (Kinch et al., 1961), but these are no longer in use. One of the problems of some of the early huskers was the severe impact they dealt to the nut. Although relatively few shells were cracked, kernel damage was sometimes sustained in the form of bruising or breakage.

In Hawaii, a screw-type husker is now widely used both in small- and large-scale operations. It consists of two parallel rollers around which are wound heavy wire spirals. In-husk nuts move along between the rotating rollers and are held down by a strip of rubber tire. Husks are torn away from the nuts in the process. This husker works well on nuts with both green and dry husks and has a more gentle husking action than most other huskers.

Between the husking and cracking operations, the nuts may be transferred several times from trucks to drying bins to holding bins, and so forth. During these transfers, the nuts can be dropped distances of 8 to 10 m, resulting in considerable impact to the nuts. Although there is no apparent damage to the shell, extensive physical damage may occur in the kernel (Cavaletto, 1979). This damage has been assessed by x-raying the in-shell nuts. Figures 10 through 12 are radiographs of in-shell nuts showing impact damage. The extent of damage sustained is dependent on moisture content of the nuts. In the Cavaletto study, when nuts were dropped into empty drying bins from a distance of 8 m, only slight damage was sustained by nuts with 25% kernel moisture, moderate damage at 20% kernel moisture, and severe damage at 10% or less kernel moisture. In the nuts with 10% kernel moisture, 83% of the kernels were damaged by the impact. These findings are significant because, in producing areas with relatively dry climates and infrequent harvesting, nuts may be harvested at this moisture level. Handling procedures that result in severe impact to these in-shell nuts could result in significant kernel damage.

2. Drying

After husking, nuts must be dried to 1.5% kernel moisture or less. During the drying process the kernels shrink slightly and most free themselves from the shell. This separation of kernel from shell is

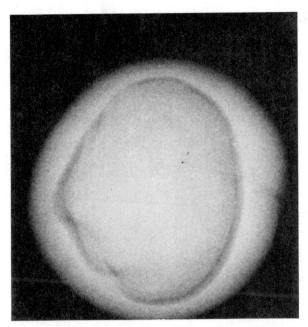

Figure 10 Radiograph of macadamia nut with slight damage resulting from impact. (*Source*: Cavaletto, 1979.)

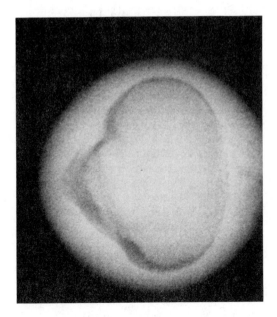

Figure 11 Radiograph of macadamia nut with moderate damage resulting from impact. (*Source:* Cavaletto, 1979.)

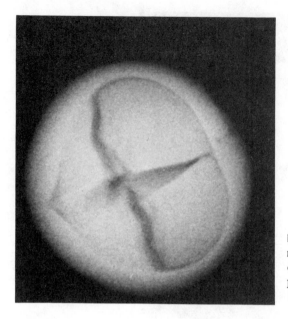

Figure 12 Radiograph of macadamia nut with severe damage resulting from impact. (*Source*: Cavaletto, 1979.)

essential if the nuts are to be cracked without damaging the kernel. Percentage of kernels sticking to the shell appears to vary with cultivar, but the problem seems to occur in most macadamias to a certain degree.

Macadamia nuts are dried first with circulating ambient air or with air heated to a maximum of 38°C. Small-scale drying may be accomplished by placing nuts no more than two or three nuts deep in trays with good air circulation for 2 to 3 weeks. A preferable method is drying the nuts in forced-draft bins for 4 to 5 days with ambient air or for 2 to 3 days at 38°C. Kernel moisture is lowered to less than 15%. In the final drying phase in which nuts are placed in forced-draft bins with heated air or left on trays in a heated room with circulating air, temperature is raised to 52°C for about 4 to 5 days. Adequate ventilation must be provided to allow moisture to exit. Final drying temperature may vary, but in no case should it exceed 60°C, and then, only in the last 1 to 2 days of drying. Actual drying time depends on initial moisture content of the nuts, dryer design and efficiency, and air velocity.

After completion of drying, kernel moisture should be 1.5% or less, at which point the nuts are ready for cracking. Alternatively, nuts may be dried to about 3.5 to 5% kernel moisture, cracked, and kernels dried at about 52°C to a final moisture content of 1.5% or less. An advantage of this system is a reduction in kernel damage during cracking and a reduction in the amount of energy required for drying.

Kernels with a moisture content of 1.5% have a water activity (a_w) of about 0.30 (Beuchat, 1978). Therefore, dry kernels must be protected from moisture because exposure to relative humidity greater than 30% will result in moisture gain.

When cracking capacity is insufficient to keep up with drying, it may become necessary to store nuts in-shell for a period of time. This may be done with no harmful effects on kernel quality provided that the nuts have been thoroughly dried and are kept dry. Cavaletto et al. (1968) showed that nuts dried to 1.2% kernel moisture and stored in dry air could be held for 12 months with no apparent effect on shelf life of the kernels following roasting. However, roasted kernels prepared from nuts stored in-shell at 3.8% kernel moisture for 6 months or longer had slightly reduced flavor quality and poorer shelf life.

3. Cracking

Various types of crackers have been devised to crack the nuts while minimizing kernel damage. Most are based on the compression principle; nuts are compressed to a constant deformation between two rollers or between a roller and a fixed plate. Nearly all compression-type crackers require that the nuts be sized into groups before cracking. Each group of nuts is then forced through a fixed-size opening. In this this manner, the magnitude of deformation is controlled within a narrow range (Liang, 1980). However, the nuts are not truly spherical, so that if they enter the cracking space in a different orientation from the one in which they were sized, deformation control is not exact. Liang (1980) has devised an integrated sizing and cracking device that permits little change in nut orientation between the sizing and cracking operations, thus achieving better control of deformation.

Coward et al. (1974) describe a different type of cracker which makes a cut around the minor axis of the nut then wedges the two halves apart. The Shaw Cracker (Shaw, 1972) has a fixed plate with a cutting blade and a rotatable wheel adjacent to the plate. The wheel has radially arranged cutting blades that are cooperable with the plate blade. Nuts are cracked between the plate blade and one of the blades of the wheel.

4. Shell Separation and Sorting

Shell separation is usually achieved by means such as screening, air separation, hand separation, and electronic color sorting or a combination of these. Drying may follow this procedure to reduce kernel moisture to 1.5% or less.

An entirely different method is brine separation, based on specific gravity of the nuts (Liang, 1977). After cracking, the nuts flow into a salt brine which has a specific gravity calculated to achieve the desired separation. If nuts have been dried to 1.5% kernel moisture, usable kernels will float in a salt brine with specific gravity of 1.025. Shells and unusable kernels sink and are carried off for discarding. A spray rinse is customarily applied to the usable kernels to remove the salt, and the kernels are then dried again.

5. Roasting

After the kernels have been dried to 1.5% or less moisture, they are ready for roasting. One of two roasting processes is used, oil roasting or dry roasting. Either batch-type or continous roasters are used for oil roasting. The oil is heated to 132°C and the kernels are heated in it for 10 to 15 min until a golden brown color has developed. Actual roasting time depends on kernel quality, kernel moisture content, and efficiency of the roaster. However, the process is essentially the same whether on a small or large scale. Following roasting, the excess oil is removed by centrifuging (for batch roasting) or draining (for continous roasting). The roasting oil used in batch operations is usually refined coconut oil with a melting point (mp) of 24.5°C. That used in the continuous roaster is a partially hydrogenated coconut oil with a mp of 43.5°C.

After centrifugation, the kernels are coated with a small amount of coconut oil (mp 43.5°C) as an adhesive and 1.5% salt is added. For the continous roasted kernels, the oil that remains after draining acts as the adhesive and salt is added. If unsalted nuts are desired, this step is omitted.

Dry roasting can also be done on both small and large scale. Types of roasting equipment are: (a) heated rotating drum; (b) perforated rotating drum with hot air flow; and (c) continous mesh belt moving through a heated chamber. Time and temperatures for roasting vary considerably with roaster design and load. In one process, kernels are roasted and then salt is applied. In another process, gum arabic, starch, and salt are applied prior to roasting.

Some defects in macadamia nuts do not become apparent until the kernels have been roasted. Usually they are seen as brown spots or general overbrowning. These discolored kernels must be segregated from premium-grade kernels, but may be suitable for lower grades. Sorting may be done manually or by a combination of manual and electronic color sorting. The electronic color sorter examines each kernel and rejects those that do not meet predetermined color limits. Because this kind of sorting is not perfect, hand inspection must still follow.

6. Packaging

The bulk of the macadamia nuts for the retail trade are packed under vacuum in cans or glass jars. Some are packaged in laminated foil packs either under vacuum or with a nitrogen flush to reduce oxygen. Packs in flexible films such as cellophane and polyethylene are generally not satisfactory, particularly in humid climates, due to poor moisture barrier capability of the packaging material (Cavaletto and Yamamoto, 1968).

B. Products and Uses

The primary product of the industry is roasted, salted kernels. Roasted pieces of lower grade are also sold for use in bakery products, ice cream, and candies. A significant portion of the crop is sold as chocolate-coated roasted kernels. Countless other products that incorporate macadamia nuts are being marketed, including macadamia nut liqueur as well as jams and jellies incorporating macadamia nuts. A unique product is a macadamia nut soup that utilizes the fines (finely ground kernels). Perhaps the most unique use reported for macadamia nuts is in treatment of a sexual phobia (Tarler-Benlolo and Love, 1977).

Researchers in California have investigated the potential for use of macadamia oil as a cosmetic oil (Saleeb, 1975). It is described as a "vanishing oil," one that is rapidly absorbed by the skin. Other uses for the oil, such as cooking oil and as an ingredient for margarine, have been proposed (Saleeb, 1976). However, the current cost of macadamia nuts to produce oil for such purposes is so high as to preclude oil production. Cull nuts are much lower in costs but lower in oil content available in insufficient quantities for significant oil production at the present time.

C. Byproducts

Macadamia husks are generally returned to the field or used for compost material. Shells are sometimes used by flower growers for growing media, but their best use is as fuel. Several processors utilize shells to fuel boilers providing steam for their processing plants. No other byproducts of commercial significance have been developed.

D. Product Stability and Spoilage

Moisture is the single most important factor affecting the stability of macadamia nuts, both processed and unprocessed. Product stability is maximized when the nuts are shake-harvested or harvested soon after falling, dried immediately to 1.5% kernel moisture or less, and kept at that low moisture level. Since the a_w of macadamia kernels at 1.5% moisture is 0.30, exposure to a relative humidity above 30% results in moisture gain. At 0.60 a_w, equilibrium moisture content is 3% (Beuchat, 1978), meaning that kernels exposed to 60% relative humidity, in time, will equilibrate at 3% kernel moisture. Thus, adequate moisture protection must be provided. The effects of high kernel moisture on kernel stability have been discussed earlier.

Oxygen also plays a role in product stability. Oxidative rancidity can be reduced or prevented by vacuum packaging or by the addition of antioxidants to the final product. Cavaletto and Yamamoto (1970) showed that vacuum-packed kernels were more stable than those packed without vacuum. However, those kernels coated with 76 ppm of antioxidant (butylated hydroxyanisole and butylated hydroxytoluene combination), even with no vacuum, had greater stability than the untreated vacuum-packed kernels. However, at the present time, these antioxidants are not being used.

Although most macadamia production is in *M. integrifolia*, small amounts of *M. tetraphylla* have made an entry into the market in recent years. This development has prompted renewed interest in the comparative stability of *M. tetraphylla* versus *M. integrifolia*. There have not been extensive studies in this area, but Leverington (1962) compared kernels of the two species roasted under identical conditions and found no difference in stability. The shorter shelf life of *M. tetraphylla* found in his earlier studies was attributed to the lower cooking temperature for *M. tetraphylla*. Winterton (1966) found the storage life of *M. tetraphylla* kernels roasted in oil at 127°C for 25 min was almost double that of the same kernels dry roasted at 135°C for 20 min. Early development of rancidity in the dry-roasted kernels was attributed to incomplete enzyme destruction during processing. Using the active oxygen method (AOM) for determining stability, Winterton (1966) found a long heating period, 280 hr, was required for development of a distinct rancid smell in oil from *M. tetraphylla*, suggesting the presence of natural antioxidants.

Insect infestation can be a problem in stored nuts and kernels or in chocolate-coated nuts. Large infestations can also build up in shells that are stored for use later as fuel. The most common insect pest is *Ephestia cautella*, also known as the almond moth. Several beetles, among them the merchant grain beetle [*Oryzaephilus mercatur* (Fauvel)] and the dried fruit beetle [*Carpophilus hemipterus* (Linnaeus)] are also known to infest macadamia nuts. Proper sanitation of storage and processing facilities is essential to avoid infestation.

E. Quality Control Methods

1. Raw Material Sampling

Upon receipt at the processing plant, nuts are sampled to determine moisture content and quality of the lot. Commonly, the grower is paid on these bases. Moisture content may be determined by any one of several rapid moisture-testing methods. This information is also important in determining the drying schedule.

Because kernel oil content is one of the most important quality considerations, it has traditionally been used as a basis for determining grades. Moltzau and Ripperton (1939) showed a high correlation between specific gravity and kernel oil content. Dry kernels with a specific gravity of 1.000 or less contain 72% or more oil. These are considered grade no. 1 provided they are free of other defects. Lower grades may also be segregated according to specific gravity. The grading is easily accomplished by placing the sample of dry kernels in tap water. Those that float are grade no. 1. Those that sink may be separated into lower grades by floating in salt brine with a pre-specified specific gravity. The sample is also examined for defects that may include insect damage, rodent damage, mold or yeast growth, discolorations, germinating kernels, and undersized and twin nuts.

Kernel yield from dry in-shell nuts is also important to the processor. The difference between 34 and 44% yield is very large because it is kernel and not shell that the processor will eventually market. Value of the lot is determined slightly differently by each processor, but, basically, it should reflect the amount of sound dry kernels obtained from a given weight of in-shell nuts.

2. Moisture Control

Because the relationship between moisture content and drying temperature is so critical and because moisture content of incoming nuts is so variable, it is necessary to monitor moisture content. Various types of radiant heat and dielectric-type moisture testers are used. These instruments provide a rapid means for determining moisture content, but should be calibrated against a method using a vacuum oven.

3. Cooking Oil Quality

Color, viscosity, and free fatty acid levels are used as indexes of cooking oil quality.

4. Microbiological Quality

Routine testing should be conducted to determine presence of coliforms. Total plate counts should also be run.

5. Color Control

No standards are used to control the degree of roasted color except for the subjective standard used by the person in charge of the roasting operation. However, electronic color sorters are normally used together with visual inspection to sort out overroasted or discolored kernels.

6. Packaging

Factors requiring monitoring are the adequacy of the original seal, maintenance of adequate vacuum in the container, and net weight.

7. Shelf Life

Samples of various processed products from selected lots are retained for extended periods of time for determination of shelf life. Storage is normally at ambient temperature, but sometimes under accelerated storage at 38°C. Informal sensory testing is the most common method for evaluation. At the present time, processors are not using chemical tests.

REFERENCES

Beuchat, L. R. (1978). Relationship of water activity to moisture content in nuts. J. Food Sci. 43:754-755, 758.

Beuchat, L. R., and Worthington, R. E. (1978). Fatty acid composition of tree nut oils. J. Fd. Tech. 13:355-358.

Cavaletto, C. G. (1979). Assessment of in-shell damage to macadamia kernels. Proc. 19th Ann. Mtg. Hawaii Macadamia Producers Assoc., pp. 65-80.

Cavaletto, C. G. (1980). Macadamia nuts. In Tropical and Subtropical Fruits: Composition, Nutrition Values, Properties, and Uses (S. Nagy and P. E. Shaw, eds.). Westport Conn., Avi Publishing Co., pp. 542-561.

Cavaletto, C. G. (1981). Unpublished data.

Cavaletto, C. G., and Yamamoto, H. Y. (1968). Criteria for selection of packaging materials for roasted macadamia kernels. Food Technol. 22(1):97-99.

Cavaletto, C. G., and Yamamoto, H. Y. (1970). Factors affecting macadamia nut stability. 3. Effects of roasting oil quality and antioxidants. J. Food Sci. 36(1):81-83.

Cavaletto, C. G., Ross, E., and Yamamoto, H. Y. (1968). In-shell storage effects on quality of processed macadamia nuts. Food Technol. 22(4):172-174.

Cavaletto, C., Dela Cruz, A., Ross, E., and Yamamoto, H. Y. (1966). Factors affecting macadamia nut stability. I. Raw kernels. Food Technol. 20(8):108-111.

Chu, A. C., King, G. S., and Sherman, G. D. (1953). Macadamia storage studies. Hawaii Agric. Exp. Stn. Prog. Notes, pp. 90.

Coward, L. D. G., Beaumont, J. H., and Manser, P. J. (1974). The decortication of some tropical nuts. Proceedings of IV International Cong. of Food Sci. and Technol., Valencia, Spain, Instituto Nacional de Ciencia y Technologia de Alimentos, Consejo Superior de Invastigaciones Cientificas. V:407-411.

Crain, W. O., Jr., and Tang, C. S. (1975). Volatile components of roasted macadamia nuts. J. Food Sci. 40:207-208.

Dela Cruz, A., Cavaletto, C., Ross, E., and Yamamoto, H. Y. (1966). Factors affecting macadamia nut stability. II. Roasted kernels. Food Technol. 20(9):123-124.

Francis, W. D. (1928). The anatomy of the Australian bush nut (*Macadamia ternifolia*). *Proc. Roy. Soc. Queensland* 39:43-53.

Hamilton, R. A. (1981). New macadamia cultivars. *Proc. 21st Ann. Mtg. Hawaii Macadamia Producers Assoc.* (in press).

Hamilton, R. A., and Fukunaga, E. T. (1959). Growing macadamia nuts in Hawaii. *Hawaii Agric. Exp. Stn. Bull. 121.*

Hamilton, R. A., and Ito, P. J. (1976). Development of macadamia nut cultivars in Hawaii. *Calif. Macadamia Soc. Yrbk.* 22:94-100.

Hamilton, R. A., and Ito, P. J. (1980). Macadamia nut prospects in New Zealand. *Proc. 20th Ann. Mtg. Hawaii Macadamia Producers Assoc.*, pp. 22-32.

Hamilton, R. A., and Young, R. L. (1966). Transfer of bitterness in *Macadamia integrifolia* by grafting. *Calif. Macadamia Soc. Yrbk.* 12:66-69.

Hansen, G. P., and Gough, M. C. (1977). Moisture characteristics of macadamia nuts in relation to storage. *J. Sci. Fd. Agric.* 28:990-995.

Hartung, M. E., and Storey, W. B. (1939). The development of the fruit of *Macadamia ternifolia*. *J. Agric. Res.* 59(6):397-406.

Hawaii Agricultural Reporting Service (1981). *Statistics of Hawaiian Agriculture*, Honolulu, Hawaii, p. 34.

Higaki, T., and Dedolph, R. R. (1963). The storage of macadamia nuts (*Macadamia integrifolia*, Maiden and Betche). *Proc. Am. Soc. Hort. Sci.* 83:359-369.

James, L. E. (1978). The variety situation in California to 1978. *Calif. Macadamia Soc. Yrbk.* 24:49-52.

Jones, W. W., and Shaw, L. (1943). The process of oil formation and accumulation in the macadamia. *Plant Physiol.* 18(1):1-7.

Kawano, Y., Matsumoto, H., and Hamilton, R. A. (1961). Plant products of economic potential in Hawaii. II. Tannins. *Hawaii Agric. Exp. Sta. Prog. Rep.* 130:3,13.

Kinch, D. M., Wang, J. K., and Strohman, R. E. (1961). Equipment for husking macadamia nuts. *Hawaii Agric. Exp. Stn. Bull. 126.*

Kinlin, T. E., Muralidhara, R., Pittet, A. O., Sanderson, A., and Walradt, J. P. (1972). Volatile components of roasted filberts. *J. Agr. Food Chem.* 20:1021-1028.

Lambertsen, G., Myklestad, H., and Braekkan, O. R. (1962). Tocopherol in nuts. *J. Sci. Food Agric.* 13:617-620.

Leverington, R. E. (1962). Evaluation of methods of roasting macadamia nut. *Queensland J. Agric. Sci.* 19(1):131-132.

Liang, T. (1977). A new processing system for maximizing macadamia nut lernel recovery. *Trans. ASAE* 20(3):438-443.

Liang, T. (1980). Designing a constant deformation macadamia nut cracker. *Trans. ASAE* 23(5):1093-1096.

Liang, T., and Lopez-Madrazo, L. (1973). Systems approach to the designing of suspended net harvesting systems for macadamia nuts. *Trans. ASAE 16* (6):1064-1067, 1071.

McConachie, I. (1980). The macadamia story. *Calif. Macadamia Soc. Yrbk.* 26:41-75.

Moltzau, R. H., and Ripperton, J. C. (1939). Processing of the macadamia. *Hawaii Agric. Exp. Stn. Bull. 83.*

Monroe, G. E., Liang, T., and Cavaletto, C. G. (1972). Quality and yield of tree-harvested macadamia nuts. *U.S. Dept. of Agric. ARS. 42-196.* Beltsville, Md., U.S. Department of Agriculture.

Prichavudhi, K., and Yamamoto, H. Y. (1965). Effect of drying temperature on chemical composition and quality of macadamia nuts. *Food Technol.* 19(5):129-132.

Ripperton, J. C., Moltzau, R. H., and Edwards, D. W. (1938). Methods of evaluating the macadamia nut for commercial use and the variation occurring among seedling plantings in Hawaii. *Hawaii Agric. Exp. Stn. Bull. 79.*

Saleeb, W. F. (1975). Macadamia by-products research continues. *Calif. Macadamia Soc. Yrbk.* 21:27-28.

Saleeb, W. F. (1976). Macadamia nut and its by-products. *Calif. Macadamia Soc. Yrbk.* 22:82-84.

Saleeb, W., Yermanos, D. M., and Storey, W. B. (1975). Macadamia shell as a profit by-product. *Calif. Macadamia Soc. Yrbk.* 21:73.

Saleeb, W. F., Yermanos, D. M., Huszar, C. K., Storey, W. B., and Labanauskas, C. K. (1973). The oil and protein in nuts of *Macadamia tetraphylla* L. Johnson, *Macadamia integrifolia* Maiden and Betche, and their F_1 hybrids. *J. Am. Soc. Hort. Sci.* 98(5):453-456.

Shaw, P. W. (1972). Nut cracking apparatus. U.S. Patent No. 3662799.

Storey, W. B. (1956). The work of many people. *Calif. Macadamia Soc. Yrbk.* 2:9-12.

Storey, W. B. (1969). Macadamia. In *Handbook of North American Nut Trees* (R. A. Jaynes, ed.). Knoxville, Tenn., North American Nut Growers Assoc., pp. 321-325.

Strauss, D. von. (1970). Über die mikroskopie fremder früchte. II. Mitteilung macadamia integrifolia-eine Nuss aus Hawaii. *Deutsche Lebensmittel-Rundschau* 66(7):225-226.

Stumpf, P. K. (1980). Biosynthesis of saturated and unsaturated fatty acids. In *The Biochemistry of Plants. A Comprehensive Treatise, Vol. 4. Lipids: Structure and Function* (P. K. Stumpf, and E. E. Conn, eds.) New York, Academic Press.

Tarler-Benlolo, L., and Love, W. A., Jr. (1977). A sexual phobia treated with macadamia nuts. *J. Behav. Ther. Exp. Psychiatry.* 8(1):113-114.

Vickery, J. R. (1971). The fatty acid composition of the seed oil of the Proteaceae: A chemotaxonomic study. *Phytochemistry* 10:123-130.

Walradt, J. P., Pittet, A. O., Kinlin, T. E., Muralidhara, R., and Sanderson, A. (1971). Volatile components of roasted peanuts. *J. Agr. Food Chem.* 19:972-979.

Wang, P.-S., and Odell, G. V. (1972). Characterization of some volatile constituents of roasted pecans. *J. Agr. Food Chem.* 20:206-210.

Wang, Y-Y. D. (1972). Factors affecting the tocopherol content in macadamia kernels. Unpublished M.S. thesis, Honolulu, University of Hawaii.

Wenkam, N. S., and Miller, C. D. (1965). Composition of Hawaii fruits. *Hawaii Agric. Exp. Stn. Bull. 135.*

Winterton, D. (1962). Use of thiobarbituric acid number as a measure of the degree of oxidation of roasted macadamia nuts. *Queensl. J. Agric. Sci.* 19:291-294.

Winterton, D. (1966). Macadamia nut roasting studies. *Food Tech. Aust.* 19(2):74-77.

Winterton, D. (1968). The macadamia nut industry: problems and prospects. *Food Tech. Aust.* 20:119-121.

Young, R. L., and Hamilton, R. A. (1966). A bitter principle in macadamia nuts. *Proc. Hawaii Macadamia Producers Assoc.,* pp. 27-30.

10

Mango

Allan E. Stafford Agricultural Research Service, U.S. Department of
Agriculture, Albany, California

I. INTRODUCTION

A. Botanical Description and Varieties

The mango is a member of the family Anacardiaceae which includes a large number of genera, mostly trees or shrubs. The cashew nut (*Anacardeum occidentale*) and the pistachio nut (*Pistacia vera*) are well-known members of this family. The cultivated mangos belong to the single species *Mangifera indica* L. The genus *Mangifera* L., contains 41 valid species (Mukherjee, 1976) that are widely distributed throughout tropical and subtropical areas of the world. The genus can be separated into two sections containing 34 species and 7 species based on the characteristics of the flower disc. Further separation of the species within these two sections has been made on the basis of leaf, inflorescence, and floral characters (Mukherjee, 1967).

The mango tree is evergreen and varies widely from dwarf size to trees having a spread of 38.1 m and a trunk of 7.6 m in circumference. The mango has a long taproot that usually continues to grow until it reaches the water table. After this, surface roots develop and form a dense network just below the surface. The crown of the tree is usually oval or broad and round-topped. The leaves are lanceolate, commonly to 30.5 cm in length, ridged, deep green, almost glossy, borne upon slender petioles, 2.5 to 10 cm long (Popenoe, 1939).

Inflorescence or flowering occurs in large panicles at the ends of the branchlets. The flowers are small and pinkish white in color. Flowering can occur two to three times a year and sometimes in only part of the tree. The mango is polygamous, producing both male and hermaphrodite flowers on the same panicle, with the male flowers in the majority.

The fruit varies widely in size, shape, flavor, seed size, fiber, and composition. The shape can be oval to round. The skin is smooth and usually yellow, but can have a reddish blush; others are green even when ripe. Mango flesh is yellow to orange and can vary in fiber content from fiber-free in the best cultivated varieties to very fibrous in inferior seedling varieties.

Mangos produce both monoembryonic and polyembryonic seeds. Seedlings grown from polyembryonic seeds produce progenies true to their type in most respects. This is not true of seedlings grown from monoembryonic seeds. Most varieties in India are monoembryonic. The few varieties in India that are polyembryonic occur in the humid tropical region of the west coast. Whether this character is genetic or due to environmental conditions has not yet been established (Mukherjee, 1972).

The four main groups of mango varieties are the Indian, Floridian, Indonesian, and Philippine (Mukherjee, 1976). There are hundreds of mango varieties grown in different areas of the world, with India, because of the monoembryonic nature of its seed and its long history of propagation and selection of the mango, having the largest number.

Table 1 Mango Varieties of Selected Countries

Country	Varieties
Australia	Kensington
Brazil	Bourbon, Carlota, Extrema, Haden, Non-Plus-Ultra
Cuba	Bizcochuelo, Haden, Macho
Egypt	Mabroka
India	Alphonso, Bombay Green, Bangalora, Banganpalli, Dashehari, Dushri, Fazli, Gulabi Khas, Him Sagar, Kesar, Langra, Malkurad, Mulgoa, Neelum, Pairi, Rumani, Safeda Lucknow, Samar Bahist Chausa, Swarnarekha, Zardaloo
Indonesia	Aroomanis, Gadoong, Golek, Wangi
Israel	Haden, Maya, Mabroka, Nimrod, Sarafend
Haiti	Madame Francis
Mexico	Ataulfo, Diplomatico, Esmeralda, Haden, Irwin, Keitt, Kent, Manila, Manzana, Naranja, Oro, Pina Canario, Sensation, Tommy Atkin
Philippines	Carabao, Pico
Pakistan	Sindhri and several Indian varieties
Puerto Rico	Colombo, Kidney, Haden, Mangotino, Mayaguezano
United States	Gouveia, Haden, Irwin, Keitt, Kent, Momi K, Palmer, Pope, Sensation, Smith, Tommy Atkin

Sources: Malo (1970), Singh (1972), Wiltbank (1977), Lakshminarayana (1980), and Valmayor (1972).

Most varieties in other parts of the world are polyembryonic. The names of mango varieties grown in a sample of the more important producing countries are shown in Table 1. A brief description of four important mango varieties is as follows.

Alphonso (India): The fruit is medium, ovate oblique; base obliquely flattened, stalk inserted squarely; ventral shoulder broader and higher than dorsal; beak absent or just a point; apex rounded; skin medium thick, yellow; flavor delightful; taste very sweet; juice moderate to abundant (Singh, 1967).

Duschri (India): The fruit is small to medium, oblong to oblong oblique; base rounded to obliquely rounded; stalk inserted squarely; shoulders equal; beak absent; apex rounded; skin medium thick, smooth yellow; flesh firm, fiberless, yellow; flavor pleasant; taste sweet; juice scanty to moderately abundant (Singh, 1967).

Carabao (Philippines): The fruit is medium to large, shape oblong with blunt apex and rounded base, slightly flattened but with full cheeks; beak rather indistinct and variable, sometimes coinciding with the apex; skin smooth, yellow, and thin; flesh yellow, very tender, and melting; flavor very delicate, aromatic, and spicy; fiber medium coarse but short and confined almost entirely to the edge of the seed (Valmayor, 1972).

Haden (United States): The fruit is large or very large, oval to heart-shaped and plump, base rounded with the ventral shoulder larger and slightly higher than dorsal; apex broadly rounded; no beak; nak small to inconspicuous and rounded about 2.5 cm above apex; slightly fibrous (sometimes objectionably so); flavor rich and sweet with a trace of turpentine; yellowish-orange flesh which is firm and quite juicy; skin butter yellow with a crimson to dark-red blush spreading over most of the surface, and numerous yellow dots (Sturrock, 1951).

B. Origin and Distribution

Based on the presence of wild forms of *M. indica* and related species in the area, the consensus of researchers on the subject is that the mango (*M. indica* L.) originated in or near the Assam-Burma region (Mukherjee, 1972; Singh, 1960). The earliest recorded history of mango cultivation goes back 4000 years in India. Approximately 400 to 600 years ago traders, missionaries, and explorers began spreading the mango to the rest of the world. The widespread success of their efforts is shown in Table 2 which lists the countries with significant mango production.

C. Economic and Nutritional Significance

The main economic importance of mangos is shown in Table 2. As can be seen, almost all the production is located in developing countries. The mangos grown in these countries are mainly consumed locally with only a small percentage being exported. The mango, therefore, serves an important role in the diet of these people as a source of calories, vitamins, and minerals. Fruit trees in tropical areas where polyembryonic varieties are located can be grown from readily available seeds at low or no cost and still produce quality fruit. Also, the mango does not require intensive cultural practices to produce fruit for home or local comsumption, and the yield per acre in terms of calories of food value is higher in this fruit than in many grain crops.

II. HORTICULTURAL ASPECTS

A. Cultivation Practices

1. Climatological and Soil Requirements

The mango can be grown in a wide range of temperatures and rainfall levels. However, to produce acceptable yields of fruit, the temperature

Table 2 Countries with Significant[a] Mango Production

Countries	1000 Tonne production[b]	Countries	1000 Tonne production[b]
Africa		N.C. America	
Benin	12 F[c]	Panama	26 F
Chad	29 F	Saint Lucia	43 F
Egypt	90 F	South America	
Ivory Coast	13 F	Brazil	680 F
Madagascar	143 F	Columbia	18 F
Malawi	26 F	Ecuador	26 F
Mozambique	30 F	Paraguay	30 F
Senegal	33 F	Peru	72 F
South Africa	13	Venezuela	118 F
Sudan	61 F	Asia	
Tanzania	172 F	Bangladesh	214
Zaire		China	240 F
N.C. America		India	9300 F
Cuba	54 F	Indonesia	300 F
Dominican Republic	168 F	Malaysia	11 F
Haiti	285 F	Pakistan	600 F
Honduras	13 F	Philippines	338 F
Mexico	570 F	Sri Lanka	57 F

[a]10,000 tonnes or more.
[b]1979.
[c]FAO estimate.
Source: Food and Agriculture Organization, 1979.

and rainfall must be within well-defined levels during certain critical
growth periods of the tree. Mango trees can grow up to 1200 m above
sea level, but they produce good crops of fruit only up to 600 m
(Cheema et al., 1954). Young trees, new growth, and blossoms are
severely damaged or destroyed when temperatures approach 0°C.
Temperatures above 42°C inhibit growth of bearing trees and can
desiccate and damage very young trees. An average mean temperature
of 26 to 28°C is regarded as an optimum temperature range.
     Optimal rainfall levels are less defined. Annual rainfall levels as
low as 20 to 25 cm with irrigation and up to 190 to 205 cm or higher
with good drainage are acceptable (K. Singh, 1967). The important aspect of rainfall is its timing; rainfall during flowering interferes with
pollination and causes mildew and other fungus diseases, and during
ripening it can cause severe fruit spoilage problems. Mangos are
grown on a wide variety of soils, but best growth and fruiting are
obtained on fertile, deep, and well-drained soils. The soil pH should
fall between 6 and 8 (Singh et al., 1963).

2. Planting Characteristics

Because mango trees have a long lifetime, site and plant material selection mean the difference between a profitable commercial orchard and a marginal one. Land tillage, leveling, proper spacing, and digging of planting holes also must be carefully planned. The site selected should be an area where mangos have been successfully grown with good soil and climatological conditions. In some areas the planting of fast-growing trees to act as a wind break is recommended before the orchard is actually planted. The soil should be first ploughed and harrowed. The land is then leveled and sloped for irrigation if needed. Proper drainage should be provided if necessary since young trees are susceptible to water stagnation.

Great care must be taken in orchard layout since mistakes in spacing cannot be corrected later without serious loss of future production. Since the mango is essentially an external bearer, close planting, especially if the trees touch, can cause loss of yield and a microclimate which is conducive to disease (Hobson, 1969). Trees on poor soil should be spaced closer together than those on rich, deep soil. Removal of trees in an orchard that is crowded will rarely result in proper spacing because of the large size of mature trees. The actual spacing of the trees will also depend on the plant material, rainfall or available irrigation, and layout system. Popular layout systems are square, hexagonal, quincunx, or diagonal, and contour. In India, seedling trees are spaced further apart (12 to 18 m) than are grafted trees (9 to 12 m) in the square system (K. Singh, 1967). Local experience and knowledge of plant material used and soil conditions are critical in spacing of trees. Mangos are best planted when the plant is not in active growth and the weather is moderate. The plants are placed in previously opened pits, the depth of which is determined by soil conditions. The plants are then watered to allow the soil to settle in and eliminate air pockets.

Young plants must be protected during early growth from temperature extremes, and if necessary shelters should be erected that allow for sunlight and air but protect the plants from drying out and from cold extremes. As with most fruit trees, young mango trees during their first 4 to 5 years should be discouraged from producing fruit so that the energy of the plant is directed to vegetative growth; this is accomplished by deblossoming. Pruning is generally unnecessary with mangos except for the removal of dead or diseased limbs.

3. Irrigation

There are many factors which govern the need for irrigation, such as age of trees, soil conditions, weather, and yearly growth cycle. The irrigation of mangos is generally divided first into two classes: (a) Nonbearing young trees 0 to 5 years old and (b) mature or bearing trees. The purpose of irrigating young trees is only to promote rapid and vigorous vegetative growth. The timing of the irrigation varies from every third day to once every 2 weeks during the first year. After the first year irrigation should be given at 7- to 21-day intervals. The irrigation need not be heavy as the root system will not be well developed. The deciding factor for timing of irrigation will be soil and climatic conditions. There is general agreement that irrigation of bearing mango trees should be withheld during fruit bud differentation and blossoming. Irrigation should be resumed after fruit set and during ripening.

4. Fertilization

The amount and types of fertilizer required by a mango tree will depend on two main factors, the natural fertility of the soil and the age of the tree. The types of nutrients required by mango trees have been divided by Singh (1960) into two categories, macro- and micronutrients. The first category includes nitrogen, phosphorus, potassium, calcium, magnesium, and sulfur, and the second category copper, zinc, manganese, boron, iron, and molybdenum. Because of its long lifetime, one or more of these elements will likely become exhausted and require replenishment if the tree is to remain fruitful and continue good vegetative growth.

The lifetime of the mango can be divided into four growth stages with respect to fertilizer needs: (a) nursery, (b) transplant, (c) nonbearing, and (d) bearing. The nursery stage begins with the planting of the seed, includes germination, and continues until the plant is transplanted, as is the case of polyembryonic varieties or the budded or grafted plant in the monoembryonic varieties. During this stage regular light doses of inorganic fertilizers, such as ammonium sulfate, are used to promote vegetative growth. In the remaining three stages there are considerable differences of opinion as to the amount of fertilizer necessary due to the many differences in soil composition in the various growing areas of the world.

In southern Florida the soil is shallow and generally infertile; there fertilization is necessary for commercial fruit production. It is generally believed that 5.5 to 6.6 kg of both nitrogen and potash per tree per year is sufficient for productive trees (Malo, 1972). Magnesium and calcium along with other micronutrients are also applied as necessary when the trees show signs of deficiency.

In India, the results of field studies (Roy et al., 1951; Mallik and De, 1952) recommend a fertilizer schedule per tree for bearing trees of 90 kg of farmyard manure, 1.8 kg of castor cake, 4.5 kg of bone meal, 0.9 kg ammonium sulfate, and 13.6 kg of wood ash. This is usually applied in two doses, one in June and the rest in October, with the ammonium sulfate doubled in heavy bearing years. The fertilizer is usually applied in shallow trenches around the trees but not beyond the tips of the branches.

The use of leguminous cover crops to enrich the nitrogen in the soil is used in some countries (Popenoe, 1939). They are usually grown in the rainy season then ploughed under so as to also increase the organic composition of the soil.

5. Insect Pests and Diseases

There are many insect pests and diseases which cause varying degrees of crop and tree damage to mangos. The extent of damage that occurs in any one year will vary with weather conditions and the preventative and control procedures used, mainly spraying and dusting. A few of the more important insect pests and diseases found in many mango-growing areas are considered next.

The mango hopper is one of the most serious insect pests in India and is found in other countries of Asia. It is a small, wedge-shaped insect that lays its egg inside the bud tissue when the blossoms appear. The nymphs and adults suck sap from the flowers and young fruit and cause premature dropping (Singh et al., 1963). The mango weevil is seen in several countries but is particularly serious for Hawaii because its presence prevents shipments of fresh fruit to the large mainland markets where it could infest other stone fruits. The mango weevil lays its eggs under the skin of the newly set fruit. When the eggs hatch, the grub moves to the stone where it continues to feed and develop. Fruit flies attack ripe fruit in many mango-growing countries. The fly lays its eggs under the skin and after a few days the eggs hatch and the larvae eat the pulp. The mango stem borer is a large, grayish-brown beetle. The adult beetle lays eggs in the cracks of the bark of trees. The hatched grubs bore into the bark and feed on the live inner tissue.

Of the diseases that affect mangos, anthracnose is the most important and widespread. It is a fungus disease that attacks flowers, flower stalks, leaves, and fruit. In fruit its appearance is in the form of black spots and the fruit is smaller in size. Rains can cause serious spread and increased severity of the disease. Powdery mildew is another common fungus disease and is found in a number of countries. Its presence is indicated by a white powdery appearance on the surface of leaves, flowers, stalks, and young fruit. Its occurrence is increased by moist weather conditions, and it can cause loss of leaves, flowers, and fruit.

B. Propagation

The mango is propagated from seed and vegetatively. In countries such as Brazil and Sri Lanka where polyembryonic varieties are found, most mango trees are grown from seed (Wiltbank, 1977; Kotalawala, 1972). Vegetative propagation of polyembryonic varieties is being used for new large commercial planting and to improve seedling trees. The main reasons for using vegetative propagation are earlier bearing of trees (5 years instead of 10), greater uniformity, and smaller and more manageable size trees. Monoembryonic varieties are vegetatively propagated to ensure true-to-type plants which are necessary for commercial orchards.

Polyembryonic seeds produce three to eight plants although more are possible. All but one of the seedlings are produced from nucellus cells and are more vigorous than the one produced from a fertilized egg cell which is normally discarded. In South Africa when the most prominent seedling reaches 20 cm in height, the weaker ones are removed. Seeds should be planted within 1 month of harvest as the seeds lose their viability during storage (Mallik, 1976).

Careful removal of the husk by cutting along the suture before planting is recommended by Lynch and Nelson (1951), although Rao (1967) does not recommend husk removal as it reduces the percentage of seed germination. Seeds should be planted flat in pots or seedbeds at a depth of 2 cm (Mallik, 1976). Inarching is one of the oldest methods of vegetative propagation of mangos and is the only commercially used method in India (Hayes, 1966). Budding is the preferred method in many other countries since it is cheaper, easier, and quicker than other grafting methods.

C. Harvest and Storage

The proper time to harvest mangos for the fresh market is reached when the fruit is physiologically mature. It takes 4 to 5 months for fruit to reach this stage after flowering, and 90 to 115 days from fruit set depending on climate and variety. Several methods have been used to determine this stage of maturity. Fruit characters such as weight, size, shape, color, flesh color, firmness, and specific gravity have been used. It is also believed that when a few fruit drop to the ground the rest of the fruit is ready for harvest. In the final judgment, grower experience and the use of one or more of the fruit characters of maturity will best determine the proper time of harvest. All of the fruit is usually harvested from the tree at one time for economic reasons but, because the mango tree blooms over a period of time, up to a month, the harvested fruit will be of varying maturity. Harkness and Cobin (1951) recommend grading the harvested fruit by specific gravity and discarding those fruits with specific gravities less than 1.01 to 1.015 to eliminate immature fruit. Immature fruit will not ripen properly but will result in ripened fruit with poor flavor, color, and aroma. The use of acetylene (Mukherjee, 1972) or ethylene (Barmore, 1974) to degreen immature fruit should be avoided; while the color will be improved, the eating quality will remain poor. Fruit harvested at a physiologically overmature stage show uneven ripening with a low sugar:acid ratio, tissue breakdown, and reduction in storage life (Lakshminarayana, 1975).

Picking of the fruit is accomplished by cutting or breaking the fruit stem. Fruit which are beyond the pickers' reach are harvested using a bag attached to a long pole with a cutter or loop. Harvesting is also aided with a ladder or hydraulic lift. In picking mangos, approximately 1 cm of the stalk should be left on the fruit to prevent bleeding. This bleeding which occurs when the stem is detached from the fruit during harvest causes the affected portion of the fruit to become black in cold storage and the fruit to be more susceptible to spoilage during ripening.

Fruit must be handled carefully during harvest and marketing as bruising and scratch marks caused by rough handling will cause unsightly blemishes on the ripened fruit, thus reducing its marketability. Severe bruising will increase the fruit's susceptibility to spoilage because of the increased ripening rate of the bruised area of the fruit.

The use of cold storage to prolong the life of the fruit and provide for the orderly marketing and transportation of the crop to market has been studied by many researchers (Abou Aziz et al., 1976; Saucedo Veloz et al., 1977; Subramanham et al., 1972; Sundararaj et al., 1972; Chatper et al., 1972; Mukherjee, 1972). The main drawback that limits the usefulness of cold storage with mangos is chilling injury to the fruit. Chilling injury upsets the normal ripening processes of the fruit and causes pitted areas and dark spots on the skin, nonuniform ripening, and increased susceptibility to microbial spoilage. Tissue damage can occur in the pulp area although it is usually limited to the skin. The temperature at which chilling injury occurs is reported to vary with variety, horticultural conditions, and stage of maturity. Pairi and Taimour mangos were successfully stored at 5°C−80 to 90% relative humidity (RH)−for 28 days compared with room temperature storage 20 to 25°C (60 to 75% RH) of 6 to 8 days for Pairi and 12 to 14 days for Taimour (Abou Ariz et al., 1976). The high relative humidity is used to avoid moisture loss during cold storage. Thompson (1971) reported that Julie and Ceylon varieties had a shelf life at tropical temperatures of 10 to 14 days after harvest. Fruit stored at 4 to 7°C for 21 days after shipment to Trinidad went through normal marketing channels and were judged to be in excellent condition although they were slightly overripe for orderly marketing. Storage studies on Kent mangos at 8, 10, and 13°C (85 to 90% RH) showed chilling injury at all three temperatures with the amount of injury related to time in storage (Veloz et al., 1977). Chatper et al. (1972) reported on the storage of Alphonso mangos for up to 75 to 78 days using an antifungal compound, wax coating, and cold storage at 5 to 10°C.

The use of controlled atmosphere storage has received some attention by researchers with mixed results. Alphonso and Raspuri were stored in 7.5% CO_2 for 5 weeks at 9.2 and 6.4°C, respectively, with less than 10% loss after ripening (Kapur et al., 1962). The ripening time of 3 days was shorter than the 5 to 6 days usually desired for orderly marketing. Results with Florida variety, Keitt, stored at 12.8°C and 5% O_2 with 5% CO_2, showed insignificant improvement over air storage during a 3-week period (Hatton and Reeder, 1966).

Subatmospheric storage studies were carried out on three mango varieties, Pairi, Maya, and Haden, by Apelbaum et al. (1977) with mixed results. Fruit stored at 13°C and atmospheric pressure started to ripen in 16 days, while at 100 and 75 mmHg the fruit started to ripen in 25 and 35 days, respectively. Fruit stored at less than 50 mmHg desiccated, while at 250 mmHg no increase in storage life was recorded. Color development at reduced pressure with Maya and Haden was poor, and treatment with 0.5% ethephon or gassing with 50 μl/liter ethylene for 48 hr after removal from storage slightly improved color development.

Coating the skin with a thin wax film has been shown to increase the storage life of mangos and reduce weight loss (Sundararaj et al., 1972; Chatper et al., 1972). The coating reduces transpiration and gas exchange and slows ripening. Similar effects are achieved with sealed film bags although this can cause CO_2 and ethylene buildup which causes physiological disorders in the fruit. For this reason ventilation holes covering 0.4% of the area were used by Sundararaj et al. (1972). The solids in the wax emulsion used in studies by Mathur and Subramanyam (1956) ranged from a low of 1.7% to a high of 2.7%. Extension of storage life in nonrefrigerated storage of 50% with Badami (Alphonso) using 2.7% solids and a fungicide, o-phenylphenol, in the wax emulsion dip was obtained. Problems with proper flavor and color development of skin-coated mangos are reported by Dharkar et al. (1966b).

Hot water treatment is used commercially in many countries to control decay during storage and ripening. Subramanham et al (1972) used a 5-min dip at 52 ± 1°C to reduce microbial spoilage. A hot water dip treatment at 47°C for 20 min was effective in controlling anthracnose decay after fruit harvest in Hawaii (Akamine, 1977). Mukherjee (1972) recommends a 15-min dip in 50 to 53°C water for controlling anthracnose, with adjustments in time and temperature made for different varieties. The hot water treatment in combination with the fungicide Benomyl has been found effective in Australia in controlling anthracnose during storage (Akamine, 1976).

The use of gamma irradiation alone (Dharkar et al., 1966a) and in combination with skin coating (Dharkar et al., 1966b) has been shown to effectively increase the storage life of Alphonso mangos. The optimum dose of 25 Krads extended the storage life 2 to 3 days at 25 to 30°C as determined by changes in the fruit composition when compared with control fruit and up to 6 days comparing skin color and firmness. The best storage quality was obtained when the fruit was kept in a nitrogen atmosphere during irradiation. Coating the fruit with a 6% emulsion prior to irradiation further extended the storage life an additional 4 to 5 days without the loss of flavor sometimes associated with skin coating of mangos.

Dose rates of gamma irradiation at 75 Krad and above have been shown to cause serious darkening of the skin and pulp (Dharkar et al., 1966a; Thomas and Janave, 1973). However, mangos irradiated under a nitrogen atmosphere with 200 Krad showed no apparent effects after 10 days of storage, whereas the controls were seriously darkened. The darkening of mangos irradiated with 75 Krad and above was attributed to an activation of polyphenol oxidase by the radiation (Thomas and Janave, 1973). They attributed the observed 6-day delay in darkening to the protective effects of ascorbic acid which was significantly reduced in the 200-Krad-irradiated mangos.

In a comprehensive series of papers on the effects of gamma irradiation on selected tropical fruits that included mangos, Beyers et al. (1979), Blakesley et al. (1979), Thomas and Beyers (1979), and Beyers and Thomas (1979) concluded that there were no statistical differences in the composition of control and irradiated fruit at the doses recommended for commercial irradiation. Analysis of a wide variety of nutritional and flavor components of mangos was carried out after the fruit had softened during storage at ambient temperature (20 to 24°C). More variation in results was caused by variety, seasonal variations, and analytical methodology than by the effects of irradiation. In contrast, losses of 50 to 70% of ascorbic acid and total sugars occurred during canning and freezing of mangos.

The use of gamma irradiation at dose levels that are tolerated by mangos has been shown to be effective in controlling fruit flies and the mango seed weevil (Balock et al., 1966; Maxie et al., 1971; Seo et al., 1974).

Much of the reported research on the irradiation of fruits and vegetables has been done on a laboratory scale with very careful handling before and after irradiation. This handling is much better than could be expected in a commercial operation and should be considered when drawing conclusions on commercial applicability of irradiation treatment for mangos (Maxie et al., 1971). The use of gamma irradiation to extend storage life and eliminate insect infestation holds promise, but the process is still regarded with suspicion by consumers; thus, its full potential may not be realized for many years.

Fumigation with ethylene dibromide is used for mangos intended for export from countries with fruit fly infestations. Experiments conducted by Shaw and Lopez (1954) found that with Manila mangos, Mexican fruit flies were eliminated by fumigation with 12 mg of ethylene dibromide at 25°C for 2 hr. Flavor appraisals of mangos treated with 16 to 24 mg/l showed no loss of flavor. There was also no loss of ascorbic acid or effect on appearance of the fruit. Spalding et al. (1975) fumigated four commercial varieties for 2 hr with 12 and 24 mg/liter of ethylene dibromide at 23.3°C. These treatments did not injure the fruit or affect ripening. Ethylene dibromide residues decreased to 0 during ripening and shipping.

III. BIOCHEMICAL AND NUTRITIONAL COMPOSITION

A. Nutritional Composition

Mangos are an excellent source of vitamins A and C. In comparison with oranges and apricots, which are generally considered to be above average in nutritional qualities, they rank equal or superior in the nutritional elements listed in Table 3. The nutritive values shown are representative values, and a wide variation in the nutritional composition exists for specific varieties, seasonal variation, and maturity differences.

B. Changes in Nutrient Composition

1. During Fruit Development

Mangos reach physiological maturity in approximately 14 to 16 weeks from fruit set depending on variety and seasonal conditions. Additional time is required either on the tree or in storage for the fruit to reach the edible ripe stage. The mangos' nutrient composition during these two stages is very different. Only a small quantity of carotenoids are

Table 3 Nutrient Composition of Three Fruits (100 g Edible Portion)

	Mango	Orange[a]	Apricot
Water	81.7 %	88.3 %	85.3 %
Food energy	66 cal	45 cal	51 cal
Protein	0.7 g	0.7 g	1.0 g
Fat	0.4 g	0.2 g	0.2 g
Total carbohydrate	16.8 g	10.4 g	12.8 g
Fiber	0.9 g	0.1 g	0.6 g
Ash	0.4 g	0.4 g	0.7 g
Calcium	10 mg	11 mg	17 mg
Phosphorus	13 mg	17 mg	23 mg
Iron	0.4 mg	0.2 mg	0.5 mg
Sodium	7 mg	1 mg	1 mg
Potassium	189 mg	200 mg	281 mg
Vitamin A value	4,800 IU[b]	200 IU	2,700 IU
Thiamine	0.05 mg	0.09 mg	0.03 mg
Riboflavin	0.05 mg	0.03 mg	0.04 mg
Niacin	1.1 mg	0.4 mg	0.6 mg
Ascorbic acid	35 mg	50 mg	10 mg

[a]Florida (all commercial varieties).
[b]International units.
Source: Watt and Merrill, Composition of foods, *Agriculture Handbook No. 8* (1963).

found in mangos during fruit development up to the physiological mature fruit stage. Subbarayan and Cama (1970) found only 41 µg/ 100 g total carotenoids in hard unripe (physiologically mature) Badami (Alphonso) mangos. In contrast, Lakshminarayana (1973) found 8263 µg/100 g in tree-ripe Alphonso mangos. A similar situation exists with total sugars. Alphonso mangos contain approximately 2% total sugars from the fourth week after fruit set until the sixteenth week (Lakshminarayana et al., 1970) with 9.5% total sugars in tree-ripe Alphonso mangos (Lakshminarayana, 1973). Ascorbic acid and total acidity, in contrast to total carotenoids and sugars, decrease during fruit development from a high at 6 weeks after fruit set of 192 mg/100 g and 3.67% to 96.1 mg/100 g and 2.88%, respectively, at 16 weeks (Lakshminarayana, 1973).

2. During Postharvest Storage

The degree of change in nutrient composition occurring during post-harvest storage is determined by maturity at harvest, variety, and storage temperature. Soft, tree-ripe fruit picked for local markets or immediate processing show only small changes during their limited storage life. Fruit intended for distant markets, export, or later processing are harvested earlier at the physiological mature stage (green, hard unripe fruit). This fruit changes dramatically in nutrient composition during storage as shown in Table 4. Mangos stored at refrigerated temperatures (Table 5) for prolonged time periods do not show the same ripening patterns as fruit stored at 25 to 34°C. Chilling injury occurs if the storage temperature is too low for the variety, and this results in serious physiological disorders which adversely affect fruit quality.

The most significant changes that occur in nutrient composition during storage at refrigerated temperatures, compared with room-temperature-ripened fruit, are reduced carotenoid and sugar content and increased vitamin C and total acid content. These changes are increased by lower storage temperatures and longer storage periods, and the overall organoleptic qualities of the fruit are poorer (Veloz et al., 1977). These changes can be partially reversed by bringing the fruit out of refrigerated storage before they are ripe and ripening the fruit at room temperature (Thomas, 1975).

3. During Processing and Storage

Changes in nutrient composition during processing vary widely depending on the severity of the processing. The degree of cell disruption, fruit temperature, and time involved during processing are the main factors affecting loss of nutrients. The degree of cell disruption will govern the release and mixing of enzymes and substrate with resultant increases in browning caused by polyphenol oxidase and off-flavor development by catalase and peroxidase during processing and

Table 4 Changes in Nutrient Composition at Room Temperature

Variety	Days from harvest	Storage temperature (°C)	Ascorbic acid (mg/100 g)	Total carotenoids (µg/100 g)	Total sugars (%)	Total acids (%)	pH
Kent[b]	1	–	18.6	308	5.24	0.33	4.6
	10	25	21.8	5560	14.62	0.18	5.2
Alphonso[c]	1	–	88.0	955	7.0[a]	3.0	2.87
	14	29 ± 3	27.9	15,800	15.0[a]	0.21	4.57
Carabao[d]	1	–	68,8	720	8.5[a]	1.9	3.6
	6	30 ± 2	35.1	2080	18.5[a]	0.4	4.7
Langra[e]	0	–	254.3	–	11.0[a]	2.66	–
	7	30.2 ± 2.5	171.6	–	20.0[a]	0.13	–
Anwar Ratual[f]	0	32 ± 2	–	–	4.15	2.12	3.1
	8	–	–	–	14.63	0.39	4.30

[a]Total soluble solids (%).
[b]Veloz et al. (1977).
[c]Thomas (1975).
[d]Morga et al. (1979).
[e]Mukherjee (1972).
[f]Elahi and Khan (1973).

Table 5 Changes in Nutrient Composition in Refrigerated Storage

Variety	Days from harvest	Storage temperature (°C)	Ascorbic acid (mg/100 g)	Total carotenoids (μg/100 g)	Total sugars (%)	Total acids (%)	pH
Kent[b]	1	–	18.6	308	5.24	0.33	4.6
	22	13	60.0	390	8.79	1.03	4.1
Alphonso[c]	1	–	88.0	955	7.0[a]	3.00	2.87
	43	15	105.9	5400	12.25[a]	0.14	4.78
Langra[d]	0	–	176	–	4.78[a]	1.25	–
	49	9	216	–	20.5[a]	0.54	–

[a]Total soluble solids.
[b]Veloz et al. (1977).
[c]Thomas (1975).
[d]Mukherjee (1972).

storage unless the enzymes are heat-inactivated. An example of this was reported by Brekke et al. (1975) in which off-flavor did not develop in frozen mango slices but did develop in frozen purée. Thermal processing will cause losses in carotene and vitamin C, with the latter being more heat-labile. Vitamin C losses of from 44.3 to 71.5% were reported by de Leon and de Lima (1966) during the canning of mango juice from four varieties at a selected stage of maturity. Storage temperature of the processed product is important to the retention of nutrients, texture, appearance, and flavor. Pasteurized refrigerated mango slices had a 9-month storage life at 2°C and 4 1/2 months at 10°C (Falcone et al., 1975).

C. Biochemical Composition

Carotenoids are mainly responsible for the color of ripe mangos. The composition of the carotenoids in Badami (Alphonso) mangos were characterized by Subbarayan and Cama (1970) at three stages of maturity—unripe, partially ripe, and fully ripe. They found 15, 14, and 17 different carotenoids at the three stages of maturity. In fully ripe mangos, β-carotene constituted 50.64% of the total, with phytofluene (11.7%), auroxanthin (11.4%), *cis*-violaxanthin (7.08%), and phytoene (6.32%) comprising the other major carotenoids. The red blush in Haden mangos is attributed to the presence of the anthocyanin, peonidin-3-galactoside (Proctor and Creasy, 1969).

The major sugars in Haden mangos were determined by Chan and Kwok (1975) to be 20.6% fructose, 5.3% *D*-glucose, and 74.1% sucrose. Two sugars, mannoheptulose and sedoheptulose, were found in trace amounts in four varieties of mangos by Ogata et al. (1972).

Preclimateric (physiologically mature) mangos contain significant levels of organic acids, but during ripening most of these are lost. Shashirekha and Patwardhan (1976) found $3.36 \pm 0.1\%$ total acids in preclimateric Alphonso mangos and only $0.39 \pm 0.27\%$ total acids in ripe fruit. The organic acids in the ripe Alphonso mangos were citric (61.0%), malic (24.0%), succinic (10.0%), and uronic acid (5.0%).

Bandyopadhyay and Gholap (1973) related the changes in fatty acid composition and glyceride content to the aroma and flavor characteristics of Alphonso mangos ripened at $10 \pm 2°C$ and $27.5 \pm 2.5°C$. The mangos ripened at $10 \pm 2°C$ for 55 days showed no changes in pulp oil content or percent glycerides in the pulp oil. These fruit were judged ripe after 55 days as judged by texture and sweetness but lacked aroma and were bland in flavor. The mangos ripened at $27.5 \pm 2.5°C$ showed a steady rise in both pulp oil (19 to 82%) and glycerides (42 to 62%) in the pulp oil during 15 days of storage. A similar situation occurred in the fatty acid composition during storage. Mangos stored at $10 \pm 2°C$ showed no changes in fatty acid composition during the 55 days of storage, whereas those stored at $27 \pm 2.5°C$ showed a decrease in linoleic acid and an increase in linolenic and palmitoleic acid. They also found a strong correlation between the ratio of palmitic to palmitoleic acid and the aroma and flavor qualities of Alphonso mangos. A ratio of less than 1 correlated well with strong flavor and aroma qualities.

The edible portion of Haden mangos was studied by Brekke et al (1975) for the presence of peroxidase, catalase, polyphenolase, pectin methyl esterase, and polygalacturonase. Peroxidase activity was found at all stages of maturity, but was most active in green and half-ripe fruit. Peroxidase tests on clear filtrates of mango fruit homogenates were negative; however, peroxidase was detected in the filter cake. The peroxidase was apparently bound to the insoluble portions of the fruit tissue. Ripe mango slices gave positive catalase reactions, and no activity was seen in green slices; however, a trace of catalase activity was found in a homogenate of green mangos. The catalase activity was greatly increased by raising the pH of the homogenate from 3.7 to 4.2 with sodium acetate. Polyphenolase was found in green mangos with only trace amounts detectable in ripe fruit. Only a trace amount of pectin methyl esterase activity was seen in any samples. Polygalacturonase activity was not detected in any sample by the cup plate method.

IV. MANGO PROCESSING

Mangos are processed at two stages of maturity. Green fruits are utilized to make chutney, pickles, curries, and dehydrated products. The green fruit should be freshly picked from the tree. Fruit that are injured, damaged, or that have prematurely fallen to the ground should not be used (Narayana, 1976). Ripe mangos are processed as canned and frozen slices, purée, juices, nectar, and various dried products. Mangos are processed into many other products for home use and by cottage industry.

The processing of mangos presents many problems to its industry and to market expansion. Alternate bearing and short storage life affect the orderly processing of the crop. The large number of varieties with their various attributes and deficiencies affects the quality and uniformity of processed products. The lack of simple, reliable methods for determining the stage of maturity of varieties for processing also affects the quality of the finished products. Many of the processed products require peeled or peeled and sliced fruit. The lack of mechanized equipment for the peeling of ripe mangos is a serious bottleneck for increasing the production of these products (Bhatnagar and Subramanyam, 1973). A significant problem in developing mechanized equipment is the large number of varieties available and their different sizes and shapes. The cost of processed mango products is also too expensive for the general population in the areas where most mangos are grown. There is a considerable export potential to wealthier countries, but in these countries the processed mango products must compete with established processed fruits of high quality and relatively low cost.

A. Green Mango Processing

1. Pickles

The optimum stage of maturity should be determined for each variety used to make pickles. Sastry and Krishnamurthy (1974) and Habibunnisa (1975) found that pickles made from 6- to 10-week-old Amlet mangos were of good quality, but those from 8- and 9-week-old mangos were superior in color and flavor. Pickles made from fruit less than 6 weeks old were hard and had a flat taste, whereas those from fruit older than 10 weeks were soft and mashy with a fruity flavor. Narayana (1976) reports that most mangos in the unripe stage lack strong flavors, but some are known to have a characteristically harsh flavor and thus should be avoided for the manufacture of pickles. He also recommends that the fruit weigh at least 250 g for pickle making. High-acid mangos (5 to 6%) were found to produce the best quality pickles (Sastry and Krishnamurthy, 1974).

There are two classifications of pickles—salt pickles and oil pickles. They are processed from whole and sliced fruit with and without stones. Salt is used in most pickles. The many kinds of pickles vary mainly in the proportions and kinds of spices used in their preparation (Bhatnagar and Subramanyam, 1973). The following basic recipe was used by Sastry and Krishnamurthy (1974) in their study of the preparation and storage of pickles in oil.

Mango Pickles

Mango pieces	250 g	Tumeric powder	2 to 4 g
Salt	60 g	Fenugreek seeds	2 to 4 g
Mustard powder	20 to 40 g	Bengal gram seeds	2 to 4 g
Chili powder	20 g	Gingelly oil	20 to 30 g

The ingredients were mixed together and filled into wide-mouthed bottles of 454-g capacity. Three days later the contents were thoroughly mixed and refilled into the bottles. Extra oil was added to form a 1- to 2-cm layer over the pickles. Srivastava (1967) lists 42 different traditional Indian recipes of mango pickles. These recipes are used for either home-scale or cottage-scale preparation of mango pickles.

2. Chutney

This product is prepared from peeled, sliced, or grated unripe or semiripe fruit by cooking the fruit with sugar, salt, spices, and

vinegar to a thick consistency (Bhatnagar and Subramanyam, 1973).
Other ingredients such as dried fruits, onions, garlic, and nuts are
added according to regional preferences. The following recipe for
Naurattan chutney was given by Puri and Puri (1969).

Mango Chutney (Naurattan)

Raisins	71 g	Nigella	2 teaspoons
Dates or chawaras	85 g	(optional)	
(optional)		Red chili	1 to 2 teaspoons
Blanched or	57 g	powder	
halved almonds		Black cumin	1 teaspoon
Pistachio nuts	28 g	seeds	
(optional)		Ground cinnamon	1 teaspoon
Vinegar	142 ml	Ground (dry)	1/4 teaspoon
Grated mangos	454 g	ginger	
Sugar	454 g	Cardamon seeds	A few
Salt	3 teaspoons	(optional)	
Cloves	2 teaspoons	Nutmeg	2 teaspoons

The shredded mangos are cooked with salt over medium heat for 5 to
7 min, mixed, and sugar, vinegar, cumin seeds, ground cloves,
cinnamon, chili powder, ginger, and nutmeg are added. Crushed
nigella and cardamon seeds are added if desired. Cook over moderate
heat until the product resembles a thick purée, add remaining ingredients, and simmer another 5 min. Cool and preserve in sterilized jars.

3. Dehydration

Immature fruit is peeled and sliced for sun-drying. The dried mango
slices can be powdered to make a product called amchoo (Singh, 1960).
The use of blanching, sulfuring, and mechanical dehydration gives a
product with better color, nutrition, storability, and fewer microbiological problems.

Green mango pulp has been successfully drum-dried by Gangopadhyay
et al. (1976). The mangos were first heated in boiling water for 15 min,
peeled, and pulped in a pulper fitted with a 30-mesh screen. The pH
of the pulp was adjusted to 5.0 and heated to 80 to 85°C at which time
corn starch and tricalcium phosphate were added to improve the flow
characteristic of the finished products. This mixture was then dried
in an atmospheric 15-cm-diameter × 20-cm-wide chrome-plated steel
double drum drier heated by steam at 50 psig and rotation at 4 rpm.
Contact time was approximately 15 sec. The powdered flakes were best
stored in sanitary cans or polyaluminum foil laminates. The powdered
product is suggested as a base material for the preparation of green
mango drinks and thick mango chutney.

B. Ripe Mango Products

1. Purée

Mangos are processed into purée for remanufacture into products such as nectar, juice, squash, jam, jelly, and dehydrated products. The purée can be frozen, canned, and stored in barrels. This allows for a supply of raw material during the remainder of the year when fresh mangos are not available. It also provides a more economical means of storage compared with the cost of storing the finished products, except for those which are dehydrated, and provides for more orderly processing during peak availability of fresh mangos. Mangos can be processed into purée from whole or peeled fruit. Because of the time and cost of peeling this step is best avoided, but with some varieties it may be necessary to avoid off-flavors which may be present in the skin.

The most common way of removing the skin is hand-peeling with knives, but this is time-consuming and expensive. Steam and lye-peeling have been accomplished for some varieties (Breeke et al., 1975). Removal of the peel by exposure to atmospheric steam for 2 1/2 min and cooling in a water bath allowed the peel of mangos which had been previously slit to be slip-peeled. The heated tissue immediately below the peel took on a translucent appearance that made it easy to determine visually how deep the heating had taken effect. Catalase activity was destroyed in the heated tissue.

Four varieties, Haden, Buchannan, Joe Welch, and Pirie were lye-peeled. The severity of the lye treatment depended on the variety and maturity. In all cases it was desirable to add a wetting agent (about 0.2% sodium lauryl sulfate) to the lye bath and to score the surface of the fruit with a stainless steel wire brush before the lye treatment.

Pirie was the easiest to lye-peel because of its thin skin. Treatment in 20% sodium hydroxide (NaOH) at 90°C for 3 min was sufficient for removing the exocarp. Haden was the most difficult to peel. Lye treatment in 20% NaOH at 100°C for 5 min removed only the outer layers of the exocarp, the cuticle, and pellicle. Generally, green fruit was more difficult to peel than ripe fruit. The peeling was completed by a rotary rod washer after lye treatment. The combination of water washing and gentle abrasive action caused by the fruit in the washer removed 90% or more of the peel.

Several methods have been devised to remove the pulp from fresh ripe mangos without hand-peeling. A mechanical scraping device described by Stafford et al. (1966) was used to separate the pulp from the peel of Haden mango slices. The purée from this process was compared with that produced by putting unpeeled slices through a cutting mill and paddle pulper fitted with a 0.084-cm screen. Nectar produced by the latter method had a better flavor (Brekke et al., 1968).

With these results, a simplified method was devised. The whole mangos were exposed to atmospheric steam for 2 to 2 1/2 min in a loosely covered chamber, then transferred to a stainless steel tank. The steam-softened skins allowed the fruit to be pulped by a power stirrer fitted with a saw-toothed propeller blade mounted 12.7 to 15.2 cm below a regular propeller blade (Brekke et al., 1975). The pulp was removed from the seeds by a continuous centrifuge designed for use in passion fruit extraction (Kinch, 1959). The pulp material was then passed through a paddle pulper fitted with a 0.084-cm screen to remove fiber and small pieces of pulp.

Benero and Rodriquez (1971) developed a similar method using Mayaguezano mangos. In one method the fruit was exposed to 93.3°C steam for 2.5 min, and in the other the peel was removed with a peel cutter which consisted of a rotating drum with knives protruding 0.32 cm from the surface of the drum. The pulp was then removed with a pulper fitted with nylon brushes revolving at 650 rpm fitted with a 0.15 cm screen. The steamed fruit gave higher recoveries of pulp (84.1 to 86.9%) compared with fruits mechanically peeled (75.6 to 79.4%). Both purées produced were of similar good quality. Mango purée can be frozen, canned, or stored in barrels for later reprocessing. In all these cases, heating is necessary to preserve the quality of the mango purée.

Brekke et al. (1968) found that purée pumped through a plate heat exchanger allowed for rapid heating to inactivate the enzyme catalase and rapid cooling to preserve the flavor. In the heat exchanger the purée was heated to 90°C for 1 min and cooled to 35°C before filling into 30-lb tins with polyethylene liners and frozen at -23.5°C. These studies found that the heated purée when made into nectar had a significantly better aroma and flavor before and after storage of the purée for 8 months than unheated purée.

In the canning of purée, Benero and Rodriquez (1971) adjusted the pH to a range of 3.5 to 3.8 with citric acid. The purée was then flash-pasteurized at 90°C in a Votator pasteurizer, packed in no. 10 cans, and cooled in a tap water bath. The purée stored well at 29.5°C for up to 305 days.

Because of the high cost of cans, Shrikhande et al. (1976) tested the storage stability of purée packed and stored in high-density polyethylene bulk containers. In this process the pulp was acidified to pH 3.5, pasteurized at 90°C, and hot-filled into 6-kg polyethylene containers that had been previously sterilized with boiling water. The containers were then sealed and cooled in water. During a 6-month storage period no abnormal odors were detected in nectars prepared from the stored purée and, furthermore, the nectars were indistinguishable from the nectars prepared from conventionally canned purée.

Wooden barrels are used to store mango pulp in the manufacture of jams and squashes. The pulp is acidified with 0.5 to 1.0% citric acid, fitted with a 0.15 cm screen, heated to boiling, cooled, and SO_2 is added 1000 to 1500 ppm in the pulp. The pulp is then filled into barrels for future use (Bhatnagar and Subramanyam, 1973).

2. Slices

Mango slices can be preserved by canning or freezing, and recent studies have shown the feasibility of pasteurized-refrigerated and dehydro-canned slices. The quality of the processed product in all of these procedures will be dependent upon selection of a suitable variety along with good processing procedures.

Thermal process canning of mango slices in syrup is the most used preservation method. Several researchers have studied the suitability of different varieties for canning. In a study by Palaniswamy et al. (1973), 20 varieites of mangos were canned and evaluated. They found four varieties, Alphonso, K.O. 8, Baneshan, and Mulgoa, were superior, four others were rated good, and the remainder was found not suitable for canning.

Ther thermal processes involved in canning mango slices and other products were studied by Nanjundaswamy et al. (1973). They used Badami (Alphonso) mangos in their studies. The thermal death time for a strain of yeast isolated from a can of spoiled mango slices in syrup and thermal inactivation time for peroxidase were determined to aid in developing process time requirements. For the heat penetration studies, 520 g of slices were filled into 401 × 411 cans and covered with hot 50° Brix syrup containing 0.25% acidity (pH 4.2) and exhausted at 97.8 to 98.9°C for 7 min and sealed. They found that in canned slices, both heating and cooling take place by convection. The thermal process time by calculation for mango slices was found to be 7 min at 100°C. The validity of the calculations for process time was tested at a commercial processing plant. No spoilage of the samples packed was detected after processing and storage.

The freezing of mango slices has been studied by several researchers because of its potential to provide improved flavor and nutritional quality retention during processing and storage compared with the canned product. Several varieties of mangos grown in Hawaii were frozen as cheeks and slices in various packs by Orr and Miller (1955). The quality of the thawed samples was compared after several months of frozen storage. The samples frozen in syrup were superior to those packed in dry sugar or with no added sugar or syrup. Ascorbic acid addition produced no improvement in quality. In freezing studies conducted by Brekke et al. (1975) significant differences were found in the texture of thawed frozen slices of different varieties, with Haden and Irwin having fair firmness and Buchannan, Kensington, and Waterhouse having a poor texture. Steam-blanching (1, 2.5, and 4 min) as a pretreatment was also investigated. Taste panel evaluation determined that the flavor and stability of the frozen slices were not enhanced by steam-blanching. The 4-min blanch caused excessive softening and imparted a cooked flavor to the slices. The recommended procedure is to fill slices into containers and cover with syrup (25 to 30° Brix), seal, freeze in a blast freezer at -23°C, and store at -18°C or lower. The use of calcium chloride ($CaCl_2$) to firm the texture of Alphonso frozen mango slices was explored by Cooke et al. (1976). They found presoaking mango slices with a syrup containing 2% (w/v) $CaCl_2$ firmed the slice excessively so as to be perceived as more fibrous by the taste panel. They recommended further studies to determine the concentration of $CaCl_2$ necessary to optimize the texture of the slices. The addition of ascorbic acid to the cover syrup had no effect other than to enhance the vitamin C and dehydroascorbate concentration, although they reported other researchers working with different varieties had found vitamin C effective in improving the color retention of frozen slices.

A process for pasteurized-refrigerated (P/R) mango slices was developed by Dougherty and Koburger (1972). It was adapted from a P/R process developed for peaches by Harris (1963). In their process the pH of the mango slices (Keitt) was reduced by soaking overnight in a 2% citric acid solution containing 30% sucrose at 2°C. The fruit was drained for 30 min and pasteurized at 70°C for 1 min. The slices were packed in sterile 236-ml jars at the same temperature and with a syrup containing 0.1% citric acid and 30% sucrose, also at 70°C. The jars were sealed and inverted for 5 min and stored at 2°C. Taste panel results showed no adverse sensory changes during the 3-month storage period, and the color remained stable. Commercial processing conditions may require the use of a preservative.

The process was modified by Falcone et al. (1975) to reduce slice handling and promote continuous processing. Gomez et al. (1980) adapted the process to flexible pouch packages. This allowed for rapid heating and cooling without the hazard of thermal shock.

3. Beverages

The commercial beverages are juice, nectar, and squash. Mango nectar and juice contain mango purée, sugar, water, and citric acid in various proportions depending on local taste, government standards of identity, pH control, and fruit composition of the variety used. Mango squash, in addition to the above, contains SO_2 or sodium benzoate as a preservative. Other food-grade additives such as ascorbic acid, food coloring, or thickeners may be used in mango beverages.

Bhatnagar and Subramanyam (1973) describe mango juice as being prepared by mixing equal quantities of pulp (purée) and water together and adjusting the total soluble solids (TSS) and acidity to taste (12 to 15% TSS and 0.4 to 0.5% acidity as citric acid). Mango nectar containing 25% purée was prepared by Breeke et al. (1975) as shown below. Commercial processing conditions may require the use of a preservative.

| | Brix of purée | | |
Nectar components	15°	17°	20°
Purée	100	100	100
Sugar	45	43	40
Water	255	257	260

The pH was adjusted to approximately 3.5 by adding citric acid as a 50% solution (w/w).

The time of heat processing will vary with filling temperature, can size, and viscosity of the juice or nectar. In a study by Nanjundaswamy et al. (1973) using 401 × 411 cans, they heated the nectar juice (pH 4.2) to 74°C before filling hot and sealing the cans. The nectar required 8 min at 100°C, and the juice required 7.5 min. Brekke et al. (1975) recommend filling hot at 85°C and heat-processing in boiling water for 10 min for cans containing 570 g of nectar.

Mango squash is described by Bhatnagar and Subramanyam (1973) to contain 25% juice, 45% TSS, and 1.2 to 1.5% acidity, and preserved with sulfur dioxide (350 ppm) or sodium benzoate (1000 ppm) in glass bottles.

4. Dried

Ripe mangos are dried in the form of pieces, powders, and flakes. Drying procedures such as sun-drying, tunnel dehydration, vacuum-drying, vacuum-puff drying, foam-mat-drying, osmotic dehydration, and freeze-drying are used commercially or have undergone laboratory studies. Packaged and stored properly, dried mango products are stable and nutritious. Economic advantages in packaging, transportation, and storage are realized by reductions in the bulk and weight of the dried products.

Studies on the dehydration of *Dasheri* mangos using various treatments before dehydration were carried out by Teaotia et al. (1976) using an electric cabinet through flow drier operated at 60°C. Eight to twelve hours were required and the dehydrated samples were packaged in 250-gauge polythene bags, heat sealed, and stored in friction-top tins at room temperature for 1 year. The treatments involved steeping the peeled slices for 18 hr in various solutions (1:1) with fruit and containing different combinations of sugar, citric acid, ascorbic acid, sulfur dioxide, and water. The dehydrated samples were examined immediately and after 1 year of storage. There was no browning in the sulfited, sugared samples. Steeping mango slices in a solution containing 40° Brix sugar, 3000 ppm SO_2, 0.2% ascorbic acid, and 1% citric acid produced the best dehydrated product.

Drum-drying of mango purée is an efficient, economical process for producing dried mango powder and flakes. Its major drawback is that the severity of heat processing can produce undesirable cooked flavors and aromas in the dried product. The drum-dried products are also extremely hydroscopic, and the use of in package desiccant is recommended during storage (Copley et al., 1956).

Brekke et al. (1975) reported on drum-drying several varieties of mangos that were reconstituted into nectar for flavor and aroma evaluation after storage. The pilot scale drier had drums 19 cm long and 15 cm in diameter heated internally by steam under pressure. A drum spacing of 25.4 mm, product residence time of about 25 sec on the drum surface, and steam pressure of 3160 g/cm^2 (gauge) was used. The dried purée was removed as a thin sheet that was bright yellow and had a flavor like that of cooked mango. The mango purée had to be dried to a moisture content of 3% or less to be easily handled in powder or flake form.

A 10-member panel rated nectars made from dried purée stored at 24°C for periods up to 6 months as fair in flavor and aroma. Also, no significant color changes were observed in dried flakes stored at 24°C for 6 months. Drum-dried mango pulp (Dusheri) reduced to 2 to 3% moisture lost about a third of its carotenoids and half its ascorbic acid (Baldry et al., 1976). Their dried product was impossible to rehydrate.

Mango pulp (Badami) was drum-dried in combination with skim milk powder (added 1:1 on the basis of Brix of the pulp) or fresh whole milk or curd (mango:milk/curd = 1:2) by Jayaraman et al. (1976). The mixture was diluted with water to give 15 to 20% total solids content in order to facilitate drying. A pilot scale drier was used with a rotational speed of 2 to 3 rpm and steam pressure of 3515 g/cm^2. The drum-dried mango-milk curd was reconstituted in cold water and remained acceptable for up to 4 months at 37°C when packed under nitrogen.

Freeze-drying produces dried products with very little loss of flavor or aroma, but the cost of production is expensive compared with other methods of dehydration because of large capital equipment and operating cost. Freeze-drying mango pulp with a moisture content of 82% required 11 1/2 hr to reduce the moisture content to approximately 1% (Ammu et al., 1976). The freeze-dried powder was packed in cans under nitrogen and air and stored at ambient temperature (26 to 30°C) and 37°C. The sample with 0.8% moisture kept well for 1 year.

The addition of sucrose to the pulp before freeze-drying increased the shelf life of fruit juice powders (Subramanian et al., 1976).

In foam-mat-drying the purée is whipped to form a heat-stable low-density foam, the foam is spread in a thin layer on perforated metal trays or continuous belt, and dried with hot air. Because of the thin coat and large surface area, drying is rapid at moderate temperatures. Most fruit juice concentrates require about 15 min in 71°C air to dry to 2% moisture for a layer 0.22 cm thick (Van Arsdel and Copely, 1964).

Mango pulp (Badami) with 0.05% potassium metabisulfite was foam-mat-dried by Jayaraman et al. (1976). The powder reconstituted with cold water and remained acceptable at room temperature for over 6 months in paper-foiled-polythene-laminate pouches. Foam-mat-dried mango purées (Alphonso) made by Cooke et al. (1976) were made into nectar for sensory evaluation. The nectar was rated poor and possessed a distinct off-flavor and color.

Spray-drying is accomplished by atomizing or spraying the juice or enzyme-treated purée into a stream of hot air. The atomized particles are dried to powder as they fall. Cooke et al. (1976) spray-dried mango purée (Alphonso) after treatment with 0.1% w/v Ultrazyme (Ciba-Geigy Ltd., Basel, Switzerland) for 2 hr at 30°C and dilution with distilled water (2:1 v/v, respectively). Taste panel evaluation of nectar made from the spray-dried powder rated the color as bright and attractive but slightly lacking in flavor compared with a control nectar.

REFERENCES

Abou Aziz, A. B., El-Nabawy, S. M., Abdel Wahab, F. K., and Abdel-Kader, A. S. (1976). The effect of storage temperature on quality and decay percentage of 'Pairi' and 'Taimour' mango fruits. *Scientia Horticulturae* 5:65-72.

Akamine, E. K. (1976). Problems in shipping fresh Hawaiian tropical and subtropical fruits. *Acta Hortic.* 57:151-160.

Akamine, E. K. (1977). Tropical and subtropical crops in Hawaii. *CSIRO Fd. Res. Q.* 37:13-20.

Ammu, K., Krishnappa, K. G., Subramanian, V., Sharma, T. R., and Nath, H. (1976). Freeze drying of mango pulp. *Food Technol. Aust.* 28:339-341.

Apelbaum, A., Zauberman, G., and Fuchs, Y. (1977). Subatmospheric pressure storage of mango fruits. *Scientia Horticulturae* 7:153-160.

Baldry, J., Breag, G. R., Caygill, J. C., Cooke, R. D., Ferber, C. E, M., and Kanagasabapathy, L., (1976). Alternative methods of processing mangoes. *Indian Food Packer* 30:56-62.

Balock, J. W., Burditt, Jr., A. K., Seo, S. T., and Akamine, E. K. (1966). Gamma radiation as a quarantine treatment for Hawaiian fruit flies. *J. Econ. Entomol.* 59:202-204.

Bandyopadhyay, C., and Gholap, A. S. (1973). Relationship of aroma and flavour characteristics of mango (*Mangifera indica L.*) to fatty acid composition. *J. Sci. Fd. Agric.* 24:1497-1503.

Barmore, C. R. (1974). Ripening mangos with ethylene and ethephon. *Fla. State Hortic. Soc.* 87:331-334.

Benero, J. R., and Rodriquez, A. J. (1971). Mango pulp extracting method. *J. Agric. Univ. P. R.* 55:513-515.

Beyers, M., and Thomas, A. C. (1979). γ Irradiation of subtropical fruits. 4. Changes in certain nutrients present in mangoes, papayas, and litchis during canning, freezing, and γ irradiation. *J. Agric. Food Chem.* 27:48-51.

Beyers, M., Thomas, A. C., and Van Tonder, A. J. (1979). γ Irradiation of subtropical fruits. I. Compositional tables of mango, papaya, strawberry, and litchi fruits at the edible-ripe stage. *J. Agric. Food Chem.* 27:37-42.

Bhatnagar, H. C., and Subramanyam, H. (1973). Some aspects of preservation, processing and export of mango and its products. *Indian Food Packer* 27:33-52.

Blakesley, C. N., Loots, J. G., du Plessis, L. M., and de Bruyn, G. (1979). γ Irradiation of subtropical fruits. 2. Volatile components, lipids, and amino acids of mango, papaya, and strawberry pulp. *J. Agric. Food Chem.* 27:42-48.

Brekke, J., Cavaletto, C., and Stafford, A. E. (1968). Mango puree processing. *Hawaii Agric. Exp. Sta. Tech. Prog. Report No. 167.*

Brekke, J. E., Cavaletto, C. G., Stafford, A. E., and Chan, H. T., Jr. (1975). Mango: Processed products. *W-23 Agricultural Research Service*, USDA.

Chan, H. T., Jr., and Kwok, S. C. M. (1975). Identification and determination of sugars in some tropical fruit products. *J. Food Sci.* 40:419-420.

Chatper, H. S., Geetha, G. Mattoo, A. K., and Modi V. V. (1972). Some problems pertaining to storage and ripening in mango fruit. *Acta Hortic.* 24:243-250.

Cheema, G. S., Bhat, S. S., and Naik, K. C. (1954). *Commercial Fruits of India.* London, Macmillan, p. 51.

Cooke, R. D., Breag, G. R., Ferber, C. E. M., Best, P. R., and Jones, J. (1976). Studies of mango processing I. The foam-mat drying of mango (Alphonso cultivar) puree. *J. Fd. Technol.* 11:463-473.

Cooke, R. D., Allison, C. J., Baldry, J., Caygill, J. C., Ferber, C. E. M., Kanagasabapathy, L., and Veale, M. J. (1976). Studies of mango processing II. Deep freezing of mango slices. *J. Fd. Technol.* 11:475-484.

Copley, M. J., Kaufman, V. F., and Rasmussen, C. L. (1956). Recent developments in fruits and vegetable powder technology. *Food Technol.* 10:589-595.

de Leon, S. Y., and de Lima, L. (1966). Acceptability of canned mango juice from four varieties and three color stages of maturity. *Philippine J. Sci.* 94:401-409.

Dharkar, S. D., Savagaon, K. A., Srirangarajan, A. N., and Sreenivasan, A. (1966a). Irradiation of mangos. I. Radiation-induced delay in ripening of Alphonso mangos. *J. Food Sci.* 31:863-869.

Dharkar, S. D., Savagaon, K. A., Srirangarajan, A. N., and Sreenivasan, A. (1966b). Irradiation of mangoes. II. Radiation effects of skin-coated Alphonso mangoes. *J. Food Sci.* 31:870-877.

Dougherty, R. H., and Koburger, J. A. (1972). Preparation and storage of pasteurized refrigerated mango fruit. *Proc. Fla. St. Hort. Soc.* 85:190-192.

Elahi, M., and Khan, N. Physico chemical changes in some Pakistani mango varieties during storage ripening. *J. Agr. Food Chem.* 21:229-231.

Falcone, E. G., Bates, R. P., and Koburger, J. A. (1975). Process refinement and storage characteristics of pasteurized-refrigerated mango slices. *Proc. Fla. St. Hort. Soc.* 88:482-486.

Food and Agriculture Organization (1979). *FAO Production Yearbook, Vol. 33*, Rome, Food and Agriculture Organization of the United Nations.

Gangopadhyay, H., Chaudhuri, D. R., and Mukherjee, S. (1976). Dehydration of green mango pulp in double drum drier. *Indian Food Packer* 30:51-54.

Gomez, J. B., Bates, R. P., and Ahmed, E. M. (1980). Flexible pouch process, development and evaluation of pasteurized-refrigerated mango slices. *J. Food Sci.* 45:1592-1594.

Habibunnisa, (1975). Studies on Indian pickles—Part III. Physico-chemical variations during growth of mangoes (Amlet variety) and storage studies of pickles from them. *Indian Food Packer* 29:39-54.

Harkness, R. W., and Cobin, M. (1951). Haden mango maturity observation during 1950. In *Mango Studies*. Stuart, Fla. Florida Mango Forum, pp. 141-146.

Harris, H. (1963). Pasteurized refrigerated peach products. *Alabama Agric. Exp. Sta. Highlights of Agri. Res.* 10:11

Hatton, T. T., Jr., and Reeder, W. F., (1966). Controlled atmosphere storage of Keitt mangos, 1965. *Proc. Tropical Region Am. Soc. Hort. Sci.* 10:114-119.

Hayes, W. B. (1966). *Fruit Growing in India*, 2nd ed. Allakabad, India, The Indian University Press, p. 169.

Hobson, L. (1969). Mango growing. In *Proceedings of the Conference on Tropical and Subtropical Fruits*. London, Tropical Products Institute, pp. 211-215.

Jayaraman, K. S., Ramanuja, M. N., Goverdhanan, T., Bhatia, B. S., and Nath, H. (1976). Technological aspects of use of ripe mangoes in the preparation of some convenience foods for defense services. *Indian Food Packer* 30:76-82.

Kapur, N. S., Rao, K. S., and Srivastava, H. C. (1962). Refrigerated gas storage of mangos. *Food Sci.* 11:228-231.

Kinch, D. M. (1959). A continuous-process centrifuge. *Am. Soc. Agr. Engin. Trans.* 2:52-57.

Kotalawala, J. (1972). Techniques of propagation of mango in Ceylon. *Acta Hortic.* 24:82-84.

Lakshminarayana, S. (1973). Respiration and ripening patterns in the life cycle of the mango fruit. *J. Hort. Sci.* 48:227-233.

Lakshminarayana, S. (1975). Relation of time of harvest on respiration, chemical constituents and storage life of mangos. *Fla. State Hortic. Soc.* 88:477-481.

Lakshminarayana, S. (1980). Mango. In *Tropical and Subtropical Fruits* (S. Nagy and P. E. Shaw, eds.). Westport, Conn., Avi Publishing, pp. 184-257.

Lakshminarayana, S., Subhadra, N. V., and Subramanyam, H. (1970). Some aspects of developmental physiology of the mango fruit. *J. Hort. Sci.* 45:133-142.

Lynch, J. S., and Nelson, R. (1951). Mango budding. In *Mango Studies,* Stuart, Fla. Florida Mango Forum, pp. 149-152.

Mallik, P. C., and De, B. N. (1952). Manures and manuring of the mango and economics of mango culture. *Ind. J. Agr. Sci.* 22:151-166.

Mallik, S. C. (1976). Different methods for raising of mango seedlings. *Indian Food Packer* 30:33-35.

Malo, E. (1972). Mango Culture in Florida. *Acta Hortic.* 24:149-154.

Malo, S. E. (1970). Mango and avocado cultivars present status and future developments. *Proc. Fla. State Hortic. Soc.* 83:357-362.

Mathur, P. B., and Subramanyam, H. (1956). Effect of a fungicidal wax coating on the storage behaviour of mangos. *J. Sci. Food Agric.* 7:673-676.

Maxie, E. C., Sommer, N. F., and Mitchell, F. G. (1971). Infeasibility of irradiating fresh fruits and vegetables. *Hortscience* 6:202-204.

Morga, N. S., Lustree, A. O., Tunac, M. M., Balagot, A. H., and Soriano, M. R. (1979). Physico-chemical change in Philippine Carabao mangoes during ripening. *Food Chemistry* 4:225-234.

Mukherjee, P. K. (1972). Harvesting, storage and transport of mango. *Acta Hortic.* 24:251-258.

Mukherjee, S. K. (1967). History, origin and botany. In *The Mango: A Handbook* (C. G. Raghava Kurup, U. Narasinga Rao, P. Kachroo, S. N. Tata, eds.). New Delhi, Indian Council of Agricultural Research, pp. 1-13.

Mukherjee, S. K. (1972). Origin of mango *(Mangifera indica). Econ. Bot.* 26(3):260-264.

Mukherjee, S. K. (1976). Current advances on mango research around the world. *Acta Hortic.* 57:37-42.

Nanjundaswamy, A. M., Saroja, S., and Ranganna, S. (1973). Determination of thermal process for canned mango products. *Indian Food Packer* 27:5-13.

Narayana, B. S. (1976). Some technological aspects of the preparation of popular varieties of green mango pickles. *Indian Food Packer* 30:40-44.

Ogata, J. N., Kawano, Y., Bevenue, A., and Casarett, L. J. (1972). The ketoheptose content of some tropical fruits. *J. Agr. Food Chem.* 20:113-115.

Orr, K. J., and Miller, C. D. (1955). Description and quality of some mango varieties grown in Hawaii and their suitability for freezing. *Hawaii Agr. Expt. Sta. Tech. Bul. 26.*

Palaniswamy, K. P., Muthukrishnan, C. R., and Shanmugavelu, K. G. (1973). Studies on the evaluation of certain mango varieties of Tamil Nadu for canning. *Indian Food Packer* 27:9-14.

Popenoe, W. (1939). *Manual of Tropical and Subtropical Fruits.* New York, Macmillan, pp. 83, 105.

Proctor, J. T. A., and Creasy, L. L. (1969). The anthocyanin of the mango fruit. *Phytochemistry* 8:2108.

Puri, G. S., and Puri, K. (1969). Mangoes and mango products. In *Proceeding of the Conference on Tropical and Subtropical Fruits* London, Tropical Products Institute, pp. 221-225.

Rao, M. V. N. (1967). Propagation practices. In *The Mango: A Handbook* (C. G. Raghava Kurup, U. Narasinga Rao, P. Kachroo, and S. N. Tata, eds.). New Delhi, Indian Council of Agricultural Research, p. 35.

Roy, R. S., Mallik, P. C., and De, B. N. (1951). Manuring of the mango *(Mangifera indica Linn).* *Am. Soc. Hort. Sci.* 57:9-16.

Sastry, M. V., and Krishnamurthy, N. (1974). Studies on Indian pickles—1. Preparation and storage of pickles from mangoes. *Indian Food Packer* 28:32-44.

Sastry, M. V., Krishnamurthy, N., and Habibunnisa. (1975). Studies on Indian pickles—Part III. Physico-chemical variations during growth of mangoes (Amlet variety) and storage studies of pickles from them. *Indian Food Packer* 29:39-54.

Saucedo Veloz, S. C., Esparza Torres, F., and Lakshminarayana, S. (1977). Effect of refrigerated temperatures on the incidence of chilling injury and ripening quality of mango fruit. *Proc. Fla. State Hort. Soc.* 90:205-210.

Seo, S. T., Kobayashi, R. M., Chambers, D. L., Steiner, L. F., Lee, C. Y. L., and Komura, M. (1974). Mango weevil: Colbalt-60 γ-irradiation of packaged mangoes. *J. Econ. Entomol.* 67:504-505.

Shashirekha, M. S., and Patwardhan, M. V. (1976). Changes in amino acids, sugars, and nonvolatile acids in a ripening mango fruit *(Mangnifera indica,* Badami variety). *Lebensm-Wiss. U. -Technol.* 9:369-370.

Shaw, J. G., and Lopez, D. F. (1954). Ethylene dibromide as a fumigant for mangoes infested with the Mexican fruit fly. *J. Econ. Entomol.* 47:891-893.

Shrikhande, A. J., Srirangarajan, A. N., and Nadkarni, G. B. (1976). A thermal process for bulk packaging of mango pulp. *Indian Food Packer* 30:65-67.

Singh, D. (1967). Varieties and nomenclature. In *The Mango: A Handbook* (C. G. Raghava Kurup, U. Narasinga Rao, P. Kachrco, and S. N. Tata, eds.). New Delhi, Indian Council of Agricultural Research, pp. 14-31.

Singh Kirpal, K. (1967). Climate and cultivation. In *The Mango: A Handbook* (C. G. Raghava Kurup, U. Narasinga Rao, P. Kachroo, and S. N. Tata, eds.). New Delhi, Indian Council of Agricultural Research, pp. 70-98.

Singh, L. B. (1960). *The Mango.* London, Leonard Hill Books Limited, pp. 5, 251, 380.

Singh, R. N. (1972). An assessment of some of the existing and also potential commercial cultivars of mango in India. *Acta Hortic.* 24: 24-28.

Singh, S., Krishnamurthi, S., and Katyal, S. L. (1963). *Fruit Culture in India.* New Delhi, Indian Council of Agricultural Research, pp. 16, 103.

Spalding, D. H., Reeder, W. F., Von Windeguth, D. L., and Brudett, Jr., A. K. (1975). Effect of ethylene dibromide fumigation on appearance, decay and ripening time of mangos. *Proc. Fla. State Hortic. Soc.* 88:471-476.

Srivastava, H. C. (1967). Grading storage and marketing. In *The Mango: A Handbook* (C. G. Raghava Kurup, U. Narasinga Rao, P. Kachroo, and S. N. Tata, eds.). New Delhi, Indian Council of Agricultural Research, pp. 99-149.

Stafford, A. E., Cavaletto, C., and Brekke, J. (1966). Papaya purée processing. *Hawaii Agric. Exp. Sta. Tech. Prog. Report No. 157.*

Sturrock, T. T. (1951). A study of the identification of mango varieties in Florida. In *Mango Studies,* Stuart, Fla. Florida Mango Forum, pp. 71-83.

Subbarayan, J. J. C., and Cama, H. R. (1970). Carotenoids in 3 stages of ripening of mango. *J. Food Sci.* 35:262-265.

Subramanham, H., Narayana Moorthy, N. V., Lakshminarayana, S., and Krishnamurthy, S. (1972). Studies on harvesting, transport, and storage of mango. *Acta Hortic.* 24:260-264.

Subramanian, V., Sharma, T. R., and Nath, H. (1976). Freeze dehydration of mango as pulp and as a ready-to-serve beverage. *Indian Food Packer* 30:70-75.

Sundararaj, J. S., Muthuswamy, S., and Sadasivam, R. (1972). Storage of mango fruits. *Acta Hortic.* 24:265-270.

Teaotia, S. S., Mehta, G. L., Tomar, M. C., and Garg, R. C. (1976). Studies on dehydration of tropical fruits in uttar pradesh-I. Mango (*Mangifera indica* L.). *Indian Food Packer.* 30:15-19.

Thomas, A. C., and Beyers, M. (1979). γ-Irradiation of subtropical fruits. 3. A comparison of the chemical changes occurring during normal ripening of mangoes and papayas with changes produced by γ-irradiation. *J. Agric. Food Chem.* 27:157-163.

Thomas, P. (1975). Effects of post-harvest temperature on quality, carotenoids and ascorbic acid content of Alphonso mangoes on ripening. *J. Food Sci.* 40:704-706.

Thomas, P., and Janave, M. T. (1973). Polyphenol oxidase activity and browning of mango fruits induced by gamma irradiation. *J. Food Sci.* 38:1149-1152.

Thompson, A. K., (1971). Transport of West Indian mango fruits. *Trop. Agric. (Trinidad)* 48:71-77.

Valmayor, R. V. (1972). The Philippine mango industry—Its problems and progress. *Acta Hortic.* 24:19-23.

Van Arsdel, W. B., and Copley, M. J. (1964). *Food Dehydration.* Westport, Conn., Avi Publishing, p. 529.

Watt, B. K., and Merrill, A. L. (1963). *Composition of Foods, Agriculture Handbook No. 8.* Washington, D.C., United States Department of Agriculture.

Wiltbank, W. J. (1977). Mango and avocado cultivars in Brazil. *Proc. Fla. State Hortic. Soc.* 90:243-244.

11
Palm Oil

Kurt G. Berger Palm Oil Research Institute of Malaysia,
Kuala Lumpur, Malaysia

I. INTRODUCTION

A. Origin

The palm oil of commerce is the product of *Elaeis guineensis* Jacq. Its origin is generally accepted to be in the tropical area of west Africa. Evidence in support of this origin has been found in fossil pollen and is deduced from the distribution pattern of the wild plants and from historical evidence. However, some authorities argue in favor of a South American origin, in common with that of most allied genera, and early transportation to Africa. Be that as it may, there are historical records of the oil palm and its use for food in west Africa dating from at least the beginning of the sixteenth century.

B. Distribution

The oil palm does not grow in primary jungle, but it grows wherever the forest has been partly cleared, along the banks of rivers, and in many swampy areas. It is distributed in wild and semicultivated groves in the wet areas of west Africa, mainly between latitudes 10° north and 10° south (Hartley, 1979).

C. Economic Significance

The oil palm is an important traditional source of food to the people indigenous to west Africa. Consumption was almost entirely confined to the oil obtained from the flesh, by primitive rendering methods, until recent times. In common with all fats it is a good source of energy. In addition, the crude oil is a rich source of carotenoids (provitamin A) and of tocopherols (vitamin E).

The beginnings of an international trade in palm oil were stimulated early in the nineteenth century by the need to find alternative cargoes

consequent to the abolition of the slave trade. At that time, the oil
was suitable only for soap and other technical purposes. Up to 14,000
tons were exported annually in the 1830s, and the trade reached
30,000 tons in the 1860s and 87,000 tons by 1911. The oil invariably
had a high content of free fatty acids resulting from the native processing methods. In the middle of the nineteenth century a trade in palm
kernels also developed. The nuts had not been regarded as a food
source in west Africa, and the kernels could be relatively easily collected into commercial quantities after hand-cracking of the shells. By
1911, 232,000 tons of kernels were exported, mainly from Nigeria.

D. Development of Plantations

The year 1911 also saw the establishment of the first oil palm plantation, all the foregoing production being from wild or semicultivated
groves. This plantation, however, was established not in West Africa
but in Southeast Asia on the island of Sumatra. The oil palm had been
introduced into the botanic gardens at Bogor in Java as early as 1848
when four seedlings of African origin were planted. Although the
useful properties of the oil were already known, this introduction did
not lead to commercial plantations for a long time. In the first place
some progeny of the original four plants was grown in Deli, Sumatra.
Further planting for purely ornamental purposes then occurred on a
number of estates in Sumatra, using seedlings of the Deli palms.

The first commercial palms in Sumatra were planted in 1911 by
M. A. Hallet, a Belgian with some experience of oil palms in Africa,
and he used progeny of the Deli palms. It is a most fortunate fact,
which was already recognized at that time, that the Deli palms were
highly productive, with a fruit composition that was superior to the
west African palms. Shortly afterwards an associate of Hallet's
planted some Deli palms in Malaysia in the Kuala Selangor district,
and developed commercial plantings at Tennamaram Estate in 1917. At
first the industry grew more rapidly in Sumatra than in Malaysia, and
by 1938 there were some 90,000 ha planted in Sumatra and 30,000 in
Malaysia. The development of plantations in West Africa was very slow
between the wars and was encouraged much more in Zaire (then
Belgian Congo) than in Nigeria.

Notable developments in palm oil production and oil palm plantations
have taken place since 1945. In some West African countries developments have been hampered by internal political and organizational difficulties, an exception being the Ivory Coast where, with significant
French participation, a substantial plantation and oil processing industry has been established, and Zaire where there are more than
250,000 ha of large and small plantations.

E. Palm Oil as a Worldwide Commodity

Production in Southeast Asia has increased dramatically, principally as a result of a partial replacement of rubber plantations by oil palm in Malyasia, which has now taken first place as producer and exporter. By 1960, relatively small plantations also existed in South and Central America, particularly Venezuela, Colombia, Ecuador, Costa Rica, Nicaragua, and Honduras; and today these areas have a total of more than 100,000 ha of oil palm. Further increases in planted area may be expected, especially in countries that require more edible oils for local consumption. Recent growth in palm oil production and exports is illustrated in Figs. 1 and 2, derived from Food and Agriculture Organization (FAO) data.

Figure 1 shows clearly that the main part of the increase in world production comes from the Far East. In the export field (Fig. 2), Far Eastern production is completely dominant, and African exports have shown a substantial decline, mainly due to the increased domestic consumption. From its position as the original exporter of palm oil, Nigeria has recently become an importer.

F. Productivity

In terms of yield per acre, the oil palm is the most efficient of all edible oil-producing plants. The following figures are based on average yields of oil, as shown in Table 1. Much higher yields than those

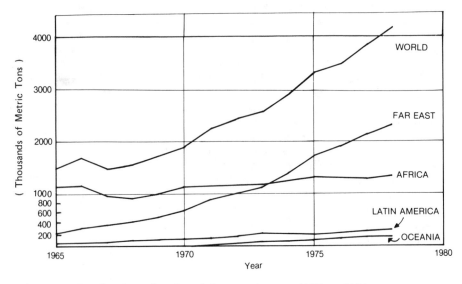

Figure 1 Production of palm oil by continents 1965 to 1978.

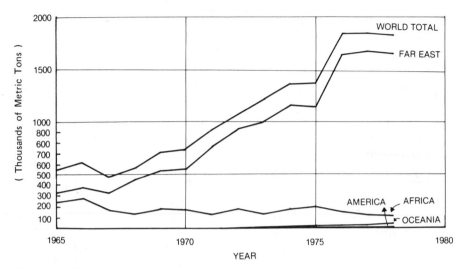

Figure 2 Export of palm oil of each continent 1965 to 1978.

mentioned in Table 1 are now being obtained from oil palm in Malaysia, as indicated in Table 2. Production costs of palm oil have been calculated at about $0.07 to $0.09/lb of oil (World Bank, 1976), and in consequence palm oil is competing successfully in the world market.

II. CULTURAL PRACTICES

A. Climate and Soil

The oil palm requires a tropical climate with a minimum of 65 in. rainfall per year, preferably spaced evenly throughout the year. While it will grow in areas that have a dry season of 2 to 3 months, this affects

Table 1 Productivity of Various Oil-Producing Plants

Oil	Lb/acre/year	
Palm oil	3300	} 3670
Palm kernel oil	370	
Coconut		1120
Groundnut		780
Soybean		340

Source: Adapted from Bek-Nielsen (1977).

Table 2 Yield of Fresh Fruit Bunches and Oil
Equivalent in Malaysia

	Tons/acre	Palm oil equivalent (tons/acre/year)
Best	16	3.2
Average	Up to 14	2.8
Small holders' cooperative	8-10 tons	1.8
Independent small holder	6-8 tons FFB/acre	1.4

flower formation and hence reduces the overall yield. It is normally
grown within 10° north and south of the equator, but suitable climatic conditions enable it to be grown in some localities outside these
latitudes.

The most suitable land for oil palm cultivation is flat, with a deep,
well-drained soil that is moderately permeable. Very sandy or very
clayey soil is not suitable, a pH of 4 to 6 is preferred. In Malaysia,
oil palm is grown successfully on soils of widely varying nutrient
status, deficiencies being made good by the use of appropriate fertilizer.
Successful procedures have been developed for cultivating oil palm on
peat soils and even under the extreme conditions found in acid sulfate
soils, which may have a pH as low as 2.0 to 2.6. In this case the
acidity results from the oxidation of iron sulfide deposits, and this may
be prevented by raising the water table to create anaerobic conditions
in the sulfide layer.

B. Production of Selected Seeds

There are two distinct fruit forms of *E. guineensis*—dura, having thick,
hard shell, and pisifera, having no shell, and a rather small kernel
surrounded by a ring of fibers. When these two types are crossed,
using pisifera as the male parent, the tenera type of fruit is obtained,
with an intermediate thickness of shell, surrounded by fiber. Tenera
palms are now those most widely grown on plantations, and are usually
raised from seed obtained by crossing parents of known yield
performance.

Controlled pollination is achieved by protecting the chosen male and
female flowers with bags. When the male flower is mature, its pollen is
collected and, if necessary, may be preserved by deep-freezing or
freeze-drying. It may be diluted with talcum powder before being
dusted onto the female flower. The latter is further protected for a
time from other pollen. When the treated fruit bunch is ripe, it is

harvested, the fruit stripped manually, and the mesocarp removed mechanically. The seed is recovered, sorted, and then heat-treated to assist germination. This process involves drying to 17% moisture, heating in sealed bags at 40°C for 40 days or more, and rewetting to 22% moisture followed by storage at ambient temperature until germination takes place. The seeds are sorted frequently to remove any that are damaged or diseased. Germination takes about 10 days, and after a further 2 weeks the seed is ready for planting in the nursery. During the heat treatment and germination, seeds are often treated with a fungicide as a precaution. Subsequent to germination the seeds may be dispatched over long distances to the nursery requiring them.

C. Planting Out

Planting out takes place after about 14 days of germination. The best system (Turner and Gillbanks, 1974) is to plant directly into individual containers, preferably large polybags. The main advantage being a minimal transplanting shock. Shading of seedlings is desirable for the first 10 weeks, and daily watering is required. A specially formulated compound fertilizer is applied in a regular program. The seedlings are ready for field planting after 11 to 12 months.

The density of planting is an important factor in determining the yield. Planting too close causes excessive competition and elongation of the trunks. However, a density of 55 to 60 palms per acre is most usual. Corley et al. (1973) have developed a formula relating mean leaf area of developed palms to optimal density, which can be used to calculate the density appropriate for a particular location. The planting pattern used is triangular, palms in one row being placed halfway between the palms in the two adjacent rows. For detailed descriptions of cultural and fertilizer practices the reader is referred to standard textbooks (Turner and Gillbanks, 1974; Bevan et al., 1966; Bevan and Gray, 1969). The full development of the plant and subsequently the production of high yields of fruit are highly dependent on regular applications of fertilizer, judged on the basis of the local conditions. In order to assist plant growth and avoid the production of excessively small fruits with low oil content, it is usual practice to remove flowers developing during the first 20 to 26 months after planting.

D. Pollination

Until very recently (see, for example, Turner and Gillbanks, 1974) it was thought that the oil palm was wind-pollinated. It is now known, however, that in west Africa and in peninsular Malaysia pollination is by insects that feed on the male flower and visit the female (Syed, 1980).

In west Africa the insects are weevils, *Elaeidobius* species, the main species being *E. kamerunicus*, whereas in peninsular Malaysia

Thrips hawaiiensis is responsible. Neither of these insects frequents
the oil palm in east Malaysia (Sabah and Sarawak on the island of
Borneo). Young palms have relatively few male flowers, and pollination is poor. Therefore, assisted pollination is usually practiced on
young palms, and is most necessary in locations without an insect
pollinator.

E. Propagation

As previously indicated, seedlings for plantations are usually produced
from seed obtained by the crossing of carefully selected parents with
a record of high yield of oil and other desirable characteristics. However, within the last 3 years the technique of cell culture has been
successfully used to produce plantlets by vegetative propagation. The
process involves taking a sample of tissue (root, leaf, flower, or meri-
stem may be used) and growing it aseptically on a selected sterile
medium (Corley et al., 1979). A callus is formed, and by changing
the hormones and other chemicals in the medium the callus is eventually
induced to produce plantlets. This process produces oil palms identical
with the parent, and it is estimated that an increase in yield of 20 to
30% may be obtained by selecting exceptional plants as parents. The
commercial production of selected clones by cell culture is expected to
begin within the next 2 to 3 years in Malaysia and in west Africa.

F. Harvesting

Fruits ripen 5 months after pollination. As much as 80% of the oil content in the mesocarp is synthesized during the last 2 weeks of ripening,
and therefore the correct timing of harvesting has an important effect
on oil yields. However, the individual fruits in a bunch ripen over a
period of 2 to 3 weeks, starting at the tip of the bunch. When fruit
becomes ripe, it detaches from the bunch and may fall to the ground.
Overripe fruit bruises easily, releasing a very active lipolytic enzyme
and resulting in rapid development of free fatty acids and a loss in
quality. Therefore, the moment of harvesting has to be a compromise,
usually decided by counting the number of fruits already detached and
fallen to the ground. A common criterion is two fallen fruits per kilogram of bunch weight. If oil of especially low free fatty acid content is
required for special purposes, then somewhat earlier harvesting with
some loss of oil yield is necessary. Each area is inspected for ripe
bunches every 7 to 10 days.

Harvesting of young palm is carried out with a chisel or knife and
of old tall palms with a sickle tied to a long cane. The frond immediately below the bunch is first cut, followed by the bunch itself.
Bunches may weigh 20 kg or more, and some bruising is inevitable as
they fall. As already indicated, bruising of cells releases lipolytic

enzymes that cause a rapid increase in free fatty acids. Therefore, bunches are transported as rapidly and gently as possible to the oil mill for processing.

III. PROCESSING

A. Primitive Methods

Primitive methods of obtaining palm oil from fruit are described by Adam (1910). These traditional methods of recovering the oil are still in use in the villages of west Africa. Fallen and loose fruit are collected, the fruit bunch is cut off and then broken up and left for a few days, when the rest of the fruit can be detached. The subsequent treatment varies somewhat from place to place, but the following steps can be distinguished:

1. Softening of the pericarp by boiling in water or by fermentation or both.
2. Mashing with a pestle and mortar or by treading underfoot.
3. Addition of hot water and separation of the oil. The residue is often reprocessed to obtain more oil.
4. Purification by heating to drive off water, and by removal of scum.

Only the simplest equipment is used. For boiling, the container is a large earthenware pot or a 44-gal steel drum. Fermentation may take place in this container, or in a cement-lined pit, or where available, in a canoe dragged on land. The separation of oil is usually achieved by skimming, but some interesting variations may be noted. In Guinea, the mash is placed in wicker baskets that are plunged into a succession of containers of boiling water, on which the oil separates. Thus, the fruit debris is kept separate from the oil. In Mellacor'ee the mash after dilution with water is filtered through a bed of straw (Adam, 1910). The oil emulsion, now substantially free of debris, is then boiled dry. Storage of the finished product is typically in earthenware jars of about 20-liter capacity. It will be appreciated that the quality of the oil produced in this way is very variable in color and flavor.

Two main types of product are obtained, depending on whether the fruit is softened by boiling or by fermentation (Nwanze, 1965). In the former case the endogenous lipase is inactivated and a relatively low free fatty acid content (7 to 12%) is usual with an oil yield of 40 to 50%. This is classified as *soft oil*. When there is fermentation, the acidity developed is much higher and may be 30 to 50%, whereas only 20 to 40% of the oil is recovered. This *hard oil* is preferred in some areas, for example the Niger Delta, and requires less labor and fuel. Faulkner and Lewin (1923) calculated that to produce 1 ton of soft oil required 420 work days, whereas for 1 ton of hard oil only 133 work days were needed.

The reason for the difference in physical consistency is that the formation of free fatty acids is accompanied by the formation of diglycerides, which form eutectic mixtures with triglycerides. The eutectic point is at a diglyceride content of 20% according to Moran (1962). However, Loncin (1958) found the eutectic point at 12% diglyceride and reported a minimum melting point and maximum softness (measured by penetrometer) for palm oil of 7% free fatty acids. Palm oil with 25% free fatty acids was much firmer and higher melting, and in fact similar in physical properties to a neutral refined product.

B. Processing: Intermediate Technology

Attempts to provide simple small-scale equipment that would give more efficient oil extraction and have greater productivity than the primitive village methods have been made since the 1900s. The most successful process operating since the 1930s (Hartley, 1979) consisted of:

1. Boiling the fruit in a 40-gal mild steel drum
2. Pounding with wooden pestles
3. Transferring while hot to a curb press similar to those used for wine

The press consists of a cage of wooden slats standing on a metal base fitted with a screw-threaded shaft. The fruit is loaded into the cage and pressure is applied by screwing down a metal plate. The oil escapes between the wooden slats and collects in a channel in the base plate. About 65% of the oil content can be recovered in one pressing.

The next improvement came in the 1950s with the introduction of the hand-operated hydraulic press, which could expel about 95% of the oil and had a capacity of about 50 kg fruit per charge. A manually operated horizontal drum for stripping the fruits from the bunches was introduced. Additionally, the fruit was reheated in drums both before pounding and again before pressing—a significant factor in obtaining efficient oil extraction.

C. Large-Scale Processing

1. The Present-Day Oil Mill

Oil mills are usually sited on or close to large areas of oil palm. The size of the mill is matches to the quantity of fruit to be processed. Mills usually have a capacity between 20 and 80 tons/hr of fresh fruit bunches. The following processing steps are involved in the oil mill.

1. Tipping of trucks on the unloading ramp.
2. Loading fruit bunches into sterilizer cages.
3. Sterilization: This destroys the lipase and stops acid development, and also softens the fruit and loosens it on the bunch.

4. Unloading of the sterilizer and tipping of the sterilized fruit from
   the cages into the bunch stripper. This is a horizontal rotating
   cylinder in which the bunches are tumbled until the fruit separates.
   Empty bunches are removed for disposal, usually by burning, and
   the fruit passes on to the digester.
5. In the digester, the fruit is thoroughly mashed and passed to the
   press.
6. Modern oil mills are usually equipped with continuous screw presses
   which are more efficient and economical than the hydraulic presses
   formerly used. The screw press discharges an oil stream that at
   this stage contains a large amount of comminuted vegetable matter
   and water, and a solids stream consisting of fairly dry fruit fiber
   and kernels. The oil stream is passed to settling tanks where the
   oil is siphoned from the top and cleaned in a clarifying centrifuge
   before being dried, cooled, and stored. The lower layer from the
   settling tank is passed to a sludge centrifuge. This puts out an
   oily stream, which is fed back to the settling tank for further
   clarification, and an aqueous stream, the *palm oil sludge,* containing
   large amounts of organic matter, which is discharged for appropriate
   effluent treatment.

The solid discharge from the screw press is dried somewhat and
then the fibers are separated from the nuts by an air stream. The
fibers are used to feed the boilers that provide steam for the mill.
The nuts are cracked in a centrifugal cracker, and the shell is separated from the kernel in a hydrocyclone. The kernel is dried and
packed for dispatch. The shell is used partly in the boiler and partly
as hard core on estate roads, although experiments have also shown
it to be a suitable starting material for active charcoal. Figure 3 gives
a flow sheet for the oil mill process.

The palm kernels are further processed to yield palm kernel oil
and a protein cake for animal feed. This may be done in a solvent
extraction plant or by means of presses. In the latter case the cake
has significant residual oil content.

2. Products and Byproducts of the Oil Mill

The various products and waste streams of the oil mill are shown in
Fig. 4; the figures in brackets indicate the quantities obtained, starting with 100 parts of fresh fruit bunches. (See also Kirkaldy and
Sutanto, 1976.) Experiments have been carried out to demonstrate
the use of surplus fiber and of the sludge solids for animal feed, and
these are discussed in Sec. V.C.

D. Processing: Refining

Whereas the consumption of palm oil in west Africa is still largely in
the crude state, in all other user countries the oil is first refined

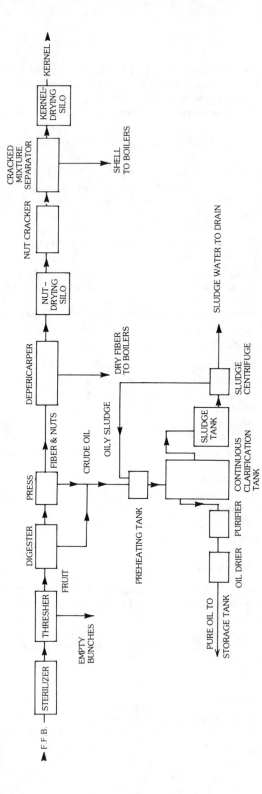

Figure 3 Flow diagram of a typical oil mill. (From Cawkwell, 1969.)

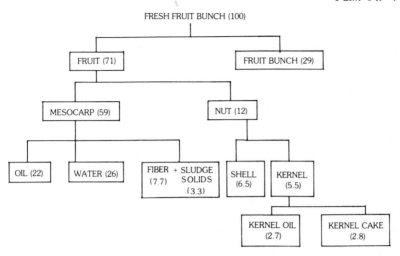

Figure 4 Yields of products from the palm oil mill. (Adapted from Young, 1976.)

by processes common to all edible oil and fats. Two alternative sequences are suitable.

1. Alkali refining
   a. Degumming with phosphoric acid
   b. Neurtalization with strong caustic soda, followed by removal of the soap
   c. Treatment with bleaching earth followed by filtration
   d. Deodorization under vacuum, using superheated steam to distill out flavor volatiles.
2. Physical refining
   a. Degumming with phosphoric acid
   b. Treatment with bleaching earth, followed by filtration
   c. Distillative deacidification and deodorization

The latter process takes place in a modified deodorizer, which enables a larger amount of steam to be used, and the considerable amount of distillate which includes the free fatty acids to be efficiently recovered. The physical process is particularly suitable for palm oil of 3 to 5% free fatty acids, since the losses of neutral oil are significantly smaller than in the alkali process. The refining processes may be carried out after transport to the consuming country, or prior to shipment, as is the case increasingly in Malaysia and the Ivory Coast. A flow sheet for the two processes is given in Fig. 5.

E. Processing: Fractionation

An additional process step has been widely adopted for palm oil in the last 10 years. Owing to its chemical composition, palm oil is readily

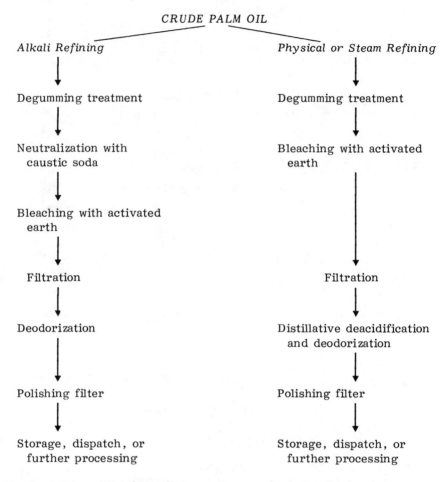

Figure 5 Flow sheet for refining processes for palm oil.

separated into a more liquid (olein) and a more solid (stearin) fraction.
The process consists essentially of two steps. Crystallization is carried
out under controlled conditions at a chosen temperature. In some
processes a solvent is used. Separation of the solid from the liquid
phase is effected by filtration or by centrifugation. Finally, where
necessary the solvent is removed from both fractions. The products
of fractionation, having significantly different physical properties
from the original oil, find additional applications mainly in food
products.

IV. COMPOSITION

A. Palm Oil

A typical gross composition of crude palm oil is given in Table 3. As stated previously, the free fatty acid content is variable because it is the result of natural enzymic action before the fruit is sterilized. Higher free fatty acid contents will result in higher partial glyceride and lower triglyceride contents.

1. Fatty Acid and Glyceride Composition

The fatty acid composition of palm oil and typical fractionated palm oils is given in Table 4. For the palm oil fractions a range of compositions is given. This range represents oleins and stearins obtained from a number of commercial plants operating under different process conditions. It will be noted that the composition of palm olein does not vary much, but that stearins of widely differing compositions can be obtained.

The composition of palm oil from widely differing sources shows a relatively narrow range of variation. Most of the published data for the triglyceride composition of palm oil relates to oil of Malaysian origin, but it will be seen from Table 5 that Sumatra and Congo palm oils are quite similar.

2. Minor Constituents of Palm Oil

The unsaponifiable matter of palm oil contains a number of substances of nutritional and technological importance. Analysis from several sources are given in Table 6. More detailed analytical information about several of the components of the unsaponifiable matter is given in subsequent sections.

Carotenoids. A feature of considerable practical importance in crude palm oil is its relatively high content of carotenoids that gives it its bright yellow-red color. β-Carotene is the largest component, α-carotene being most of the remainder, as shown in Table 7.

Table 3 Percentage Composition of Palm Oil

Free fatty acids	3.2
Monoglycerides	Trace
1,2-Diglycerides	0.8
1,3-Diglycerides	1.2
Triglycerides	94.3
Unsaponifiable matter	0.5

Table 4 Fatty Acid Composition (Mole %) of Crude Palm Oil and Palm Oil Fractions

	Palm oil					Fractionated palm oil (Malaysia)	
	Mean of 215 Malaysian samples[a]	Sumatra[b]	Papua New Guinea[b]	Codex[e]	Zaire[c]	Olein Range[d]	Stearin Range[d]
C12:0	0.1	0	0	<1.2	0.1	0.1-1.1	0.1-0.6
C14:0	1.0	1.3	1.0	0.5-5.9	1.0	0.9-1.4	1.1-1.9
C16:0	43.7	45.6	48.8	32-59	45.5	37.9-41.7	47.2-73.8
C16:1	0.1	—	—	<0.6	0.1	0.1-0.4	0-0.2
C18:0	4.4	4.1	2.5	1.5-8.0	5.9	4.0-4.8	4.4-5.6
C18:1	39.9	39.6	35.5	27-52	34.6	40.7-43.6	15.6-37.0
C18:2	10.3	9.4	12.2	5.0-14.0	11.8	10.4-13.4	3.2-9.8
C18:3	—	—	—	<1.5	0.4	0.1-0.6	0.1-0.6
C20	0.3	—	—	<1.0	0.3	0.2-0.5	0.1-0.6
Other	0.2	—	—	—	0.3	—	—

[a]Chin et al. (1980).
[b]Harrisons and Crosfield (1974).
[c]Loncin et al. (1970).
[d]Tan et al. (1983).
[e]Codex Alimentarius. Draft standard (1979).

Table 5 Triglyceride Composition of Palm Oil[a]

No. of double bonds	Gly- ceride	Unilever (1965) Congo	Jurriens and Kroesen (1965) Sumatra	Deroanne et al. (1975) Malaysian	Barrett et al. (1963) Malaysian	Jacobsberg (1975) Malaysian	Faulkner et al. (1976)	Tan (1979) Malaysian (1)	Tan (1979) Malaysian (2)
0	PMP	0.3	0.3			0.5			
	MPP	0.2	0.6			0.2			
	PPP	4.3	6.1	8.66	10	4.8		9.0	10.2
	PPS	1.1	0.9			0.8			
	PSP	0.4	0.3			1.2			
	Others		0.3			0.3			
Subtotal		6.3	8.5	8.66	10	7.9	11.2	9.0	10.2
1	MOP	1.2	1.1			1.0			
	POP	24.1	25.9	30.17	32.5	28.7		30.6	30.8
	POS	7.0	3.1			4.7			
	SOS	0.5	—			0.3			
	PPO	3.6	6.0	5.87	8.0	3.5		6.3	7.3
	SPO	0.5	0.3			0.3			
	PSO		0.5			0.8			
	Others		0.8			0.4			
Subtotal		36.9	37.7	36.04	40.5	39.7	44.7	36.9	38.1
2	MOO	0.6	18.9	22.09		0.4			
	POO	18.9			26	19.6		21.5	22.0
	SOO	2.8	2.6			1.8			
	OPO	1.0	1.2	1.07		0.5		1.1	1.3
	PPL	0.4	1.7	1.05	1.0	0.9		1.4	1.2

Table 5 (Continued)

No. of double bonds	Glyceride	Unilever (1965) Congo	Jurriens and Kroesen (1965) Sumatra	Deroanne et al. (1975) Malaysian	Barrett et al. (1963) Malaysian	Jacobsberg (1975) Malaysian	Faulkner et al. (1976)	Tan (1979) Malaysian (1)	Tan (1979) Malaysian (2)
	MLP	0.5				0.3			
	PLP	7.8	6.8	9.33	6.5	6.9		9.3	8.7
	PLS	2.3	1.9			1.2			
	Others		1.9			0.9			
Subtotal		34.3	35.0	33.54	33.5	32.4	27.7	33.3	33.2
3	OOO	2.7	3.2	4.19		3.3		3.8	3.9
	MOL	0.2				0.1			
	POL	4.0	2.6	4.12	13	5.5		4.8	3.7
	SOL	0.6				0.5			
	MLO	0.3				0.1			
	PLO	4.5	4.3	7.08		4.8		6.5	6.2
	SLO	0.6	0.5						
	OPL	0.3	0.5	0.40		0.4		0.5	0.4
	Others		0.6			0.1			
Subtotal		13.2	11.7	15.79		14.8	11.5	15.6	14.2
4	OOL	1.8	1.5	2.86		1.9		1.7	1.3
	OLO	1.4	1.3	1.60		0.8		1.1	1.1
	PLL	2.2	2.6	1.57	3	1.4		1.5	1.0
	SLL	—	0.5						
	LPL	0.4	—	0.04		0.1		0.1	

		OSLe, SOLe, SLeO							
OSLe, SOLe, SLeO		0.8							
Others	0.7		0.2			0.9		0.8	0.5
Subtotal	6.5		6.9	6.07		5.1	4.8	5.2	3.9
Summary									
0	6.3		8.5	8.66	10	7.9	11.2	9.0	10.2
1	36.9		37.7	36.04	40.5	39.7	44.7	36.9	38.1
2	34.3		35.0	33.54	33.5	32.4	27.7	33.3	33.2
3	13.2		11.7	15.79	13	14.8	11.5	15.6	14.2
4	6.5		6.9	6.07	5	5.1	4.8	5.2	3.9
Grand Total	97.2	99.8	99.8	100.3	100.0	99.9	99.9	100.0	99.6

[a] Key: S = stearic; P = palmitic; M = Myristic; O = oleic; L = linoleic; Le = linolenic.

Table 6 Unsaponifiable Matter of Palm Oil (ppm)

| | Crude | | | |
| | Faulkner et al. (1976) | Jacobsberg et al. (1978) | Weir (1975) | |
			Crude	Refined
Carotenoids	473	640	450-820	—
Tocopherols	447	850	620-830	460
Sterols	271	300	300	250
Triterpene alcohols	387	800	760	n.a.
Xanthophylls	240			

(n.a. = not available.)

Tocopherols. The level of total tocopherols in crude palm oil was reported by Jacobsberg et al. (1978) as 760 ppm (Malaysia), 860 ppm (Zaire), and 465 ppm for a low grade of Nigerian palm oil. The same author (1975c) obtained a mean value for 990 ppm for 117 samples taken at the time of shipment and representing a large proportion of Malaysian production. On arrival at destination the mean value for the shipped oil was 720 ppm. Palm oil is unique among vegetable oils in that most of the tocopherols are present as tocotrienols. Detailed analyses for individual tocopherols in Malaysian crude palm oil have been carried out recently (Table 8).

After refining, the total tocopherol content normally falls to 50 to 80% of the value found in the crude oil. Some of the tocopherols are present in the deodorizer distillate, and some are destroyed.

Table 7 Percentage Composition of Carotenoids of Palm Oil

	Faulkner et al. (1976)	Weir (1975)	Loncin et al. (1970)
α-Carotene	19.5	21.3	36.4
β-Carotene	43.4	69.6	54.4
γ-Carotene	—	5.0	3.3
Lycopene	—	—	3.8
Xanthophylls	24	4.1	2.2

Table 8 Tocopherols in Crude Palm Oil (ppm)

	α-Tocopherol	α-Tocotrienol	γ-Tocopherol	γ-Tocotrienol	γ-Tocotrienol	Total
	99[a]	136[a]	30[a]	209[a]	105[a]	579[a]
Range for three samples[b]	146-160	90-205	—	273-439	78-94	638-890

[a]Jacobsberg et al. (1978).
[b]Gapor and Berger (1980).

Table 9 Percentage Composition of Sterols in Palm Oil

	Faulkner et al. (1976)	Seher and Vogel (1971)[a]	Matsumoto (1974)	Manino and Amelotti (1974)	Weir (1975)	Guyot (1969)
β-Sitosterol	58.7	60.2	62.4	60.1	59.9	64
Campesterol	24.6	22.8	21.2	24.4	21.4	19
Stigmasterol	13.2	13.4	12.9	12.3	12.1	10
Cholesterol	1.9	3.6	1.4	3.1	6.6	7
Δ-5-Avenasterol	1.8	—	2.1	—	—	—

[a]Mean of 50 analyses.

Table 10 Percentage
Composition of Lipids
from Palm Fruit

Neutral lipids	93.7
Phospholipids	2.6
Glycolipids	1.4
Losses	2.3

Sterols. β-sitosterol is the major component of the sterols of palm oil, whereas campesterol and stigmasterol make up most of the rest. Detailed analyses are given in Table 9. These results represent oil from a variety of sources and show very little variation.

Polar Lipids. The phospholipid content of crude palm oil varies between 500 and 1158 ppm according to Weir (1975); other authors also give figures within this range. A detailed analysis of the phospholipids present in commercially produced palm oil does not appear to be available. However, Tan (1977) carried out analyses on phospholipids and on glycolipids obtained in oil extracted from fresh palm fruit mesocarp with mixed solvents. He obtained 25% total lipids based on fresh fruit. Fractionation on acid-treated Florisil gave the composition of the lipids shown in Table 10.

Phospholipids. The composition of the phospholipids is given in Table 11 from a later publication by Goh et al. (1982).

Glycolipids. The composition of the glycolipids is given in Table 12.
It should be noted that the polar lipid content of crude palm oil produced by large-scale methods is much lower than the amount extracted by Tan with solvents, and its composition may be somewhat different from the above.

Table 11 Phospholipids of Fresh Palm Fruit (mol %)

Phosphatidyl choline	36
Phosphatidyl ethanolamine	24
Phosphatidyl inositol	22
Phosphatidyl glycerol	9
Diphosphatidyl glycerol	4
Phosphatidic acid	3
Lysophosphatidyl ethanolamine	2

Source: Goh et al. (1982).

Table 12 Glycolipids of Fresh
Palm Fruit (%)

Monoglycosyl diglyceride	26.8
Diglycosyl diglyceride	23.1
Cerebrosides	12.9
Steryl glycosides	20.7
Unknown and loss	16.5

Source: Khor et al. (1980).

B. Palm Kernel Oil

1. Fatty Acid Composition

The fatty acid composition of palm kernel oil is given in Table 13.
It will be noted that it is very different from palm oil. The kernel
oil is a typical lauric oil, rich in saturated fatty acids of short and
intermediate chain length.

2. Glyceride Composition

Palm kernel oil contains a high proportion of saturated triglycerides
of short and medium chain length. Table 14 gives the proportions
of the main triglyceride groups present by carbon number, being the
sum of the carbon atoms in the three fatty acids chains, and the main

Table 13 Fatty Acid Composition of Palm Kernel Oil (%)

Fatty acid	Typical commercial sample	*Codex Alimentarius* Draft Standard (1979)	Bugaut and Bezard (1977)
C6:0	0.5	<0.5	0.5
C8:0	4.4	2.4-6.2	6.1
C10:0	6.0	2.6-7.0	4.9
C12:0	44.2	41-55	52.5
C14:0	14.4	14-20	15.8
C16:0	8.2	6.5-11	6.3
C18:0	2.5	1.3-3.5	1.8
C18:1	16.9	10-23	10.2
C18:2	2.9	0.7-5.4	1.5
Other	—		0.4

Table 14 Component Triglyceride Groups and Main Types in Palm Kernel Oil

Carbon number	Mole (%)	Main types
30	1.3	6, 12, 12
		8, 10, 12
32	8.6	6, 12, 14
		8, 12, 12
34	9.8	8, 12, 14
		10, 12, 12
36	25.7	12, 12, 12
38	16.8	12, 12, 14
40	9.5	12, 12, 16
		12, 14, 14
42	7.8	8, 16, 18
		12, 12, 18
		12, 14, 16
44	5.8	8, 18, 18
		12, 14, 18
		12, 16, 16
46	4.0	12, 16, 18
		14, 14, 18
48	4.4	12, 18, 18
		14, 16, 18
50	2.2	14, 18, 18
		16, 16, 18
52	2.2	16, 18, 18
54	1.8	18, 18, 18

Source: Bezard (1971).

triglycerides in each group. The position of the fatty acids in the glycerides was not determined.

3. Minor Constituents of Palm Kernel Oil

A typical value for the unsaponifiable matter of palm kernel oil is 0.4%. The unsaponifiable matter contains 11 to 118 ppm tocopherol and 2 to 8 ppm carotenes (Jacobsberg, 1975b).

V. NUTRITION

The nutritional qualities of palm and palm kernel oil can be considered
in relation to the foregoing compositional data. An interesting feature
is that the chemical composition of the oil obtained from the mesocarp
(palm oil) is substantially different from that obtained by extraction
of the kernel (palm kernel oil). In common with other natural fats,
palm oil and palm kernel oil are fully digested and are excellent sources
of energy, having more than twice the energy value of carbohydrates
or proteins.

A. Palm Oil

Palm oil has a useful content of linoleic acid, an essential fatty acid
for which the recommended minimum dietary level is about 3% of the
calorie content of the diet (FAO, 1977). Studies on the nutritional
properties of palm oil were reviewed recently by Gottenbos and Vles
(1980). Palm oil has been used in a number of nutritional experiments
in comparison with other oils. In general, the results show that according to the classic criteria of growth, food efficiency, and absorption, palm oil behaves like the other common food fats. Its effect on
mortality and pathological abnormalities is not different from other oils
studied (Timmer and Vles, 1978; Hornstra and Vles, 1978).

Its behavior was in conformity with its composition. For example,
there was some atherogenic effect in the rabbit, as expected from the
polyunsaturated-to-saturated acid ratio of palm oil. This would, however, be counteracted in a normal mixed diet by polyunsaturated acids
present in other components. However in some experiments on arterial
thrombosis, palm oil behaved more favorably than would be predicted
from its fatty acid composition, and was approximately equivalent to
sunflower seed oil in its effect (Hornstra, 1975).

Two minor components of palm oil have nutritional significance.
These are the carotenes and tocopherols. The carotenes are precursors of vitamin A. They are fully available only when the oil is consumed in crude form as is the case in West Africa. The bleaching
process carried out in the refinery is specifically designed to remove
or destroy the carotenes so as to obtain the white color required by
most customers. The tocopherols are important not only for their
natural antioxidant activity, but also because they are physiologically
active as vitamin E.

B. Palm Kernel Oil

Specific studies of the nutritional properties of palm kernel oil have
not been reported. It would be expected from its fatty acid composition
(about 82% saturated) that some increase in blood lipid level would

Table 15 Percentage Composition of Palm Oil Byproducts

	Press fiber[a]	Oil palm sludge[a,b]	Palm kernel cake		
				Expeller[b]	Expeller plus solvent = extracted[a]
Dry matter	86.2	90.3	89.6	89.04	90.6
Crude protein	4.0	9.6	10.2	17.6	19.0
Crude fiber	36.4	11.5	11.4	15.6	16.0
Ether extract	21.0	21.3	16.6	14.3	2.0
Ash	9.0	11.1	11.3	3.02	4.2
Nitrogen-free extract	29.6	46.5	40.1	38.5	58.8
Calcium	0.31	0.28	0.50	0.30	0.34
Phosphorus	0.13	0.26	0.75	0.60	0.69
Magnesium	0.52	0.25	–	–	0.16
Gross energy (MJ/Kg)	18.1	18.7	21.0	21.2	17.3

[a]Devendra and Muthurajah (1977).
[b]Webb et al. (1977).

result if fed at high levels of the diet. However, as a relatively minor component of dietary fats, no significant effect would be expected.

C. Palm Fruit Byproduct

As indicated in Sec. II, some of the byproducts of the oil mill have actual or potential value as animal feed. Analytical data for the pressed fiber, palm oil sludge, and palm kernel meal are given in Table 15. Palm kernel cake is an established protein-rich animal feed component. By comparison with soybean and groundnut meals, it is somewhat high in fiber and low in protein. Nonetheless, it is widely used in compound feed concentrates, forming about 1% of the world trade in oil seed meals. The use of press fiber and oil palm sludge in animal feeds has been the subject of a number of successful experiments, but has not to date been commercialized.

VI. UTILIZATION

A. Food Uses of Palm Oil

The nature of palm oil as a semisolid fat at ambient temperature (20°C), indicates that it should be a useful ingredient in fat products of similar consistency. Its position is most readily appreciated by comparing its solids content over a range of temperatures with that of appropriate fat products, as shown in Table 16.

Table 16 Solids Content of Palm Oil Products and Some End Products

Temperature (°C)	Solids content (%)					
	10	15	20	30	40	50
Palm oil (average)[b]	52	35	23	9	3	—
Palm olein (average)[b]	37	19	6	0	—	—
Palm stearin [b,c]	54-91	42-91	31-87	16-73	7-57	0-40
Block margarine[a]	27	—	18	8	—	—
Tub margarine[a]	13	—	8	4	—	—
Bakery shortening[a]	—	39	29	11	—	—
Indian vanaspati[d]	74	65	53	21	1	—
Palm kernel oil[a]	49	—	38	1	—	—

[a]Berger (1977).
[b]Tan et al. (1983).
[c]The composition of palm stearin can be varied widely by adopting different process conditions as indicated by the range of figures given.
[d]Kheiri and Oh (1983).

The consumer products listed are normally prepared from blends of oils and fats of different origin, some of which may have been partly hydrogenated. The choice of ingredients that can be mixed to obtain a solids-content profile like these products is very wide. However, it is clear that palm oil could be a major component of such blends. The extent to which it is actually used will depend on availability, price, the local taste, and some other technical and marketing factors. Thus, for example, the amount of palm oil currently used in vanaspati varies from approximately 20% in India to 40% in Pakistan and to over 90% in Iraq.

Palm oil has been a major ingredient of fat blends used for margarine manufacture in Europe for many years. The exact proportions of ingredients to be used are dependent on the type of product required and the processing plant used. However, the formulas given in Table 17 are a general guide, and can be adjusted by minor changes to meet the requirements of specific markets.

Table 17 Some Formulas of Standard-Quality Table Margarine

1.[a]	Palm oil	50%
	Hardened palm oil (melting point 44°C)	20%
	Liquid vegetable oil	30%
2.	Palm oil	20%
	Palm kernel oil	30%
	Hardened marine oil	40%
	(34-36°C melting point)	
	Liquid vegetable oil	10%
3.[b]	Hardened vegetable (for example, hardened palm oil) or marine oil (melting point 45°C)	10%
	Palm oil	50%
	Palm kernel oil	25%
	Liquid vegetable oil	15%

The following formula is suitable for tropical climate:[c]

Palm oil	80%
Palm stearin (melting point 45°C)	20%

[a]Feron (1969).
[b]Anderson and Williams (1965).
[c]Moolayil (1977).

Consumer preference in many countries is for a liquid cooking oil rather than for a semisolid fat. Palm olein, which remains completely liquid at temperatures above 20°C, is suitable as a liquid cooking oil in warm climates and is being widely used in the Arabian peninsula, India, and Southeast Asia. However, in more temperate climates it partly solidifies, and its use is then restricted to blends with other oils. For example, it is used as a 50/50 mixture with rapeseed oil in Japan.

The physical properties of palm stearin can be varied over quite a wide range depending on the fractionation procedure used. The softer grades are being used as components of shortening blends in Europe and the United States.

In addition to its incorporation into fat products for the consumer, palm oil has a number of direct uses in food manufacture, the most important being as a frying medium for snack foods and in fast-food restaurants. It shows excellent stability and resistance to breakdown in these rather severe conditions. Palm olein is equally suitable for frying and is preferred by some users. The various food uses of palm oil products are summarized in Table 18.

Table 18 Food Uses of Palm Oil Products[a]

Product	Palm oil	Palm olein	Palm stearin (soft)	Palm stearin (hard)	Hardened Palm oil
Shortenings	+++	+++	+++	+	+++
Vanaspati	+++	+++	+++	+	++
Margarines	++	++	++	+	++
Frying fats	+++	+++	++	-	+
Salad oil	-	+	-	-	-
Speciality fats for coatings	-	-	+++	-	-
Ice cream	+++	-	-	-	-
Miscellaneous	+++	+++	++	+	+

[a]Key: +++ Highly suitable; ++ suitable; + minor applicatons only; - not suitable.
Source: Adapted from Berger (1978).

B. Food Uses of Palm Kernel Oil

The unusual fatty acid composition of palm kernel oil imparts to it physical properties which make some special applications possible. It will be seen that, although there is a quite high solids content at 20°C, palm kernel oil is completely molten at 30°C. It is therefore suited for products having a high fat content that need to have rapid melt-in-the-mouth characteristics. Such products include whipped creams, bakery coatings, and sugar confectionery. For some specialized purposes, palm kernel stearin obtained by fractionation or hydrogenated palm kernel oil may be used.

In general, these products all share the property of being quite hard at room temperature but molten below body temperature. As indicated previously palm kernel oil is a suitable ingredient in margarines. In these products it is particularly useful in combination with palm oil, since the two oils form a low-melting eutectic mixture when the palm kernel oil content is about 40% (Berger, 1975). An interesterified mixture of palm oil and palm kernel oil is also useful in this context. Its glyceride composition is quite similar to that of butterfat and so in consequence is its melt-down behavior.

A special application of palm kernel oil is as a source of medium chain length fatty acids (6- to 10-carbon atom chains). These are obtained from palm kernel oil by hydrolysis and fractional distillation and resynthesized into so-called medium chain triglycerieds (MCT). Such fats are valuable dietary components in certain metabolic disorders in which long chain (16 + 18 carbon acids) triglycerides cannot be digested. This is because the MCT are absorbed and metabolized by a different route (Sickinger, 1975).

C. Direct Consumption of Palm Fruit

The following recipe for palm oil chop illustrates the direct use of palm fruit in cookery as practiced in west Africa. Ripe fruit is thoroughly pounded in a mortar and pestle and strained. The resulting oily suspension of vegetable matter is placed in a cooking pot with chilies, some onions, a few hard-boiled eggs, and a jointed chicken. The mixture is stewed over a fire for several hours and served with boiled rice (*The Planter*, 1979).

VII. STABILITY AND QUALITY PROBLEMS

In common with most oils and fats, palm oil and palm kernel oil are subject to two main forms of deterioration: oxidation leading to rancid flavors and hydrolysis leading to the production of free fatty acids.

A. Oxidation

Oxidation is due to prolonged exposure to the air. The reaction is accelerated by elevated temperature, the presence of trace metals acting as catalysts, and by strong daylight. In comparison with more highly unsaturated vegetable oils palm oil shows considerable resistance to oxidation, partly because of the virtual absence of linolenic acid and partly because of the high content of natural antioxidants (tocopherols).

The variable features of the primitive production methods described earlier, that is, prolonged boiling, heavy contamination from iron derived from rusty drums, and exposure to air, result in a variable degree of deterioration. These adverse factors are also potentially present in the large-scale modern production processes, but in general sufficient control is excerised to minimize their effect. Therefore, most crude palm oil arrives at its destination in good condition. Deterioration, when it occurs, may result in difficulties in the oil refinery in reducing the color to the low levels desired in a fully refined oil. This deterioration appears to involve changes in the carotenoids, resulting in a fixed color.

B. Free Fatty Acids

The hydrolysis of palm oil is promoted by free moisture, elevated temperature, and an acid or alkaline environment, but also by lipolytic enzymes, which may be endogenous to the plant tissue or derived from bacterial or fungal action. It has already been noted that the endogenous lipase is very active until it has been destroyed by heat treatment. If the oil is dry and is stored cool and under reasonably clean condition, further hydrolysis will be rather slow.

The village processing and storage procedures are very variable from this point of view, but since the traditional West African taste is for a crude oil with a fairly high (soft oil) or a very high (hard oil) acidity, the degree of hydrolysis is probably not important when the oil is intended for local comsunption. When, however, the oil is intended for export, its value is enhanced by low acidity. The small-scale processes described previously are inherently capable of producing a low-acidity oil, and considerable success was obtained in west Africa by an incentive scheme directed to this end (Iwuchukwu, 1965).

In 1949, the Nigerian Oil Palm Produce Marketing Board prescribed five grades of palm oil for export having free fatty acid (FFA) contents as follows: below 9%, 9 to 18%, 18 to 27%, 27 to 36%, and above 36%. A higher price was paid by the marketing board according to grade. The response was so good that in 1950 it was already possible to introduce a special grade with FFA below 4.5%. By 1954, the proportion of oil in this grade has risen from 0.2% in 1950 to over 50%. The FFA limit was later reduced to 3.5%, and by 1965 more than 80% of the oil was produced in this grade.

Production in Southeast Asia, geared to the export trade from the beginning and using large-scale processes, has generally been of low FFA oils (Jacobsberg, 1975c). During large-scale bulk transport in ships' tanks, a moderate increase in FFA of about 0.25%/month is regarded as normal.

The hydrolysis of palm kernel oil presents particular problems in food use. A low level of hydrolysis releases short chain fatty acids with very low flavor thresholds. Consequently a very low level of microbiological activity, due to yeast, fungal, or bacterial contamination in a food system containing palm kernel oil gives rise to objectionable flavors and renders the food unpalatable.

C. Quality Control

The control of quality in the oil mill requires chemical analysis of at least some of the parameters of deterioration. The following list includes the most common analyses, together with some comments on their significance.

1. Free fatty acid content (FFA) measures the extent of hydrolysis of the glycerides occurring either in the fruit before sterilization or during subsequent handling and storage. Palm oil is traded internationally on the basis of 5% FFA contracts specifying a premium for lower figures and a rebate for higher figures. However, crude palm oil is mainly produced at about 3 to 3.5% FFA. A lower content of 2 to 2.5% can be obtained by special harvesting procedures, and such crude palm oil is available as a special grade at a premium.

2. The moisture content of crude palm is normally about 0.15%, a figure close to the natural solubility of water in palm oil. Appreciably higher figures are usually the result of contamination during transport.

3. Nonvolatile impurities should be below 0.1%; higher figures are evidence of significant contamination.

4. Peroxide value is a measure of the peroxide oxygen that has combined with the unsaturated components, that is, of primary oxidation products, and is an indication of deterioration.

5. Anisidine value is a measure of aldehydic secondary oxidation products resulting from the decomposition of peroxides. This together with peroxide values provides a useful basis for predicting the likely quality of the oil after refining.

6. Trace metals content: Traces of iron and copper in particular act as pro-oxidants. Crude palm oil should contain no more than 4 ppm iron and 0.2 ppm copper. However, the latter level is already high enough to have an adverse effect.

7. Ultraviolet absorption at 232 and 269 nm gives some measure of the extent of primary and secondary oxidation products present, and some good correlations with peroxide value and anisidine value have been reported.

Table 19 Quality Specifications of Crude Palm Oil

	Karlshamn[a]	Harrisons and Crosfield standard	Harrisons and Crossfield lotox	Zaire regular[b]	Grade SPB[b]
Moisture	0.5% max	0.12	0.12	0.1	0.1
Dirt		0.02	0.02	0.01	0.002
FFA	3.0 max.	3.5	2.5	3-5	1-2.5
Peroxide value meq/kg	5 max.	5 max.	3 max.	–	–
Anisidine value	6 max.	–	4 max.	–	–
Carotene	–	–	650	500-700	500
Iron ppm	3.5 max.	5	3	10	5
Copper ppm	0.05 max.	0.2	0.2	0.2	0.2
AOM stability	53 hr	–	–	–	–

[a]Johansson and Pehlergaard (1977).
[b]Loncin et al. (1970).

8. The carotene content of crude palm oil should be higher than 550 ppm. Lower figures indicate oxidation of the oil and probable difficulties in refining.
9. Accelerated stability tests (active oxygen method or oxygen absorption test): These tests, usually carried out at about 100°C, give some indication of the keeping properties or shelf life of the oil, in terms of its ability to resist oxidation.

D. Quality Standards

Table 19 sets out quality standards for crude palm oil indicated as desirable by a large European refiner and specifications offered in Malaysia and from Zaire.

REFERENCES

Ab. Gapor, Md. T. and Berger, K. G. (1983). In *Palm Oil Technology in the '80s* (E. Pushparajah and M. Rajadural, eds.). Kuala Lumpur, Incorporated Society of Planters, p. 145.

Adam, J. (1910). *Le Palmier A' Lhuile* Paris, A. Challamel.

Anderson, A. J. C., and Williams, P. N. (1965). *Margarine*. London, Pergamon Press, p. 72.

Barrett, C. B., Dallas, M. S. J., and Padley, F. B. (1963). *J. Am. Oil Chem. Soc.* 40:581.

Bek-Nielsen, B. (1977). *International Developments in Palm Oil*. Kuala Lumpur, Incorporated Society of Planters, p. 160.

Berger, K. G. (1975). *Chemistry and Industry*, London, Society of Chemical Industry, p. 910.

Berger, K. G. (1977). *International Developments in Palm Oil*. Kuala Lumpur, Incorporated Society of Planters, p. 435.

Berger, K. G. (1978). *Market Development of Palm Oil Products*. Geneva, International Trade Centre, p. 104.

Bevan, J. W. L., and Gray, B. S. (1969). *The organisation and Control of Field Practice for Large Scale Oil Palm Plantings in Malaysia*. Kuala Lumpur, Incorporated Society of Planters.

Bevan, J. W. L., Fleming, T., and Gray, B. S. (1966). *Planting Techniques for Oil Palms in Malaysia*. Kuala Lumpur, Incorporated Society of Planters.

Bezard, J. A. (1971). *Lipids* 6:630.

Bugaut, M., and Bezard, J. (1977). *Oleagineux* 32:277.

Cawkwell, B. K. (1969). *The Planter* 45:85.

Chin, A. H. G., Oh, F. C. H., and Siew, W. L. (1982). *MARDI Research Bulletin* Serdang Selangor, Malaysian Agricultural Research and Development Institute.

Codex Alimentarius (1979a). Draft standard for edible red palm oil. Rome, F.A.O.

Codex Alimentarius (1979b). Draft standard for palm kernel oil. Rome, F.A.O.

Corley, R. H. V., Wooi, K. C. , and Wong, C. Y. (1979). *The Planter* 55:377.

Corley, R. H. V., Hew, C. K., Tan, T. M., and Lo, K. K. (1973). In *Advances in Oil Palm Cultivation* (R. L. Wastie and D. A. Earp, eds.). Kuala Lumpur, Incorporated Society of Planters.

Deroanne, C., Wathelet, J. P., and Severin, M. (1975). *Rev. Franc. Corps Gras* 22:599.

Devendra C., and Muthurajah, R. N. (1977). *International Developments in Palm Oil.* Kuala Lumpur, Inc. Soc. of Planters, p. 105.

Faulkner, H., Bonfand, A., and Naudet, M. (1976). *Proceedings of I.S.F. Congress, Marseilles, Symposium 4.* (M. Naudet, ed.). Paris, ITERG, p. 19.

Faulkner, O. T., and Lewin, C. J. (1923). *Second Annual Bulletin.* Agric. Dept. Nigeria, p. 3.

Feron, R. (1969). In *Margarine* (H. J. Van Stuyvenberg, ed.). Liverpool, Liverpool University Press, p. 101.

Food and Agriculture Organization (1977). *Food and Nutrition Paper no. 3.* Rome, Food and Agriculture Organization.

Goh, S. H., Khor, H. T., and Gee, P. T. (1982). *J. Am. Oil Chem. Soc.* 59:296.

Gottenbos, J. J., and Vles, R. O. (1978). *Nutritive Value of Palm Oil,* presented at I.S.F. Congress New York, April 1980.

Guyot, A. (1969). *Bull. Rech. Agron. Genbl.* 4(314):484.

Harrisons and Crosfield Ltd. (1974). *Palm Oil Technical Brochure,* London.

Hartley, C. W. S. (1979). In *The Oil Palm.* London and New York, Longman.

Honstra, G. (1975). In *The Role of Fats in Human Nutrition* (A. J. Vergroesen, ed.). London, Academic Press, p. 303.

Hornstra, G., and Vles, R. O. (1978). *International Conference on Atherosclerosis* (A. Carlson et al., eds.). New York, Raven Press, p. 471.

Iwuchukwa, A. N. (1965). *The Oil Palm Conference Proceedings.* London, Tropical Products Institute, p. 74.

Jacobsberg, B. (1975a). *Oleagineux* 30:271.

Jacobsberg, B. (1975b). *MARDI Workshop Proceedings.* Kuala Lumpur, Serdang, Selangor, Malaysian Agricultural Research and Development Institute, p. 130.

Jacobsberg, B. (1975c). *Oleagineux* 30:319.

Jacobsberg, B. Deldime, P., and Gapor, A. (1978). *Oleagineux* 33:239.

Johansson, G., and Pehlergaard, P. O. (1977). *International Development in Palm Oil.* Kuala Lumpur, p. 203.

Jurriens, G., and Kroesen, A. C. J. (1965). *J. Am. Oil Chem. Soc.* 42:9.

Kheiri, M. S. A. and Oh, F. C. H. (1983). In *Palm Oil Technology in the '80s* (E. Pushparajah and M. Rajadurai, eds.). Kuala Lumpur, Incorporated Society of Planters, p. 449.

Khor, H. T., Goh, S. H., and Tan, W. I. (1980). *Oil Palm News.* London, Tropical Products Institute 24:12.

Kirkaldy, J. L. R. and Sutano, J. B. (1976). *Planter.* Kuala Lumpur, 52:118.

Loncin, M. (1958). *Oleagineux* 13:33.

Loncin, M., Jacobsberg, B., and Evrard, G., (1970). In *Palm Oil, A Major Tropical Product.* Brussels, Congo Palm.

Manino, S., and Amelotti, G. (1974). *Twelfth I.S.F. Congress,* Milan (Abstract).

Matsumoto, T. (1974). Primate communication quoted in G.D.S. Weir, (1975).

Moolayil, J. (1977). In *International Developments in Palm Oil* (D. A. Earp, ed.). Kuala Lumpur, Incorporated Society of Planters, p. 411.

Moran, D. J. P. (1962). Quoted in J. B. Rossel (1967), *Advances in Lipid Research, vol. 5,* London, Academic Press, p. 353.

Nwanze, S. C. (1965). *The Oil Palm Conference Proceedings.* London, Tropical Institute, p. 63.

The Planter (1979). Kuala Lumpur, Quoted in *History of the Incorporated Society of Planters,* p. 498.

Seher, A., and Vogel, H. (1971). Paper presented at D.G.F. Meeting, Munich.

Sickinger, K. (1975). In *The Role of Fats in Human Nutrition* A. J. Vergroesen, (ed.). London Academic Press, p. 126.

Syed, R. A. (1980). *Pollinating Insects of Oil Palm.* London, Commonwealth Institute of Biological Control.

Tan. B. K. (1979). Palm oil studies: The effect of fractionation on palm oil triglycerides. Unpublished Ph.D. thesis, Liverpool Polytechnic, p. 81.

Tan, W. I. (1977). Chemical studies on the fruit of *Elaeis guineensis.* Unpublished M. Sc. thesis, University of Malaya, p. 108.

Tan, B. K., Oh, F. C. H., Siew, W. L., and Berger, W. G. (1983). In *Palm Oil Technology in the '80s.* (E. Pushparajah and M. Rajadurai, eds.). Kuala Lumpur, Incorporated Society of Planters, p. 127.

Timmer, W. and Vles, R. O. (1978). *Proceedings 5th Int. Rapeseed Conference, Malmö, Sweeden, Vol. 2,* p. 105.

Turner, P. D. and Gillbanks, R. A. (1974). *Oil Palm Cultivation and Management.* Kuala Lumpur, Incorporated Society of Planters.

Unilever (1965). The chemistry of glycerides. *Education Booklet no. 4,* London.

Webb, B. H., Hutagalung, R. I., and Cheam, S. T. (1977). *International Development in Palm Oil.* Kuala Lumpur, Incorporated Society of Planters, p. 134.

Weir, G. D. S. (1975). The stability of palm oil towards oxidation. Unpublished Ph.D. thesis, Reading University, p. 51.

World Bank (1976). Prospects for palm oil. *Commodity Paper No. 23.* Washington, D.C. International Bank for Reconstruction and Development.

Yong, M. L. (1976). Abstract presented at Chicago meeting of Am. Oil Chem. Soc.

12
Papaya

Harvey T. Chan, Jr. Tropical Fruit and Vegetable Research
Laboratory, U.S. Department of Agriculture, Hilo, Hawaii

I. INTRODUCTION

Papaya (*Carica papaya* L.) is a tropical plant grown between latitudes
of 32° north and south. Fruit size ranges from less than 1 lb to 20 lb.
Papaya is indigenous to southern Mexico and Costa Rica. It was taken

by the Spaniards to Manila in the mid-sixth century and reached Malacca shortly afterwards. From there it was introduced to India. It was reported in Zanzibar in the eighteenth century and in Uganda in 1874 (Purseglove, 1968). The introduction of papaya to Hawaii is usually credited to Don Martin, an early Spanish settler and horticulturist, who brought the seeds from the Marquesas Islands sometime between 1800 and 1823.

Since that early period, papayas have become one of Hawaii's major agricultural export crops. In 1977 about 9.6 million lb of cull papayas were processed into purée, nectar bases, canned slices, and frozen chunks (Souza, 1978). In the United States the majority of the fresh fruit is consumed when ripe. However, in many Southeast Asian countries, especially the Philippines, the fruit is consumed as a vegetable while still in the green stage.

II. HORTICULTURAL ASPECTS

A. Climatological and Soil Requirements

The papaya tree is able to grow on many different soils that have good drainage and a soil pH of 6.5 to 7.0. At present, 90% of the papayas in Hawaii is grown in a rocky volcanic soil called aa that is composed primarily of porous lava, volcanic ash, weathered rock material, and some organic matter.

The papaya has adapted to a wide range of rainfall conditions in Hawaii, ranging from 1.5 to over 2.5 m/year. Papayas are grown in the Puna area of Hawaii which experiences rainfalls greater than 2.5 m/year due to the highly porous nature of the aa soils. Most of the papayas grown in Hawaii are in areas considered warm, on lands from a few feet to 500 ft above sea level. Papayas grown at higher elevations with lower temperatures usually produce fruit with lower sugar content and poor market quality.

B. Propagation

Papaya plants are usually started with seeds from ripe fruit that have been processed and dried. The seeds are processed by allowing the fresh seeds to ferment in a bucket of water for a few days. The fermentation facilitates the removal of the gelatinous seed coat. The sarcotesta is washed off with vigorous scrubbing and the remaining seed is dried. The seeds are planted directly in the field. Five or more seeds are placed in a hole. Germination occurs within 10 to 14 days. The papaya seedlings are thinned out 4 to 6 weeks after germination. Only the three strongest seedlings are allowed to remain. The second and final thinning occurs when the papaya flowers are large enough to determine if the tree is hermaphroditic or female. Only a hermaphroditic tree is selected to grow per planting hole.

C. Harvesting and Yield

Papayas at the proper maturity for harvesting show a tinge or more of yellow at the apical end of the fruit. These fruits are harvested manually when the trees are short. With older mature trees whose fruits are beyond the reach of the picker, mechanical harvesting aids are employed. These mechanical aids are self-propelled tractors upon which the picker platforms are elevated on booms. Each picker has a fruit conveyor running the length of the boom to a bin. Each bin holds about 900 lb of papayas, and the machine capacity is eight bins.

In commercial orchards, papaya trees that are harvested manually are cultivated for 3 years since after 3 years the trees are too tall for harvesting. Those orchards that are mechanically harvested may be harvested for an additional 1 or 2 years due to the added height advantage of the harvesting machines.

D. Postharvest Handling

Papayas are treated to reduce storage decay by immersing in hot water at 120°F for 20 min, then cooled in running water for 20 min (Akamine and Arisumi, 1953). The shelf life of papayas can be extended further by controlled atmosphere storage of 1 to 1.5% oxygen.

Disinsectation methods for fruit flies in papayas involve the use of vapor heat and fumigation. In the vapor heat treatment, the papayas are first preconditioned to dry heat [40% relative humidity (RH)] at 110°F for 6 to 8 hr. The papayas are next subjected to moist heat (100% RH) such that the center temperature of the fruit reaches 117°F and is held for 4 hr. The fruit are then air-cooled. In the fumigation method, the fruits are fumigated with ethylene dibromide at a dosage of 1/2 lb/1000 cubic ft of fumigation chamber space for 2 hr (Yee et al., 1970).

III. BIOCHEMICAL AND NUTRITIONAL COMPOSITION

A. Nutritional Composition

Papaya has been described as an excellent source of provitamin A and ascorbic acid (Wenkam and Miller, 1965). Because of its year-round availability, papayas are an important source of vitamin C in the diet of the rural population of tropical Latin America (de Arriola et al., 1980). A table of the nutrient composition for the Hawaiian Solo papaya is given in Table 1. As shown in Table 1, the edible portion of papaya is composed mostly of water, 86.80%, and carbohydrates, 12.18%, which together make up 98.98% of the fruit.

Table 1 Nutrient Composition of
Papaya var. Solo, Per 100 g of
Edible Portion

Moisture	86.80	%
Food energy	46	cal
Protein	0.36	g
Fat	0.06	g
Total carbohydrate	12.18	g
Fiber	0.58	g
Ash	0.57	g
Calcium	29.9	mg
Phosphorus	11.6	mg
Iron	0.19	mg
Vitamin A	10.93	mg
Thiamine	0.27	mg
Riboflavin	0.043	mg
Niacin	0.33	mg
Ascorbic acid	84.00	mg

Source: Data from Wenkam and
Miller (1965).

B. Changes in Composition

1. During Fruit Development

Several changes occur within the papaya during its development.
Presently only the changes in sugar content and papain concentration have been reported in the literature. Changes in the sugar
content and composition were reported by Chan et al. (1979). The
results are shown in Fig. 1. Total sugar content progressively increased at a relatively slow rate during the first 110 days of fruit
development to 3.4% (w/w) about 135 days after anthesis. Sucrose,
which comprised less than 35% of the total sugars 10 days after
anthesis, declined to less than 15% after 70 days. Sucrose remained
low until it reaches 18% 110 days after anthesis, then it increased
rapidly until it comprised 80% of the sugars about the time the total
sugars peaked. After the 135th day, sucrose rapidly decreased,
and glucose and fructose increased correspondingly, indicating the
inversion of sucrose to the single sugars. The dramatic changes in
sugar composition immediately after the 110th day of anthesis corresponded with the commencement of color change of seeds from white
to black, followed by the change in color of the pulp from white to
yellow in the periphery of the fruit cavity several days later (120
days after anthesis). About the 130th day, first indication of

fruit-surface yellowing (color-break stage) on the blossom end of the fruit occurred. About the 135th day when the second dramatic change in sugar composition occurred, the fruit was at its prime stage for consumption. Papain concentration in papaya latex reaches its maximum just before ripening of the fruit. However, observations with the Solo variety indicate that the papain concentration in papaya flesh decreases with ripening.

2. During Postharvest Storage

Chemical changes during the postharvest ripening of papaya have been reported by Chen (1963). A change in surface color from green to orange-yellow is due to the destruction of chlorophyll in the epidermis and the unmasking and development of carotenoids in the flesh. The carotenoid content of the pericarp reaches its maximum at the three-quarters-ripe stage and remains at that level. During ripening, the texture of the fruit changes from firm to soft, and there is an apparent increase in the sweetness of the fruit. The subepidermal latex disappears and the weight of the fruit decreases. A climacteric rise in CO_2 production with the ripening of the fruits was reported by Jones and Kubota (1940). Maturing papaya also emits ethylene and application of ethylene initiates respiratory rise and ripening in detached fruits (Akamine and Goo, 1979).

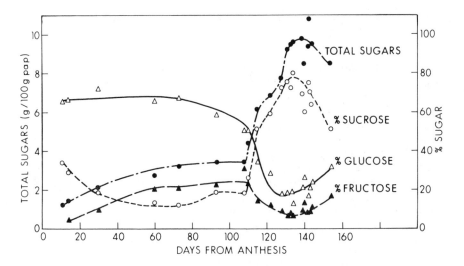

Figure 1 Changes in sugar composition during fruit development.

3. During Processing and Storage

Several chemical and biochemical changes can occur in processed papaya products during processing and storage. These changes can be classified as enzymatic, nonenzymatic, and microbial.

Enzymatic Changes. Enzymatic changes are generally initiated in the manufacture of papaya purée when the fruit undergoes a pulping operation whereby fruit tissues are disrupted causing the release and mixing of enzymes and substrates. Several deleterious enzymatic reactions that affect the product can then ensue. The development of off-flavors and off-odors due to both enzymatic and microbial activity has been reported by Chan et al (1973). Butyric, hexaonic, and octanoic acids and their methyl esters were found in purées prepared by commercial methods in which the enzymes had not been inactivated by acidification and heat. A pungent sulfury odor has also been known to evolve from papaya purée, especially purée made from green fruit. Gelation of papaya purée due to pectin esterase activity is an important problem facing a processor. Immediately after papaya is pulped, a gel is formed unless certain steps are taken to inhibit or inactivate pectin esterase activity. The formation of gels may be prevented by the use of sucrose (Yamamoto and Inouye, 1963) or the application of heat and acidification (Brekke et al., 1973). Another enzymatic problem facing the processor is the action of invertase which hydrolyzes the nonreducing sugar to glucose and fructose. The conversion is rapid in papaya purée, with 50% of the sucrose being hydrolyzed within 2.6 min after the tissue is macerated (Chan and Kwok, 1975). The conversion of nonreducing sugars to reducing sugars increases the potential susceptibility of processed papaya products to nonenzymatic browning during high temperature or prolonged storage conditions.

Microbial Changes. Several microbial changes can occur when papaya products are improperly handled or stored. The development of off-flavors and odors such as volatile and nonvolatile acids has been described by Chan et al. (1973). The presence of sulfury off-odors in papaya products was attributed to the production of H_2S (Tang et al., 1972). Homogenates of papaya seed or pulp supplemented with (BITC) produced H_2S during incubation. The source of H_2S was proved to be from the endogenous and supplemented BITC. Benzylamine was also found to be another breakdown product. The responsible microorganism was isolated and identified as *Enterobactor cloacae*. An overall reaction was proposed by Tang et al. (1972):

$$C_6H_5 - CH_2 - N = C = S + 2H_2O$$

$$\xrightarrow{\text{Bacterial enzymes}} C_6H_5 - CH_2 - NH_2 + H_2S + CO_2$$

Nonenzymatic Changes. The quality and nutritive value of papaya products may be altered by nonenzymatic changes occurring during processing. Changes in ascorbic acid, carotenoids, and sensory quality during the manufacture of papaya purée and papaya concentrate were reported by Chan et al. (1975). Ascorbic acid losses were significant during purée processing and concentration. Statistically significant losses occurred during pulping (P = 0.05) and during concentration (P = 0.01). The loss during pulping represented 5.5% of the initial ascorbic acid. Loss in ascorbic acid was greater, 14.3%, in the concentration step. Heat applied during this process probably contributed to the destruction of ascorbic acid. Retention might be improved by cooling the concentrate after concentration. The total ascorbic loss from crushed fruit to concentration was 20.3%.

Absorption spectra differed for total carotenoid extracts of fresh papayas, purée, and concentrated purée. Adsorption maximum for the total carotenoid of fresh papaya was at 445 nm, with minor peaks at 469 and 425 nm. After the acidification to pH 3.5 in the processing of purée, the spectrum shifted with increased absorption at 425 nm and decreased absorption at 445 nm. The difference became pronounced after concentration when absorption at 425 nm was clearly the major peak. The hypsochromic effect increased progressively with the processing sequence.

Of the total carotenoids, about 15% cryptoxanthinmonoepoxide was detected in fresh papaya purée, 9.8% in processed purée and none detected in papaya concentrate. The isomerization of 5,6-monoepoxy-cryptoxanthin to 5,8-monoepoxycryptoxanthin under acidic conditions (pH 3.5) would explain the hypsochromic shift of the total carotenoid extract in the purée and concentrate samples.

The carotenoid composition of Solo papaya has been reported by Yamamoto (1964). β-Carotene and cryptoxanthin, carotenoids with provitamin A activity, were reported to be 4.8 and 38.9% of the total carotenoids, respectively. Cryptoxanthinmonoepoxide was reported to be 15.6%; it too, may be provitamin A depending on the position of the epoxide group. Since there is a question at this time on whether the epoxy group is 5,6 or 5',6', the provitamin A activity of this carotenoid is uncertain. However, the isomerization from the mono-epoxy form to the furanoid form should not affect the provitamin A activity of the purée, because 5',6', epoxycryptoxanthin would not affect the β-ionone (provitamin A) portion of the molecule.

Total carotenoids, as determined from the absorbance of carotenoid extracts at 445 nm, decreased from an initial value 2.83 mg% in fresh fruit to a final value after purée concentration of 2.12 mg%. Because of the hypsochromic effects, such losses in total carotenoid values should not be construed as destruction of carotenoids and provitamin A.

Changes During Storage. Changes in product quality of papaya nectar in plain tin- and enamel-lined cans stored at 55, 75, and 100°F for 1 year were reported by Brekke et al. (1976). Quality of the samples held at 100°F deteriorated the most rapidly. Can corrosion increased with temperature, as indicated by the rate of accumulation of tin and iron in the nectar. Nectars in tin-lined cans held at 100 and 55°F for 51 weeks had 400 and 60 ppm of tin, respectively. Nectars in enameled cans stored at 100°F darkened or browned substantially, and color at 32 weeks was judged unacceptable. It was concluded that papaya nectar should be stored at 75°F or below for optimum quality retention.

C. Biochemical Composition

1. Sugars

The principal carbohydrate in papayas is the sugars, with little or no starch being present (Chan et al., 1978a). Total soluble solids in papaya purée have been found to vary between the values of 11.5 to 13.5° Brix (Brekke et al., 1973). The composition of sugars in papayas has been reported by numerous workers. The reported values for sucrose conflict and vary considerably. King et al. (1951) and Pratt and Del Rosario (1913) reported that sucrose comprised 1.2 to 1.3% of the total sugars. Pope (1930) and Thompson (1914) reported sucrose was 0 to 13.2% of the total sugars. Stahl (1935) reported sucrose was from 0 to 4.4%, whereas Jones and Kubota (1940) reported sucrose as 18% of the total sugars. Chen (1963) using a hot-alcohol extraction method reported that 60% of the sugars were sucrose. Dollar et al. (1969) reported that sucrose was not present at any time during postharvest ripening. The discrepancy in the reported values was shown by Chan and Kwok (1975) to be caused by an invertase enzyme in papayas. By inactivating the enzymes with microwave heating before extracting the sugars, we determined the sugar composition of ripe papayas to be 48.3% sucrose, 29.8% glucose, and 21.9% fructose. Trace quantities of sedoheptulose in papaya were reported by Ogata et al. (1972).

2. Organic Acids

Among fruits, papaya is notably low in acid. Data acquired at the United States Department of Agriculture-Agricultural Research, Hawaii Fruit Laboratory, over the past several years show the Solo papaya to be at pH 5.0 to 5.5. Chan et al. (1971) extracted and purified papaya acids by ion exchange. The acids were quantitatively determined by gas-liquid chromatography to be comprised of malic, citric, and α-ketoglutaric acids, which were 0.464, 0.525, and 0.042 meq/100 g wet wt, respectively.

The total titratable acidity of papaya was 1.54 meq/100 g or 0.099% acid calculated as citric acid. Papaya purée had 0.279 meq of ascorbic acid per 100 g (49.2 mg/100 g) which, together with the malic, citric, and α-ketoglutaric acids, totaled 1.31 meq/100 g, about 85% of the total titratable acidity. Total volatile acids in papaya were 0.123 meq/ 100 g and contributed 8% of the total titratable acidity. The remaining 7% (0.11 meq/100 g) was attributed to galacturonic and unidentified nonvolatile acids. The results show that papaya is significantly low in organic acids, and this perhaps accounts for its pleasant sweet taste.

3. Volatile Compounds

The volatile flavor compounds of papaya have been reported by Katague and Kirch (1965), Tang (1970a), Chan et al. (1973), and Flath and Forrey (1977). Most of the other references deal with the presence of benzyl isothiocyanate and its glucosinolate precursor (Ettlinger and Hodgkins, 1956; Gmelia and Kjaer, 1970; Tang, 1970b, 1971; Tang et al., 1972b). Flath and Forrey (1977) examined the volatiles of fresh papaya fruit by combined gas chromatograph-mass spectrometery and a total of 106 compounds were identified. Linalool was the major component with smaller amounts of benzyl isothiocyanate. Minor quantities of butyric, hexanoic, and octanoic acids and their corresponding methyl esters were also present. Other compounds that were present were phenylacetonitrile and linalool oxide.

4. Pigments

The color of ripe papaya flesh is due to its carotenoid pigments. Yamamoto (1964) isolated and identified the carotenoids in both the yellow- and red-fleshed papaya. The major differences between the two varieties was the complete absence of lycopene in the yellow-fleshed type. The relative composition of carotenoids of both types is shown in Table 2.

Table 2 Percentage Composition of Carotenoid Pigment in Papaya

Pigment	Yellow-fleshed fruit	Red-fleshed fruit
β-Carotene	4.8	4.8
ζ-Carotene	24.8	5.9
Cryptoxanthin-monoepoxide	15.6	4.4
Cryptoxanthin	38.9	19.2
Lycopene	0.0	63.5
Unresolved mixture	15.9	2.2

Source: Data from Yamamoto (1964).

The total carotenoids obtained were 3.7 mg/100 g and 4.2 mg/100 g for the yellow- and red-fleshed fruits, respectively. From these results red-fleshed fruits would have approximately one-half the provitamin A activity of the yellow-fleshed type.

5. Enzymes

Papain (3.4.22.2). Papain is one of the more important proteolytic enzymes used in food, cosmetic, leather, and drug manufacturing industries. Papaya latex is tapped from the green fruit by cutting the surface with a sharp blade. The latex is either sun-dried or oven-dried under temperatures below 70°F. Because of its labor-intensive nature, production of crude papain is dominated by tropical countries with ample low-cost work power.

Commercial papain varies in quality ranging from crude, dried latex without further purification to products described as "high purity" by the manufacturers. All these different grades of papain contain benzyl glucosinolate, a naturally occurring thioglucoside in papaya latex (Tang, 1974). The isothiocyanates formed by the hydrolysis of benzyl isothiocyanates have been shown to inhibit papain activity (Tang and Tang, 1976). The crude papain contains at least two types of proteolytic enzymes, papain and chymopapain (Kunimitsu and Yasunobu, 1967).

Papain is routinely purified from papaya latex by the method of Kimmel and Smith (1954). It involves extraction of the latex, removal of insoluble material at pH 9, ammonium sulfate precipitation, and recrystallizations. The resulting crystalline protein contains three states of papain: active papain, activatible papain, and nonactivatible papain.

Thioglucosidase (3.2.3.1). Tang (1971) found that approximately 10% of the dry weight of latex can be attributed to a single thioglucoside (e.g., benzylglucosinolate). This compound is hydrolyzed by the enzyme thioglucosidase (myrosinase), and benzyl isothiocyanate is formed according to the following reaction.

$$B_z\!-\!C\!\!\underset{N}{\overset{\displaystyle\diagdown}{\,-\!S\!-\!}}\!C_6H_{11}O_5 \xrightarrow[\;H_2O\;]{\text{Thioglucosidase}} B_z\!-\!N\!=\!C\!=\!S\ +\ C_6H_{12}O_6$$

$$SO_4^-$$

(benzyl isothiocyanate)   (glucose)

$$+\ SO_4{+}{+}\ H^+$$

(benzylglucosinate)

The thioglucosinolate is probably localized in idioblasts, a special type of cell found in glucosinolate-bearing plants such as *Crucifer* (Kjaer, 1960).

Pectin Esterase (3.1.1.11). Chang et al. (1965) determined the opitimum conditions for papaya pectin esterase (PE) activity to be

pH 7.5 and 0.2 NaCl. They demonstrated that PE was inhibited by
sucrose, thereby delaying the gelation of purée. The inhibitory effect
was linear with sucrose concentration. Evidence was obtained against
competitive inhibition, transferase activity, and an effect on the binding of PE as possible mechanisms for inhibitions. Aung and Ross (1965)
determined the average PE activity in ripe papaya flesh to be 0.013
meq/min/g. They also determined the heat inactivation of PE in acidified purée (p_H 4.2) in the range 169 to 186°F which gave a Z value of
11°F and a D_{180} of 10 min.

Invertase (3.2.1.26). The presence of an invertase enzyme in
papayas was shown by Chan and Kwok (1975, 1976) to be responsible
for the conflicting and low sucrose values reported in the literature.
They reported positive evidence for the presence of high concentrations of both sucrose and invertase in papayas. This work also showed
that if invertase was not inactivated prior to extraction of the sugars,
50% of the sucrose would be lost within 2.6 min. The invertase in papaya was extracted, partially purified, and characterized. Substrate
specificity studies showed the enzyme to be a β-fructofuranosidase.
The enzyme has an optimum pH of 4.6 and a temperature optimum of
40°C. Its pH optimum indicated that it was an acid invertase. The
Km of the enzyme with sucrose as a substrate was 7.7 mM. Heat
inactivation of papaya invertase was biophasic, and the kinetics of both
phases were first-order. The activation energies for the thermal inactivation of the two phases were 33.5 and 53.6 kcal. The enzyme's
apparent molecular weight as determined by gel filtration was 275,000.
The heat-inactivation studies and chromatography of the enzyme on
DEAE Sephadex indicate the possiblility of at least two isozymes of
papaya invertase.

Catalase (1.11.16). Chan et al. (1978a) extracted, purified, and
characterized papaya catalase. The enzyme has a pH optimum of 6.1
and was stable when refrigerated or frozen. The enzyme was inactivated by acidification to pH 3.5 Heat inactivation of papaya catalase
was biphasic at 55 and 60°C and monophasic at 65°C. Kinetics of both
phases were first-order. The activation energies for the thermal inactivation of two phases were 95.9 kcal/mol and 97.0 kcal/mol.
The apparent molecular weight of the enzyme as determined by gel
filtration was 160,000. Because the enzyme was irreversibily inactivated by acidification to pH 3.5 and was also found to be much too heat-
labile, it was concluded to be unsuitable as a biochemical indicator for
heat inactivation of enzymes.

Peroxidase (1.11.17). Sawato (1976) determined the heat-inactivation and isozymic pattern of papaya peroxidase following gamma
irradiation at 0, 75, and 300 krad. The heat inactivation of papaya
peroxidase followed by first-order in the temperature ranges
studied (100 to 130°F). D values for 0-, 75-, and 300-krad-treated

papayas heated to 130°F were 1.3, 2.0, and 3.0 min, respectively.
The activation energies for the three treatments were statistically
insignificant and averaged 61.1 kcal/mol indicating that irradiation
up to 300 krad did not change the thermal destruction properties
of papaya peroxidase.

Nitrate Reductase (1.6.6.2). The presence of nitrate reductase in
papayas has been reported by Menery and Jones (1972). The enzyme
plays an important role in controlling high nitrate levels in Australian-
grown papayas. The high nitrate levels were reported to be causing
severe detinning in canned fruit products. Highest nitrate reductase
activity was found in the exocarp with much lower activities in the
mesocarp, endocarp, and seeds. Nitrate levels and reductase activity
varied with maturity of fruit. Reductase activity in green exocarp fragments was greatly increased by exposure to light. It was proposed to
use light exposure as a postharvest treatment of papayas to accelerate
the enzymic reduction of mesocarp nitrate.

Acid Phosphatase (3.1.3.2). Carreno (1979) reported an acid phosphatase in papaya. This enzyme may be responsible for changes in pH
during processing and storage of the pulp. The enzyme has a pH optimum of 5.2 and the Km was 5.55 mM of p-nitrophenol/min/g pulp,
using the sodium salt of p-nitrophenyl phosphate as the substrate.

Lipoxydase (1.13.1.13). Carreno(1979) found a lipoxydase in papaya. The enzyme has a pH optimum of 4.5 and may be involved in the
development of off-flavors during the processing of the fruit.

D. Composition of Seeds

Papaya seeds, which constitute 22% of the waste product from the papaya purée industry in Hawaii, were characterized by Chan et al. (1978b)
to evaluate their possible utilization. The incorporation of seed particles in papaya purée is also known to lower the quality of the purée.

The proximate composition of papaya seeds is shown in Table 3.
On a dry weight basis the oil content of papaya seeds was 32.9%, and

Table 3 Percent Composition of Papaya Seeds

Moisture	71.89
Fat	9.50
Protein	8.40
Ash	1.47
Total carbohydrate	9.44

Source: Data from Chan et al. (1978). Reprinted from *J. Food Sci.* 43:255-256. Copyright © by Institute of Food Technologists.

Table 4 Characteristics of Papaya
Seed Oil

Refractive index (40°C)	1.4627
Specific gravity (25°C)	0.9130
Unsaponifiable matter	2.11%
Saponification value	193.4
Iodine no.	74.77
Free fatty acids	1.11%
Viscosity (centipoises)	339.41

and the protein content was 29.16%. Ether extraction of papaya seeds
yielded a slightly green oil. The results of a further anaylsis of this
oil are shown in Table 4. The isdine number for papaya seed oil was
74.8, indicating, that the oil was relatively low in polyunsaturated fatty
acids. The indication was supported by gas liquid chromatography
analysis of the fatty acids (Table 5). The major fatty acids in order
of decreasing abundance were oleic acid, palmitic, linoleic, and stearic
acid. Trace quantities of lauric, myristic, linolenic, arachidic, and
behenic acids were also found. Defatted papaya seed meal was found
to have high amounts of crude protein (40. 0%) and crude fibers (49. 9%).

Table 5 Fatty Acid
Composition of Papaya
Seed Oil

Fatty acid	Percent
Lauric	0.13
Myristic	0.16
Palmitic	15.13
Stearic	3.61
Oleic	76.60
Linoleic	7.68
Linolenic	0.60
Arachidic	0.87
Behenic	0.22

Source: Chan et al.
(1978). Reprinted from
J. Food Sci. 43:255-256.
Copyright © by Institute
of Food Technologists.

The principle minerals of the papaya seed meal were calcium (1.66%), phosphorus (0.84%), and manganesium (0.64%).

Papaya seeds are sometimes used as a substitute for pepper because of their spicy pungent flavor. They have also been used as an adulterant in ground pepper. Ettlinger and Hodgkins (1956) attributed the spicy, pungent flavor to the presence of benzyl isothiocyanate, which has been shown by Tang (1973) to be formed from benzylglucosinolate by the action of thioglucosidase. The enzyme is found in the sarcotestae but not in the endosperms, whereas the reverse is true for the substrate glucosinolate, which constitutes more than 6% (w/w) of the endosperms. Both the enzyme and substrate are present in the embryo (Tang, 1970b,1973). The BITC content in the seed oil was found to be 0.56% (w/w) (Chan et al., 1978b).

IV. PAPAYA PROCESSING

A. Purée Manufacture

As stated previously, deleterious enzymatic activity is initiated in papayas whenever the fruit is pulped. These deleterious changes were subsequent gelling of the purée and development of off-odors and flavors. A new method for producing papaya purée has been developed which overcomes the enzymatically induced changes (Brekke et al., 1973) (Fig. 2).

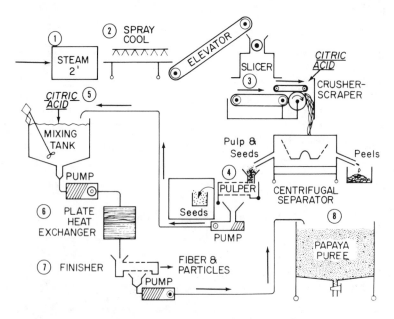

Figure 2 Flow sheet for papaya purée production.

The papayas are first steamed for 2 min. Steaming the whole fruit before processing has the dual effect of preventing exudation of latex from the skin during slicing and of softening the outer 3 to 4 mm of the fruit, thus, increasing yields by 4 to 10%. Steaming the fruit also inactivates the enzymes in the outer 2 to 3 mm of the fruit. Steaming also serves to surface sterilize the fruit, thereby lowering the microbial load. The steamed fruits are then spray-cooled after which they are sliced. The sliced fruits are fed into a crusher-scraper device. Within this device the papaya slices are squeezed through a narrow gap, and the flesh and seeds are loosened and removed from the peel by the action of a rapidly rotating cylinder. Breakage of seeds is minimized by the use of the crusher-scraper in contrast to the use of conventional pulpers. Minimization of breakage of seed and sacotestae minimizes the release of the enzyme myrosinase and its substrate benzyl glucosinolate, thereby minimizing the development of off-flavors. The crushed flesh is then separated from skins and seeds in a centrifugal separator. The separation of skins and seeds by the centrifugal separator prior to pulping further minimizes the breakage of skins and seeds and their inclusion in the purée. The crushed flesh is then pulped in a paddle pulper fitted with a 0.033-in. screen. The pulped flesh is then acidified with citric acid to pH 3.5. Acidification inhibits the action of pectin methyl esterase, the enzyme responsible for the gelation of papaya purée. Acidification to pH 3.5 also inhibits the growth of microorganisms. The acidified purée is then pumped through a paddle finisher fitted with a 0.020-in. screen which removes coarse fiber and whatever seed-coat particles are present to yield a smooth purée. The purée is then pumped through a plate heat exchanger where the temperature is raised to 205°F, held for 2 min, then lowered to 85°F, in a continuous flow. The heat treatment serves to inactivate the enzymes and destroy the microorganisms. The cooled purée is packaged into 25-lb containers and frozen at -10°F.

The purée made by this method has proven to be superior to purées made by other methods. Purées manufactured by the new method are devoid of off-flavors and odors, do not gel during frozen storage, are lower in microbial counts, and possess less seed particles.

B. Dehydrated Products

A dried powder can be made from papayas as follows. Whole ripe papayas with seeds removed are cut into slices 4.8 mm thick (peel included) and dried on screen trays at 60 to 66°C to a moisture content of 6%. The dried slices are ground to pass through standard 20-mesh screens (King et al., 1951).

Papaya fruit leathers (known commercially as fruit rolls) are manufactured by the dehydration of papaya purée into leathery sheets (Chan and Cavaletto, 1978). To make the leather, papaya purée is first mixed with sugar 10% (w/w), and then 49 kg/m^2 is poured out evenly onto Teflon-coated pans or pans sprayed with a lecithin release agent. Sodium bisulfite ($NaHSO_3$) is mixed in at 552 ppm as an SO_2 treatment that protects flavor and color during drying and storage. The purées can then be either dried in the sun or in a forced-draft oven at an air velocity of 110 fpm at 84°C until they reach about 12 to 13% moisture content or an a_w of 0.50 to 0.52. The leathers are removed from the pans, wrapped with a plastic film, and rolled into scrolls.

C. Canned Papaya

Canned papaya dices can be prepared by the following procedure. Wash, peel, and deseed firm, fully ripe fruit. Dice the fruit into 19- to 25-mm cubes. Fill 383 g of diced fruit into a no. 2 can. Add boiling-hot 40° Brix syrup containing 0.75% citric acid to a gross head space of 7.9 mm. Exhaust in steam or hot water to 71°C, close cans, and process to a minimum product temperature of 90.6°C. This may take 10 min in boiling water. The processed cans should be cooled immediately to 37.8°C (Lynch et al., 1959).

D. Frozen Papaya Products

Frozen papaya products generally experience a loss of texture becoming soggy and mushy. Hence, greener (one-half to three-quarters), firmer fruit are generally selected as the raw material for frozen papaya products. An assortment of frozen papaya products and freezing processes has been attempted with varying degrees of success. Papaya halves in which whole papaya were sliced and the seeds removed have been frozen. This product has also been marketed with the seed cavity filled with scoops of ice cream or sherbet. Frozen papaya chunks and slices have also been manufactured and test marketed. The various freezing methods used were air blasting at -40°C, immersion in a combination of sodium chloride ethanol at -23°C, smothering with a layer of flaked carbon dioxide, and drenching with cryogenics such as freon or liquid nitrogen.

A contributing factor to the limited commercialization of frozen papayas is the lack of commercial equipment for deseeding and peeling. A laboratory scale-prototype-contour peeler was developed by Atlas Engineering Co. of Emeryville, California. A mechanical means for removal of papaya seeds has been reported by Chan (1977). The principles of the seed removal process are based on the application of a fluid jet through an orifice in the papaya, thereby forcing the seeds out through an opening in the blossom end of the fruit. Both the contour peeler and the seed removal process are in the developmental stages.

E. Papaya Concentrates

A method for preparing papaya concentrates as reported by Chan et al. (1979) is given as follows. Papaya purée is treated with a pectinolytic enzyme (Pectinol 10-m, Rohm and Haas) to reduce its consistency before concentration. The enzyme is added to purée at the optimum temperature for the enzyme (50 to 60°C) at levels of 0.05 to 0.2%, and depectinization is allowed to proceed for 1.5 to 2.0 hr before concentration. The depectinized purée is concentrated 2.4- to 3.0-fold in an Alpha Laval Centritherm vacuum evaporator. Operating parameters for the evaporator are as follows: vapor temperatures 38 to 50°C, vacuum 27 to 29 in. Hg, condenser water temperature 24 to 27°C.

F. Aseptic Processing

A method of aseptically processing papaya is given as follows (Chan and Cavaletto, 1982). Papaya purée which has been acidified to pH 3.6 to 3.9 with citric acid is pumped into a swept surface heat exchanger and held at 93°C for 60 sec. The sterilized purée is then cooled in a scraped surface heat exchanger to 24°C, pumped to a Scholle aseptic filler which is used to fill 1- to 300-gal bags. The multi-ply, aluminized, polyester/evapolyethylene bags are sterilized by the supplier using gamma irradiation.

Aseptic processing has been used in the food industry for many years, but is generating renewed interest because of rising energy costs. Tropical fruit products such as papaya purée being shipped transoceanic are likely candidates for adoption of aseptic processing since refrigerated transport and storage are not needed with this system.

REFERENCES

Akamine, E. K., and Arisumi, T. (1953). Control of post-harvest storage decay of fruits of papaya (*Carica papaya* L.) with special reference to the effect of hot water. *Proc. Am. Soc. Hort. Sci.* 61:270-274.

Akamine, E. K., and Goo, T. (1979). Concentrations of carbon dioxide and ethylene in the cavity of attached papaya fruit. *Hort. Sci.* 14(2):138-139.

Aung, T., and Ross, E. (1965). Heat sensitivity of pectin esterase activity in papaya purée and of catalase-like activity in passion fruit juice. *J. Food Sci.* 30:144-147.

Brekke, J. E., Chan, H. T., Jr., and Cavaletto, C. G. (1973). Papaya purée and nectar. *Res. Bull. 170.* Honolulu, Hawaii, Hawaii Agric. Exp. Sta.

Brekke, J. E., Cavaletto, C. G., Nakayama, T. O. M., and Suehisa, R. (1976). Effects of storage temperature and container lining on some quality attributes of papaya nectar. *J. Agric. Food Chem.* 24: 341-343.

Broderick, H. T., Jacobs, C. J., Swartz, H. D., and Mulder, N. J. (1972). The control of storage diseases of pawpaws in Southern Africa. *The Citrus Grower and Sub-Tropical Fruit Journal.* November:5, 7, 9, 21.

Carreno, R. (1979). Some factors related with the changes in the quality of papaya pulp, during processing and freezing storage. Unpublished Ph.D. thesis, Universidad Central de Venezuela, Facultad de Ciencias Escuela de Bioligica, Caracas.

Chan, H. T., Jr. (1977). Method for removing seeds from papayas. *U.S. Patent No. 4,002,744.*

Chan, H. T., Jr., and Cavaletto, C. G. (1978). Dehydration and storage stability of papaya leather. *J. Food Sci.* 43:1723-1725.

Chan, H. T., Jr., and Cavaletto, C. G. (1982). Aseptically packaged papaya and guava purée. Changes in chemical and sensory quality during processing and storage. *J. Food Sci.* 51.

Chan, H. T., Jr., and Kwok, S. C. M. (1975). Importance of enzyme inactivation prior to extraction of sugars from papaya. *J. Food Sci.* 40:770-771.

Chan, H. T., Jr., and Kwok, S. C. M. (1976). Isolation and characterization of β-fructofuranosidase from papaya. *J. Food Sci.* 41:320-323.

Chan, H. T., Jr., Tam, S. Y. T., and Koide, R. T. (1978). Isolation and characterization of catalase from papaya. *J. Food Sci.* 43:989-990.

Chan, H. T., Jr., Chang, T. S. K., Stafford, A. E., and Brekke, J. E. (1971). Nonvolatile acids of papaya. *J. Agric. Food Chem.* 19:263-265.

Chan, H. T., Jr., Hibbard, K. L., Goo, T., and Akamine, E. K. (1979). Sugar composition of papaya during fruit development. *Hort. Sci.* 14:140-141.

Chan. H. T., Jr., Flath, R. A., Forrey, R. R., Cavaletto, C. G., Nakayama, T. O. M., and Brekke, J. E. (1973). Development of off-odors and off-flavors in papaya purée. *J. Agric. Food Chem.* 21:566-570.

Chan, H. T., Jr., Heu, R. A., Tang, C-S, Okazaki, E. N., and Ishizaki, S. M. (1978). Composition of papaya seeds. *J. Food Sci.* 43:255-256.

Chan, H. T., Jr., Kuo, M. T-H, Cavaletto, C. G., Nakayama, T. O. M., and Brekke, J. E. (1975). Papaya purée and concentrate: Changes in ascorbic acid, carotenoids and sensory quality during processing. *J. Food Sci.* 40:701-703.

Chang, L. W. S., Morita, L. L., and Yamamoto, H. Y. (1965). Papaya pectinesterase inhibition by sucrose. *J. Food Sci.* 30:218-222.

Chen, N. K-L. (1963). Chemical changes during the post-harvest ripening of papaya fruit. Unpublished M.S. thesis, University of Hawaii, Honolulu.

de Arriola, M. C., Calzada, J. F., Menchu, J. F., Rolz, C., Gracia, R., and de Cabrera, S. (1980). Papaya. In *Tropical and Subtropical Fruits: Composition, Nutritive Values, Properties, and Uses* (S. Nagy and P. E. Shaw, eds.). Westport, Conn., Avi Pub. Co., pp. 316-340.

Dollar, A. M., Hanaoka, M., Moy, J. H., Cinnamon, A. D., Hamill, E., Helber, D., Hsia, S. T., and Wenkam, D. (1969). Physiological, chemical, and physical changes during ripening of papaya. In *Radioisotope and Radiation Applications, NVO-347-17, TID-4500.* Division of Isotopes Development, U.S. Atomic Energy Commission, p. 86.

Ettlinger, M. G., and Hodgkins, J. E. (1956). The mustard oil of papaya seed. *J. Organic Chem.* 21:204-205.

Flath, R. A., and Forrey, R. R. (1977). Volatile components of papaya (*Carica papaya* L., Solo variety). *J. Agric. Food Chem.* 25:103-108.

Gmelia, R., and Kjaer, A. (1970). Glucosinolates in the caricaceae. *Phytochemistry* 9:591-593.

Jones, W. S., and Kubota, H. (1940). Some respirational changes in the papaya fruit during ripening and the effects of cold storage in these changes. *Plant Physiol.* 15:711.

Katague, D. B., and Kirch, E. R. (1965). Chromatographic analysis of the volatile components of papaya fruit. *J. Pharm. Sci.* 54:891-894.

Kimmel, J. R., and Smith, E. L. (1954). Crystalline papain: I. preparation, specificity, activation. *J. Biol. Chem.* 207:515.

King, G. S., Sakanashi, A., and Soong, E. (1951). Rich powder from papaya. *Food Engineering* 23:147.

Kjaer, A. (1960). Naturally derived isothiocyanates (mustard oils) and their parent glucosides. *Prog. Chem. Organic National Products* 18:122-176.

Kunimitsu, D. K., and Yasunobu, K. T. (1967). Chymopapain: The chromatographic fractionation of partially purified chymopapain and the characterization of crystalline chymopapain B. *Biochem. Biophys. Acta* 139:405-417.

Lynch, L. J., Chang, A. T., Lum, J. C. N., Sherman, G. D., and Seale, P. E. (1959). *Hawaii Food Processors Handbook, Circular 55.* Hawaii Agric. Exp. Sta. Honolulu, Hawaii.

Menery, R. C., and Jones, R. H. (1972). Nitrate accumulation and reduction in pawpaw fruits. *Aust. J. Biol. Sci.* 25:531-542.

Ogata, J. N., Kawano, Y., Bevenue, A., and Casarett, E. J. (1972). The ketopheptose content of some tropical fruits. *J. Agric. Food Chem.* 20:113-115.

Pope, W. T. (1930). *Papaya culture in Hawaii. Bulletin 61.* Honolulu, Hawaii, Hawaii Agric. Exp. Sta.

Pratt, D. S., and Del Rosario, J. I. (1913). Philippine fruits: Their composition and characteristics. *Philippine J. Sci.* 8A:59.

Purseglove, J. W. (1968). *Tropical Crops: Dicotyledons, Vol. 1.* New York, Wiley, p. 45-51.

Sawato, M. (1969). Changes in isozyme pattern and kinetics of heat inactivation of peroxidase enzyme of papaya following gamma irradiation. Unpublished M. S. thesis, University of Hawaii, Honolulu.

Souza, R. A. (1978). Private communication.

Stahl, A. L. (1935). Composition of miscellaneous tropical and subtropical Florida fruits. *Bulletin 283.* Gainsville, Florida, Florida Agric. Exp. Sta.

Tang, C. S. (1970a). Hydrogen sulfide production in relation to benzyl isothiocyanate in papaya fruit (*Carica papaya L.*), *Paper No. 92, 160th Annual ACS Meeting, Chicago, Illinois.* (Abstract)

Tang, C. S. (1970b). A simple method for demonstracting an enzymatic reaction. *J. Chem. Ed.* 47:692.

Tang, C. S. (1971). Benzyl isothiocyanate of papaya fruit. *Phytochemistry* 10:117-121.

Tang, C. S. (1973). Localization of benzylglucosinolate and thioglucosidase in *Carica papaya* fruit. *Phytochemistry* 12:769-773.

Tang, C. S. (1974). Benzyl isothiocyanate as naturally occurring papain inhibitor. *J. Food Sci.* 39:94-96.

Tang, C. S., Bhothiopaksa, K., and Frank, H. S. (1972). Bacterial degradation of benzyl isothiocyanate. *Appl. Microbiol.* 23:1145-1148.

Tang, C. S., Syed, M. M., and Hamilton, R. A. (1972b). Benzyl isothiocyanate in the Caricaceae. *Phytochemistry* 11:2531-2533.

Tang, C. S., and Tang, W. J. (1976). Inhibition of papain by isothiocyanates. *Biochem. Biophys. Acta* 452:510-520.

Thompson, A. R. (1914). The composition of Hawaiian fruits and nuts. *Annual Report 1914.* Honolulu, Hawaii, Hawaii Agric. Exp. Sta.

Wenkam, N. S., and Miller, C. D. (1965). Composition of Hawaii fruits. *Bulletin 135.* Honolulu, Hawaii, Hawaii Agric. Exp. Sta.

Yamamoto, H. Y. (1964). Comparison of the carotenoids in yellow- and red-fleshed *Carica papaya*. *Nature* 201:1049-1050.

Yamamoto, H. Y., and Inouye, W. (1963). Sucrose as a gelatin inhibitor of commercially frozen papaya purée. *Tech. Prog. Rpt. 137.* Honolulu, Hawaii, Hawaii Agric. Exp. Sta.

Yee, W., Akamine, E. K., Aoki, G. M., Haramoto, F. H., Hine, R. B., Holtzmann, D. V., Hamilton, R. A., Ishida, J. T., Keeler, J. T., and Nakasone, H. (1970). Papayas in Hawaii. *Cir. 436.* Honolulu, Hawaii, Coop. Ext. Ser., University of Hawaii.

13

Rice in the Tropics

Albert P. Mossman Western Regional Research Center,
U.S. Department of Agriculture,* Albany, California

---

*Reference to a company or a product name does not imply approval or recommendation of the product by the USDA to the exclusion of others which might be suitable.

I. INTRODUCTION

A. The Importance of Rice in the Tropics

Rice is the most important food in the tropics and one of the two leading food crops of the world. Over a billion people depend on rice for
more than half of their calories. On a world basis, production of wheat,
the other leading crop, exceeds that of rice, but over 90% of the wheat
crop is produced and consumed outside the tropics (Fellers, 1979).
Maize (corn), sorghum, and millet are significant staple crops in the
tropics and are found in many areas, but their usage is much less than
that of rice. Thus, in the tropics as a whole, the single food most
likely to be eaten is rice (FAO, 1980a,b).

To a great many individuals, rice is not only the staple food but
also a major factor in every part of their daily lives. It dominates
daily economic and social activities and sometimes even attains religious
or political significance. To millions of subsistence and low-income
farmers and farm workers, rice is the only source of buying power, as
well as the major source of nutrients. Thus, the improvement of rice
technology can be an important means of improving the nutritional and
economic status of this large segment of the population, and as such is
consistent with the goals of several agencies working to better the
human condition worldwide. Chandler (1979) has published a handbook
for rice program developers that contains technical information, sources
of assistance, and an annotated bibliography on rice in the tropics.
Austin (1981) and Kahn (1981) have discussed problems in combating
malnutrition and described several of the agencies involved.

Rice is ideally suited for its important role. Lu and Chang (1980)
have shown that rice can support more human beings per hectare than
other grains. It grows in a wider variety of environments and it stores
as well as, or better than other foods. The following sections of the
chapter give a concise overview of rice production and utilization in the
tropics. Further technical information on each phase is available in the
literature, which is quite extensive for rice, and references to appropriate reviews are given with each section.

Much in the rice literature describes optimum practice, an ideal seldom achieved in the tropics due to the harsh conditions against which
the tropical worker must struggle. Additionally, some information derived in the more temperate zones simply does not pertain to the tropical situation. On the other hand, it is not possible to discuss rice in
the tropics without discussing the world rice situation. Nevertheless,
in the following pages, those aspects of rice technology having the
greatest impact on the quality and quantity of rice finally available to
the tropical consumer have been selected and discussed in detail. The
choices are largely based on information obtained during an assessment
tour of world rice areas in 1978 (Saunders et al., 1980).

Emphasis has thus been given to tropical practices and conditions, particularly at the village level of sophistication, since the majority of people dependent on rice operate at that level. Practices common only in the more industrialized, capital-intensive temperate zones have not been discussed unless directly related. The geographical definition of the tropics, 23.5° north and south of the equator, includes most but not all of the tropical rice area discussed.

In summary, the purpose of the chapter is to introduce the reader to this important tropical food, to point out aspects having the greatest impact on rice as food in the tropics, and to provide easy access to the rice literature.

B.   The Origin and History of Cultivated Rice

Rice as we know it today (genus *Oryza*) is a member of the grass family (Gramineae). This large family includes such exotic relatives as sugar cane and bamboo, as well as the common prairie-type grasses and the other cereal grains. The many different varieties* of rice which exist today, both under cultivation and in the wild, are grouped in about 20 species (Lu and Chang, 1980). All of the cultivated varieties are included under the species *Oryza sativa* L., except a few in Africa which come under *O. glaberrima* Steud. The wild rices, on the other hand, are distributed among many species including *O. sativa*. It should be noted that the so-called wild rice of the Great Lakes region of North America, *Zizania acuatica*, whereas it shares with rice the characteristic of water tolerance, is otherwise closer to barley and is not a member of the genus *Oryza*. The true wild rice types, which are the uncultivated varieties of *Oryza*, are important both in the historical development of the plant and in supplying germ plasm to the pool available for breeding today's cultivated varieties.

The origins of the use of rice as food and its cultivation are not known for certain because few records exist from such ancient times. The earliest human records of China, India, and the Indochina area already mention rice cultivation and even specific varieties. In contrast, the ancient Egyptian records do not mention rice, a conspicuous absence since cultivation of other grains has a prominent place. It is speculated that wild types were at first simply gathered as food. The cultivated form evolved from the annual wild form. Crosses then occurred between cultivated and wild types, as occurs in some areas today, so

---

*For simplicity, the term variety has been used to include all cultivars except breeding lines.

that a hybridization and selection took place which allowed the cultivated varieties of today to further evolve.

It is generally accepted that cultivation of *O. sativa* began independently at several sites within a broad area between India and southwest China. As cultivation spread throughout eastern Asia, three major genetic subgroups (indica, javanica, and japonica) evolved.

From eastern Asia, *O. sativa* cultivation spread to western Asia, Africa (including Madagascar), and finally to Europe and the Americas.

The African *O. glaberrima* varieties are thought to have differentiated separately with origins around the Niger River. Spread of this species has been limited although it was introduced to Central and South America with the slave trade.

Attempts to grow rice in the Americas began with Columbus, but the first sustained commercial rice production in North America began in 1685 in South Carolina with the introduction of improved varieties. Central and South America originally obtained the grain via the Spanish and Portuguese colonists, but many of the varieties grown there later came from seed stock obtained from South Carolina around 1700. Commercial rice production began in Australia in 1923.

Commercial exportation of rice in quantity is a fairly recent development. Under British influence, large areas of untilled swampland were brought under cultivation in Burma and the Indochina area. A substantial export activity began from this area to the population centers in India, China, the other traditional Asian rice areas, and eventually to Europe and elsewhere. The stable supply of commercial rice was welcomed by the growing urban population of Asia who up to then depended on the uncertain supply of rice from the traditional farmers who sold only the rice that was excess to their needs. In bad years less rice would go to the cities, causing hardship.

By World War II, the Burma-Thailand-Indochina area was known as the "rice bowl" of the world. After the war, the disrupted colonial trade networks in eastern Asia were not fully restored. Population increased faster than production, Indochina exports did not keep pace, and exportation to Asia from other areas of the world increased. Today, most rice bowl countries (except Thailand) produce mainly for domestic consumption.

The future is difficult to predict. The great population increases in tropical countries continue to strain production and distribution abilities, whereas the development through selective breeding of rice varieties capable of much higher yields per acre has increased the potential for production. The origin and history of rice have been reviewed in more detail by Lu and Chang (1980), Efferson (1952), Adair and Jodon (1973), and Purseglove (1972).

C. The Geography and Character of Rice Today

Today rice is grown as far north as 53° in China, as far south as 40° in Argentina and New Zealand, at elevations as high as 3000 m in India and Nepal, and at sea level on the flood plains of the Ganges in Bangladesh. It is grown without irrigation on slopes considered too steep for many other crops, and in other areas it grows under flood waters as deep as 15 ft. In some countries it is the most highly mechanized crop, in others it is raised with no machinery and an incredible input of human and animal labor, and in still others it is grown with no attention at all between planting and harvest. This diversity is possible partly because of varietal differences, which have allowed wide adaptation to different conditions, and partly because of special characteristics such as the ability of rice to transport oxygen to its roots under water. Varieties differ in processing and eating characteristics as well as agronomic behavior, and regional preferences have evolved for partic- ular grain types which greatly influence the marketing of the grain.

This remarkable diversity makes general statements about rice diffi- cult to make and use. Nevertheless, average data are useful in show- ing some interesting features of the production, consumption, and trade of rice in the world. Table 1 shows the production figures for each continent and for the major rice-producing countries between 1977 and 1979. The largest producers are the People's Republic of China (PRC) and India. The United States, which was the largest exporter during these years (see subsequent discussion), had a production less than 10% of that of India and less than 5% that of the PRC. Asia, particularly Southeast Asia, is the major area of rice production.

Table 2 shows the major areas which exported rice between 1976 and 1978. Each year the world total of rice exported is less than 5% of the total world production. The more elaborate quality standards used in international trade therefore do not apply to the bulk of the rice pro- duced. For example, U.S. Federal grain standards apply only to grain destined for export or for government purchase.*

The small amount of the world production that moves in international trade is important. It provides needed rice for the importing countries and income for the exporting ones. It tends to stabilize prices, and to influence to some extent rice quality and quality standards. Geograph- ically there have been definite patterns for export and import, with oc- casional changes in some years. In the Americas, the United States is the largest exporter, but many of the other American countries also export modest amounts of rice (some export and also import). In gen- eral, European and African countries that use rice import rice; however, Italy and Egypt have been exporting rice consistently. In Asia the oil- producing countries of the Middle East import rice; Indonesia in South- east Asia, which produces some oil, is the world's largest importer. The heavy population centers of Singapore and Hong Kong also import rice, as do Bangladesh and Sri Lanka (Ceylon). The largest exporters

---

*An analysis of rices moving in world trade in terms of U.S. rice stand- ards has been published by Rivenburgh (1961). The stricter U.S. standards for absence of insect parts frequently resulted in low grades for the world rices.

Table 1 The Major Rice-Producing Continents and Countries in the World Between 1977 and 1979[a]

Continent or country	Rough rice production (million tonnes)[b]		
	1977	1978	1979[c]
North and Central America	6.5	8.0	8.4
United States	4.5	6.1	6.3
South America	11.5	12.2	12.9
Brazil	7.5	7.7	8.6
Columbia	1.3	1.8	1.7
Europe	1.6	1.8	1.8
Italy	0.8	0.9	1.0
U.S.S.R. (Europe and Asia)	2.2	2.1	2.2
Africa	7.6	7.8	8.2
Egypt	2.3	2.3	2.4
Malagasy	1.7	1.9	2.0
Nigeria	0.7	0.8	1.0
Asia	332.2	352.8	334.4
Bangladesh	19.6	18.5	18.8
Burma	8.8	10.5	9.8
Kampuchea	1.6	1.5	0.4
People's Republic of China	126.5	137.0	140.0
Taiwan	3.5	3.2	3.1
India	74.3	80.8	61.6
Indonesia	22.8	25.8	24.1
Iran	1.0	1.3	1.2
Japan	16.4	15.7	15.0
North Korea	3.9	4.5	4.7
South Korea	8.3	7.3	7.4
Malaysia	1.7	1.6	2.0
Nepal	2.7	2.4	2.3
Pakistan	4.3	4.9	4.8
Philippines	6.9	7.3	7.6
Sri Lanka	1.7	1.9	1.9
Thailand	15.0	16.8	16.5
Vietnam	11.0	9.8	11.0
Australia	0.5	0.7	0.7
World total	362.0	385.5	368.6

[a]Crop year beginning August 1. All continents which raise rice are included, but only countries with production exceeding 1 million tonnes are listed separately.
[b]For milled rice equivalent multiply by 0.66.
[c]Preliminary figures.
Source: USDA (1980).

Table 2 The Major Exporting and Importing Continents and Countries in the World Between 1976 and 1978[a]

	Milled equivalent traded (million tonnes)[b]					
	1976		1977		1978[c]	
	Exports	Imports	Exports	Imports	Exports	Imports
North and Central America	2.0	0.3	2.3	0.4	2.3	0.4
United States	2.0	–	2.3	–	2.3	–
South America	0.5	0.2	0.6	–	0.7	0.1
Europe (east and west)	0.8	1.6	0.7	1.7	0.9	1.7
Africa	0.2	0.8	0.2	1.5	0.2	1.8
Asia	4.9	4.8	5.6	5.2	4.2	4.3
People's Republic of China	1.4	–	1.0	–	1.2	–
Indonesia	–	1.3	–	2.0	–	1.8
Thailand	1.9	–	2.9	–	1.6	–
Australia	0.2	–	0.3	–	0.3	–
World total	9.1	8.7	10.5	9.7	9.4	9.0

[a]Calendar year. Includes continents trading rice and countries with exports exceeding 1 million tonnes in year. Pakistan and Japan have also exceeded 1 million tonnes in year. Pakistan and Japan have also exceeded 1 million tonnes in more recent years.
[b]For rough rice equivalent multiply by 1.52.
[c]Preliminary.
Source: USDA (1980).

in Asia are the PRC and Thailand with over 1 million tonnes each, followed by Pakistan (growing) and Burma (declining). Asia is thus both
an importing and exporting area.

The quantitative aspect of the trade is only part of the rice trade
picture. The overall quality of the rice demanded and paid for by the
different importing countries varies greatly. The oil-producing countries of western Asia require higher-quality rice as do most European
markets. Indonesia imports large amounts of lower-quality rice. Bangladesh and Sri Lanka may settle for lower-quality rice depending on
the nature of the purchase.

Concessional sales, that is, sales subsidized by the government of
the exporting nation, make up part of the rice traded by the large exporting nations. For example, Japan, whose internal rice price is at
least twice the world price, occasionally exports rice at the world
price, with the Japanese government making up the difference. The
United States exports rice under its Public Law 480 program, some
sections of which are a negotiated concessional-sale mechanism. About
15% of total U.S. rice exports were made through Public Law 480 in
1979 (USDA, 1980).

All of the higher-quality rice in trade is commercially produced,
that is, produced with intent to sell. Precautions are taken throughout processing and transport to maintain quality, and the buyer pays
for the quality received, based on marketing standards. The lower-
quality rice, on the other hand, may be either downgraded commercial
rice or excess rice originally produced for local consumption that has
found its way into export channels.

Most of the rice in world trade is commercial and produced by nontropical countries. Most of the rice produced in the tropics is subsistence rice grown for personal or local consumption, with only the excess being sold. The distinction between commercial and subsistence
may at first seem trivial, but the difference in purpose, attitude, and
approach profoundly affects every phase of the rice system in the
tropics. Commercial producers who sell their entire crops and buy
from the store have an investment in the end product and the entire
system. On the other hand, the subsistence producer focuses on the
rice retained and takes less active interest in the rice that is sold and
the processing and marketing system into which it enters. Very often
the best rice will be kept and inferior rice sold. Prices are often negotiated at a local market, or between farmer and miller or owner and
worker (bartered), based on local, unofficial standards that vary
greatly with supply and demand. Even rice produced primarily for
sale becomes involved in this system if most of the rice in the area is
subsistence produced. As a result, opportunities for quality loss are
greater. There are definite advantages for each system. Rice available in subsistence areas is usually of lower overall quality, but is
also lower in price. Subsistence operations are less sensitive to price
drops, since less rice is sold, but are also much less responsive to

advances in modern technology. For example, it is the commercial producers who have benefited most from the high-yielding varieties.

Asia and Africa are basically subsistence or semicommercial with some commercial areas, while South and Central America have a large commercial sector, due to their history of plantation-style agriculture. However, the tendency towards land reform is increasing the proportion of subsistence or semicommercial operations in the Americas also. Certainly the character and influence of subsistence farming must be appreciated to understand the rice situation in the tropics.

Recent trends have been analyzed by Lu and Chang (1980). Efferson (1952) gives a vivid description of the traditional practices of each country in his earlier work. Additional statistical data on production, consumption, trade, and commodity projections may be found in the publications of the Food and Agricultural Organization (FAO) of the United Nations (FAO, 1979, 1980a,b), which differ slightly from U.S. Department of Agriculture (USDA) data cited here.

II. PRODUCTION

A. Present Rice Cultural Practices

As mentioned previously, rice culture around the world is incredibly diverse. Part of the reason for the diversity is the different requirements of the different varieties. More important, however, is the ability of rice to tolerate a variety of conditions. Although rice is thought of as a water crop, it actually requires no more total water intake during growth than other cereal crops, and can be grown without flooding (upland rice), provided the required moisture is in the soil continuously throughout the growing season. Indeed, significant amounts of upland rice are grown. However, rice does have the ability to transport oxygen down to its roots allowing it to grow in standing water and to take advantage of the benefits of controlled flooding. The standing water enhances nutrient availability, nitrogen fixation, and tiller formation. It tends to neutralize the soil pH, regulate the immediate environment, and eliminate weeds which compete with the rice for nutrients. The standing water thus tends to modify any extreme conditions and helps increase grain yields. Abundant sunshine, warm soil, a rain-free ripening period, and lack of destructive factors such as storms (uncontrolled flooding) and pests also tend to favor higher yields. Yet rice grows under less favorable conditions also, but with a reduction of yield.

The choice of variety to be planted is influenced by the local climatic pattern and whether one or two rice crops will be produced during the year. The traditional tropical monsoon rice varieties (indicas) are often photoperiod-sensitive, and the seeds may require a dormant period before they will grow. These evolutionary traits allow the plant to grow during the monsoon (rainy) season but do not allow grain formation until the dry season approaches (shorter day length). For double cropping, a photo-period-insensitive variety is usually used since one crop must mature during the rainy season.

The traditional tropical rice crop is planted to take advantage of the natural rainfall pattern, that is, a monsoon followed by a dry period. Since rice requires moisture during growth and sunshine during harvest, the fields are commonly prepared before or during the rainy season and the rice is planted so that it is ready for harvest during the driest period. The standing water may be provided by irrigation or by simply trapping water from the rains within dirt walls constructed around the fields. Preparation of a field includes leveling, construction or repair of the dikes (bunds, levees) and the irrigation troughs, plowing the dirt, mixing in fertilizer (manure) if used, adding water, and working the mixture into a smooth mud (puddling). The plowing and puddling are operations that are often done with the help of animals or small hand tractors.

Transplanting is commonly practiced in tropical Asia. All of the seed is first planted in one field, and, after the primary shoots are established, they are transplanted into many prepared secondary fields. Plants are spaced to allow for growth of secondary shoots (branches called tillers). There is evidence that transplanting itself does not directly increase yields (Adair et al., 1942, cited by Johnson and Miller, 1973), but allows better management of resources which indirectly affects yields. With transplanting, all of the rice can begin growing while other fields are prepared. This is desirable for more efficient use of labor and land and allows greater latitude in multiple-cropping situations. The transplanted rice also has a head start on weeds that strongly affect yield by competition. Transplanting is often done by teams of women who stand in a row, place the shoots in the mud along a taut string, step back, and after the string is moved to mark the next row, repeat the process. Planting in straight rows allows hand weeding to be done easily, whereas broadcasting (randomly spreading the seeds directly on the field) practically eliminates the possibility of such easy weeding. Small mechanical transplanters and weeders are available, but the use of machines is very limited in the tropics.

After transplanting, the water level is raised and maintained at a height considered best for the particular variety until just before harvest. During growing, weeding is either performed twice by teams or continuously by the farmer and family. In more highly developed rice farming, chemicals are applied to control weeds, insects, fungi, and small animals. Despite efforts of the tropical farmer, birds and other pests usually do considerable damage. Information about the best methods for control of the particular pests and diseases in a given area is usually available to the farmers through local authorities or local commercial sources. As harvest approaches, the standing water is drained to allow the ground to become hard enough to walk on but not so early as to deprive the ripening plant of needed moisture. The timing of this and many other cultural operations is a matter of local art and custom.

Mikkelsen and De Datta (1980) have discussed cultural factors and have compared cultural practices in different areas of the world today. Purseglove (1972) has summarized the requirements of the plant and described its structure. The structure of the plant with a glossary of terms has also been published by Chang and Bardenas (1965). The stages of growth have been discussed by Vergara (1980).

A single seed has the potential to produce many rice plants. The seed first sends a primary shoot straight upwards, and later branches (tillers) grow up from the base of the primary shoot. Each tiller has the potential to produce a clump of rice grains (the panicle). The first part of growth (the vegetative phase) establishes the plant itself, its branches, leaves, and roots, whereas the last part (the reproductive phase) produces the rice grains. Both phases are important.

Table 3 shows the relative timing of the stages of rice growth. Four yield-determining stages are indicated: (a) number of tillers, (b) number of grains per tiller (panicle), (c) number of fertile florets (spikelets), and (d) kernel size. With varieties which are sensitive to length of day, panicle production is initiated by shorter day length and will not occur until a particular date, regardless of date of planting. The resulting differences in total growing time in a given location occur as differences in the duration of the vegetative phase. The growth duration of varieties not sensitive to day length is constant for a given variety in a given environment. It increases in the duration of both vegetative and ripening phases if planting is moved from tropical to cooler temperate environments. For example, the resulting change for IR-8 variety would be from 130 days between sewing and harvest in the tropics at sea level to 180 or more days in a cooler environment, an increase of 50 or more days.

Rice is usually more than 95% self-pollinating. At the flowering stage the spikelet (flower) opens for about 1 day. After pollination, the embryo begins development within the spikelet, and the aleurone layer produces cells that fill with starch, until the entire spikelet cavity is full (the endosperm). When dried, this filled spikelet is the rough rice kernel. The flag (top) leaf influences yield because it provides a major portion of the photosynthesis for the filling of the spikelets.

Pests and their management have not been discussed here, although they have become particularly important subjects since the introduction of the genetically uniform high-yielding varieties into many parts of the world. Reviews are available on diseases (Ou, 1980) and insects (Bowling, 1980). A popular pamphlet on rice pests has been published by the International Rice Research Institute (IRRI) (Mueller, 1970).

Table 3   Growth Stages of the Rice Plant

Stage of growth	Duration (ds)[a]	Structures visible and processes begun during stage
1. Seedling	0-14	Root, shoot, 2 leaves; seed is food, air conduction cells
2. Seedling	14-21	Roots, leaves, tiller buds; breaks water, makes own food; transplanting
3. Tillering	20-52	Very active growth of new tillers[b] and roots
4. Maximum tillers	53-60	End effective new tillers, tillers develop
5. Panicle initiation	61-70	Panicle (reproductive) differentiation within stems
6. Elongation	70-92	Spikelets develop,[b] internode elongation
7. Heading and flowering	93-105	Panicles emerge, spikelets open, fertilization[b]
8. Grain formation ("filling")	102-138	Starch builds in spikelet which fills[b]
9. Maturity	135-145	Ripe grain dries to harvest moisture, continued conversion of sugars to starch

[a]ds = days after seeding. Some overlap of stages. Wide variation in tillering time.
[b]Yield determining step: (1) no. of tillers (panicles): (2) no. of grains per panicle, (3) percent of flowers (spikelets) which are fertile; and (4) kernel size (least important).
Source: Schematic composite adapted from Williams (1980).

B.   Cultivated Rice Varieties and Breeding

All of the presently cultivated rice varieites (Sec. I. B) are included in one of four groups, the three historical subspecies of *O. sativa*: (a) indica, native of the tropical monsoon; (b) japonica, native of the temperate subtropics; (c) javonica, native of the uniform equatorial climate of Indonesia; or in (d) the African species, *O. glaberrima*. These groups represent the historic varieties that form the major genetic base upon which today's breeding programs are built. Their existence, however, does not preclude the breeder from developing varieties that do not fit into the historic groups. Although partial sterility barriers exist between the groups, successful crossings have been

made, not only between the cultivated groups, but also between cultivated rices and wild types having particular desired traits (e.g.,
varieties of *O. hivara*).

The indica (tropical) and japonica (temperate) rices are the most
important for cultivation and for breeding. Although there is a wide
variation within each group, each has typical characteristics acquired
through evolutionary adaptation to its respective natural habitat which
is particularly desirable for breeding. Tropical varieties traditionally
have been grown during the monsoon season, which is characterized
by flooding, low solar radiation (clouds), fierce competition from weeds
and pests, and temperature and day length decreasing toward maturity. They possess the traits of quick early vegetative growth, high
resistance to disease, pests, and severe conditions, a sensitivity to
day length, and a tendency to direct their energy toward vegetative
growth rather than reproductive development (lower yield and lower
yield-response to fertilizer application). The temperate varieties
have traditionally been grown under more carefully controlled conditions
with temperature and photoperiod increasing toward midseason and with
more total solar radiation and nutrients. They tend to have slower initial and vegetative growth, greater reproduction growth (greater grain-
to-straw ratio), greater sensitivity to adverse factors including disease,
and no sensitivity to length of day. The fertilizer response of temperate varieties is the more desirable because it is directed toward reproductive (grain) development rather than excess vegetative growth.
Thus, the temperate (cold-tolerant) rices tend to yield more grain if
fertilized, but the tropical rices are stronger plants that can grow under adverse conditions and resist disease and pests.

The International Rice Research Institute (IRRI) in the Philippines
has been particularly successful in combining higher yield characteristics with vigor. An early successful cross between a Taiwanese short-
stature variety (Dee-geo-woo-gen)* and a vigorous, heavy tillering,
disease-resistant tropical variety (Peta) resulted in a fourth-generation
selection, later known as IR-8, which dramatically increased yields
when grown in the tropics and began the rice portion of the "green
revolution." The breeding program was contained to increase disease
resistance and grain quality in IR-8 and was expanded by exporting
breeding material to other countries for crossbreeding with varieties
adapted to local conditions.

All breeding programs include such goals as increased yield and increased resistance to disease and pests, the latter being a continual need
because of the continual natural development of new disease and pest

---

*Dee-geo-woo-gen is like japonica varieties, but is considered to be an
indica. Other crosses have been made between japonica and indica
varieties.

strains. Additional specific goals have been included in the IRRI program. Reduced plant height (stature) has been sought in order to increase grain-to-straw ratio, and to reduce lodging, the falling over of the plant under the weight of the panicle. The elimination of photoperiod sensitivity has been important to allow off-season cropping in the tropics. Specific eating-quality characteristics, which are important for consumer acceptance, are also included in the program. Rice breeding programs which serve different needs include different specific goals. For example, varieties expected to be mechanically threshed are bred for easy release of the grains from the panicle (called high shattering), while those expected to be mechanically threshed are bred for more difficult release (low shattering) to reduce losses in handling.

There is a wide range of agronomic characteristics in the rices of the world besides those of the typical indica or japonica. Most areas have local varieties adapted to local conditions, including deep water rices that are able to grow fast enough to keep above rising waters up to 5 m deep and upland rice varieties that can survive greatly reduced soil moisture. With regard to eating characteristics, the typical indicas tend to be dry and bland whereas the japonicas tend to be moist, sweeter, and somewhat sticky. However, certain less typical varieties, called waxy (mochi) rices, produce grains devoid of amylose-type starch (i.e., 100% amylopectin) which results in a very sticky, chewy, cooked product. Other varieties are highly aromatic, a characteristic which commands premium prices in some markets. These unusual characteristics are also available to the breeder.

The characteristics bred to solve one problem may simultaneously aggravate another. For example, short stature, which resists lodging, increases disease in some areas by reducing the aeration among the tillers. The elimination of photoperiod sensitivity, necessary to allow off-season harvest (double cropping), also removes the mechanism for location-specific maturation, a very desirable trait in some areas. Greater ease of shatter, necessary for hand-threshing, allows a higher percentage of loss during reaping. One of the greatest problems is the increased pest and disease attacks in some tropical areas due to the consecutive growing of dense, genetically uniform rice crops. Varieties diverse enough to provide a genetic fallow between rice crops are needed.

Successful breeding sometimes actually causes new problems. The increased yields, especially in the off-season crop, have often overloaded drying capacity, so that spoilage losses occur. Sometimes the increased yields depress market prices enough that the extra cost of fertilizer needed with high-yielding varieties is not recovered. In some countries, mass production of seed is not controlled well enough to prevent mixed seed being distributed, (e.g., Ecuador) giving poor results even though the newly bred variety is superior.

Most countries producing significant amounts of rice have national breeding centers that have developed their own varieties and techniques. Many have played an important part in introducing high-yielding varieties, especially those from IRRI, and providing IRRI with local germplasm. Successful non-IRRI varieties have become more accessible as a result of this interchange, and the IRRI Germplasm Bank has grown steadily (66,000 accessions by the early 1980s) (Chang and Li, 1980). Some countries have also built up national germplasm collections (the United States, Japan, PRC, and India) (National Research Council, 1972).

The IRRI, which is supported by several national governments and donor agencies, is probably the most important tropical rice center today, not only because of its successful breeding but also because of its research and teaching in chemistry, engineering, and economics as related to rice in the tropics. It has one of the world's largest collections of publications on tropical rice production, including many translations into English. Bibliographies, annual reports, research papers, and books are also published by the IRRI, and a list may be obtained by contacting: IRRI, P.O. Box 933, Manila, Philippines.

A history of rice breeding up to 1960 (when the IRRI began) and a review of world programs from 1960 to 1972 has been published by the IRRI (1972). Recent work in the area has been reviewed by Chang and Li (1980). Purseglove (1972) has summarized varietal characteristics and improvement by breeding.

III. PROCESSING

A. Reaping, Threshing, and Drying

1. Reaping and Threshing

Reaping is the cutting and removal of the entire rice stalk from the field, whereas threshing is the removal of the grain from the stalk. Reaping, threshing, and drying are processing steps that normally occur in or nearby the field although further drying may occur at the mill. In most of the tropics, both reaping and threshing are hand operations. Small gasoline-powered (or diesel) threshers are common in some areas (e.g., Taiwan and parts of Thailand), and their popularity is growing. Rice combines, machines that reap and thresh at once, are used only in capital-intensive, commercial operations in the tropics (e.g., Central and South America) and in the temperate areas.

In a typical tropical harvest the rice stalks are gently cut by hand, and either bundled to dry further before threshing or threshed immediately. Threshing may be done in the field or at a nearby central location. Hand-threshing methods include treading on the panicles, beating them with flails, beating them against a stationary object, and drawing small bundles of panicles across forked spikes.

When available, animals are used to thresh by walking them in a circle over a thick layer of the reaped stalks. The grain falls to the floor below the straw, which provides a cushion against abuse of the grain from the weight of the animal. Tractors can be used similarly to thresh; but they cause grain damage, and the fuel would be better used to provide power for proper mechanical threshers.

The mechanical thresher consists of a large drum, fitted with short protruding spikes or loops, which rotates within a concave half-shell. The shell holds the panicles against the rotating drum while the spikes knock off the grain. The loose grains are separated from the straw by screening and aspiration. Some models are small enough to be carried into a field by two men or an animal.

The chief advantage of mechanical threshing is the great increase in speed (capacity) with which the job can be done, allowing an entire field to be harvested quickly with less likelihood of spoilage. A second advantage is the replacement of inefficient human energy with motor power. Disadvantages include the cost of machine and fuel, transport difficulties, and the need for a more complex social organization than is present in some areas. Human-powered mechanical threshers exist, but are usually quickly replaced by gasoline- or diesel-powered models. Threshers are sometimes mounted on wheels and pulled from field to field by tractor or truck. In some areas, harvest teams travel through a district working field after field in return for a percentage of the rice. In other areas a thresher owned by one may serve the needs of several farmers in turn, through cooperative teamwork. Occasionally, the threshers are situated in the rice mills (e.g., Bolivia and Malaysia). Unlike the complex rice combines, the small threshers are easily produced by village-level industries. The advantages of mechanical threshing and the types of threshers available in the tropics have been discussed by Kahn (1976). Saunders et al. (1980) have described country by country, harvest and threshing methods in use in the tropics.

2. Drying

Drying of the grain after harvest is the single most important step in the production of rice in the tropics. There are three reasons for this: (a) lack of drying can cause the complete loss of a rice crop by spoilage; (b) improper drying can cause partial spoilage, scorching, later breakage, and other quality deterioration; and (c) the lack of drying capacity deters production of large amounts of additional grain sorely needed in the tropics. Drying is more important in the tropics than in temperate areas because the climate is warmer and more humid, transportation problems from field to drier are more frequent, and the impact of grain losses is greater. In the tropics, drying, or the lack of it, affects every phase of rice production and consumption, including growing (planning), harvest (timing), storage (spoilage), milling (breakage), and even marketing (supply). The advent of higher-yielding varieties and second crops that mature during the wet season has put an even greater load on the already insufficient capacity to dry rice. Mechanical driers have become a necessity, although their use is substantially below the need, and much rice spoils as a result.

Rice tends to gain or lose moisture from the surrounding air until an equilibrium is reached based on the relative humidity (RH) of the

air and the moisture content of the grain. The equilibrium points are
shown in Table 4. For example, at 27°C, grain at 16% moisture content
will gain moisture from the air that is above 84% RH and lose moisture
to air that is below that value. The RH is important for two reasons:
(a) high-RH air supports spoilage organisms, and (b) low-RH air passing through the grain dries it in mechanical driers. The drying power
of the air depends primarily on how full it is (RH) rather than how
much moisture it contains (absolute humidity). The water-holding capacity of air approximately doubles with every 11°C-rise in temperature
so that air which is 100% RH (saturated) at one temperature will be 50%
RH (half full) at a temperature 11°C higher, with no change in the
actual air moisture content. Air with the same RH at a higher temperature would contain more moisture. Thus, moist air (high RH) may be
made into dry air (low RH) by raising its temperature. Since heat is

Table 4   Relative Humidity of Air at Given Temperatures in
Equilibrium with Rough Rice of Given Moisture Contents

Rice moisture content (%wb)[b]	Temperature of air and rice (°C)[a]			
	21	27	32	38
	Relative humidity (%)			
5	9	11	14	17
10	45	48	51	54
11	53	56	59	61
12	61	63	65	68
13	68	70	72	73
14	74	76	77	79
15	79	80	82	83
16	83	84	85	86
17	87	88	89	89
18	90	91	91	92
19	92	93	93	94
20	94	95	95	95
25	99	99	99	96

[a]Temperatures are Celsius approximations of 70, 80, 90,
and 100°F used in reference.
[b]%wb = percent wet basis. The equilibrium attained in
practice will deviate from values shown (<1%) due to
hysteresis, that is, values will be low if approached from
below, and high if approached from above.
Source: Adapted from data of Wratten and Kendrick in
Wasserman and Calderwood (1972).

required to evaporate water, there is a need for heat input in drying, which is supplied by the heated air or by the sun.

If very moist grain is confined, the surrounding air soon gains moisture enough to raise its RH significantly, although the grain may not decrease much in percentage moisture because the grain-to-air-weight ratio is so high. Thus, the equilibrium RH of the air may be very near that for the original grain moisture as shown in Table 4 for that temperature. Table 5 shows critical RH values necessary to support common spoilage organisms. Grain 13% moisture or below would equilibriate with air below 75% RH and should store safely, whereas grain at 18% or above would equilibriate with air above 90% RH and will spoil rapidly.

In most drying operations, the low-RH air is not confined with the grain, but moves through it, so that equilibrium is never reached and the grain continues to dry. In sun-drying or with heated mechanical driers the air and grain are heated, which accelerates the drying process. In nonheated, aerated, bulk drying and storage bins, spoilage prevention depends largely on the amount of air movement through the grain. These unheated bulk-storage driers are not common in the tropics although some experimental installations exist (Tambun, Indonesia), and the amounts of air throughput needed in the tropics have been described (Rawnsley, 1976).

Table 5   The Effect of Relative Humidity Level on Mold and Bacterial Activity

Critical RH levels	Activity expected
Above 90% RH	Normal growth and proliferation of food spoilage bacteria and molds; profuse growth if other conditions are optimum[a]
Below 90% RH but above 75% RH	Normal growth and proliferation of molds (slower than at 90% RH); no bacterial growth, but spores survive
Below 75% RH	Bacteria and most molds do not develop, although some molds (*Aspergillus* species) grow very slowly; dormant forms do survive desiccation

[a]Optimum temperature for many spoilage microorganisms is about 27°C, a typical ambient temperature for the tropics. Insects (vectors for microorganisms) also proliferate at higher moistures, but vary widely in their temperature requirements, some not surviving higher tropical temperatures.

Source: Adapted from Rawnsley (1976).

Most tropical rice is sun-dried. The traditional crop has always matured at the time of maximum sun. It is partly dried before harvest, and after harvest may be further dried in bundles in the field before threshing. Threshed rice is dried with the hull still attached. In this form it is called rough rice or paddy. After threshing, the rough rice is taken to a drying yard. The yard may be a concrete or mud and dung platform, the edge of an asphalt highway, or any similar flat place. The rice is spread in a layer several centimeters deep to catch the sun. It is periodically stirred during drying to prevent overdrying of the top layer, and gathered in piles and covered in the evening or in case of rain. In a few days the rice is dry enough to store. Because of the increased yields from the new rice varieties and the clouds and rain during the off-season harvest, the sun-drying capacity is no longer great enough to handle the drying load. However, many producers continue to rely on sun-drying alone because it is free. As a result, a considerable amount of partly spoiled rice enters the tropical marketing channels.

Mechanical driers consist of a container for the rough rice, a blower to force the air through it and, in the tropics, most driers also have a heater to heat the air. Some common drier designs are described in Table 6. The main advantage of the mechanical drier is the greater amount of rice that can be dried per day. An additional advantage is the higher-quality product that is possible if care is taken in the drier design and the drying procedure used.

Table 6 Descriptions of Some Common Types of Mechanical Driers[a]

Common name	Design features	Characteristics
Deep bed drier	Sealed warehouse or silo with false floor or tunnels for air input below grain, which is typically 3 to 10 m deep	High-powered fans move air through deep bed of rice from bottom to top; gentle heat may be applied; first rice hit dries fastest; grain is static; structure doubles as storage bin
Nonmixing column drier	Rice descends between two vertical parallel screens set 10 to 20 cm apart, forming tall, double-wall cylinder or box with air passing horizontally from center outwards	Heated air passes through thin layer of continuously moving rice; inside layer dries fastest, but less difference than in deep bed; mixing only between passes, if multipass used; not used for storage; heat control is important

Table 6   Continued

Common name	Design features	Characteristics
Mixing column drier	Similar to nonmixing but with baffles or other provision for mixing grain as it falls	Similar to nonmixing, but rice which receives hot air first is continually changed, which results in uniform drying; tempering between passes recommended
L.S.U. drier	A popular vertical (column) drier of any size but special design; solid column of rice descends while air enters inverted v tunnels which cross grain path horizontally in rows; similar exit tunnels staggered; air path is distance between tunnels (10 to 20 cm)	Tunnels effectively mix grain, drying is uniform; air path is same for all drier sizes; design was promoted by Louisiana State University, thus the L.S.U. name; tempering between passes recommended; not used for storage
Flat bed drier (small farm type)	Coverless box about 2 m X 3 m with perforated or screen false bottom; rice depth to 1 m (50 cm is maximum recommended)	Care is needed to seal container against air leaks; sufficient blower needed for depth used; heat provided (husk available only at mill), control important; can temper rice in drier (rice static); to empty, must scoop rice out; promoted by several groups.
Vertical batch drier	Same size as flat bed type but rice is in compartments on side; air passes from center out, path about 50 cm	Rice static; blower and heater similar to flat bed; individual small lots may be kept separate, unloading is easy; promoted by IRRI, SEARCA, UPLB, and other groups
Recirculating drier	A column drier which consists of a storage box above, feeding into drier, and mechanism	Grain receives several drying passes with a short temper between; popular in Japan, temper

Table 6 (Continued)

Common name	Design features	Characteristics
Recirculating drier (cont.)	to move grain from bottom of drier to top of storage	is too short as usually used (i.e., it is equivalent to one pass, not multipass, drying)
Sack tunnel drier	Bags of rice are stacked so as to make a tunnel through the center; axial fan heater forces air into tunnel and theoretically through bags to outside	This attempt to remove moisture directly from bagged rice quickly and cheaply is attractive to some South American millers, but is not as effective as column driers; drying is very uneven, causing cracking and spoilage; bags often contain uneven moisture to begin with (from standing on the ground)
Seed drier	Long closed retangular tunnel with series of holes along top, each just smaller than the side of rice bag; single bags placed on holes, hot air forced up through bag	Used in jungle areas of Peru and other South American countries; drying is uneven though better than sack tunnel

[a]Illustrations of driers may be found in Wasserman and Calderwood (1972), Beck and de Padua (1976), or Steffe et al. (1980).

Rice tends to resist drying. Its shape impedes air flow, and its high-starch content tends to hold water. Because of the low water diffusion rate and low coefficient of heat transfer, water at the center of the grain does not move rapidly to the surface as the surface is dried. At grain moistures below 18%, the difference in contraction due to the moisture difference between surface and interior during drying, causes stress which may result in breakage during later milling. Rapid, continuous drying results in breakage, however, breakage may be avoided by either: (a) alternating short periods of rapid, active drying with periods of moisture equilibriation to relieve the stresses, or, (b) drying so slowly that the internal moisture differences between center and surface are never great enough to cause stress. The latter method is practiced in commercial bulk facilities for finish drying, but rarely in the tropics. In the first method, about 2 to 3% moisture is removed at a time by active drying, followed by a tempering (equilibriating) period of at least 6 hr before the next period of active drying. Since the drying rate is fastest at first when surface moisture is being removed (as with fresh or equilibriated rice), tempering between drying passes reduces the total active drying time and the cost. If tempering is done in separate bins, the drier is free to dry other rice, increasing the effective drier capacity. Unfortunately, tempering during drying is not usually practiced in the tropics, and higher milling breakage is experienced as a result. Perhaps it is enough that the crop is dried at all, and gross spoilage is prevented.

Rice drying, including theory, drier designs and practices in the subtropics and tropics, and drying of rice for seed, has been reviewed by Wasserman and Calderwood (1972). Beck and de Padua (1976) have discussed rice-drying theory and drier designs. Saunders et al. (1980) have discussed the importance of drying to prevent postharvest loss and described tropical practices.

B. Storage

Rice is almost always stored for some period of time between production and consumption. Fortunately, it is one of the easiest foodstuffs to store provided certain criteria are met: (a) a physical barrier against outright consumption by predators is established; (b) a storage environment and grain condition fostering lowered metabolism within the rice kernels are maintained; and (c) an atmosphere between the kernels that retards the growth of bacteria, mold, fungi, insects, and other such spoilage organisms is maintained. Sound, clean grain that has been well dried will keep indefinitely if sealed and kept uniformly cool, yet spoilage losses are significant in the tropics because the criteria for safe storage are not met (Mallick and Nandi, 1981).

Sound grain possesses, in its siliceous husk, a very hard natural barrier against attack. Damaged grain has lost this advantage. Partly spoiled or very dirty grain already has a high population of spoilage organisms, whereas clean grain is not so highly inoculated. Without a physical barrier, such as a sealed container, even dry grain can be eaten by predators (as commonly occurs in naturally dry Ecuador, for example). If the warm tropical air is humid enough and allowed to circulate in the grain, it will create conditions that support spoilage organisms. If it is dry (low enough RH), circulation may be desirable to keep the grain dry and cool and to prevent localized buildup of moisture and heat. Because the grain is such a poor conductor of heat and retards air movement, any localized buildup of heat and moisture will not normally be dissipated and could easily become high enough to support spoilage. Evaporation and condensation within the storage container, as it is alternately heated and cooled by

by the tropical day and night, can quickly bring about such local moisture buildup in the rice. Certainly air circulation is to be preferred if
the grain is not very dry or clean and is stored in bulk. Majumder
(1974) has devised a large storage jar of special design to remove condensate, thus taking advantage of the alternating day and night temperatures to further dry grain sealed in the jar.

Aeration (and sometimes changing bins) is common in commercial
bulk operations, especially in the temperate areas. However, most rice
in the tropics is stored in bags in warehouses, homes, or out of doors
(covered). Up to 100 kg rough rice is put in each bag. The bag material (usually burlap) offers little resistance to predators. Barriers
must be installed to deny rats entrance to the warehouse. The bags,
which can be transported by human workers or animals, are stacked
so as to allow air to circulate freely. Moisture content of the rice (RH
of the air in contact) is the primary factor in the proliferation of fungi,
which are the major causes of spoilage and may produce toxic metabo-
lites (Scott, 1973). The stacks may be fumigated for insects and other
predators after covering them temporarily with a plastic tarpaulin.
Since insects are vectors for fungi, fumigation helps reduce fungi
also. Spoilage from fungi is much faster at grain moisture contents
above 18% (complete spoilage in a couple of days if confined). The
usual technique in the tropics is to reduce the rice moisture to 14 or
16% quickly by sun-drying and then to allow equilibrium in sacks as
described. The purpose of these operations is simply to retard, not
to eliminate, spoilage and infestation. The warehouse operator keeps
watch on the condition of the stored grain and will have it moved or
even redried, if necessary, using plentiful labor. The commercial
operator in the temperate areas likewise watches, moves, and aerates
the bulk grain using mechanical means. The difference between them
is that the temperate zone operator prefers 11 to 12% moisture for storage of much cleaner grain, whereas the tropical operator operates much
closer to the borderline of safe storage with higher temperatures, higher moisture, less of a barrier against pests, and usually with rice that
is initially much more highly infested. Thus, the tropical operator is
more at the mercy of the ambient conditions, and some grain spoilage
or loss of quality is practically inevitable (Mallick and Nandi, 1981).

Schroeder and Calderwood (1972) have reviewed rough rice storage,
including deterioration factors and storage techniques for combating
them. Rawnsley (1976) has discussed tropical storage of rice. Cogburn (1980) has described insect pests of stored rice. Additional
references have been reviewed by Steffe et al. (1980). General works
on grain storage (Christensen, 1974) are devoted mostly to grains
other than rice, though much of the information may apply.

In addition to any changes in the rice due to spoilage or infestation,
there are also chemical and physical changes which occur during storage due to natural aging. Some of the changes have an important effect on cooking and eating properties. For example, stickiness tends

to decrease during storage so that aging is considered deterioration by people who favor sticky rice (Japan, Korea, Laos, Puerto Rico), and improvement by those who do not (India, Indonesia, southern Thailand).

The changes due to natural aging have been studied most in milled, rather than rough rice. Fresh, sound rice is alive. The synthesis reactions begun during kernel maturation may continue during the early part of storage (Sinha, 1973). Respiration results in the conversion of starch to CO_2 and water, which evaporate and modify the storage atmosphere if confined. Grain heating and weight loss also result. Non-respiration reactions occur slowly in the intact grain, but much more rapidly after milling. This is due to the intimate mixing of enzymes and substrates due to the disruption of cell structures during the milling process. Ordinarily these effects are not important nutritionally, as storage changes do not seem to alter the basic food value of the rice in any major way. A varying amount of vitamin loss does occur. Storage changes, particularly in milled rice, have been reviewed by Barber (1972).

C. Milling

1. The Purpose of Milling

The rice grain is surrounded by a brittle, siliceous husk. Just below the husk are several bran layers consisting of dried cells fused tightly together as a result of being crushed between the husk and endosperm as the grain filled with starch during kernel development. The aleurone layer, which is below the bran, that is, below the seed coat and pericarp layers, is part of the endosperm, and manufactures the other endosperm cells during seed development. It is largely removed with the bran during milling. The germ, which is the embryo of the potential new plant, protrudes somewhat into the endosperm from one corner of the grain. It is similarly removed during milling, although small amounts of germ material usually remain attached to the milled kernel.

After the husk is removed, the grain, called the brown rice kernel, has a surface which is not smooth. Ridges and valleys run the length of the kernel. Due to the uneven surface, streaks of bran material remain in the low spots after milling even though the high spots may have been cut deep enough to expose the starchy endosperm. Some of the inner bran and some germ material may thus remain on the grain even after milling is considered complete.

The purpose of milling is to remove the husk, bran, and germ without damaging the residual kernel. The husk is siliceous and inedible. The bran contains material which many tropical consumers find objectionable. Both bran and germ contain oil and enzymes that cause the oil to spoil within a short time. The husk, which is brittle, can be cleanly separated from the brown rice underneath, whereas the bran, which adheres tenaciously, must be scraped or abraded off. The germ is usually scraped off with the bran. The amount of bran removal, termed the degree of milling, varies with the type of mill, the amount of time

the rice remains in the mill, the milling pressure, and the quality of
the rice. The product after milling is termed white or milled rice, and
the amount of product is called the total milling yield. The term white
rice sometimes implies that the grain was severely polished (10% or more
bran removal), whereas the term milled rice carries no such connota-
tion. Six to 8% bran removal is common in the tropics. Undermilled
rice may have only 4% or even less removal. In the tropics, the total
milling yield, including both whole and broken kernels, is often the
product of commerce. If broken kernels are separated, the amount of
whole rice, termed head rice, is called the head yield. Yield figures
are usually expressed as a weight percentage of the weight of the original rough rice milled. If trade standards place a limit on the amount
of broken rice allowed in the principal product, excess brokens represent an economic loss because they go into a lower-grade product.
Whether standards apply or not, excessive breakage always results in
some real losses, as the finer particles usually end up in the husk
which is discarded or the bran which is usually fed to animals.

2. Milling Methods

Hand-milling is still widespread in Asia and Africa, although machine-
milling has become available in most areas. Wooden implements such as
mortar and pestle are used, powered typically by human beings or
sometimes by water or animals. The mortar consists of a stump hol-
lowed to form a bowl, which is half filled with rough rice and into which
is repeatedly dropped the pestle, a long pole rounded at the bottom.
The husk is removed from the grain by the friction of the grains rubbing against themselves as the pole plunges into the rice and forces
the rice up the side of the bowl. Although the operation is often called
hand-pounding, in the best practice of the art, actual pounding is a-
voided. Every few minutes the operation is stopped and the batch of
rice removed and tossed into the air by means of a flat basket, to win-
now away the loose husk and bran. The basket is then held at an angle
and shaken gently, whereupon the milled grain separates from the
rough rice and is removed (the same principle is used in the gravity
separators in large mills). The milled rice thus escapes further treatment and the unmilled rice is returned to the bowl. Needless to say,
with hand-milling the degree of bran removal is limited and the potential for breakage high.

The next level above hand-milling is the use of a single machine to
replace the human-powered operation. Invariably the machine used is
the Engelberg-style mill, called a huller because it was originally used
to remove the hulls from coffee beans.* The huller consists of a long

---

*When the huller is used for bran removal only, as sometimes occurs
with multistage mills, it continues to be called a huller in spite of the
confusion in terminology.

solid steel cylinder that revolves on a horizontal axis within a perforated metal shell called a screen. The cylinder has horizontal projections (flutes) which tend to sweep the rice around with it as the grain
travels the horizontal path between cylinder and screen. The stationary screen, on the other hand, is fitted with a single, long adjustable
resistance bar called a brake, which tends to keep the rice from revolving. The result is a great amount of friction, especially grain against
grain, which grinds off hull and bran. Usually the rice is passed
through the machine twice, the first pass with the brake bar adjusted
back, and the second with it tightened down. In theory the hulls are
expected to come off in the first pass and the bran in the second, each
passing through the holes in the screen as powder. In practice, however, hull, bran, a good bit of broken rice, and whatever dirt, straw,
or small stones entered the huller with the rice come through the screen
in both passes. In spite of its inefficient use of power and excessive
loss in broken rice, the huller is found everywhere in the tropics. It
was estimated that India alone had 72,000 huller mills in 1978 (Saunders et al., 1980).

The use of separate machines for hull* and bran removal is much
more efficient, both in terms of power utilization and milled rice yield,
but a much larger minimum volume is required for economic feasibility
because of the larger capital investment. Multistage mills, as these are
called, include accessory pieces of equipment for precleaning the rough
rice and for separating mixtures into components at various stages in
the process. Milling capacity for multistage mills in the tropics varies
from about 200 kg/hr to as much as 20 tons/hr in larger commercial enterprises (Programa Nacional del Arroz, 1978). Most are less than 2
2 tons/hr. Although the individual machines available differ in capacity
to some extent, most of the capacity increase in the larger mills is
gained by using several machines in parallel. Because removing the
bran in steps reduces breakage, several machines in series are used
for bran removal in the larger mills. Since the machines at the different stages may vary in capacity, the numbers used must also vary.
The layout of a large mill, using both parallel and sequential streams,
can be quite complex. Table 7 describes the types of individual milling machines used in the tropics. The minimum stages for a typical
multistage mill are: precleaner (dirt and stones removed), sheller
(husk removed from kernel), aspirators (husk separated from brown
rice), paddy separator (unhusked rice separated from brown rice),
whitening mills (bran removed), and bran screens or aspirators (bran
separated from milled rice). Any rough rice that passed through the
sheller is usually returned to a separate sheller with closer settings.
Thus, the larger grains are husked in the first sheller and the smaller
in the second.

---

*The machines which remove the hulls are sometimes called shellers.

Table 7 Characteristics of Some Mills Used in the Tropics[a]

Name	Design features	Use	Characteristics
Rubber roll sheller	Two rubber-surfaced rolls, differential rotation, opposite direction, rough rice passes between rolls	Husk removal	Gentle to rice, faster wear, can be damaged, will husk damp rice
Underrunner sheller	Two, grooved pancake-shaped stone discs (emery), horizontal, bottom rotor, top stator, about 1 cm apart, tapered; rough rice moves from center outwards by centrifugal force, husk opened by jamming	Husk removal	Scratches brown rice surface, not easily damaged, wears well, can be resurfaced at mill, rice must be about 14% H_2O
Engelberg-type huller	Fluted cylinder revolving within screen (see text), sometimes a brush and blower attached below	Single-stage mill, or bran removal stage in multimill	Low capital cost, higher power and rice loss, popular as village toll mill
Cono mill	Stone (emery) cone revolving within screen, usually vertical, apex down, screen has brakes	Bran removal	Can remove bran in single step from parboiled or regular brown rice
Japanese abrasive	Stone (emery) cone revolving within screen (or solid shell), horizontal, weighted exit gate	Bran removal	Similar to cono, may clog with wet rice, cuts surface
Japanese friction mill	Metal cylinder rotor, shaped like Engelberg (see text), screen is hexagonal with dimples and perforations for friction, weighted exit	Bran removal, especially last step (pearling or polishing)	High speed, low pressure for polishing, higher pressure for full bran removal

Table 7   (Continued)

Name	Design features	Use	Characteristics
Pin kaeu (pin cow)	Stone (emery) cylinder revolving in screen; a smooth, abrasive Engelberg	Husk or bran removal or both	Used only in Thailand, use varies, also called apollo
Centrifugal	Rubber-lined wall surrounding high-speed rotor, rough rice thrown against wall by rotor	Husk removal	Promoted in India as first stage of two-stage mini mill to replace Engelberg

[a]Accessory machines not included. Illustrations of some of these mills may be found in Borasio and Gariboldi (1979), van Ruiten and Wimberly (1976), Spadero et al. (1980), and Gariboldi (1974a). Others are described by Saunders et al. (1980).

In earlier times the world typically used machines of traditional European design that included: underrunner abrasive* disc shellers, compartment separators to separate rough from brown rice, and vertical abrasive cone mills for whitening. Larger mills included machines with rotating leather brushes for final polishing. More recently, Japanese-style machines have become very popular, especially in Asia. A Japanese-style mill would include rubber roll shellers, specific gravity paddy separators, and horizontal abrasive cylinders for partial bran removal (optional, see subsequent discussion), with horizontal metal (friction) cylinders for final bran removal. Polishing brushes are also occasionally used. The brushes remove the last abraded bran which tends to stick to the kernel and defy removal by aspiration or any other means except physical brushing. The bran powder thus removed is termed polish and is higher in starch, sugars, and other nutritious components than the other bran. Both Japanese and European systems include many machines for cleaning, separating brokens, and other related tasks. The rubber roll sheller was introduced in Japan to avoid scratching the bran on the surface of the brown rice, because in that country brown rice is often stored as is for some time before

---

*The word "abrasive" is commonly used to refer to mills using an emery surface, and the word "friction" to those which do not. The friction mills used for bran removal usually employ metal surfaces with ridges or dimples to grip and abrade the rice.

milling to white rice. Scratching the bran allows the oil and enzymes
to mix, resulting in rancidity during storage. Although there is a definite trend away from using machines with abrasive surfaces, especially
in the shelling step, both the abrasive and friction styles are still heavily used.* One disadvantage for the rubber roll sheller is that the rubber surface is easily damaged by stones, which can escape precleaning
if they are the same size as the rough rice. An advantage for rubber
rolls is their ability to remove husk satisfactorily from higher-moisture
rice.

Tropical milling systems have been discussed by Van Ruitten and
Wimberly (1976), with particular attention given to common errors in
operating the individual machines and to a comparison of traditional
and modern mills. Milling machinery and causes of breakage during
milling have been reviewed by Spadaro et al. (1980). The relationship
and purpose of the individual machines to the whole system are described by Witte (1976). The operation and maintenance of milling
equipment have been described (Gariboldi, 1974a), and a glossary of
milling in five languages, with diagrams, has been published (Borasio
and Gariboldi, 1979).

D. Parboiling

1. The Basic Parboiling Process

The parboiling process consists of the following steps: (a) cleaning
and soaking the rough rice to 30% or more moisture, (b) steaming the
soaked rice, and (c) drying the steamed rice. Parboiled rice is always
milled before being used, but is usually stored in bulk as parboiled
rough rice. The term parboiled rice is applied to both the rough and
milled form. Milling of parboiled rice does not differ from conventional
rice milling except that the parboiled kernel is physically harder.

Several transformations occur to the components of the rice kernels
during parboiling. The starch component is gelatinized by the heat in
the presence of the moisture. Protein is denatured (enzyme activity
reduced or halted). The lipids and other components are also affected,
and some of the more mobile ones tend to migrate within the kernel
(whether migration occurs is controversial). Parboiled rice must usually be cooked longer than white rice before it is soft enough to eat.

The soaking and other precleaning operations remove much foreign
material, including dirt and living contaminations, which could otherwise contribute to spoilage or infestation during storage. The steaming

---

*It is interesting to note that the modern friction mills, such as the
Satake Jet Pealer, which are replacing the abrasive mills for bran removal, have the same general construction and operation as the Engelberg, but because of the extensive modification provide much superior
results.

step kills residual organisms and thus further increases storage stability. The drying operation alters the color to one of a range of yellow-browns depending on the temperature, time, and moisture levels during steaming and drying. Gelatinization not only hardens the kernel, resulting in increased resistance to insects and altered milling characteristics, but it also tends to repair cracks and stresses which would otherwise cause breakage during milling. Because the grain becomes harder, there is a tendency to undermill it, that is, to remove less bran during milling. Undermilled rice is richer in vitamins, minerals, and protein than the corresponding fully milled product because the natural concentration of these components is greatest at the surface of the kernel. Because of undermilling, the bran from milling parboiled rice tends to have a higher oil concentration, making it more suitable for oil extraction.

Parboiling increases the flavor of the rice, making it stronger but not unpleasant. One unfortunate change occurs when soaking extends over several days. Fermentation and general microbial growth cause the development in the product of a very undesirable flavor, which cannot be removed by repeated washings. This off-flavor development is reduced or eliminated by soaking at higher temperatures for less time, increasing cleanliness (prewashing the rice and changing water during soaking), or by adding chemicals to retard microbial growth. However, these preventive steps increase the cost of production. The producer is therefore reluctant to make the changes, and the consumer, who is unwilling to pay more, continues to endure the undesirable flavor.

2. Parboiling in the Tropics

Parboiled rice is the traditional form of consumption in eastern and southern India, Bangladesh, parts of Sri Lanka, and in some parts of Africa. Village-level parboiling installations are numerous in these areas. Some large commercial plants with reasonably modern equipment, processes, and quality control are also found in these same areas and a few other locations in the tropics (e.g., Colombia, for export only). In the traditional areas, a small amount of rice is parboiled in the home, a bag at a time, and stored for future use. Also, rough rice given to farm workers as payment will be given an abbreviated parboiling treatment (1-hr soak followed by roasting), if the rice is too wet to store or mill by hand.

Typically, traditional village-level parboiling involves soaking the rough rice in cold water in concrete tanks for up to 3 days, steaming in separate metal tanks until the husks split open (about 1/2 hr), and sun-drying until nominally 14% moisture. The use of hot soak water (preheated to 85°C, maintained at 70°C) reduces the soak time to 3 hr. The goal of either soaking method is 30% moisture content which is necessary for complete gelatinization using atmospheric steam. Higher moisture contents and shorter steaming times or other combinations of conditions may be used at the commercial level. Most parboiled rice in the tropics is produced using atmospheric steam, although the use of higher pressures is increasing. Pressure parboiling is well established in the temperate zone.

Short descriptions of various parboiling procedures used around the world have been given by Ali and Ojha (1976), along with detailed descriptions of techniques used in India. One pressure method used commercially in India is described later (Sec. V. B). The basic parboiling process and various items of equipment are discussed by Gariboldi (1974b), who also compares village and modern processes with regard to the changes during parboiling and the overall nutritional effect (Gariboldi, 1972).

IV. UTILIZATION

A. Utilization of Milling By-Products

Rice milling by-products include husk, bran, some straw (most of the straw produced remains at the field or threshing point), and polish and brokens from mills which separate these fractions. Each is discussed subsequently. The major outlet for milling by-products is animal feed. Lesser amounts go to special food uses or industrial applications. If no other use is available, the by-product is disposed of as waste. Which of the four outlets receives a particular by-product depends upon economic factors such as proximity of the supply to the user (or transportation costs) and the technical requirements of the various uses.

Domestic livestock differ in their feed requirements. The ration fed is typically a mixture of various grains, by-products, and additives formulated in the proper proportion to satisfy the needs of the particular animal. The amount of the ration made up by a particular ingredient, rice bran for example, ideally depends upon its composition and cost. In sophisticated feeding operations where many feed sources are available, least-cost formation is a complex task. In the rural tropics, however, where feed sources are very limited, what is available is fed, what is thought to be harmful is not fed or is diluted. Any requirements not supplied by the feed are specially added or just omitted.

Rice husk is basically a cellulose-silica material containing significant amounts of hemicellulose and lignin, but very low in starch and protein. Its vitamin, mineral (except silica), and lipid content is lower than that of bran. Rice hull has a very low bulk density (0.1 g/cc) if left uncrushed, although its true density is 0.73 g/cc. The low thermal conductivity at the hull compares well with asbestos and other common insulators. The fuel value reported is about 3500 kcal/kg, nearly half that of bituminous coal (Beagle, 1978).

Rice hull has less feed value than bran but is accepted as a component in formulated feeds. It is also used for animal bedding, soil conditioners, and a host of industrial applications, such as insulation, building materials, absorbents, and abrasives. It is a source of furfural.

Ash from the hull has many uses. However, in spite of many uses, the hull is usually burned, either for fuel or as a mean of disposal because of the low economic demand, high transport cost, and the large amount produced. Furnaces designed to use husk as fuel are available, however, as a by-product of milling, husk is available only at the milling site.

Rice straw, on the other hand, is available at the farm and could be used as fuel to dry harvested rice if furnaces for it were available. The present practice is to dispose of rice straw by burning it in the field. This also helps reduce disease and weed problems in subsequent crops. Varying amounts are fed to animals. The feed value of straw from cereal grains decreases as the plant ripens, and rice is customarily harvested when fully ripe. Minor amounts are used for making hats, for bedding, and for similar uses. Rice paper is not made from rice straw, but from the pith of a tree (*Tetrapanax papyrifera*) native to Taiwan (Purseglove, 1972).

Rice bran varies in composition with the degree of milling, the type of mill used, the rice variety, and other factors. Table 8 shows the change in bran composition as the degree of milling increases. Parboiled bran is significantly higher in fat than regular bran. Bran from huller mills (one-stage Engelberg type) contains a large percentage of hulls which dilute the fat and protein.

Most bran is fed to animals. In fact the economic value of the bran influences the profitability of the milling operation. If the bran is free from hulls, it can be used as a source of rice oil by solvent extraction and the defatted bran can still be used for feed. Some rice oil is now produced in the tropics for industrial purposes, primarily for the manufacture of soap. For food use, the oil, and therefore the bran, must be low in free fatty acids, which accumulate rapidly after milling due to

Table 8 Composition of Bran from Various Milling Stages (Dry Basis)[a]

Source in mill	Yield (%)[a]	Protein (%)	Fat (%)	Ash (%)	NFE (%)[b]	Crude fiber (%)
First cone	2.5	17.0	17.6	9.8	45	10.5
Last polisher	0.5	15.3	11.6	6.0	63	3.7
Total bran	7.0	16.8	16.9	9.0	47	9.9

[a]Percent of rough rice. This mill had six bran-removal stages that removed a total of 7% by weight based on rough rice. The first cone removed the first 2.5%, and the last polisher removed the last 0.5% (the stages between not shown). Rice and bran compositions vary widely but milling effect would be similar to trends shown here.
[b]NFE = nitrogen-free extract.
Source: Adapted from Primo et al., in Houston (1972a).

the warm tropical environment and the presence of enzymes. Such technical problems along with economic factors have tended to restrict the manufacture of food-grade rice oil to nontropical countries such as Japan, although small amounts are produced in India and the Philippines.

Polish, a powder composed of the inner bran and some endosperm is produced at the last stages in some multistage mills, and is sometimes separated and used in food products. If brokens are separated, they may also be used for food manufacture, either directly or after grinding to flour. Food uses are discussed in Sec. IV. B.

Rice bran and hulls have been reviewed by Houston (1972a,c). A bibliography and a compendium of technologies of agricultural residues have been published by FAO (1978a,b). Beagle (1978) has described current and potential use of rice husk for fuel, including furnace design and uses for the combustion products. Rice oil technology has been discussed by Chang et al (1980). Rice bran stabilization has been reviewed by Sayre et al. (1982). A symposium report on rice by-product utilization has been published (Instituto de Agroquimaca y Technologia de Alimentos, 1974).

B. Utilization of the Milled Rice

Most of the world rice production is eaten as whole grain (with or without brokens) after being cooked in some manner with water. This is by far the major use of rice in the tropics. A typical home cooking procedure is to heat the rice in boiling water until tender, usually for about 1/2 hr with a water uptake of around 200% of the original rice weight. A common modification is to heat the rice at a temperature just below boiling, in just the amount of water that will be completely soaked up. Steaming previously soaked rice to a similar end point is also a popular alternative. The product in each of these cases is plain steamed (boiled) white rice. In some areas rice is commonly prepared with oil in the water, or fried in oil before heating with water which produces a less sticky surface texture. Baking rice with or without other foods is also practiced but is more common outside the tropics. Parboiled rice is prepared similarly to white rice except that a longer cooking time is required. An interesting survey of rice cooking methods used around the world has been published (Batcher et al., 1956).

Dry milled rice destined for home use (regular or parboiled) is usually stored either in bags or packages until purchase by the householder. Dried rough rice is also stored in bags and may be purchased for home milling or home parboiling. Canned rice, frozen high-moisture rice, rice-based formulations, and whole quick-cooking rice are available but not common in the tropics. However, other ready-to-eat forms, such as roasted and rolled rice (India) and popped rice (Indonesia), are growing in popularity. The fast-food booth, where rice products are prepared on the spot in various ways, is an important outlet for rice in several tropical countries.

Rice flour, either as a by-product of milling or quite often from roller milling the brokens or whole grains, is used to make crackers, rice cakes, and noodles of various types. Some of these products are dried quick-cooking products, others are high-moisture, and a few are fermented. Extruded snack products made from rice flour are popular in some areas. Brokens and flour are also used in the manufacture of vinegar and beverages, including beer and rice wine (sake). These forms of rice are more common in the temperate areas, but are found in some tropical areas also. See Sec. V. B. for research involving rice flour.

A minor amount of rice flour or brokens is extracted to obtain rice starch for food or industrial use. Waxy rice starch or flour (100% amylopectin) is used in cooked frozen products because of its freeze-thaw stability. Rice flour is also used directly as a dusting powder. Again, these uses are more common in the temperate areas. Several chapters in two books are devoted to products from rice and rice flour (Houston, 1972b; Luh, 1980). Cooking-quality tests of rices collected from around the world have been published (Simpson et al., 1965).

C. Composition and Nutritional Aspects of Milled Rice

To most of the world's population the ability of a food to supply food energy (calories) is its most important attribute. Calories mean life, and rice is the major source of calories for many. Rice contains a large proportion of easily digested starch, some protein, and smaller amounts of essential lipids, vitamins, and minerals (Table 9). The caloric value is 363 kcal/100 g rice. The starch is the major source of calories, with the protein usually available for structure building or replacement. However, if the overall caloric intake of the consumer is inadequate, the protein and lipid would be used as a source of energy.

The quality of the protein in rice is high for a cereal grain, but nevertheless lysine is the limiting amino acid* as is the case for other cereals when compared to the reference amino acid pattern (Table 10). If rice is the only food available, sufficient amounts of the essential amino acids must be obtained by eating enough rice. Amino acids limiting in rice may also be supplied by other sources, that is, from foods eaten with rice. In this case the protein quality is determined by the amino acid pattern contributed by the total diet. The protein quality may also be increased by direct enrichment of the rice with lysine or food material rich in lysine, and such an approach has received interest from time to time as a vehicle for nutritional improvement (Austin, 1981). Conversely, lysine may be made nutritionally unavailable by

---

*Limiting amino acids are those essential amino acids present in the least quantity when they are expressed as a percentage of the reference amino acid pattern. The reference pattern is an estimate of the amino acid balance needed by a human in a particular age group.

Table 9   The Composition of Brown and White Rice

Component	Brown rice	White rice[a]
Water (%)	12.0	12.0
Protein (%)	7.5	6.7
Fat (%)	1.9	0.4
Ash (%)	1.2	0.5
Carbohydrate (total) (%)	77.4	80.4
Fiber (%)	0.9	0.3
Calcium (mg/100 g)	32	24
Phosphorous (mg/100 g)	221	94
Iron (mg/100 g)	1.6	0.8
Sodium (mg/100 g)	9	5
Potassium (mg/100 g)	21.4	92
Thiamine (mg/100 g)	0.34	0.07
Riboflavin (mg/100 g)	0.05	0.03
Niacin (mg/100 g)	4.7	1.6

[a]White rice is milled to at least 10% bran removal. The
less bran removed (7% common in tropical Asia), the more
the white rice values will shift toward those for brown
rice. Composition of rices before milling varies widely
but effect of milling would follow the trend shown above.
Source: Adapted from data of Watt and Merrill in
Houston and Kohler (1970).

high-temperature, low-moisture treatment, which would lower the protein quality of the rice. While ordinary cooking does not have this effect, roasting rice, such as is practiced in parts of India and South America, may be detrimental if the rice moisture during roasting is allowed to become too low.

Attempts have been made to increase the protein content of rice by selective breeding. The result has been partially successful in that higher-protein rice has been obtained. However, the increases were in proteins low in lysine so that the desired overall nutritional effect was not achieved. Some success in producing high-lysine rice has been achieved by new techniques (see Sec. V. B).

Rice contains enzyme as well as storage proteins. The major enzymes in rice are those concerned with the synthesis and breakdown of starch, sugars, phosphorous compounds, and lipids in the rice kernel. They seem to have no direct effect on human nutrition, but since they may become active under certain conditions during storage or processing spoilage may result, thus the quality or supply of rice available may be reduced (see Secs. B and C).

Table 10 The Amino Acid Composition of Rice Partial List) (g/16 g N)

Amino acid	Reference pattern[a]	Brown rice	White rice
Isoleucine	4.2	4.6	4.6
Leucine	4.8	7.9	8.0
Lysine	4.2	3.6	3.5
Phenylalanine	2.8	5.1	5.2
Tyrosine	2.8	4.7	4.9
Methionine	2.2	2.8	2.9
Threonine	2.8	3.6	3.5
Tryptophan	1.4	1.4	1.3
Valine	4.2	6.4	6.5

[a]FAO Provisional Reference Pattern of essential amino acids (a composite conservative for adults, not adequate for infants) used in scoring the protein quality of foods. Based on lysine, the first limiting amino acid, milled rice would be expected to supply 83% of the essential amino acids needed by a group of children and adults if the total protein and caloric intake is adequate (from FAO, 1957, as adapted by Houston and Kohler, 1970). An updated revision of this pattern has been published (FAO, 1973).
Source: Adapted from Houston and Kohler (1970).

The starch of rice is mostly amylopectin (branched) with varying amounts of amylose (linear) from 0 to 30%. Tropical varieties tend to have higher-amylose content than subtropical varieties. There appears to be no significant nutritional difference between the two starch forms. High amylopectin (lower amylose) is associated with stickiness. Very sticky varieties with no amylose, called waxy rices, are popular in some areas (e.g., Laos).

Most of the lipid in brown rice is removed during milling and the amount retained depends on the degree of bran removal. Table 11 shows that the fatty acid distribution of the total oil is roughly similar for brown and milled rice, with a significant portion in the milled rice being unsaturated (linoleic). The stability of rice oil (extracted) is reportedly due to various natural antioxidants in the oil, including tocopherols. The enzymes which accelerate spoilage are either denatured, or tend to remain in the residual bran during extraction. The oil in raw rice bran or abraded brown rice is unstable due to action between lipase and lipid.

Rice is a good source of some of the B vitamins and of phosphorous (Table 9). It contains little or no vitamins A, C, D, or B_{12}. It is also

Table 11 The Major Fatty Acids of the Lipids of
Brown and Milled Rice (% Total Oil)

Fatty acid	Brown rice	Milled rice
Myristic	1.0	0.9
Palmitic	27.5	24.0
Stearic	2.0	2.5
Oleic	43.0	29.6
Linoleic	25.1	41.6
Linolenic	1.0	1.1

Source: Data of Herting and Drury in Juliano
(1972).

low in calcium, iron, and sodium. Since the outer parts of the endosperm and the bran layers are richer than the center of the kernel in
all components except starch, milling reduces the role of rice as a
source of vitamins, minerals, and proteins. In terms of nutritional
quality, it is fortunate that various levels of undermilling are common
in the tropics (Saunders and Betschart, 1979). Often only the highly
commercial or export product is fully polished, although this varies
with local custom and with the ability of the local mills to remove the
bran. It is a matter of historical interest that the advent of machine
milling in Asia increased the availability of fully milled rice and simultaneously the incidence of beriberi, a vitamin B_1 (thiamine) deficiency
disease. Recognition of the power of rice bran (undermilled rice) to
cure the disease essentially led to the discovery of vitamin B_1 (Houston and Kohler, 1970).

Although the cooking of rice by boiling in water does not lower the
protein quality, it may cause a loss of up to 50% of the thiamine if the
cooking water is very alkaline, compared to less than 10% in acidified
water. Thiamine, which is water-soluble, may also be significantly reduced by vigorous washing and by cooking in excess water which is
subsequently discarded.

Parboiled rice is almost as rich in the B vitamins after milling as is
raw brown rice. Whether this is due entirely to its milling characteristics or due partly to the inward migration of the vitamins during parboiling is controversial. Parboiled rice also resists thiamine loss during washing, though similar cooking losses occur (Houston and Kohler,
1970).

Postharvest losses of rice vary with place, season, and customary
practice. They are equivalent to a production loss and have the overall effect of directly reducing the available food supply. A rice postharvest loss of 25% translates directly to a 25% reduction in the overall
supply. This may represent an even greater loss to some segments of
the population since the wealthiest consumers may be expected to maintain their consumption level at the expense of those with the least

purchasing power. Likewise, a reduction in the losses may have a greater positive impact on some than others. For those whose diet is principally rice and whose consumption is at the borderline of their caloric need, a reduction of supply will have a double impact of reducing the energy and restricting severly the protein and lipid which is essential for structure and functional uses as these components are used for energy. Conversely, a reduction of losses will have a corresponding double, positive impact. It is difficult to quantify the actual impact from losses since a certain amount of food may be gathered from wild plant and animal sources in times of severe need. However, the value of the rice lost is very clear. The effect of losses on the populations in tropical countries has been discussed by Saunders and Betschart (1979) and Saunders et al. (1980). The nutritional importance of protein and other rice constituents has been discussed by Saunders and Betschart (1979), Houston and Kohler (1970), and Juliano (1980). The chemical composition of rice was reviewed by Juliano (1972) and Barber (1972). Rice enzymes have been reviewed by Akazawa (1972).

V. OTHER ASPECTS

A. Economic Considerations

The production and processing of rice require input that must be paid for by the consumer. In the case of subsistence production, the farmer, family, and farm workers who eat the rice contribute to its production. In the case of commercial production, the relationship between production cost and consumer support is less direct but is just as real. For either, the only source for the input costs is the consumer payment (in terms of money or labor). To increase the input would be foolish on the part of the producer or processor without a reasonable belief that market returns would be likely to increase proportionately to cover the cost. In the Asian tropics, the market usually does not support an increase in quality and supports increases in quantity only in proper circumstances. (A huge increase in the rice supply in a local area may depress the rice price so much that actual income per hectare may be reduced.) In the tropics, any added operation that increases costs beyond the minimum necessary to produce the rice usually results in an inadequate return or outright loss to the farmer or processor, although the society as a whole benefits. This is especially true of mechanical drying or efforts taken to maintain quality.

The lack of buying power* on the part of so many in the tropics restricts the ability to increase rice quality or quantity. The necessary

---

*The production of goods or services needed by others results in buying power which can be used to demand and support increased rice production.

input simply is not there. The greatest demand is for low-priced (low-quality) rice. Government programs, which control the rice market in many countries, are usually committed to low food prices. These and other government policies may also lower the quality or supply of rice.

Economic effects may be complex. One rice mill manufacturer, a village operator, interviewed in Indonesia (Saunders et al., 1980), who produced a mill similar to that of a large Japanese company but with better quality and at one-half the price, was unable to sell his mills. The Japanese salesman who was able to offer financing, that is, was able to take his payment out of the profits of the milling, was able to sell to small operators. No doubt the salesman also advised the millers during the life of the equipment. In this case the best product at the lowest price was not enough.

Cooperatives have been formed in some areas to help with the marketing of rice by the producer. Where such an organization has been formed by the growers or processors themselves, the operation is usually successful; where the cooperative has been organized by the government, it is often beset with problems. The reasons for the distinction are not obvious though the interest and incentive for problem solving may be greater where the operation is the producers' responsibility. Also, government programs sometimes deal with artificial markets.

Success has usually come to enterprises where economic incentives have been coupled with technology. The more successful operations tend to evolve from subsistence toward commercial and tend to increase in awareness of quality standards. Highly commercial operations have already been successful and are growing with the increased input in technology, limited only by the ability and willingness of the consumer to pay (Saunders et al., 1980). A book of discussion papers on the economic consequences in Asia of the new rice technology has been published (IRRI, 1978b). Chandler (1979) gives case histories at the national level of four successful rice development programs, two in the tropics.

B. Research

The foregoing discussions have been limited to the factors in each phase of production and processing which exert the greatest influence on the rice supply and which are in actual practice in the tropics today. Methods used in the temperate zones and tropical proposals or pilot research successes in the tropics, such as the many schemes for improving parboiling in India (Ali and Ojha, 1976), have been omitted if they are not widely practiced in the tropics. Yet successful research is being done which may influence future tropical practice. Also, practices which have been successful in one area (tropical or temperate) may be transferable to another area with appropriate modifications if necessary. Transfer from related subject areas is also feasible. For example, the extensive work on drying and storage of wheat and corn has been, and continues to be, adapted to rice.

Rice research is conducted at many centers throughout the world, in and out of the tropics. A few have been mentioned previously. A more extensive list may be found in the report on postharvest losses (Saunders et al., 1980). Collections of reports on postharvest rice research that was being done worldwide from 1975 to 1978, are available from the Instituto de Agroquimica Technologica de Alimentos, Jaime Roig No. 11, Valencia 10, Spain, and is called the *Rice Report* (Barber et al., 1975).

The following are examples of recent research or development efforts, many not mentioned in the reports previously cited, which may be expected to have an impact on rice in the tropics. (a) Production: experimental rice plants with 10% more lysine than usual have been produced using tissue-culturing techniques. The experimental rice will probably be crossbred with commercial varieties. More information may be obtained from G. W. Shaeffer, Agricultural Research Center, Beltsville, Maryland. Species of *Azolla*, a tiny fern in symbiotic association with a nitrogen-fixing blue-green algae (*Anabaena azollae*), which grows in the water with rice, is being investigated by several researchers (e.g., Thomas A. Lumpkin, Zhejiang Academy, PRC) as a living source of the fertilizer absolutely essential for the greater yields from the new rice varieties. Further information may be obtained from Lumpkin, IRRI (P.O. Box 933, Manila, Philippines), or from S. Talley and D. W. Rains, University of California, Davis, California. (b) Drying: A large experimental, bulk-drying and storage installation was being constructed by Baden Urusan Logistik, the government food agency, at Tambun, Indonesia, in 1978 with the cooperation of scientists from the Tropical Products Institute (England) to test the feasibility of drying and conditioning rice using tropical air without supplemental heat (aerating only during periods of lower humidity). (c) storage: The use of nitrogen and carbon dioxide in place of pesticides to suffocate insects in sealed grain storage containers without leaving pesticide residues has been shown to be effective and has been approved for use in the United States. Further information may be obtained from P. H. Schwartz, Jr., National Program Staff, Beltsville, Maryland. (d) Milling: several comparative studies of milling systems have been undertaken recently (Andales et al., 1980; IRRI, 1978a) which focus on tropical practice. Water and abrasives such as calcium carbonate added to the brown rice just before milling has been found to reduce milling power requirements, decrease milling time, and increase milling yields (Roberts and Wasserman, 1977). Water addition is becoming more common in Japan (Satake, 1981). (e) Parboiling: India, which produces and consumes most of the world's parboiled rice, also conducts most of the current research and extension in that subject area. Much of the effort has been to apply modern technology at the village or small commercial level. One pressure parboiling method, described as experimental by Ali and Ojha (1976), has been adopted commercially with mixed results. Steam under pressure is applied to rough rice below 30% moisture (as low as 22%). At the higher temperature the moisture added by condensation is sufficient to gelatinize the rice, but the moisture after parboiling is less than with the traditional processes, thus reducing the drying load. As produced in the Punjab region, the product also gives higher milling yields, but is darker in color and often so hard that much longer cooking time is required before it is soft enough to eat, a distinct disadvantage (Nayyar, 1982). (f) Utilization: Until recently, rice flour could not be used in place of wheat flour to make wheat-type cakes and breads due to the lack of gluten in rice. Asian "rice cake" is a completely different product. Such products developed to assist people who cannot tolerate wheat, are now possible with rice flour using additives in a special formulation (Nishita et al., 1976). The general properties of rice flour have also been investigated (Bean et al., 1982; Nishita and Bean, 1979, 1982). (g) Marketing: systems of grading rice to differentiate quality levels have been proposed for domestic use in the tropics as a necessary step in bringing a greater return to producers and processors who market higher-quality rice. Although most areas have some grain standards, successful market systems involving grading have yet to be developed and implemented in most areas. Any progress is sure to have an impact.

An instrument which can detect the presence of one insect in a kilogram of grain has been developed by W. A. Bruce, Stored-Product Insects Lab, Savannah, Georgia, and is being tested for grain inspection. Although grading for the presence of insects is not strict in the tropics, such an instrument might be adaptable for grading or rice storage uses. (h) Nutrition: the importance of rice in supplying nutrients is well established, but the need to supplement rice diets is a matter of controversy. The desirability for protein (lysine) enrichment, which was predicted (U.S., 1968; Aylward and Jul, 1975), has not been shown clearly in actual practice during enrichment programs involving rice (Austin, 1981). Caloric adequacy, health, and other factors seem to be more important with rice-eating populations. Results of further studies involving rice in the areas of nutrition and composition will find immediate application in helping to understand this complex situation and to use resources more efficiently.

Information on current rice production research related to the tropics can be obtained from IRRI (P.O. Box 933, Manila, Philippines). A book on rice production with emphasis on tropical problems and practices has recently been published (DeDatta, 1981). Sources of information on postharvest research sources have been listed by Saunders et al. (1980).

C. Summary

Rice is the most important food in the tropics, and increasing the supply and availability of rice is the major concern of those involved in its production, processing, and utilization. The major factors which affect the amount of rice available have been selected for each phase of the rice system in the tropics and their significance discussed briefly.

Where possible, references have been given to reviews, where the literature is critically discussed. Examples of current research have been given along with sources for further information.

REFERENCES

Adair, C. R., and Jodon, N. E. (1973). Distribution and origin of species, botany, and genetics. In *Rice in the United States: Varieties and Production, Agricultural Handbook No. 289.* Washington, D.C., U.S. Department of Agriculture.

Adair, C. R., Beachell, H. M., Jodon, N. E., Davis, L. L., and Jones, J. W. (1942). Comparative yields of transplanted and direct sown rice. *Am. Soc. Agron. J.* 34:129-136.

Ali, N., and Ojha, T. P. (1976). Parboiling. In *Rice Postharvest Technology* (E. V. Araullo, D. B. de Padua, and M. Graham, eds.). Ottawa, Canada, International Development Research Center, p. 163.

Andales, S. C., Alvarez, E. L., and Tec, Jr., A. B. (1980). *Terminal Report of the UPLB-IDRC Project (Phase I) on Post-Production Technology.* Los Banos, Philippines, University of the Philippines.

Akazawa, T. (1972). Enzymes of rice. In *Rice Chemistry and Technology* (D. F. Houston, ed.). St. Paul, Minn., American Association of Cereal Chemistry, p. 75.

Austin, J. E. (1981). *Nutrition Programs in the Third World.* Cambridge, Mass., Oelgeschlager, Gunn and Hain.

Aylward, F., and Jul, M. (1975). *Protein and Nutrition Policy in Low-Income Countries.* New York, Wiley.

Barber, S. (1972). Milled rice and changes during aging. In *Rice Chemistry and Technology* (D. F. Houston, ed.), St. Paul, Minn., American Association of Cereal Chemists, p. 215.

Barber, S., Mitsuda, H., and Desikachar, H. S. R. (eds.) (1975). *Rice Report 1975.* Valencia, Spain, International Union of Food Science and Technology, c/o IATA.

Batcher, O. M., Helmintoller, K. F., and Dawson, E. H. (1956). Development and application of methods for evaluating cooking and eating quality of rice. *Rice J.* 59(13):4.

Beagle, E. C. (1978). Rice husk conversion to energy. *Agricultural Services Bulletin No. 31.* Rome, Food and Agricultural Organization of the United Nations.

Bean, M. M., Elliston-Hoops, E. A., and Nishita, K. D. (1982). Rice flour modification for baking applications. *Cereal Foods World* 27(a): 452, Abstract 55.

Beck, J. M., and de Padua, D. B. (1976). Drying. In *Rice Postharvest Technology* (E. V. Araullo, D. B. de Padua, and M. Graham, eds.), Ottawa, Canada, International Development Research Center, p. 107.

Borasio, I., and Gariboldi, F. (1979). Illustrated glossary of rice processing machines. *2nd Agricultural Services Bulletin.* Rome, Food and Agriculture Organization of the United Nations.

Bowling, C. C. (1980). Insect pests of the rice plant. In *Rice Production and Utilization* (B. S. Luh, ed.). Westport, Conn., Avi Pub., p. 260.

Chandler, R. F., Jr., (1979). *Rice in the Tropics: A guide to the Development of National Programs,* Boulder, Colo., Westview Press.

Chang, S. C., Saunders, R. M., and Luh, B. S. (1980). Rice oil chemistry and technology. In *Rice Production and Utilization* (B. S. Luh, ed.), Westport, Conn., Avi Pub., p. 764.

Chang, T., and Bardenas, E. A. (1965). *The Morphology and Varietal Characteristics of the Rice Plant.* Los Banos, Philippines, International Rice Research Institute.

Chang, T., and Li, C. (1980). Genetics and breeding. In *Rice Production and Utilization* (B. S. Luh, ed.). Westport, Conn., Avi Pub., p. 000.

Christensen, C. M. (ed.) (1974). *Storage of Cereal Grains and Their Products.* St. Paul, Minn., American Association of Cereal Chemists.

Cogburn, R. R. (1980). Insect pests of stored rice. In *Rice Production and Utilization* (B. S. Luh, ed.). Westport, Conn., Avi Pub., p. 289.

De Datta, S. K. (1981). *Principles and Practices of Rice Production.* New York, Wiley.

Efferson, J. N. (1952). *The Production and Marketing of Rice.* Washington, D.C., The Rice Journal.

Fellers, D. A. (1979). Wheat and wheat foods in the tropics. In *Tropical Foods, Vol. 2* (G. E. Inglett and G. Charalambous, eds.). New York, Academic Press, p. 575.

Food and Agricultural Organization (1957). *Protein requirements. FAO Nutritional Studies No. 16.* Rome, Food and Agricultural Organization of the United Nations.

Food and Agricultural Organization (1973). Energy and protein requirements. *Report of a Joint FAO/WHO Committee, FAO Nutrition Meetings Report Series No. 52.* Rome, Food and Agriculture Organization of the United Nations.

Food and Agricultural Organization (1978a). A bibliography of Agricultural residues. *Agricultural Services Bulletin No. 35.* Rome, Food and Agricultural Organization of the United Nations.

Food and Agricultural Organization (1978b). Agricultural residues: Compendium of technologies. *Agricultural Services Bulletin No. 33.* Rome, Food and Agricultural Organization of the United Nations.

Food and Agriculture Organization (1979). Agricultural commodity projections 1975-1985. *FAO Economic and Social Development Series No. 16.* Rome, Food and Agriculture Organization of the United Nations, pp. 12-17 and 25-33.

Food and Agriculture Organization (1980a). *Production yearbook 1979, Vol. 33, FAO Statistics Series No. 28.* Rome, Food and Agricultural Organization of the United Nations.

Food and Agriculture Organization (1980b). *Trade Yearbook 1979, Vol. 33, FAO Statistics Series No. 29.* Rome, Food and Agricultural Organization of the United Nations.

Gariboldi, F. (1972). Parboiled rice. In *Rice Chemistry and Technology* (D. F. Houston, ed.). St. Paul, Minn., American Association of Cereal Chemists, p. 358.

Gariboldi, F. (1974a). Rice milling equipment operation and maintenance. *Agricultural Services Bulletin No. 22.* Rome, Food and Agricultural Organization of the United Nations.

Gariboldi, F. (1974b). *Rice Parboiling.* Rome, Food and Agricultural Organization of the United Nations.

Houston, D. F. (1972a). Rice bran and polish. In *Rice Chemistry and Technology.* St. Paul, Minn., American Association of Cereal Chemists, p. 272.

Houston, D. F. (ed.) (1972b). *Rice Chemistry and Technology.* St. Paul, Minn., American Association of Cereal Chemists.

Houston, D. F. (1972c). Rice hulls. In *Rice Chemistry and Technology.* St. Paul, Minn., American Association of Cereal Chemistry, p. 301.

Houston, D. F., and Kohler, G. O. (1970). *Nutritional Properties of Rice.* Washington, D.C., National Academy of Sciences.

Instituto de Agroquimica y Technologia de Alimentos (1974). *Proc. of International Conf. on Rice Byproduct Utilization.* Valencia, Spain, Instituto de Agroquimica y Technologia de Alimentos.

International Rice Research Institute (1972). *Rice Breeding.* Los Banos, Philippines, International Rice Research Institute.

International Rice Research Institute (1978a). *A Report on Rice Postproduction Technology Project Submitted by IRRI and University of Philippines of Los Banos to the Bicol River Basin Development Program.* Los Banos, Philippines, International Rice Research Institute.

International Rice Research Institute (1978b). *Economic Consequences of the New Rice Technology.* Los Banos, Philippines, International Rice Research Institute.

Kahn, A. U. (1976). Harvesting and threshing. In *Rice Postharvest Technology* (E. V. Araullo, D. B. de Padua, and M. Graham, eds.). Ottawa, Canada, International Development Research Centre, p. 85.

Kahn, S. G. (1981). World hunger: an overview. *Food Technol.* 35: 93-98.

Johnston, T. H., and Miller, M. D. (1973). Culture. In *Rice in the United States: Varieties and Production, Agricultural Handbook No. 289.* Washington, D.C., p. 110.

Juliano, B. O. (1972). The rice caryopsis and its composition. In *Rice Chemistry and Technology* (D. F. Houston, ed.). St. Paul, Minn., American Association of Cereal Chemists, p. 16.

Juliano, B. O. (1980). Rice: Recent progress in chemistry and nutrition. In *Cereals for Food and Beverages* (G. E. Inglett and L. Munck, eds.). New York, Academic Press, p. 409.

Lu, J. J., and Chang, T. (1980). Rice in its temperal and spatial perspectives. In *Rice Production and Utilization* (B. S. Luh, ed.). Westport, Conn., Avi Pub., p. 1.

Luh, B. S. (ed.) (1980). *Rice Production and Utilization*. Westport, Conn., Avi Pub.

Majumder, S. K. (1974). *Control of Microflora in Stored Grains*. Mysore, India, Central Food Technology Research Institute, p. 70a.

Mallick, A. K., and Nandi, B. (1981). Research on rice storage in India. *Rice J.* 84(2):8, (3):3.

Mikkelsen, D. S., and De Datta, S. K. (1980). Rice culture. In *Rice Production and Utilization* (B. S. Luh, ed.). Westport, Conn., Avi Pub., p. 147.

Mueller, K. E. (1970). *Field Problems of Tropical Rice*. Los Banos, Philippines, International Rice Research Institute.

National Research Council (1972). *Genetic Vulnerability of Major Crops*. Washington, D.C., National Academy of Sciences.

Nayyar, D. (1982). Private communication.

Nishita, K. D., Roberts, R. L., Bean, M. M., and Kennedy, B. M. (1976). Development of a yeast-leavened rice-bread formula. *Cereal Chem.* 53:626.

Nishita, K. D., and Bean, M. M. (1979). Physiochemical properties of rice in relation to rice bread. *Cereal Chem.* 56:185.

Nishita, K. D., and Bean, M. M. (1982). Grinding methods: their impact on rice flour properties. *Cereal Chem.* 59:46.

Ou, S. H. (1980). Rice plant diseaes. In *Rice Production and Utilization* (B. S. Luh, Ed.). Westport, Conn., Avi Pub., p. 235.

Programa Nacional del Arroz (1978). *Piladoras Existentes en el Pais*. Guayaquil, Ecuador, Programa Nacional del Arroz, Ministerio de Agricultura y ganaderia.

Purseglove, J. W. (1972). *Tropical Crops Vol. I, Monocotyledons*. New York, Wiley, p. 164.

Rawnsley, J. (1976). Storage: Constraints. In *Rice Postharvest Technology* (E. V. Araullo, D. B. De Padua, and M. Graham, eds.). Ottawa, Canada, International Development Research Center, p. 113.

Rivenburgh, D. V. (1961). Analysis of selected varieties and grades of rice moving in world trade in terms of U.S. standards. *Marketing Research Report No. 460*. Washington, D.C., F.A.S., U.S. Department of Agriculture.

Roberts, R. L., and Wasserman, T. (1977). Effect of milling conditions on yields, milling time and energy requirements in a pilot scale Engelberg rice mill. *J. Food Sci.* 42:804.

Satake (1981). Moisturizing polished rice without risk of cracking grains by restricting moisture addition rate to 0.3% per of weight of rice. *German Patent No. 3,030,091*. Tokyo, Japan, Satake Engineering Co., Ltd.

Saunders, R. M., and Betschart, A. A. (1979). Rice and rice foods: Chemistry and nutrition. In *Tropical Foods: Chemistry and Nutrition, Vol. I* (G. E. Inglett, and G. Charalambous, eds.). New York, Academic Press, p. 191.

Saunders, R. M., Mossman, A. P., Wasserman, T., and Beagle, E. C. (1980). *Rice Postharvest Losses in Developing Countries.* Washington, D.C., U.S. Department of Agriculture Publication ARM-W-12, USDA.

Sayre, R. M., Saunders, R. M., Enochian, R. V., Schultz, W. G., and Beagle, E. C. (1982). Review of rice bran stabilization systems with emphasis on extrusion cooking. *Ceral Foods World.* 27:317.

Schroeder, H. W., and Calderwood, D. L. (1972). Rough rice storage. In *Rice Chemistry and Technology* (D. F. Houston, ed.). St. Paul, Minn., American Association of Cereal Chemistry, p. 166.

Scott, P. M. (1973). Mycotoxins in stored grain, feeds, and other cereal products. In *Grain Storage: Part of a System* (R. N. Sinha and W. E. Muir, eds.). Westport, Conn., Avi Pub., p. 343.

Simpson, J. E., Adair, C. R., Kohler, G. O., Dawson, E. H., Deobald, H. J., Kester, E. B., Hogan, J. T., Batcher, O. M. and Halick, J. V. (1965). Quality evaluation studies of foreign and domestic rices. *Tech. Bulletin No. 1331.* Washington, D.C., U.S. Dept. Agriculture.

Sinha, R. N. (1973). Interrelations of physical, chemical, and biological variables in the deterioration of stored grains. In *Grain Storage: Part of a System* (R. N. Sinha and W. E. Muri, eds.). Westport, Conn., Avi Pub., p. 15.

Spadaro, J. J., Matthews, J., and Wadsworth, J. I. (1980). Milling. In *Rice Production and Utilization* (B. S. Luh, ed.). Westport, Conn., Avi Pub., p. 360.

Steffe, J. F., Singh, R. P., and Miller, G. E. Jr. (1980). Harvest, drying and storage of rough rice. In *Rice Production and Utilization* (B. S. Luh, ed.). Westport, Conn., Avi Pub., p. 311.

United Nations (1968). *International Action to Avert the Impending Protein Crisis.* New York, United Nations.

United States Department of Agriculture (1980). *Agricultural Statistics.* Washington, D.C., U.S. Department of Agriculture.

Van Ruitten, H., and Wimberly, J. (1976). Milling. In *Rice Postharvest Technology* (E. V. Araullo, D. B. De Padua, and M. Graham, eds.). Ottawa, Canada, International Development Research Centre, p. 207.

Vergara, B. S. (1980). Rice plant growth and development. In *Rice Production and Utilization* (B. S. Luh, ed.). Westport, Conn., Avi Pub., p. 75.

Wasserman, T., and Calderwood, D. L. (1972). Rough rice drying. In *Rice Chemistry and Technology* (D. F. Houston, ed.). St. Paul, Minn., American Association of Cereal Chemistry, p. 188.

Williams, J. (1980). Rice growth and timing of management practices. In *Rice Field Day*. Biggs, Calif., Rice Experiment Station, p. 3.

Witte, G. C. (1976). Conventional rice milling in the United States. In *Rice Chemistry and Technology* (D. F. Houston, ed.). St. Paul, Minn., American Association of Cereal Chemists, p. 188.

14

Tropical Fruit Wines

Tommy Nakayama University of Georgia Experiment Station, Experiment, Georgia

I. INTRODUCTION

The term wine generally connotes the fermented beverages made from grapes and, when more broadly applied, refers to the fermentation products of fruits. In its broadest sense it can refer to a product made from plant materials other than fruit which have alcohol levels similar to that of grapes. Even fermented products made from honey are designated as honey wine when the material is fermented in

accordance with the procedures of the Alcohol, Tobacco, and Firearms
Division of the United States Internal Revenue Service. Thus, a variety of plant products and derivatives may be used in the making of
wine. The materials specifically disallowed are grains, cereals, malt,
or molasses. These are specifically designated as materials which, when
fermented, do not produce products considered to be wine. Hence, no
ready definition of wine is apparent, and specificity becomes more dif-
fuse as one moves farther from grapes.

This chapter focuses upon alcoholic beverages derived from plants
growing within the area of the world generally known as the tropics, a
region where frost is not encountered and pest are endemic. The fact
that tropical plants endure in a climate of constant attack indicates
that they have developed defense mechanisms which often are reflected
in their composition. These may take the form of repellents in the
skin, thick hulls, proteolytic enzymes, tannins, high acidities, and
other means.

Although the number of fruits grown in the tropics is very large,
their composition generally is not as suitable as that of grapes for
making wine; oftentimes they may lack sufficient sugar to produce at
least 7% v/v and preferably 11 to 12% alcohol by ordinary fermentation
or may contain adventitious materials which may be detrimental. Another factor in the development of wine making on an industrial scale
is the availability of fruit in amounts sufficient to warrant industraliz-
ation. A discussion of pineapple, papaya, and passion fruit is presented
to illustrate some of the adaptations necessary for production of wine
from tropical fruits. Extension of these principles may be helpful in
dealing with other types of fruits.

II. WINE-MAKING PROCEDURES

The procedures discussed in this chapter are technically possible and
not limited to those falling within the regulations of the Bureau of Alcohol, Tobacco, and Firearms of the United States Internal Revenue
Service, as the latter are promulgated for the regulation of wine commerce in the United States (U.S. BATF, 1976). Because most of the
fruits grown in tropical areas lie principally outside the United States,
the regulations may be entirely different. However, it is to be noted
that wines imported into the United States should be properly identified
with government authorities.

For details in the technology of winemaking, the reader is referred
to the classic texts by Amerine et al. (1980) and Cruess (1948). There
are two possibilities for producing an alcoholic beverage containing
approximately 11% alcohol from fruit products. One is to prepare the
must (juice) in such a way that when fermentation has subsided, the
end product will contain the requisite alcohol. The other procedure is
to calculate the dilutions to be experienced upon adding alcohol of

appropriate strength to the fruit so that the final alcohol in the liquid will be of the desired strength. Intermediate practices consisting of adding alcohol to a fermenting must at various stages are widely used. This fortification is often used to stop fermentation and produce wines containing approximately 20% alcohol which are stabilized against further fermentation. However, this discussion will be limited to making those wines which may be experienced in a natural production cycle typified by a product containing 11% alcohol.

A. Preparation of Must

The diversity of operations in preparing juice is due to the type of fruit, its seeds, enzymes, and so forth. These procedures vary for each fruit, and this section is devoted to preparation for fermentation. The reader is referred to the chapters by Chenchin, Chan, and others for juice preparation. In preparing the must for fermentation, one of the first requirements is to have sufficient sugar to produce a wine of appropriate alcohol content. Generally, this is interpreted to mean a must having an original Brix of 22° which may be attained by addition of sugar or sugar and water. The use of water may be required when sugar or acid levels are excessively high. Generally, the total acid of must in grapes varies from about 5 to 9 g/liter must, calculated as tartaric. In the case of passion fruit, therefore, a very large dilution with water is necessary in order to reduce the acidity to a palatable level. For this reason, it has not been possible to produce passion fruit wines within the limits imposed by the Alcohol, Tobacco, and Firearms Division. However, the process is technically feasible and would involve a dilution of severalfold to bring the acidity to a reasonable range. This extreme dilution, however, necessitates a large addition of sugar. This may also, but not necessarily, necessitate addition of growth factors common to more normal grape juice. Addition of ammonium phosphate (10 g/liter) will sometimes overcome this.

Further preparation of must involves the elimination of excessive amounts of tannins or astringent substances that may interfere with palatability of the finished wine. Although these compounds may be adsorbed by protein or polyvinyl-polypyrollidone (PVPP), their removal is often done postfermentation. Excessive extraction of tannin from the fruit is to be avoided. Likewise, gums of various nature that will precipitate in the wine upon storage need to be removed. Treatments for excessive amounts of pectin and gums are enzymatic, and appropriate pectin-degrading enzymes or gum-splitting enzymes may be used, generally with elevated temperatures for short periods of time.

Another requisite is that the must be cleaned microbiologically. This means that much of the natural flora needs to be neutralized by means of heat or antiseptics such as sulfur dioxide. For the latter, sulfur dioxide as a gas or potassium metabisulfite (KMS) may be added. Sulfur dioxide is calculated directly whereas potassium metabisulfite is generally recognized as yielding 50% effective sulfur dioxide. Generally, sulfur dioxide in the range of 50 to 100 ppm is deemed sufficient to provide initial neutralization of the natural flora.

B. Fermentation (Vinification)

An active culture of yeast at the rate of 2 to 3% v/v may be used for fermentation. The usual wine yeast in an active dry form such as Montrachet strain 522 University of California-Davis or champagne yeast *S. bayanus* may be used, as well as others which may be more attuned to the particular must. The general method is to inoculate a sterilized must from an agar slant or with the dry yeast and to use the resulting fermenting culture as inoculum.

Nakahama (1956) reports that *Saccharomyces sake* ferments passion fruit juice faster than *S. cerevisiae* and yields a wine with a flavor reminiscent of sake. Chye and Meng (1975), using rice cake yeast to ferment pineapple waste with cooked sago, found maximum activity at about 38°C and an alcohol concentration as high as 13% compared with 8.9% for *S. cerevisiae* under these conditions.

Some of the fruits may contain gums which produce a persistent foam upon fermentation. For these, allowance must be made for escape of the foam or provisions made to accommodate the large foam blanket.

Cooling is often advantageous in maximizing the yield of alcohol and preventing overheating due to the generally warm ambient temperatures. It is necessary to keep the temperature below 37 to 38°C. Cooling by water appears to work satisfactorily if the requirements are not too great. After fermentation has subsided and the wine is properly protected against oxidation by means of traps, the usual cellar operations of racking and fining can be carried out. A host of fining agents including tannin-gelatin, casein, bentonite, isinglass, egg albumin, polyvinyl-polypyrollidone, carbon, and some proprietary mixtures is used. The reader is advised to make laboratory tests that consist of adding small amounts of the agents properly prepared to 100-ml portions of the wine, shaking, and allowing to stand for several hours. A visual inspection is used to determine the lowest effective concentration which may then be used to extrapolate for larger amounts. Chill-stabilizing by holding at cool temperatures to precipitate tartrates is used in the grape wine industry. Although not mandatory for precipation in tropical fruit wines, it does appear to aid in precipitating materials that are marginally soluble. The final act in filtration can be accomplished by using filter aids and pads.

C. Stabilization

Because of the unknown nature of the wines, it is generally good practice to stabilize then against microbiological changes by use of antiseptics such as sorbic acid or its potassium and sodium salts in amounts ranging from 300 to 1000 ppm. An alternative is to pasteurize the wines after bottling. Another alternative may be to flash-pasteurize, fill into clean bottles, and seal using clean closures. Sterile filtration utilizing membrane filters and followed by aspetic bottling would no doubt be feasible, but extensive experience in tropical fruit wines is lacking. Closures can be the usual wine types including corks, screw caps, and crown caps. During storage, changes will be evident in the wine. The papaya and passion fruit wines appear to be quite stable except for a very slight darkening of color. With pineapple wine, a slight haze will develop as well as a darkening, both being accelerated with warm temperatures.

D. Sparkling Wines

Steinkraus et al. (1969) have described conditions for producing sparkling wines from pineapples. There appear to be no overt difficulties once the wine base is made to produce the sparkling wine by usual procedures. These operations include proper preparation, secondary fermentation using champagne yeasts, disgorging, and finishing. Bulk carbonation methods should undoubtedly be effective. For details, the reader is advised to consult the text of Amerine et al. (1980).

III. PINEAPPLE WINE

Pineapple (*Ananas comosus*) probably originated in Brazil or Paraguay. It is a member of the Bromeliaceae family. A comprehensive account of its composition, developmental biochemistry, and physiology is covered by Dull (1971). A major producer of pineapple is Hawaii, with Taiwan, Malaysia, Australia, the Philippines, Thailand, Africa, South America, and Mexico also now engaged in production. Although pineapple juice is readily available in Hawaii and single-strength juice is produced in abundance, the production of wine has yet to attain much success. Some of the surplus is used in conversion to distilled alcohol, mainly for production of vinegar.

The natural inclination to prepare alcoholic drinks has also been applied to pineapples. One of the earliest records of pineapple wine is contained in the writings of Columbus who reported that beverages made from pineapples had the finest character (Irving, 1887). It is also mentioned in the writings of Gonzalo Fernadez de Oviedo y Valdes who was sent in 1513 to the New World by King Ferdinand of Spain (Collins, 1960).

Various pineapples have been fermented under natural conditions which result in a low-alcohol drink known in Hawaii as swipe. Although

it is clearly possible to make a low-alcohol wine from pineapple
(Amerine et al., 1980), the product has not yet attained full commercial acceptability. Although some is produced in Puerto Rico,
Hawaii, and elsewhere, the requisite technology for introducing it to
the world of commerce has not yet been exploited. A recipe for making pineapple wine is given by Anderson (1973). Steinkraus et al.
(1969) reported that satisfactory wines could be made from Philippine
pineapple. Similarly, wine produced from pineapple concentrate was
commercially produced in California. This wine was fortified with
alcohol and thus may be comparable to a dessert wine.

A typical composition of Hawaiian pineapple flesh is shown in
Tables 1 and 2. The extract composition varies from summer to
winter, with summer crops being sweeter and less acid (Mehrlich,
1961). Conceivably, problems arising from extreme variations in
acidity may necessitate considerable process modification.

Among the carbohydrate constituents are gums such as hexosans,
pentosans, and pectin. A particular characteristic of fermentation
of pineapple juice is the large amount of foam which is generated.
During fermentation it is not unusual to have 50% of the working
capacity of the fermenter full of foam. The predominate acids consist of citric, malic, succinic, and phosphoric (Chan et al., 1973a).
Small amounts of phenolic acids such as p-coumaric and ferulic also
occur.

The flavor of pineapple has been the object of much investigation
which has been summarized by Silverstein (1971). Of the large
number of compounds exemplified, one in particular, 2,5-dimethyl-
4-hydroxy-3(2H)-furanone, is a major contributor described as
"burnt pineapple" or "fruity carmel." Among the other volatile
compounds, the sulfur-containing esters methyl β-methylthiopropionate

Table 1 General Analysis of Ripe Pineapple
Fruit Flesh

Analysis	Fresh weight (%)
Brix	10.8-17.5
Titratable acid (as citric)	0.6-1.62
Ash	0.30-0.42
Water	81.2-86.2
Fiber	0.30-0.61
Nitrogen	0.045-0.115
Ether extract	0.2
Esters (ppm)	1-250
Pigments (ppm of carotene)	0.2-2.5

Source: Dull (1971).

Table 2 Carbohydrate Constituents
of Ripe Pineapple Fruit Flesh

Constituent	Fresh weight (%)
Glucose	1.0-3.2
Fructose	0.6-2.3
Sucrose	5.9-12.0
Starch	<0.002
Cellulose	0.43-0.54
Hexosans	0.10-0.15
Pentosans	0.33-0.43
Pectin	0.06-0.16

Source: Dull (1971).

and ethyl β-methylthiopropionate were indicated to be major components. In grape wines, however, sulfur compounds invariably arise from fermentations, forming 3-methylthiol-1-propanol from methionine (Schreir, 1979).

A. Pineapple Gums

Dull (1971) has indicated that gums constitute approximately 0.3 to 0.5% of pineapple flesh. These gums, if not removed, will persist in the wine and will cause a haze to form upon storage, even though the wine may have been filtered brightly through the use of filter aids. In the case of certain mill juices which are recovered from those pieces of pineapple not canned, the subsequent heating and precipitation, as well as treatment with charcoal, remove much of this material. The composition of the gum has been analyzed by Chenchin and Yamamoto (1978), who identified mannose followed by galactose and raffinose as the principal constituents in the hydrolysates. Small amounts of glucose and xylose were also found. The gum, along with a small amount of pectin, may be responsible for the viscosity of the juice. Pineapple juice is filtered traditionally by heavy use of filter aid on a rotary vacuum filter. Chenchin and Yamamoto (1978) identified several enzymes that are capable of decreasing the viscosity of the juice. The pectinases, cellulases, and hemicellulases were the most effective.

Mill juice resulting from heating, pH corrections, and other processing steps renders a wine that is quite different from that obtained from fermentation of juice; it is quite stable for at least 2 years. Natural fermentation of the juice collected by pressing chopped, ripe fruit results in a beverage which, although containing alcohol, has an undesirable odor similar to that of a rotting pineapple. Therefore, it is concluded that the juice needs preparation. One of the most important preparations for the fermentation of a must is to eliminate many of the undesirable organisms already present. This is deemed to be absolutely necessary in dealing with pineapple under the usual conditions of juice production and the generally high temperatures prevailing. The usual practice of using sulfur dioxide in amounts of 50 to 100 ppm is satisfactory.

Another method of preparation of juice is encountered in production of concentrate. In this process, juice is concentrated by vacuum evaporation and the volatiles are removed. The advantage of using concentrate is that the material can be standardized and space conserved during storage. On the other hand, the concentrate must be stored at freezing temperatures. Otherwise, darkening will ensue. Reconstituted concentrate differs slightly from fresh juice in that the volatiles have been removed to some extent, resulting in a more neutral and less intense pineapple flavor in the fermented product. The end product is immediately identifiable as pineapple, nevertheless. The use of heat appears to have a favorable effect as shown by the report of Alian and Musenge (1977) that boiled pineapple waste produced a wine that was favored over that produced from unboiled waste or pulp.

After fermentation has ceased, yeasts and other flocculant matter should be removed; separation is aided considerably by cooling and can also be accomplished by centrifugation. After racking, it is suggested that a small amount of enzymes be added to the wine. Preliminary experiments have shown that treatment of the wine with enzymes will keep the wine clear and prevent the formation of opalescence. Fining by the use of bentonite is also effective; Steinkrauss et al. (1969) used 1% tannic acid and 0.5% gelatin. Pasteurization can be by the usual method of heating to 70°C for 15 min. Alternative methods of preservation include use of sorbic acid in amounts of 300 to a maximum of 1000 ppm, as well as sterile filtration.

B. Production of Alcohol from Pineapple Waste

Alcohol production from pineapple waste utilizes a significant amount of material, particularly where pineapple canneries are located. Waste from trimming tables, mill juice, and centrifuge underflows can all be fermented to alcohol which is then recovered by distillation. The material can be fermented in large open tanks with a minimal amount of cooling. The foam which results, however, allows only about half the working volume to be occupied by juice. Fermentation is rapid and in most cases accomplished in a matter of hours, particularly if the amount of sugar is low due to having been diluted with wash water. No particular precautions are taken in this fermentation process except for temperature control. The distillate is generally separated from the bulk of the material in a single pass and then redistilled in a column still with numerous plates to yield 190-proof alcohol. This material has traditionally been used for production of distilled vinegar. However, it can also be used for wine production. In cases where the recovery of alcohol is the primary aim, the juice of pineapple wastes can be enriched by adding molasses or sago to yield a beer with an alcohol content of at least 7% which is more economically feasible (Chye and Meng, 1975; *Taiwan Sugar*, 1975).

A typical process for making pineapple wine consists of using single-strength juice or diluting concentrate to a Brix of 12° and 0.82% total acidity calculated as citric acid which will vary. To 1000 liter of this juice, add 432 liter of water and 248 kg of sugar. Add 50 ppm of sulfur dioxide, let stand for several hours, and innoculate with about 3% v/v of an actively fermenting wine yeast prepared the day before. Allow to ferment at temperature not exceeding 30°C taking care to remove the excess foam. When the fermentation has subsided in about 10 days, the Brix will be near 5.5, the alcohol content near 10.5% v/v, and the total acidity about 0.59%. After completion of fermentation, the wine can be racked and fined by adding 550 g of activated carbon and, after mixing, 365 g of bentonite that has been soaked overnight, racked and filtered. Sulfur dioxide may be added at this point to a total of 100 ppm. This wine may be preserved with sorbate or pasteurized.

An alternate process utilizing 190-proof alcohol from pineapple waste is as follows. To 1000 liter of the reconstituted concentrate or juice, add 528 liter of water and 80 kg of sugar. After fermentation is essentially complete, rack and add 105 liter of the alcohol, and proceed as in the nonfortified process. The alcohol will be between 10 and 11% v/v and the Brix near 3.5.

IV. PAPAYA WINE

Papaya, also called paw paw or papaw,* is indigenous to Mexico and Costa Rica and has spread to other tropical and subtropical countries. A common variety in Hawaii is the *Carica papaya* L. cultivar 'Solo', cultivated principally for the fresh market, and is the species referred to here. The earliest record of cultivation has been recorded by Oviedo in the early sixteenth century. In contrast to pineapple, there does not appear to be a record of its use for alcoholic beverages by the native peoples of the West Indies (Purseglove, 1968).

---

*These terms are also applied to the North American tree *Asimina triloba* and its fruit.

The use of papaya for wine making has not evolved commercially, although it is possible to make wine from papayas and recipes have been developed which include the addition of other fruits and sugar (Anderson, 1973). Its wine was said to resemble a Moselle with its tart, light body and light-gold color. Preparation of wine from papaya without acidification yields a product with an exceptional stench. However, a modified process for preparing papaya purée which was developed by the Hawaii Fruit Laboratory USDA (Chan et al., 1973b) allows rapid acidification and minimizes the formation of this objectionable odor. The process is depicted in Fig. 2 of Chap. 12.

From the composition of papaya purée (Table 3), it is obvious that the product requires acidification in order to make a wine as we generally know it. Thus, acidification will bring the pH from 5.4 to 3.5. Utilization of this modified purée to produce a wine, yields one which is greatly improved in flavor.

The presence of other compounds in papaya has long evoked interest from a medical standpoint. Although papain has been utilized extensively in foods, leathers, cosmetics, and so forth, the medical use of papain has been mainly as a digestive aid. For a comprehensive account, see Chan and Tang (1979). The ingredients of the papaya plant have been utilized principally for their protease activity. Other parts appear to have effect due to pharmacologically active compounds which are either extracted or used as is. Among these are benzyl glucosinolate or benzyl isothiocyanate (BITC), choline, carpaine, serocarpaine, dehydro carpaine I, and dehydro carpain II

Table 3 Chemical Composition of Pineapple, Papaya, and Passion Fruit Juices

Material	Chemical analysis		
	° Brix	pH	Total acid g/100 cc
Pineapple	10-17.5[a]	4.2-3.5[b]	0.6-1.64[a]
Papaya	11.5-13.5[c]	5.0-5.5[c]	0.05-0.10[c]
Passion fruit (yellow variety)	17.3[d]	2.8[d]	3.4[d]

[a]Dull (1971).
[b]Mehrlich (1961).
[c]Brekke et al. (1972).
[d]Boyle et al. (1955).

(Tang, 1979). Of these, the benzyl glucosinolate and its hydrolysis product benzyl isothiocyanate are important because they occur in the seed and give wine a bitter taste. The gelatinous seed coating (sarcotesta) is a good source of the enzyme which effects its cleavage. Carpaine and its derivatives, on the other hand, are found largely in the green parts as well as the seeds. The latex and seed contain only traces. BITC has been reported as a potent germicidal compound as well as an insecticide. Therefore, its use in folk medicine is readily understandable. In wine, however, BITC is bitter, and processing methods should not damage the sarcotesta. This occurs in experimental wine making where certain purées that have been maltreated have a bitter taste in the wine.

Another aspect of papaya purée is the fact that it contains an active pectin esterase which leads to the gelation of the purée. Interestingly, although pectin esterase is readily detected, the presence of polygalacturonase has so far not been unequivocally demonstrated. Therefore, in order to produce wine through normal fermentation, it is necessary to use depectinizing enzymes which yield a purée similar to that of grape must. Failure to use such enzymes results in gelation and formation of a very viscous purée which is inhibitory to fermentation.

Following these general precautions, a stable wine can be made which holds up well in storage. A notable characteristic of the fruits is that they have a high concentration of ascorbic acid. Papaya in this respect is typical. The Solo variety contains approximately 84 mg/100 g portion. A typical process using the acidified fruit purée would be to treat it with 0.2% pectin-degrading enzymes, heat gradually to 140°F for 30 min, and cool. Sulfur dioxide can then be added to the must.

Because the purée consists of 9 to 10% solids and has a total acidity of about 1%, it is necessary to ameliorate with water and sugar to bring the total acid to approximately 6 to 7 g/liter and the soluble solids to 22° Brix. The must can then be inoculated with a strain of wine yeast. An actively growing culture can be added at 3% v/v. If fermentation proceeds normally, at the end of 8 to 10 days the wine may be settled in the cold and racked.

Filtration with pads and filter aid will produce a clear wine which will be maintained. The wine can then be pasteurized or preserved with sorbic acid; it is reasonably stable in storage and intensifies slightly in color as it ages. During storage for a year, it darkens only slightly. Due to the extremely strong flavor of papaya, it can be used as a flavoring adjunct for other more neutral wines (Miyanabe, 1974).

V. PASSION FRUIT WINE

Passion fruit (*Passiflora edulis* flavicarpa) is another tropical fruit grown in Hawaii. The yellow variety is of recent origin compared to the purple variety (*P. edulis* Sims). The purple passion fruit originated in Brazil and is now grown in most of the tropical and subtropical countries (Pruthi, 1963). Although wine from passion fruit juice has been made and judged to be pleasant (Czyhrinciw, 1966; Anderson, 1973), there is no indication that the wine could be produced under the regulations of the U.S. Internal Revenue Service. Since passion fruit can contain approximately 4% acid, it is obvious that the juice must be diluted several fold to make it similar to grapes.

The composition of passion fruit is shown in Tables 4 and 5. As can be seen, the acidities of the yellow and purple varieties differ slightly. The unique and very intense odor of passion fruit has attracted attention from researchers as well as users. The predominant compound in the volatile fraction of the yellow variety is

Table 4 Pilot Plant Studies on the Manufacture of Passion Fruit Squash: Technical Data on Extraction, Yield, and Physicochemical Composition of Passion Fruit Juice

| | | Range of variation | |
Particulars	Overall average	Max.	Min.
Wt per 1000 fruits (lb)	64.4	80.0	56.3
Time for cutting (min)	29.9	27.4	21.9
Time for scooping out pulp (hr)	6.5	7.5	6.0
Peel (%)	49.9	53.8	45.6
Residue (%)	13.5	14.7	11.5
Juice (%)	36.5	40.1	32.6
Analysis of juice			
Refractometric solids	17.7		
Acidity (% w/w)	3.6	4.0	3.3
Brix/acidity	5.0	5.5	4.4
pH	2.79	2.88	2.70
Ascorbic acid mg/100 g	33.6	33.8	28.7
Reducing sugars (%)	5.4	6.1	4.8
Nonreducing sugars (%)	5.1	5.9	4.3
Total sugars as invert (%)	10.8	11.4	10.2

Source: Data summarized from Pruthi and Lal (1955).

Table 5 Quantitative Determination of Organic Acids in Yellow Passion Fruit (*P. flavicarpa*) and Purple Passion Fruit (*P. edulis*)

Acid	*P. flavicarpa* (meq/100 g)	*P. edulis* (meq/100 g)
Citric	55.0	13.0
Malic	10.55	3.86
Lactic	0.58	7.49
Malonic	0.13	4.95
Succinic	trace	2.42
Ascorbic	0.06	0.05
Volatile acids	0.11	0.12

Source: Chan et al. (1972).

n-hexyl caproate (70%) along with its esters (Hui and Scheuer, 1961). The purple variety, on the other hand, has only 5% of this compound (Parliment, 1972). It has been suggested that subtle differences in flavor between the yellow and purple varieties may be due to this quantitative difference. Other volatile compounds in passion fruit wine from the yellow variety were identified by Muller et al. (1964) who found only trace quantities of n-hexyl caproate.

The processing for passion fruit wine may be assumed to be somewhat similar to that for preparation of juice. The greatest hindrance to making a passion fruit wine appears to be the high acidity. Therefore, it is used primarily as an adjunct for flavor purposes. A typical process for passion fruit wine would be to dilute the juice with about three volumes of water and enough sugar to raise the Brix to 22°. The sugar can be added at several stages during fermentation. Because of the high-acid content, a small amount of sulfur dioxide, to 50 ppm, can be used. The wine will ferment out and should contain approximately 11 to 12% alcohol. The deep-orange color of the juice is lost on fermentation because the color is largely carotenoid, and thus the wine will be a pale yellow; however, the flavor will be immediately recognizable as passion fruit. If dilutions greater than this are anticipated, a small amount of ammonium phosphate, 10 g/liter, may be added to enhance fermentation. Even at this great dilution, the wine can be mixed with less flavorful species to enhance their flavor (Miyanabe, 1974).

VI. VINEGAR PRODUCTION

In general, most of the wines which are produced can be converted to vinegars. The general procedure is to dilute the wine to about 8%

alcohol v/v and add a vinegar (*Acetobacter*) culture and growth
factors as follows: ammonium phosphate, 0.1%; yeast extract 0.5%;
hydrolyzed casein, 0.05%; magnesium sulfate, 0.1%; glucose, 0.5%
(Maldonado et al., 1975). Alternatively, malt extract may be substituted for the yeast extract. The wines made from tropical fruits
offer no real problem with vinegar manufacture, although occassionally
suprises do ensue. In a trial of several different fermenters, aerated
and still, Lee (1975) found that wine made from papaya would not
acidify without aeration. Whereas in a period of 3 months the pineapple wine had exceeded 4% acetic acid, the papaya wine remained constant; this condition can be overcome by aeration. A submerged
process which utilized agitation and a generator filled with shavings
produced satisfactory results. Nutrients are necessary to establish
the culture, but they appear to have no effect on the rate of acetifica-
tion. The vinegars are typically inoculated by using one-third of the
working volume of a previous batch. If vinegar stock is to be stored
for any length of time, it is advisable to acidify the material to 2%
acetic acid in order to prevent formation of film yeasts which would
utilize the alcohol. The finished vinegars may be filtered and pasteurized by heating for a few seconds at 60° (Cruess, 1958). It has
not yet been determined what the inhibitory factors are in papaya wine.

VII. OTHER TROPICAL FRUITS

Various other tropical fruits are discussed here, with emphasis on the
peculiarities which may be experienced in their use for wine. Pomegranate, *Punica granatum*, is an example of a fruit which contains an
abundance of soluble tannins which will be readily extracted into the
juice. If excessive crushing is avoided, however, by pressing the
whole fruit under moderate pressure, juice of pleasing flavor and a
red color can be obtained. Cruess (1958) indicates that excessive
astringency can be removed by the judicious use of gelatin. This
juice can then be handled in a normal manner. Java plum, *Eugenia
cuminii*, resembles the pomegranate in having an excessive amount of
tannins. Methods of using it, therefore, necessitate treating the juice
or fruit to eliminate the astringency. Governor's plum, *Flacourtia indica
syn. F. ramonchi*, resembles java plum and has a ready tendency to
brown. Although cooking can inhibit browning, it does not eliminate the
excessive amount of soluble tannins. Jaboticaba, *Myrciaria caulifora*
cultivar Sabara, is a large, grape-size fruit that yields a brilliantly
purple juice and a mildly astringent wine. Tamarind, *Tamarindus
indica*, has been used as a source of wine by Maldonado et al. (1975).
The preparation consisted of manual removal of the outer part, soaking
the pulp in cold water for 24 hr, followed by manual separation of the
seed. The suspension was then pulped through a 20-mesh screen.

Bananas, *Musa* species, have been used as a substrate for wine fermentation. The general procedures involved manual removal of the peel and passing the fruit through pulpers with added water. Additional pulping with smaller screens can be used to remove seeds. Czyhrinciw (1966) has described the making of wine from mango, *Mangifera indica*. Sanchez-Nieva et al. (1959) have described the processing and canning of mango nectars. For most of these fruits, it is necessary to add sugar to bring the fermentables to reasonable values. The precautions taken by Maldonado et al. (1975) in adding ammonium sulfate (10 g/liter), disodium phosphate (0.5 g/liter), and magnesium oxide (0.5 g/liter) to initiate fermentation can be used.

Many other fruits are potential canidates for the making of wine; however, it is hoped that by illustrating some of the adjustments necessary with these exotic fruits, the reader will be guided toward a rational development plan for wine production.

ACKNOWLEDGMENT

The author wishes to acknowledge the considerable help of Dr. Sigmund H. Schanderl, Visiting Professor, University of Hawaii (1973) and Ms. Michiko Miyanabe and Mr. Jin Woo Lee, graduate students, for their interest and participation.

REFERENCES

Alian, A., and Musenge, H. M. (1977). Effect of fermentation and aging on some flavoring components in tropical fruit wines. *Zambia J. Sci. Technol.* 2(1):10-17.

Amerine, M. A., Berg, H. W., Kunkee, R. E., Ough, C. S., Singleton, V. L., and Webb, A. D. (1980). *The Technology of Wine Making*, 4th ed. Westport, Conn., Avi Pub.

Anderson, R. H. (1973). *Wines of Samoa and How To Make Them*. Pago Pago, American Somoa, Department of Education.

Boyle, F. P., Shaw, T. N., and Sherman, G. D. (1955). Wide uses for new passion fruit juice. *Food Eng.* 27(9):94,184.

Brekke, J. E., Chan, H. T., Jr., and Cavaletto, C. G. (1972). Papaya purée: A tropical flavor ingredient. *Food Prod. Dev.* 6(10):36-37.

Chan, H. T., and Tang, C. S. (1979). The chemistry and biochemistry of papaya. In *Tropical Foods Vol. I*, (G. E. Inglett and G. Charalambous, eds.). New York, Academic Press, pp. 33-53

Chan, H. T., Chang, T. S. K., and Chenchin, E. (1972). Nonvolatile acids of passion fruit juice. *J. Agr. Food Chem.* 20(1):110-112.

Chan, H. T., Jr., Chenchin, E., and Vonnahme, P. (1973a). Nonvolatile acids in pineapple juice. *J. Agr. Food Chem.* 21:208-211.

Chan, H. T., Jr., Flath, R. A., Forrey, R. R., Cavaletto, C. G., Brekke, J. E., and Nakayama, T. (1973b). Development of off-odors and off-flavors in papaya purée. *J. Agr. Food Chem.* 21:566-570.

Chenchin, K. L., and Yamamoto, H. Y. (1978). Isolation, characterization and enzymic hydrolysis of pineapple gum. *J. Food Sci.* 43:1261-1263.

Chye, T. T., and Meng, L. C. (1975). Industrial alcohol from pineapple wastes. *J. Singapore Natl. Acad. Sci.* 4(3):152-154.

Collins, J. L. (1960). *The Pineapple: Botany, Cultivation and Utilization.* New York, Interscience, p. 294.

Cruess, W. V. (1948). *Commercial Fruit and Vegetable Products,* 3rd ed. New York, McGraw Hill, pp. 698-761.

Cruess, W. V. (1958). *Commercial Fruit and Vegetable Products,* 4th ed. New York, McGraw Hill, pp. 681-707.

Czyhrinciw, N. K. (1966). The technology of passion fruit and mango wine. *Am. J. Enol. Viticult.* 17:27-30.

Dull, G. G. (1971). The pineapple: General. In *The Biochemistry of Fruits and Their Products, Vol. 2* (A. C. Hulme, ed.). New York, Academic Press, pp. 308-323.

Hiu, D. N., and Scheuer, P. J. (1961). The volatile constituents of passion fruit juice. *J. Food Sci.* 26:557-563.

Irving, W. (1887). *Life and Voyage of Columbus,* Vol. I. New York, John B. Alden.

Lee, J. W. (1975). Vinegar production from papaya and pineapple by four different fermenters. *Termination Report, Project S-566.* Honolulu, Hi., University of Hawaii, College of Tropical Agriculture.

Maldonado, O., Rolz, C., and Schneider de Cabrera, S. (1975). Wine and vinegar production from tropical fruits. *J. Food Sci.* 40:262-265.

Mehrlich, F. P. (1961). Pineapple juice. In *Fruit and Vegetable Juice: Processing Technology* (D. K. Tressler, and M. A. Joslyn, eds.). Westport, Conn., Avi Pub. pp. 746-786.

Miyanabe, M. (1974). Sensory evaluation of tropical fruit wines. Unpublished M. S. thesis, University of Hawaii.

Muller, C. J., Kepner, R. E., and Webb, A. D. (1964). Some volatile constitutents of passion fruit wine. *J. Food Sci.* 29:569-575.

Nakahama, T. (1956). Studies on alcoholic beverages of passion-fruit juice. *Saikyo U. Faculty Agri. Sci. Rpt. No. 8.* Saikyo, Japan, Saikyo University, pp. 34-37.

Parliment, T. H. (1972). Some volatile constituents of passion fruit. *J. Agr. Food Chem.* 20(5):1043-1045.

Pruthi, J. S. (1963). Physiology, chemistry and technology of passion fruit. *Adv. Food. Res.* 12:203-282.

Pruthi, J. S., and Lal, G. (1955). Some technological aspects of manufacture of passion fruit squash. *Chem. Age (India)* 6(2):42.

Purseglove, J. W. (1968). *Tropical Crops. Dicotyledons.* New York, Wiley.

Sanchez-Nieva, F., Rodriquez, A. J., and Benero, J. R. (1959). Processing and canning mango nectars. *Bulletin 148.* Rio Piedras, Puerto Rico, Agric. Expt. Stat., Univ. of Puerto Rico. pp. 1-23.

Schreir, P. (1979). Flavor composition of wines: A review. In *CRC Critical Reviews in Food Science and Nutrition*, Vol. 12(1) (T. E. Furia, ed.). Bora Raton, Fla. pp. 59-111.

Silverstein, R. M. (1971). The pineapple: Flavor. In *The Biochemistry of Fruits and Their Products Vol. 2* (A. C. Hulme, ed). New York, Academic Press, pp. 325-331.

Steindraus, K. H., Ramos, L. J., Layse, G. E., Yap, A., and Banzon, J. (1969). Production of still and sparkling wines from Philippine pineapple juice. *Philippine Agriculturists* 52(9/10): 619-625.

Taiwan Sugar (1975). *A study on production of alcohol from pineapple skin-juice.* 22(1):14-16.

Tang, C. S. (1979). Macrocyclic piperidine and piperideine alkaloids in *Carica papaya.* In *Tropical Foods Vol. I*, (G. E. Inglett and G. Charalambous, eds.). New York, Academic Press, pp. 55-68.

United States Bureau of Alcohol, Tobacco and Firearms (1976). Wine. *Title 27, Part 240. Code of Federal Regulations.* Washington, D. C., U.S. Government Printing Office.

15

Yams

D. G. Coursey Tropical Development and Research Institute, London, England

I. INTRODUCTION

A. Botanical Description and Varieties

Yams are traditional food crops of great antiquity in cultivation, grown in many parts of the tropics. They are members of the genus *Dioscorea*, which is far the largest genus of the Dioscoreaceae, which in turn is the principal family of the Dioscoreales, an order close to the Liliales, within which the Dioscoreaceae were formerly included. Also included in the Dioscoreaceae are several monotypic or very small satellite genera, one of which, *Rajania*, also includes minor yamlike food plants. The Dioscoreales are classified as Monocotyledons, but nevertheless show several morphological features that are more typical of the Dicotyledons, some species even having a nonemergent second cotyledon. They also appear to be among the most primitive of the angiosperms. True yams must not, of course, be confused with the sweet potato, *Ipomoea batatas* (L.) Lam., which is often incorrectly referred to as yam, especially in the United States (Coursey, 1967; Ayensu, 1972; Burkill, 1960).

The genus *Dioscorea* contains several hundred species, widely distributed throughout the tropics of both the Old and New Worlds, with a few members occurring in temperate or montane regions. Asian, African, and American species are quite distinct from each other, morphological differences between American and Old World species being greater than between African and Asian. The species of the Old World normally have chromosome numbers based on $\times = 10$, being thus further distinguished from the American species, all of which studied so far have numbers based on $\times = 9$, although in both cases most cultivated forms are high polyploids (Coursey, 1976a).

Yams are perennial plants, with a strong marked annual cycle of growth and dormancy. The organ of dormancy is a rhizome in a few species, but all the edible species and most others develop one or more tubers: these tubers are annually renewed in edible yams although in some nonedible species the tuber is a perennial organ, increasing in size and becoming increasingly lignified from year to year. In the typical *Dioscorea*, the stems are produced annually at the onset of the rainy season, and are initially erect, but soon commence to climb by twining, extending often for many meters through trees or undergrowth; in cultivation, artifical support is usually provided. The stems of many species are spiny or alate. The leaves are borne on long petioles, usually simple, and cordate or acuminate, but in some species they are lobed or palmate. The flowers are individually small and borne in long racemes, with male and female always being separate and usually borne on separate plants. The female flowers are followed by dehiscent capsules containing six seeds, which in most species are winged for wind dispersal. Many of the cultivated forms have become partially (often highly) sexually sterile as a result of centuries of vegetative propagation.

In all, probably some 50 or 60 *Dioscorea* species are sometimes used as food plants: most of these have been discussed in detail by Coursey (1967) and by Martin and Degras (1978b). The majority of these are only of local, minor importance. Only a much smaller number are regularly grown as food crops to any significant degree: these are listed in Table 1.

The greater part of the world's production of yams for food is, in fact, derived from four species, *D. rotundata*, *D. cayenensis*, *D. alata*, and *D. esculenta*. These species exist in a great variety of cultivars. As with most crop plants which are important mainly in tropical sub-sistence economies, much confusion exists among the cultivated forms, which in most parts of the world have never been properly scientifically classified. A description of many cultivated forms in Nigeria (Waitt, 1965) although of some use is not entirely satisfactory. Much

Table 1 Major Food Yam Species

	Africa	Asia	America
Major economic species	*D. rotundata* Poir[a]	*D. alata* L.	*D. trifida* L.f.
	D. cayenensis Lam.[a]	*D. esculenta* (Lour.) Burk.	
Secondary species	*D. bulbifera* L.[b]	*D. bulbifera* L.[b]	*D. convolvulacea* Cham. et Schlecht.
	D. preussii Pax.	*D. hispida* Dennst.	
	D. praehensilis Benth.	*D. pentaphylla* L.	*Rajania cordata* L.
	D. sansibarensis Pax.	*D. nummularia* Lam.	
	D. dumetorum (Kunth) Pax.	*D. opposita* Thunb.[c]	
		D. japonica Thunb.[c]	

[a]Some authors regard *D. rotundata* as only a subspecies of *D. cayenensis*.
[b]*D. bulbifera* is the only species common to both Africa and Asia. The African form is however, quite distinct and is sometimes regarded as a separate species, *D. latifolia* Benth.
[c]These are often together known incorrectly as *D. batatas* Decne. They are temperate species native to China and Japan.

Table 2 Elite Cultivars of *D. alata* Selected in Puerto Rico[a]

Cultivar	Origin	Advantage	Disadvantage
Alowinrin	Nigeria	Uniform shape and color	Poor kitchen qualities
Belep	West Africa	Good yield	Poor shape
Florido	Puerto Rico	Compact shape, good flavor, high yields	Disease, nematode susceptibility
Forastero	Puerto Rico	Vigor, good quality and yield	Susceptible to leaf spot
Gemelos	Puerto Rico	Perfect shape, multiple tubers	
Murapoi	Fiji	Good shape, thick bark	Polyphenolic oxidation
Nae Onwula	Nigeria	Excellent shape and flavor	Poor yields
Pacala	Ivory Coast	Good shape, color, and yield	Quality not as high as desired
Puka	Ghana	Good shape and flavor	Low viability
Smooth Statia	Caribbean	Excellent shape and flavor	Susceptible to virus
Suidie	Ivory Coast	Excellent flavor	Poor keeping quality
Veeven	Nigeria	Globular shape, good yield	Only normal cooking quality
White Lisbon	Trinidad	Best cooking characteristics	Poor shape
Unnamed	Nigeria	Heavy yields, good flavor	Irregular shape

[a] All forms of this species are originally from Southeast Asia. The origins are given here to indicate the countries from which these accessions to Martin's collection were made.
Source: Martin (1976).

more detailed studies have been made in Puerto Rico (Martin, 1974a; Martin and Sadik, 1977), and a number of elite cultivars have been selected and are available for distribution (Martin and Rhodes, 1973; Martin et al., 1975). Most attention was paid to *D. alata*, the species most favored in Puerto Rico, and the characteristics of the elite culti- vars described (Table 2); but some superior cultivars of *D. rotundata* and *D. cayenensis* were also included (Table 3).

In the case of *D. bulbifera*, it is generally accepted that the Asiatic form, with round bulbils, is a better food yam than the African form, which has angular bulbils (Martin, 1974b). A substantial improvement program on *D. trifida* (which unlike other yams is highly sexually fer- tile) in Guadeloupe has developed a form, INRA 25, which is being distributed. Many other cultivars of varying quality are known. Three main cultivars of the temperate *D. opposita* are grown commercial- ly in Japan, Tsukue-Imo, Icho-Imo, and Naga-Imo. The first is con- sidered the best, but the last is more cold-tolerant and can be grown as far north as Hokkaido (Kawakami, 1970). It should be mentioned that a number of *Discorea* species are exploited for medicinal purposes as sources of precursors for sterodial drugs. Many others find occa- sional use in traditional medicine in various parts of the world. These are, however, quite distinct species from those used as food plants (Coursey, 1967; Coursey and Martin, 1970).

Table 3 Elite Cultivars of *D. rotundata* and *D. cayenensis* Selected in Puerto Rico

Name	Origin[a]
Guinea Blanco	Puerto Rico
Grosse Caille Corrosol	Ivory Coast
Negro	Jamaica
Zaria	Iwo, Nigeria
Etentu	Iwo, Nigeria
Fele	Kaiola, Nigeria
Boki	Iwo, Nigeria
Unknown	Nigeria
Awada	Umudike, Nigeria
Unknown	Nigeria
Baniore Bagarou	Benin
Kourokouragourouko	Benin

[a]All forms of this species are originally from Africa
Source: Martin and Sadik (1977).

B. Origin and Distribution

It has already been indicated that various *Dioscorea* species occur naturally in most parts of the tropical world, and the domestication of the species of yams native to Asia, Africa, and tropical America must have taken place entirely separately, as intercontinental contacts are only comparatively recent. Earlier writers often supposed that yam-based agriculture evolved only through external cultural influences, subsequent to the initiation of grain-crop agriculture in the Neolithic Revolution of southwest Asia. There is little doubt that culture contacts between grain-using intrusive and nongrain-using aboriginal populations did take place particularly in Asia and Africa around 5000 years ago, contributing to the present form of yam-based agriculture (Alexander and Coursey, 1969), but the origins of yams as crop plants lie even earlier in history, within the aboriginal cultures of different areas.

The Asiatic cultigen *D. alata* appears to have been selected by man from wild forms, probably of *D. hamiltonii* and *D. persimilis* or their hybrids in the north-central parts of the Southeast Asian peninsula. *D. esculenta* is indigenous to the same region, and cultivated forms appear to have been developed simply by selection from the wild (Alexander and Coursey, 1969; Coursey, 1976b). The greatest diversity of cultivars of both these species is now in Papua New Guinea, but the lesser diversity in other areas may have resulted from erosion of a former greater variability, although Martin (1976) considers that much of the evolution, at least of the former species, in cultivation, took place in Indonesia. These processes are likely to be very old, being initiated as much as 10,000 years ago. Domesticated yams evolved far enough to be taken across the Pacific in the Polynesian migrations, which left the Asiatic mainland around 3500 years ago, and to associated with fairly sophisticated mesolithic cultures in Melanesia even earlier. Both species were taken to Madagascar and the east African coast by Malaysian migrations starting about 1500 years ago, but only reached the main yam-growing areas of west Africa later after European contact (Coursey, 1972, 1976b). The temperate-climate *D. opposita* is confined to Japan and China, where related wild forms are known. It was introduced to Europe as a substitute for potato at the time of the potato blight epiphytotic in the 1860s, but has not persisted there in cultivation.

"To the African himself is entirely due the invention of *D. cayenensis* as a crop plant" (Burkill, as quoted by Ayensu and Coursey, 1972), and this applies equally to *D. rotundata*. Of these two species, *D. cayenensis* is native to the forests of Africa whereas *D. rotundata*, which is a cultigen like its Asiatic counterpart *D. alata*, is so close to *D. cayenensis* that it has been regarded as a subspecies (Ayensu and Coursey, 1972). This, the most important of the African yams, appears to be of hybrid origin, one parent undoubtedly being *D. cayenensis*, which as a forest species is adapted to a short dry season and limited tuber

dormancy, whereas the other must be a savanna species, probably
D. praehensilis, although *D. abyssinica* and *D. togoensis* may also
have contributed to its ancestry. Hybrids probably arose spontaneously in the forest/savanna ecotone of west Africa, and were selected
by mesolithic people whose concepts of protection of food plant resources and recognition of a superior food plant led by vegetative
propagation to the clonal cultivars known today. As in Asia, this initial phase appears to have been ancient, perhaps as much as 11,000
years ago (Ayensu and Coursey, 1972; Coursey, 1976b).

Little is known of the origins of New World yams. They were of
secondary importance in pre-Colombian America, perhaps because of
the ready availability of cassava, although *D. trifida* is clearly an
Amerindian domesticate, distribution of cultivars suggesting an origin
on the borders of Brazil and Guyana, followed by spread through the
Caribbean (Ayensu and Coursey, 1972). Yams are primarily Old World
domesticates, but have become important in the New World, especially
the Caribbean, since the paleocolonial Portuguese and Spanish expansion into the tropics began around 500 years ago and brought the
Indo-Pacific area, Africa, and America into regular contact. Asiatic
yams were extensively used for supplying sailing ships returning from
the Far East, and by this means *D. alata* was taken to west Africa: a
little later the Atlantic slave trade resulted in both this species and
the African *D. rotundata* and *D. cayenensis* being taken to the Caribbean. Historical records of *D. alata* in west Africa and of African yams
in the Americas date back to the sixteenth century (Coursey, 1967).
This mechanism of transfer resulted in only selected cultivars, usually
those superior as food and of good storage life, being taken beyond
their native continents. The Asiatic *D. esculenta*, which does not
store well, was only taken to Africa and America within the last century
and is still little grown outside the Indo-Pacific area. There has been
essentially no comparable transfer of yams from America to the Old
World or from Africa to Asia except experimentally in the last decade
(Coursey, 1967, 1976b).

Spontaneous hybridization is believed to have contributed to the
ancestry of some yams, but propagation in cultivation is entirely
vegetative, each cultivar being a single clone, and improvements have
therefore been by selection of somatic mutants. Vegetative propagation over many centuries has led to reduced sexual fertility, resulting
from limited production and incomplete opening of flowers and failure
of pollen release. The high polyploidy of many cultivars may also contribute to infertility. The infertility appears most extreme in the
Asiatic *D. alata* and *D. esculenta* where seed set is normally unknown
(Coursey, 1976a). Seed set in *D. rotundata* takes place rather more
readily, and the difficulties of obtaining fertile seed are less than was
earlier believed (Sadik and Okereke, 1975a,b). Attempts to breed
improved food yams have recently been made in Nigeria, using this

species and *D. cayenensis*. It is of interest to note that seedling yam plants are much more highly sexually fertile than the normal clonal cultivars, and a higher proportion of hermaphrodite plants occurs in a seedling population.

Plans for the further development of yams as food crops need to be aimed both towards improved clones for the small farmer for manual cultivation, under virtually horticultural conditions and accepting relatively high cost, and to attempt to modify the crop to adapt it better to mechanized agriculture. Parameters to be considered in improvement program have been indicated (Coursey and Martin, 1970; Ayensu and Coursey, 1972): particularly to be emphasized is the need to eliminate staking, which can account for almost a third of total production costs.

C. Economic and Nutritional Significance

Yams are essentially crops of subsistence agriculture although in recent years there has been some development towards small-scale commercial production for urban markets in parts of west Africa and the Caribbean. In west Africa, particularly, such trade involves the transportation of large quantities of fresh yam over distances of several hundred kilometers (Coursey, 1978). International trade, other than some transfrontier or interisland regional trade, is limited to a few thousand tons a year, directed to the needs of immigrant communities in Europe or North America. As with all crops of the subsistence sector, statistics of production are somewhat unreliable, but world production has consistently been estimated by the Food and Agriculture Organization (FAO) of the United Nations as around 20 million tonnes/year (Table 4).

Table 4 Global Production of Yams[a]

	Area (× 10^3 ha)	Production (× 10^3 tonnes)	Yield (kg/ha)
Average			
1961-1965	2138	16,243	7598
1973	2029	19,380	9554
1974	2073	20,188	9740
1975	2110	20,198	9571

[a]The last year for which FAO statistics are available is 1975: in subsequent years yams are grouped with minor root crops.
Source: FAO Production Yearbook (1975).

Table 5 Yam Production and Utilization in Principal Producer Countries

	Production		Utilization
	(1000 tonnes)	(% of global total)	(g/person/day)[a]
Nigeria	15,000	74.3	652
Ivory Coast	1700	8.4	695
Ghana	800	3.9	222
Togo	750	3.7	914
Benin	610	3.0	543
Ethiopia	270	1.4	26
Sudan	260	1.3	47
Papua New Guinea	168	0.8	169
Japan	138	0.7	3
Jamaica	134	0.7	180
Guinea	55	0.3	34
Upper Volta	48	0.2	23
Venezuela	48	0.2	11
Dominican Republic	31	0.15	16
Philippines	30	0.15	2
Haiti	25	0.12	15
Madagascar	24	0.12	8
Barbados	16	0.07	179
Panama	16	0.07	16
Puerto Rico	13	0.06	12
Solomon Islands	13	0.06	190

[a]Without allowance for postharvest losses or wastage.
Source: FAO (1975).

The principal countries in which yams are important are listed in Table 5. This shows that well over 90% of the world's yam production derives from west Africa, specifically the five countries of the "yam zone" (Coursey, 1967)—Nigeria, Benin, Togo, Ghana, and Ivory Coast. Indeed, Nigeria alone produces three-fourths of the world's yams. Within Nigeria, almost half the total yam crop is grown in the Igbo-speaking areas, so that this single ethnic group produces almost a third of the yams in the world.

Many of the smaller, non-African countries in Table 5 make only a very small contribution to world yam production, but the per capita consumption figures indicate the importance of the crop in the diets of their populations. Outside west Africa, yams are especially important in the Caribbean and in parts of the Pacific, notably Papua New Guinea and the Melanesian and Micronesian islands.

It is often said that yam production is declining. There has indeed been a relative decline over recent decades, compared with staples such as cassava and rice. Nevertheless, as is shown in Table 4 this has not been an absolute decline; indeed, global production has risen slightly in the last two decades. The temporary decline from 1966-1970 can be explained by the civil distrubances and subsequent war in Nigeria that affected mainly the Igbo areas (Onwueme, 1978).

The role of yams in the diet is essentially that of a starchy or carbohydrate staple, and as such it occupies a similar position to cassava, plantains, taro, and sweet potatoes, or to food grains and their products. Almost throughout the West African yam zone, however, yams are much more highly favored than any of the alternatives, and indeed this applies also in most other yam-growing parts of the world. The reasons are traditional or ethnocultural in origin, but are nonetheless sufficient to ensure that yam commands a considerable premium in price over other carbohydrate foods. Market studies in various parts of West Africa have shown that prices for yam can be anything from two to five times those of equicaloric amounts of rice. Yam should not therefore be regarded as tropical equivalent to the potato, which is usually cheap food: it is rather a preferred or prestige food, the consumption of which in quantity is a status symbol (Coursey, 1967).

The high cost of yam compared with other staples is also a reflection of the high production costs: the crop demands good soil; much attention at all stages of growth; staking; and a large amount (sometimes as much as a quarter) of the crop is used up as planting material.

Although the place of the yam in the diet is primarily as a source of a carbohydrate, the protein content is high enough to make a very significant contribution to protein nutrition. It has been estimated (Coursey, 1967) that the quantities of yam that are habitually consumed in those parts of the world where it is a major staple supply almost a quarter of the daily protein requirement.

II. HORTICULTURAL CONSIDERATIONS

A. Climatological and Soil Requirements

The majority of the edible yams are truly tropical plants, and do not thrive at temperatures below 20°C. They are killed by chilling below about 10°C. It has been shown that even within the range 25 to 30°C the growth improves with increasing temperature, and such temperatures are of course normal in most yam-growing countries. Excessively high temperatures, especially if associated with drought can, however, be damaging. An exception is D. opposita which is cultivated in Japan and neighboring countries, and is adapted to growing during warm.

temperate summers and to survival in the dormant condition even through winter frost.

The total rainfall requirement for all economic species is at least 1000 mm/year, and for must cultivars 1200 to 1500 mm is optimal, whereas some yams are grown under as much as 3000 mm. The tuberous development of yams is an adaptation to an annual cycle of growth and dormancy, which occurs during rainy season and dry season, respectively. The lengths of the rainy and dry seasons are in many ways more important than the total rainfall, but the reaction of different species and cultivars to different pluvial regimes varies greatly. Forest species, such as *D. cayenensis* and some forms of *D. trifida* and *D. esculenta*, cannot tolerate a rain-free period of more than 2 or 3 months, whereas most cultivars of *D. alata* and *D. rotundata* need only 7 or 8 months of rain to complete their phase of vegetative growth. Some need even less. Little is known of the photoperiodic response in yams, but it appears that long days favor growth above ground, and short days, tuber formation.

Although adapted to a period of drought which coincides with dormancy, yams are extremely sensitive to droughts occurring during the phase of active growth. Unseasonably dry periods are particularly damaging during the third to fifth months of growth, when the reserves of the planting set are exhausted, but bulking of the new tuber has only just been initiated.

Yams need a reasonably loose, flexible soil of considerable depth: shallow, clayey, or stoney soils impede the development of the tuber or cause it to be malformed. A relatively high nutrient status is required, and under normal tropical subsistence agriculture conditions yams are usually grown as the first crop after the clearing and burning of the forest or bush fallow to take advantage of the accretion of nutrients. Sandy soils are usually too poor to produce a good yam crop, but free drainage is essential, as any degree of waterlogging can lead to rotting of the tubers. Yams are tolerant of a wide range of pH. Moderately acid soils are favored, but they will grow even on limestone-derived soils. The soil in which yams are to be planted is usually formed into mounds or ridges, in order to concentrate the top soil, to increase the depth of soil available for tuber development, and to reduce the chances of waterlogging. Mulching of the heaps or ridges is highly beneficial and virtually essential in yams planted during the dry season in savanna climates, which is normally also the hottest time of the year. This serves to keep soil temperature at a lower level and reduce moisture loss.

Under subsistence farming conditions, fertilizers are rarely applied, apart from the ashes and vegetable refuse from the bush fallow. Yams generally respond to N and K, but relatively slightly to P, as they appear to remove P very efficiently from the soil. Soils over which bush has been burnt are likely to be rich in K, so that a simple application of N as ammonium sulfate is often recommended, although NK and comparable NPK fertilizers are also used. Applications of 100 to 250 kg/ha are used. Fertilizer is most beneficial if applied 2 to 3 months after growth commences, split into two or more applications, or if slow-release fertilizers are used, as the early growth of the plant is supported mainly by the nutrients present in the largeplanting sets used (Coursey, 1967; Onwueme, 1978; Diehl, 1982).

B. Planting Characteristics

Yams are normally grown from vegetative setts, planted manually, either during the dry season or at or shortly after the beginning of the rains. Some farmers presprout the setts in pits or barns before planting, in order to achieve more rapid development. Emergence after the rains begin is followed by rapid growth, and at this stage weed control is most important. Support for the growing vines is normally provided, generally using either stakes or trellises, or strings or light ropes attached to horizontal wires or to trees, but occasionally by allowing the vines to climb on bushes, or on the standing remains of a previous crop such as corn or cotton. Such support is usually considered necessary to ensure good canopy development, but a few cultivars, especially of *D. alata* and *D. esculenta*, are adapted to trailing on the ground without support.

As already mentioned, the ground is usually ridged or formed into mounds: the latter may be as small as 0.5 m high and twice as wide at the base, accommodating a single plant, or well over 1 m high, and of similar proportions, several plants being grown on one mound. Yams are sometimes planted on the flat, expecially in deep, rich soils. They are also, when especially large tubers are needed for cermonial or show purposes, planted in pits which have been filled with organic matter.

When grown as a monoculture, planting density of around 10,000 plants per hectare is normal, but under subsistence farming conditions densities are often low, to allow for intercropping. It is often customary to plant short-lived annual crops between the yams, and harvest them before the main yam harvest, at the same time planting cassava for the next year's crop. There are, however, variations in intercropping practice, while with the increasing exploitation of marketing channels in developing countries, there has been a marked trend towards the cultivation of yams in monoculture, for sale (Coursey, 1967; Onwueme, 1978; Diehl, 1982).

C. Productivity

The productivity of yams varies enormously with species, cultivar, and condition of cultivation. Under optimal conditions, yams are among the most efficient producers of human food (de Vries et al., 1967; Coursey and Martin, 1970). Some recorded high yields obtained for various

Table 6 Selected High Yields of Various
Yam Species

Species	Country	Yield (kg/ha)
D. *alata*	Malaysia	42,500
D. *alata*	Trinidad	46,800
D. *alata*	St. Vincent	58,200
D. *alata*	Fiji	25,400
D. *esculenta*	Malaysia	24,600
D. *esculenta*	Trinidad	32,200
D. *esculenta*	West Irian	70,000
D. *rotundata*	Ghana	20,800
D. *rotundata*	Nigeria	16,200
D. *cayenensis*	Trinidad	31,500

Source: Coursey and Martin (1970).

species are given in Table 6. The yields obtained under normal
farming conditions, however, are usually much lower, and the following ranges can be regarded (Coursey, 1967) as the norm:

West Africa: 7500 to 18,000 kg/ha
Caribbean: 12,500 to 25,000 kg/ha
South East Asia: 20,000 to 30,000 kg/ha

These, however, are gross yields. A very substantial proportion of
the crop has to be reserved as seed material for the following season.
The quantity so used varies, but it is often of the order of 2500 kg/ha,
which has a serious effect on net yield, especially if the gross yield is
low.

It must be emphasized that under subsistence farming conditions
many cultivars are preserved which may be poor or very poor yielders,
but which are valued for early maturity, organoleptic acceptability,
adaptation to peculiar local ecological conditions, or simply for traditional, ethocultural reasons.

The productivity of many early maturing cultivars of D. *rotundata*
is enhanced by the practice of double harvesting. A first harvest is
taken during the growing season, usually about 4 or 5 months after
emergence, by clearing the soil away from the developing tuber and
severing it from the growing plant. Great care has to be taken to
avoid disturbance to the roots. The soil is replaced after removal of
the tuber, and the plant develops one or more further tubers. These
latter are harvested with the main crop yams, when the vines have
completely senesced at the end of the rainy season (Onwueme, 1978).

D. Propagation

In normal farming practice, yam propagation is invariably by the use
of vegetative setts. These sets may be small tubers, comparable to
seed potatoes, or pieces of large tubers, subdivided into smaller fragments. Fragments from the proximal end of the tuber, that is, where
it was joined to the plant, are known as heads, those from the distal
end as tails, and those from the central parts as middles. Bulbils are
also used in those forms that regularly produce them.

Best results are usually obtained with entire, small tubers or with
heads, which latter more readily produce the bud primordia from which
new growth will occur. There is little preference between middles and
tails, although conflicting reports have been published. When tubers
have to be cut to manufacture setts, 2 or 3 days must be allowed before
planting for wound healing and suberization of the cut surface, or
rotting is likely to occur. Sett sizes of 150 to 300 g are normally adopted.
The larger the sett, the more rapid establishment and growth of the
plant may be expected to be, with favorable effects on ultimate yield,
but above 300 g the increased yield per unit weight of planting material is not usually economic. Some farmers use setts as large as 450 g,
however, and for the production of outsize yams for ritual or exhibition purposes, even full-sized tubers of up to 4 kg may be used
(Coursey, 1967; Haynes and Coursey, 1969; Onwueme, 1978).

An exception to this is with *D. trifida*, which is sexually fertile,
and is often grown from seed, although two seasons are often needed
to produce a worthwhile crop. Although under experimental conditions
both *D. rotundata* and *D. cayenensis* have successfully been grown
from seed (Sadik and Okereke, 1975a,b), this has not yet been applied
commercially. Seedling populations are highly variable and contain a
large proportion of plants with undesirable characteristics that need to
be rougued out.

Multiplication of material by conventional vegetative methods is extremely slow. Rapid multiplication of selected or improved strains may
be achieved by means of stem or vine cuttings. These are segments
of mature but still fairly young stems containing one, or occasionally
two, three, or four nodes: they are planted in a mist propagator or
under a cover to retain humidity. Growth commences with the formation of an amorphous mass of tuberlike tissue in the leaf axil, from
which a shoot and ultimately roots emerge. Such cuttings should be
taken early in the growing season to allow a plant of sufficient size to
develop before senescence and dormancy set in, otherwise a tuber
large enough to be viable will not be formed (Ferguson, 1972).

E. Postharvest Handling Methods

The harvesting of yams is almost invariably manual, a simple wooden
or occasionally iron-shod digging stick being the tool most commonly

employed, together with bare hands and a machete under subsistence agriculture conditions. Those species that form several small tubers (e.g., *D. esculenta, D. trifida*) can easily be lifted mechanically with conventional or modified potato-lifting equipment, but the more important large-tubered species (*D. rotundata, D. cayenensis, D. alata*) are extremely difficult to lift mechanically, on account of the very large volume of soil that needs to be shifted. Various tractor-drawn implements have been used experimentally, but none has been entirely successful. Damage to the large tubers has been a major problem.

Yam tubers, being organs of dormancy, have inherently long storage life, which, however, varies greatly between species and cultivars. Natural breakage of dormancy ultimately determines the end of storage life, although attack by fungal and bacterial pathogens or nematodes can enhance losses in storage prior to the end of the natural dormant life (Coursey, 1967; Booth, 1974). The various sprout inhibitors which are so successfully applied to stored potatoes to enhance storage life have little or no effects on yams, as the bud primordia on which they act are not formed in yam tubers until well after harvest (Passam, 1978).

Being crops of peasant farmers, who operate on a small scale, yams are generally stored in comparatively small quantities, and storage techniques are necessarily simple. Centralized storage, as often used for potatoes, is virtually unknown. Even in the markets, yams are usually handled and stored in individual parcels of only a few tons. Storage by traders or middlemen is of short duration, as stocks are turned over rapidly. Yams for consumption outside the harvest season are usually held by the producers on the farms, and are sold off gradually. A substantial proportion of the yam crop never appears even in local trade, but is used by the cultivators or their immediate families.

The fundamental requirements of yam storage differ from those of the temperate root crops that are harvested at the end of summer and are stored through winter so that protection from cold is therefore one of the main requirements. Yams, on the other hand, are grown in tropical countries and are usually stored through the dry season, the hottest part of the year. Protection from cold is not therefore needed; rather, the avoidance of high temperatures and the provision of adequate ventilation are of the greatest importance in yam storage.

The simplest storage technique for yams is simply to leave them in the ground until needed. This practice is still followed to a limited extent in some of the remoter parts of west Africa. Another simple mode of storage, still widely used in some parts of Asia and Africa, consists of stacking the tubers into heaps that may consist of only a few dozen tubers, or may be of several tonnes. The heaps are covered with straw or leafy branches. In many countries yams are stored without any special precautions in ordinary storerooms, sheds, or huts that are not otherwise in use, or are especially constructed for this purpose. Where houses are built on piles or stilts, yams (and other crops) may be stored in the space beneath.

Throught most of west Africa, the most common type of storeroom, and probably also the most satisfactory, in the yam barn. These vary considerably in detail between different parts of the region, but all consist of a vertical or nearly vertical wooden framework to which the tubers are fastened individually by means of string, or local cordage materials. The frames are usually 1 to 2 m in height, but are sometimes as much as 4 m high. They may be as short as 2 m, but are often, according to the amount of material to be stored, very much longer. They are either built in dense shade of trees or provided with a thatched roof. The main vertical poles of the frame are frequently, but not necessarily, chosen from timbers which, left unbarked, will take root and sprout when set in the ground. This reduces the danger of collapse of the structure as a result of termite attack or decay and provides additional shade.

In much of Melanesia, special houses are constructed as yam storerooms. These are generally similar to those used for human habitation, but are often more sophisticated in construction and decoration, a reflection of the great ritual importance attended to yams in that part of the world. As in west Africa, adequate ventilation is recognized as a prime consideration in successful yam storage (Coursey, 1967).

Tubers that are damaged during harvest or transportation or that are found at harvest to be infected with decay are not suitable for storage and should be reserved for early consumption or for processing. Bruising is much more likely to lead to decay than simple cuts, and bruised areas should therefore be cut out and the wounds allowed to dry out and heal (Passam et al., 1976a,b). Treatment of wounds with alkaline material such as lime or wood ashes can reduce the likelihood of reinfection.

During recent years there has been much discussion of the possibilities of using cold storage for yams, especially at centralized depots, which are becoming more needed with increasing commercial development. However, the major economic yams are liable, like many tropical crop products, to chilling injury or low-temperature breakdown (LTB) when exposed to temperatures below around 12°C (Coursey, 1968; Noon, 1978), which indicates that a sophisticated cool storage system with accurate control, comparable to those employed for bananas, would be necessary. Further, the marketing infrastructure in most developing countries is not yet adequate to provide the cool storage chains for distribution. Technically, many problems remain to be solved, in particular in relation to phytopathological aspects, since at low temperatures, even above the chilling limit of about 12°C, attack by psychrophilic pathogens, to which yams have little natural resistence, occurs (Noon, 1978). The prolongation of yam storage life by the use

of gamma irradiation has been studied experimentally, with most encouraging results (Adesuyi and MacKenzie, 1973; Adesuyi, 1978), but
this technique has not yet been put to practical commercial application.

As with other root crops, notably the sweet potato, the losses of
yams in storage may be reduced by subjecting the tubers to a curing
process before they are placed in store. Curing is especially important, indeed virtually essential, if the produce is to be kept below
ambient temperature under artificial cool storage conditions. The
curing process involves holding the tubers at relatively high temperature and humidity for a few days before they are placed in storage,
which results in hardening of the skin and the healing of any wound
damage present by suberization and periderm formation. Curing conditions reported as satisfactory for *D. rotundata* and *D. alata* are 29
to 32°C and 90 to 95% RH for 4 days (Gonzalez and Collazo de Rivera,
1972), 30°C and 91% RH for 7 days or 40°C and 98% RH for only 24 hr
(Been et al., 1977), and 35°C and 85% RH for 4 to 5 days (Passam
et al., 1976a). The latter authors describe and illustrate the histolog-
ical process involved in the would healing. Curing can also be affected
by a few days of exposure to direct sunlight (Been et al., 1977) as
often practiced by subsistence farmers, although prolonged exposure
to the sun can be highly deleterious (Coursey and Nwankwo, 1968).
Less satisfactory results with *D. esculenta* and *D. bulbifera* were obtained by Martin (1974c) at the rather lower curing temperature of 26
to 28°C. It must be noted that curing will only heal clean-cut wounds:
bruised areas will not heal, and must be excised or rapid decay will
set in (Passam et al., 1976b).

III. BIOCHEMICAL AND NUTRITIONAL COMPOSITION

A. Nutritional Composition Tables

Yams are essentially carbohydrate foods, and the main component of
the tuber, apart from water, is starch. Protein content, though variable between cultivars is generally of the same order of magnitude as
in potatoes or sweet potatoes, and so, where yams are consumed in
substantial quantities, a worthwhile contribution to protein nutrition
is made. The ranges within which typical proximate analyses for the
main edible yam species fall are indicated in Table 7. These figures
already show that, although there is a considerable variation in proximate composition among cultivars within any species, there is little
consistent difference between species.

The indications of per capita consumption of yam given in Table 5
are that in the major yam-producing countries of west Africa, Melanesia,
and the Caribbean quantities of the order of 0.5 to 1 kg of yam may be
eaten daily, as it must be borne in mind that in all these countries
there are substantial elements in the population who seldom or never

Table 7 Summarized Proximate Analyses of Yam

Species	Moisture content (%)	Carbohydrate (%)	Fat (%)	Crude protein (%)	Crude fiber (%)	Ash (%)
Alata	65-73	22-29	0.03-0.27	1.12-2.78	0.65-1.40	0.67-2.06
Rotundata/cayenensis	58-80	15-23	0.05-0.12	1.09-1.99	0.35-0.79	0.68-2.56
Opposita	70-80	16-29	0.06-1.10	1.11-3.10	0.33-1.00	0.69-1.10
Esculenta	67-81	17-25	0.04-0.29	1.29-1.87	0.18-1.51	0.50-1.24
Bulbifera	63-67	27-33	0.04	1.12-1.50	0.70-0.73	1.08-1.51
Dumetorum	79	17	0.28	2.78	0.30	0.72
Trifida	–	38	0.44	2.54	–	–

Source: Coursey (1967).

Table 8 Nutritional Value of 1 kg of Yam Daily

| | | Intake | |
	Assumed composition	Total	Recommended British Medical Association daily allowance (%)
Kilojoules	4.5 Kj/g	4500 Kj	About 35
Protein	2%	20 g	23
Calcium	15 mg/100 g	150 mg	19
Iron	1 mg/100 g	10 mg	84
Vitamin A	Trace		Negligible[a]
Thiamine	0.1 mg/100 g	1 mg	84
Riboflavin	0.03 mg/100 g	0.3 mg	17
Nicotinic acid	0.4 mg/100 g	4 mg	33
Vitamin C	5 mg/100 g	50 mg	More than adequate
Vitamin D	Trace		Negligible

[a]Except in the case of some yellow-fleshed cultivars of *D. cayenensis* as discussed in the text.
Source: Coursey (1967).

eat yams. Table 8 shows the contribution that a kilogram of yam represents in a typical diet.

Yam is thus seen to be a useful food in ways other than as a simple source of carbohydrate or energy. It is, nevertheless, far from being a balanced food, and deficiency diseases, especially kwashiorkor, are prevalent in yam-growing areas, especially among the poorer elements of the population. Yam is, however, greatly superior to cassava, expecially with regard to protein content, and the displacement of yam by this more easily grown crop that is taking place may well be a factor in the spread of kwashiorkor in many tropical countries. It is also an important source of vitamin C and to a lesser extent of other vitamins and minerals.

B. Changes in Nutrients

1. During Development

Little is known of the changes in nutritional value of the yam tuber during its development. In general, immature tubers are of higher-moisture content than mature ones, and are therefore softer, more easily damaged. Immature tubers will not store well, as they have not yet entered the dormant phase (in which the abscisic acid metabolism appears to be involved) and have very high respiratory rates, and are liable, once detached from the plant, to invasion of pathogens.

The growth physiology of the yam plant is such that the proximal (head) end of the tuber consists of older tissue than the distal (tail). Even in mature tubers, therefore, the tail tissue is softer and more easily damaged, and there is a marked gradient in moisture content down the tuber from head to tail. In the most important species, D. rotundata, immature tissue is often bitter in taste, and the extreme tail ends even of mature tubers are often sufficiently bitter to be cut off and rejected when the yam is being prepared for the table.

2. During Postharvest Handling

Similarly, little is known of nutrient changes during postharvest handling and storage of fresh yam tubers. Their storage, as already mentioned, depends on their dormancy, but even though the tubers in storage are dormant, they are still metabolically active. In particular, respiration results in steady loss of carbohydrate as carbon dioxide and water, while at the same time a transpiratory loss of water occurs. These respiratory and transpiratory losses result in a destruction of edible material, which under normal storage conditions can often reach 10% after 3 months, and up to 25% after 5 months (Coursey, 1961; Passam et al., 1978). Relatively little change in the actual nutritional value of the material remaining after this metabolic loss takes place, nevertheless (Gonzalez and Collazo de Rivera, 1972). Free sugars tend to increase as the end of the dormant phase approaches (Ugochukwu et al., 1977).

3. During Processing and Storage

Very little seroius work has been undertaken on factors involved in the processing of yams or in the storage of processed products; thus, nutrient changes are poorly understood. It may be presumed that high-temperature processes such as drum-drying will denature proteins and cause losses of vitamin C, but no definite information is available. Air-drying at 42°C and freeze-drying of thin slices of D. opposita, however, were found to result in only slight loss of vitamin C (Misawa and Matsubara, 1965). Any processing is liable to lead to changes in starch properties and often to rupture of the starch granules, but this is discussed in more detail subsequently.

Most processed products made from yams, whether traditional flours or more sophisticated products (most of which have only been made at experimental or pilot plant level), are relatively stable in storage. Various flake-type products are quoted as retaining their acceptability when stored at tropical ambients for periods of 3 months (Onayemi and Potter, 1974), 6 months (Afable, 1970), or even a year (Gooding, 1972),

although Steele and Sammy (1976b) found that their product stored
well in glass jars for up to 6 months but showed some discoloration
and rancidity after the same period when kept in sealed polyethylene
bags.

C. Biochemical Composition

1. Principal Constituents: Carbohydrates, Proteins, Lipids,
   Acids, Pigments, Etc.

Starch is the major component of yam tubers, and the properties of
Dioscorea starches, especially their rheological properties, are of
importance in relation to processing characteristics. Rheological examination of starch-water pastes from four species of yam (Rasper and
Coursey, 1967a) showed that viscosities obtained with *D. rotundata*
starches were significantly greater than those of other species, and
the gel strengths were also moderately high (see Table 9). This relates to the fact that this is the preferred species for the production
of fufu, for which a stiff dough is required. *D. alata* exhibited a very
high gel strength but a lower viscosity, but the starches of the other
two species studied, *D. esculenta* and *D. dumetorum*, were found to
have low viscosities and low gel strengths. Nevertheless, most yam
starches give viscous pastes with high gel strengths compared with
the starches of other tropical starch crops (Rasper, 1969a). These
rheological characteristics can be related to the swelling and solubility
properties of the starch (Rasper, 1969b) and also to granule size
(Rasper, 1971) (see Table 10). The starch granules of *D. rotundata,*
D. cayenensis, and *D. alata* are large (up to 50 μm) whereas those of
D. esculenta and *D. dumetorum* are much smaller (1 to 5 μm).
   Starch of *D. alata* has also been shown to be highly heat-stable.
This is indicated by the absence of a viscosity peak when the starch
is subjected to heating: instead the viscosity increases throughout
both cooking and cooling cycles (Cruz-Cay and Gonzalez, 1974). The
desirable glutinous texture of yam fufu is rapidly lost under normal
holding conditions, on account of starch retrogradation, as has been
confirmed by microscopy and x-ray diffraction studies (Ayernor et al.,
1974). These textural changes in the dough structure upon retrogradation are temperature-dependent and increase in rapidity with decreasing
storage temperature. Rapid retrogradation in *Dioscorea* starches was
also noted by Rasper (1969a), and it has been suggested that the high
content of linear amylose compared with branched-chain amylopectin
in the starch is responsible for this property (Cruz-Cay and
Gonzalez, 1974). The rate of retrogradation of yam starches is several
times faster than that of most other starches. The amylose contents of the
starches of *D. alata*, *D. rotundata*, and *D. cayenensis* lie between 21 and
24%, those of *D. esculenta* and *D. dumetorum* are 14 to 15%, and *D. trifida*
10% (Seidemann, 1964; Coursey, 1967; Rasper and Coursey, 1967a).

Table 9 Rheological Properties of Various Yam Starches

Species and cultivar	Pasting temp. °C	Viscosity (Brabender units)		Gel strength (ml) after		
		On attaining 95°C	Maximum reached before cooling	24 hr	96 hr	168 hr
D. rotundata						
Puna	76°	450	630	8.8	13.6	14.1
Labreko	78–79°	260	470	4.3	6.2	8.0
Kplinjo	77°	330	490	10.6	12.7	13.3
Tantanpruka	79°	610	650	12.4	17.2	20.5
Tempi	80–82°	430	520	7.5	10.5	10.8
D. alata						
White fleshed	85°	25	110	14.8	16.5	17.2
Purple fleshed	81°	80	200	14.8	18.5	19.4
D. esculenta	82°	25	55	2.5	4.0	4.6
D. dumetorum	82°	25	25	—	—	—

Source: Rasper and Coursey (1967 a).

Table 10 Gelatinization Characteristics of Yam Starches

Species	Pasting temperature (°C)[a]	Maximum viscosity (BU)[a]	Period of increasing viscosity (min)[a]	Apparent rate of viscosity increase	At 95°C Swelling	At 95°C Critical concentration value
D. rotundata	73.5	980	22.5	2.3	24.9	4.0
D. esculenta	78.5	500	Steadily increasing	Steadily increasing	23.0	4.3
D. cayenensis	75.0	690	16.5	2.4	21.3	4.7
D. alata	77.5	620	Steadily increasing	Steadily increasing	18.3	5.5
D. dumetorum	83.0	185	Steadily increasing	Steadily increasing	13.9	7.2

[a]Data obtained from Brabender Viscograph curves.
Source: Rasper (1969b).

Although the major part of the carbohydrate fraction of yam tubers consists of starch, some free sugars are also present, which are intermediates in the formation and breakdown of starch. The free sugars consist mainly of sucrose and glucose, with the former predominating traces of fructose and mannose have also been detected. The level of free sugar in the tuber varies with its physiological condition, but in most of the species which have been studied is less, often much less, than 1%. An exception is *D. esculenta* whose tubers contain enough sugar to give them a positively sweet taste, although total free sugar levels of around 5% would be more usual in the species (Coursey, 1967; Ketiku and Oyenuga, 1970).

It has already been indicated that, although yams are primarily carbohydrate staples, their protein contents are sufficiently high to be of dietary significance. Indeed, it has been pointed out by Idusogie (1971) that under optimal west African conditions yam can provide more protein per hectare per year than maize, rice, or sorghum, or even than soybeans. Actual protein contents vary very considerably between both species and between cultivars of a particular species: Intercultivar variation is indeed so great that it is difficult to see any consistent differences between the major species, but from the observations available to date, it appears that the large-tubered *D. alata*, *D. rotundata*, and *D. cayenensis* generally have rather higher protein levels than *D. esculenta or D. trifida* (Martin and Thompson, 1971).

A considerable number of yam samples have been examined for the amino acid composition of their protein fractions (Martin and Thompson, 1973; Splittstoesser and Martin, 1975; Splittstoesser et al., 1973; Splittstoesser, 1976; Francis et al., 1975). As with total protein, considerable variation between species and cultivars has been reported, but the figures given in Table 11 for essential amino acid composition may be taken as fairly typical for the major economic species. Further details including concentrations of nonessential amino acids may be found in the references cited. Like most other root crop proteins yam proteins are generally deficient from the nutritional point of view in the sulfur-containing amino aicds, methionine and cysteine, and also in tryptophan. Since yam is usually eaten with a stew containing meat and/or fish, the total diet will probably be adequately balanced with regard to essential amino acids. Yam proteins are relatively rich in leucine, lysine, phenylalanine, and threonine.

The lipid content of yam tuber tissue is very low, that present being entirely the structural lipid of the cell membranes. Although of importance in the cellular metabolism of the tuber, these lipids are of no nutritional significance. The fatty acid composition of the lipids of four of the major edible species have recently been determined (Opute and and Osagie, 1978) and are given in Table 12.

Yam tuber tissue is essentially neutral in reaction, and free organic acids, such as occur in many fruits, are not present in appreciable

Table 11 Essential Amino Acids in Various Yam Species (g amino acid per 100 g protein)

Amino acid	FAO reference protein[a]	Species and cultivar			
		D. alata	*D. rotundata*	*D. esculenta*	*D. trifida*
Leucine	4.8	7.5	7.6	8.6	8.6
Lysine	4.2	5.2	5.4	4.0	4.6
Methionine	2.2	1.9	1.5	1.6	1.3
Cysteine	2.0	0.5	0.1	0.5	1.6
Phenylalanine	2.8	5.8	6.1	5.9	5.2
Threonine	2.8	4.2	3.9	3.9	5.0
Tyrosine	2.8	3.2	2.8	3.0	3.1
Valine	4.2	4.2	4.6	5.3	5.1
Isoleucine	4.2	3.7	4.2	4.3	3.9
Tryptophan	1.4	0.6	0.3	1.1	0.2

[a]*FAO Nutritional Studies 24* (1970).

Table 12 Fatty Acid Composition of Yam Tuber Lipids

Fatty acid	*D. alata*	*D. rotundata*	*D. cayenensis*	*D. bulbifera*
Lauric (12:0)	Trace	Trace	Trace	1.8
Myristic (14:0)	Trace	Trace	Trace	1.0
Palmitic (16:0)	34.5	31.6	30.6	27.8
Stearic (18:0)	3.2	1.5	1.5	1.2
Oleic (18:1)	8.1	6.5	9.5	25.1
Linoleic (18:2)	48.5	51.9	52.6	33.9
Linolenic (18:3)	5.7	8.5	5.1	7.6

Source:Opute and Osagie (1978).

quantities. Ascorbic acid (vitamin C) is present in fresh yams in substantial quantities, sufficient to be nutritionally highly significant. As indicated in Table 8, the quantities of the vitamin supplied by a diet based on yam as the main carbohydrate component are at least as high as the total recommended intake. Reported levels of ascorbic acid in yams from various sources in the most detailed study made so far (Coursey and Aidoo, 1966) are summarized in Table 13, which also indicated the relatively slight losses associated with different cooking methods. Much higher losses on cooking have, however, been reported by le Berre et al. (1968).

Two types of pigment are known to occur in yams, anthocyanins and carotenoids. Several cultivars of D. alata and D. trifida contain anthocyanins, which impart a pink or purplish-red color to the tuber tissue. The quantity of anthocyanin varies greatly between cultivars. At one extreme there is only a thin, pinkish layer immediately beneath the skin, the remainder of the flesh being white, whereas at the other extreme, the entire flesh of the tuber is deep purple or purplish-red. There are many intermediate forms. The pigments consist of a mixture of cyanidin glycosides, of which cyanidin-3:5 diglucoside predominates in one West African cultivar of D. alata examined (Rasper and Coursey, 1967b) and ferrulic acid cyanidin-3-gentiobioside ester in a West Indian cultivar of the same species (Imbert and Seaforth, 1968). The anthocyanins of D. trifida have not so far been identified, but from the similarity in color has probably closely related compounds. Purple-fleshed forms of D. bulbifera are also known that presumably contain anthocyanins.

Carotenoid pigments are responsible for the yellow color of the tuber flesh in most cultivars of D. cayenensis (which is generally known as

Table 13 Levels of Ascorbic Acid and Retention During Cooking in Yams

Species	Ascorbic acid (mg/100 g)
D. rotundata	6.5-11.6
D. cayenensis	4.5-8.2
D. alata	5.0-8.2

Method of Cooking	Retention of ascorbic acid (%)
Boiling (without peeling)	95
Frying (in palm oil)	93
Roasting or baking	85
Boiling (after peeling)	65

Source: Coursey and Aidoo (1966).

the yellow yam) and of the bulbils and tubers in some forms of D. bul-bifera. The pigments of the former species include β-carotene (pro-vitamin A) in nutritionally significant quantities of between 0.4 and 1.4 mg/100 g (Martin and Ruberte, 1975), in addition to the xantho-phylls and their esters, mainly lutein, violaxanthin, neoxanthin, auroxanthin, and cryptoxanthin, which have no nutritional significance (Martin et al., 1974), and are present in the latter species.

2. Flavor Compounds

Like most staple carbohydrate foods, yams have a bland flavor, and their acceptability depends more on their textural characteristics than on flavor, so long as off-flavors, such as might be caused by decay or the bitter principles referred to later, are absent. Only two inves-tigations have been made so far of the compounds involved in the flavor of cooked D. alata and D. rotundata, those of Osinowo (1977) and Gramshaw and Osinowo (1982). They identified 35 compounds in D. alata and 30 in D. rotundata. These included 8 terpenes, 4 ketones, 10 aldehydes, 5 alcohols, 4 sulfur compounds, 2 aromatic hydrocarbons, a furan, and 3-nonyne; all the compounds identified in D. rotundata were present also in D. alata as would be expected from the similarity between the aromas of the two species during cooking.

The major flavor volatiles in both species include: 2(or 3)-methyl-butanal, α-pinene, β-pinene, 1-pentanol, 1-hexanol, hexanal, 2-pen-tylfuran, 2-heptanone, 2(or 3)-methylbutanol, 2-heptenal, 2-oxetenal, 2-nenenal, 1-octen-3-ol, benzaldehyde, linalool, α-terpineol, 4-terpineol, phenylacetaldehyde, 2,4-decadienal, and 4-phenylbutan-2-one. The complexity of chromatograms obtained suggested, however, that many further unidentified components are present, at very low levels, whereas sensory evidence suggests that some further powerful aroma components (possibility oxygenated pyrazines) are present a levels too low to be detected instrumentally. Yams have very low odor intensity, which was reflected in the low yields of volatiles obtained and pre-sented a major problem during the study.

The bitter principles that occur in immature tuber tissue of D. ro-tundata and D. cayenensis, and to a lesser extent in some cultivars of D. alata, have already been mentioned. The amounts present in young tubers, or the tips of mature ones, can be sufficient to render them completely unpalatable. The nature of these bitter principles is un-known, but phenolic or tanninlike compounds have been suggested, as it is known that relatively high concentrations of polyphenols occur in the meristematic tissue of the developing tuber tips. Bitter sub-stances also occur in the bulbils of some forms of D. bulbifera to suf-ficient quantity to render them unpalatable. These have been studied in some detail, and are found to include a previously unknown group of three furanoid norditerpenes, designated diosbulbins a, b, and c (Martin, 1974b). It is possible that these or similar compounds are involved in the bitterness of other species.

3. Toxic Principles

The major food yams are free from any known toxicity, the bitter
principles just mentioned being unpalatable but harmless. Many wild
yams, and those which are cultivated only on a relatively small scale
are, however, highly toxic owing to the presence of alkaloids which
also confer a bitter taste but must not be confused with the substances
already discussed. The most important species in this category are
the African *D. dumetorum* (often known as the bitter yam), which contains the alkaloid dihydrodioscorine, and the Asiatic *D. hispida,* which
contains the closely related dioscorine, $C_{13}H_{19}O_2H$. These compounds
have also been reported in *D. sansibarensis* and some forms of *D. bulbifera* (Coursey, 1967; Martin and Degras, 1978b) and are probably
present in several other species which are known to be toxic but which
have not been scientifically studied. These alkaloids are water-soluble
and can relatively easily be removed by soaking the sliced or grated
tubers in several changes of water, salt water often being considered
more efficacious than fresh, although running water in streams is
sometimes employed. It is interesting to note, however, that many
cultivated forms of *D. dumetorum* are sufficiently free from toxicity to
be eaten with no more precautions than thorough boiling.

Many wild *Dioscorea* species contain steroidal sapogenins, some of
which are exploited commercially as intermediates for pharmaceuticals.
Although some of these compounds are hemolytic poisons and are used
for poisoning fish, they are not toxic when ingested. Such compounds
are absent from the main edible yams, or are present only in minute
quantities (Coursey, 1967; Coursey and Martin, 1970; Anon., 1972).

4. Enzymes

The enzyme systems of yams have received very little study. The
most important from the point of view of food use of yam tubers are
those involved in the starch-sugar conversion and other aspects of
the respiratory process; the related enzymes involved in wound healing;
and the phenoloxidases which are responsible for browning reactions
in the flesh of the tubers of some cultivars.

The activities of phosphorylase, hexokinase, glucose-6-phosphate
(G-6-P) dehydrogenase, and alcohol dehydrogenase in *D. rotundata*
have been studied by Ugochukwu et al. (1977). In all cases, activities
were substantially higher by a factor of 2 to 4 in tubers which had
been kept for a year than in freshly harvested material, while at the
time of the metabolic activity peak associated with the breakage of
dormancy, phosphorylase activity reached 40 times its level in fresh
material, and hexokinase, 11 times. The authors suggest that the
high levels of G-6-P dehydrogenase and their increase with tuber age
indicate that the pentose phosphate pathway is of major importance in
the carbohydrate metabolism of yam tubers and that the contribution
of this pathway increases with age. It was also found that levels of

the same enzymes were much lower, by an order of magnitude, in tubers of *D. cayenensis* and *D. alata*.

Enzymatic changes associated with wound repair and the accompanying suberization have been investigated in *D. rotundata* by Passam et al. (1976a). During the wound repair process, there is a rapid increase in tissue respiratory activity and also a buildup of free sugars near the wound, indicative of enhanced α-amylase activity. Simultaneously, a strong invertase activity develops in the wounded tissue. The latter effect has been studied in more detail by Passam and Barrett (1977), and invertase activity was shown to develop during the aging of tissue discs from tubers of this species and also *D. cayenensis* and *D. alata*. The invertase is present in both bound and soluble forms, as has been reported in other plant storage tissues.

It is well known that some cultivars of most edible species of yam show a rapid browning reaction in the tuber flesh when it is cut and exposed to the air, whereas other, very similar, cultivars do not show this effect. The browning reaction is usually strongest at or near the extreme head and tail ends (i.e., in the regions of meristematic tissue). The effect is usually attributed to enzymatic oxidation of polyphenols present in the tissue. Polyphenol oxidases were reported in *D. opposita* by Imakawa (1967) and by Neumann et al. (1969). These were found to be specific to *o*-diphenols, although Tono (1970), who isolated dopamine from the same species, found that the polyphenol oxidases do have a high degree of activity towards this compound. Although catechins and associated tannins were detected, he considered enzymatic oxidation of dopamine to be the main feature in the browning reaction.

More recently, several African species, *D. bulbifera*, *D. cayenensis*, *D. rotundata*, *D. esculenta*, and *D. dumetorum*, have been studied (Anosike and Ayaebene, 1981), and all were found to have significant levels of polyphenol oxidase activity. That in the first-named species was an order of magnitude higher than in the others, which correlates well with the intense browning reaction shown by bulbils of this species. Within *D. alata*, it has similarly been shown (Adamson and Abigor, 1980) that cultivars having a high level of polyphenol oxidase activity are more susceptible to browning that those with lower levels. These authors refer to the enzyme as a catecholase and like that found by Anosike and Ayaebene (1981) regarded it as specific to *o*-diphenols. However, de la Rosa and Emiola (1980) found that the polyphenol oxidases isolated from *D. rotundata* did also show some activity towards some monophenols, although these were poor substrates compared with catechol. The browning effect was inhibited by bisulphite, β-mercaptoethanol, EDTA, thiourea, and cysteine. The main substrates for these enzymes in several yam species appear to be catechins (Ozo et al., in press).

It has also been suggested (Okagami, 1978) that polyphenol oxidases may be involved in the process of dormancy, apparently being one of

the complex of dormancy-inducing proteins. Levels of polyphenol
oxidase activity in the bulbils were observed to decline as sprouting
commenced.

IV. PRESERVATION METHODS

In the discussion of the preservation of yams by any form of processing, it must be emphasized that by far the greater part of the world's
yam crop is kept, and eventually consumed, in the fresh state. Traditionally, processed yam products are made in most-yam growing areas
of the world, but only in very limited quantities, usually as a way of
utilizing tubers that are not fit for storage. Industrially, several investigations into the manufacture of more sophisticated products have
been made, and a number of pilot scale processing operations initiated,
but none of these operations has long survived on an ongoing commercial basis. The salient aspects of what is known of yam processing
are discussed next, but further details may be obtained from a recent
review of the subject by Coursey and Ferber (1979).

A. Village Level

1. Products: Uses and Dietary Significance

The only processed yam product traditionally made at village level is
yam flour, the preparation of which is described in the next section.
As indicated previously, flours of this type are prepared in limited
quantities in most yam-growing districts, but mainly as a means of
preserving yams that are not suitable to be stored in the fresh condition and are in excess of immediate requirements. Typically, tubers
which have been badly damaged during harvesting or have been found
to be already partially rotten when harvested are used. In these
situations the yam flour, when rehydrated, is regarded simply as a
substitute, usually an inferior substitute, for fresh yam. An exception to this is the Yoruba-speaking area of the southwestern part of
Nigeria, especially Oyo and Ogun states, and most especially the
traditional heartland of the Yoruba people, around Ife, Ilesha, and Ede.
Here, yam flour is positively favored, and about a quarter of the total
yam crop of this area is processed into yam flour. The reconstituted
food is known in Yoruba as *amala*. Yam flour is also manufactured and
used to a much smaller extent in Benue state of Nigeria, and in Ghana,
where it is known as Yam Kokonte (Coursey, 1967). As the flour consists essentially of the entire dry matter of the peeled yam tuber, it is
presumably nutritionally similar to fresh yam, but no studies are
available on any loss of nutrients that may occur in processing.

2. Preservation Methods and Processing

To prepare yam flour, the tubers are sliced to the thickness of about 10 mm (more or less, according to whether the weather is hot and dry, which will give quick drying, or not). The slices are then parboiled and generally allowed to cool down in the water in which they are parboiled. This heating deactivates the enzymes and may partially denature the proteins. The parboiled slices are then peeled and dried in the sun to a low-moisture content.

The dried slices, which are almost as hard as soft wood, are then ground into flour. Traditionally, this is done in a wooden mortar with a wood pestle, with repeated sieving of the product, but today small hand-operated or engine-driven corn mills or hammer mills are increasingly being used.

3. Product Stability and Spoilage Problems

The processed product may be stored either as the actual flour or as the dried slices from which it is prepared. Both are essentially inert, stable products and can be stored for several months but present entirely different storage problems from fresh yam tubers. The processed material naturally suffers no autolytic deterioration while the plant pathogens which attack living tubers have no effect on the processed product. Other food-spoilage organisms may sometimes occur but should not have much effect if the material has been properly dried. The critical moisture content for safe storage has not been determined, but it has been determined in similar materials to be 12 to 14%.

Insect attack, however, can be serious. A large number of stored-products insects have been reported as infesting yam flour, the most common being *Sitophilus zeamays* Mots, *Tribolium castaneum* (Herbst.), *Lasioderma serricorne* F., and *Dinoderus* species. Pieces of dried yam arriving at mills are often riddled with holes caused by the former insect, and stores where yam flour is kept in normal sacks are usually heavily infested with one or more species. Losses from insect attack have been reported to be as high as 30 to 38% in 4 months of storage (Adesuyi, 1965). This insect attack can fairly easily be controlled, first by milling the dried yam pieces shortly after preparation, before any infestation has a chance to build up, and second by packing the flour immediately after preparation in insect-proof containers, such as polyethylene bags or polyethylene-lined sacks. Infested materials could be fumigated (e.g., with methyl bromide). Rodent attack, especially on the unmilled pieces, may be severe, but can be minimized by good storage hygiene and by conventional control measures, such as the proofing of the storage buildings or the use of warfarin-type poisons.

4. Potential for Scaling-Up Process to Industrial Level and Anticipated Difficulties

Outside the Yoruba-speaking areas of southwestern Nigeria, as possibly parts of Ghana, yam flour is probably not a sufficiently popular product to be worthy of major attention. It must also be borne in mind that many attempts to process tropical food crops, including yams, at the industrial level have failed partly because of difficulties in obtaining adequate supplied of raw material; partly because insufficient attention is paid to acceptability considerations; and partly because, even where the product is acceptable, a factory-made product often cannot compete economically with the traditional product made within the subsistence economy using family labor which is either uncosted or costed as well below official rates by the vendors.

Within the areas where a demand exists for yam flour, the market would probably be better served by the upgrading and refinement of the traditional process in small-scale plants located in the rural areas than by large-scale factories. Rural location should ease the problems of raw material supply, while the transporation to urban centers for a compact, stable, dry product is obviously more economical than that of the bulky, easily damaged, fresh tubers, that consist of at least two-thirds water and waste. Such small rural factories need not be devoid of technical sophistication (Olorunda, 1979). The traditional village-scale industry in Nigeria is already adopting some technological innovations, notably the use of engine-driven mills for grinding the dried yam slices to give a more uniform product and the use of plastic bags or plastic-film-lined sacks for storing the product to reduce or eliminate insect infestation. The use of a sulfite dip for the fresh yam slices should improve product quality but is not usually adopted.

Further modifications have been suggested by Jarmai and Montford (1968). These include the precooking of the peeled yam under controlled conditions and mashing and oven-drying the mash at 50 to 70°C for 6 to 8 hr to a final moisture content of below 10%. The authors claim that their product, when reconstituted with water, was indistinguishable from fufu made from fresh yam.

B. Industrial Level

Yams have not as yet been processed to any significant extent on a commercial basis at the industrial level, although the subject has attracted considerable interest in many parts of the world and a substantial amount of research has been done. The manufacture of processed products with longer storage lives than fresh tubers could do much to reduce food losses and also to stabilize seasonal fluctuations in supply. Dehydrated products could also minimize marketing and transportation costs, which is of increasing importance with the rapid growth of urban populations in tropical countries, while changing social conditions, especially in the urban centers, provide a stimulus to the production of convenience foods that are easily prepared in the home.

Pilot-scale commercial factories producing dehydrated yam products of a more sophisticated nature than the traditional yam flours already discussed have been operated in the Ivory Coast and in Nigeria, using *D. rotundata,* and in Barbados, using *D. alata.* None of these has remained in commercial operation for more than a few years, however, for the reasons outlined in the last section, especially problems of the supply of raw material at economical prices; as far as is known none is in production today. It is understood that a second processing operation has recently been attempted independently in Nigeria, but no details are currently available.

The manufacture of fried products from *D. alata* has recently been attempted in Puerto Rico. Although the scale of operation is only small, it is mentioned here, as these are nontraditional yam products. Both chips (in European English usage, crisps) and French fries (in European English usage, chips) have been manufactured (Martin and Ruberte, 1972; Rodriguez-Sosa et al., 1973).

Canning of yams in brine has been attempted in Nigeria, Ghana, and Jamaica, but with little success, on account of breaking up of the yam pieces, and the liberation of gelatinized starch into the brine during the retorting (Coursey and Ferber, 1979). These authors also discuss other minor industrial utilization of yams that have been proposed, such as incorporation in bread, and the manufacture of edible starch from the toxic *D. hispida* and *D. dumetorum.*

Brief mention should also be made of a nontraditional industrial use of yams peculiar to the Philippines. A particular deep-purple-fleshed cultivar of *D. alata* is used, together with vanilla, as a flavoring and coloring agent, in the manufacture of a variety of ice cream which is locally very popular. In recent years, a dehydrated product prepared by drying precooked, grated yam at 50°C has been used instead of fresh yam, with satisfactory results (Afable, 1970).

1. Process Technology

Only the dehydrated products previously mentioned are sufficiently important to warrant detailed discussion. It was anticipated (Coursey, 1966) that the established techniques used for potato and sweet potato processing should also be applicable to yams, and the matter was investigated further by Abe (1973). References to work on these other crops are given by Onayemi and Potter (1974). A considerable amount of research has subsequently been done mainly on the production, by drum-drying, of instant yam flakes, which are capable of rehydration to yield the desired product without further preparation. The first factory operation in Nigeria and also those in Barbados and Puerto Rico adopted this method of processing.

The first industrially made yam product, however, manufactured in the Ivory Coast in the mid-1960s under the trade name Foutoupret, was produced by air-drying precooked grated or mashed yam on trays in cabinets. No further details of the process are available, and the product has not been marketed for some years.

The industrial manufacutre of instant yam in Barbados has been described by Gooding (1972). This process, which was developed in collaboration with the Tropical Products Institute and the University of the West Indies, involved drum-drying of mashed yam (*D. alata*), and the factory operated for several years in the late 1960s and early 1970s under the aegis of the Agricultural Development Corporation. A generally similar process was used in a privately owned plant in Nigeria to produce a flake product sold under the trade name Poundoyam from *D. rotundata*. Studies on drum-drying of yam have also been conducted in Trinidad and Puerto Rico.

The first stage in any yam processing operation, after procurement, sorting, and washing, is peeling. The efficiency of the peeling process affects both the quality of the finished product and the amount of waste. Hand-peeling is labor-intensive and wasteful (if not carefully done, it can involve losses of 15 or even 25%), whereas mechanized peeling is difficult to apply owing to the irregular shapes and sizes of yam tubers. Lye-peeling, which utilizes combined chemical and thermal action on the tuber peel, is therefore a more attractive option.

The relationships between alkali concentration in the lye and exposure time in the boiling solutions required for satisfactory peeling of *D. alata* cultivar 'Florido' were stidued by Rivera-Ortiz and Gonzalez (1972). Various alternative peeling conditions were identified, all of which gave substantially lower wastage (between 12.2 and 14.4% peeling loss) than hand-peeling, which gave 22.2% losses on average. The lye treatment did not cause any loss of sensory quality, or increased acidity or hardness of the peeled yam. The process was less efficient with tubers which had been in storage for more than 28 days. On the basis of studies of the effect of varietal differences on the lye-peeling of yams, a 10% lye solution at 104°C, with varying immersion times depending upon cultivar, was recommended by Steele and Sammy (1976a). Peeling losses were reduced compared with hand-peeling, and there was insignificant retention of alkali from the lye in the tuber flesh. The proximal end of the tuber consisting of older tissue showed greater resistance to peeling than the distal end. Yams were successfully lye-peeled during the commercial running of the Barbados plant. After peeling, whether by hand or lye, the peeled tubers are washed, trimmed, and cut into conveniently sized slices, pieces or diced. Sulfite is often added to the wash water to inhibit enzymic browning.

Cooking by boiling may be conducted at atmospheric pressure or, more usually, in pressure cookers under steam pressure of 5 to 10 psig. In situations where it is desired to produce a nonsticky type

of product (see subsequent discussion), the inclusion in the process
of a short, distinct, precooking stage, prior to steam-cooking, appears
to lower the amount of starch damage in the final product made from
D. alata. Precooking at 71.1°C for up to 25 min was found to cause
partial starch gelatinization and so conferred resistance to further
damage during processing (Rodriguez-Sosa et al., 1974). In general,
the more intense the cooking process, the greater the stickiness of
the final product. Relationships between steam pressure in cooking on
the properties of both the dried product and the reconstituted product
made from D. rotundata were demonstrated by Ayernor (1976), a
summary of some of whose results is given in Table 14. A similar
dependence of stickiness on the degree of starch damage, which increased with increasing cooking time, was found by Rodriguez-Sosa
and Gonzalez (1972) with D. alata cultivar 'Florido.' The gelatinization temperature of the mashed yam decreased with increased cooking
time, indicating partial starch gelatinization during cooking which
gives rise to a greater degree of cell rupture during subsequent
dehydration. Stickiness can be a desirable quality, or otherwise,
according to the type of product desired. The cooked product is
then mashed and converted into a slurry. It was found in the
operation of the Barbados plant, which processed D. alata, that
ricing followed by gentle mashing in a mechanized mixer gave the
best results (Gooding, 1972).

Most investigational work on the drum-drying of yams has used
double drum-drying. Using D. rotundata, Onayemi and Potter
(1974) produced a satisfactory, sticky, fufu-type product with a
Blue Value Index (BVI) of 235. Typical operational data from their
work are quoted in Table 15. Similar processing conditions, but
using a slurry of 15% solids content, were used by Ayernor (1976).
These studies formed the basis for the Nigerian Poundoyam operation.
Double drum-drying was used by Steele and Sammy (1976 b) in
Trinidad to investigate three cultivars of D. alata and one each of
D. rotundata, D. trifida, and D. esculenta; only two cultivars of
the former species gave fluffy products that might be acceptable in
Caribbean markets, and all had BVI values of several hundred.

During the development of the Barbados instant yam process,
after initial trials with double drum-drying, a single drum-dryer
was used. Although problems were experienced with the application
of the yam slurry from the feed rolls, these were essentially solved
by sing a very close setting (i.e., using the last applicator as a
pressure roll). The operating conditions given in Table 15 gave a
satisfactory product, with a BVI of 100 to 140, and a moisture content between 2 and 4% (Gooding, 1972). After drying, the flake
product is packed in plastic bags or cardboard cartons, as may be
convenient, using standard packaging machinery.

Table 14 Influence of Cooking Conditions on Yam Product Properties

Cooking condition (Steam pressure psig)	Properties of dried product				Rheological properties of dough 15 min after reconstitution			
	Powder bulk density (g/cm^3)	Starch damage BVI	Swelling Power (cm^3/g solids)	Solubility (g/cm^3 water)	Modulus of elasticity ($\times$ 10^5 dynes/cm^2)	Ultimate (yield) deformation	Recoverable elasticity (%)	Energy ratio
0	0.31 ± 0.05	70 ± 2	11.7	2.4	5.2	0.50	66	0.77
5	0.30 ± 0.07	100 ± 3	11.7	2.6	4.9	0.48	73	0.71
10	0.28 ± 0.03	110 ± 1	13.2	3.1	4.4	0.45	81	0.55

Source: Ayernor (1976).

Table 15 Processing Conditions for Double-Drum-Dried
D. rotundata and *D. alata* Flake

D. rotundata[a]	
Solids content of slurry	20%
Steam pressure in drums	80 psig
Drum speed (6 in. diameter drums)	2-4 rpm
Clearance between drums	0.01 in.

D. alata[b]	
Total solids of mash	19-20%
Space between feed roller and drum	0.25 in
Space between first applicator roll and drum	0.25 in.
Space between second applicator roll and drum	0.006 in.
Steam pressure in drum	60 psig
Retention time	5.7 sec

[a] Onayemi and Potter (1974).
[b] Gooding (1972).

2. Flow Sheets

A flow diagram for a yam flake plant is given in Fig. 1. Essentially
the same series of processes is adopted, whatever type of dried flake
product is devised, although the species of yam used and the processing parameters may be varied.

3. Products and Uses

The only substantial industrial processing of yam has been directed to
the production of a dehydrated flake product, designed to reconstitute
with hot water to traditional-type foods. Two main types of this product exist, however, which relate to the traditional food habits in different parts of the world. In much of the Caribbean area, yam is normally
consumed boiled in pieces, either as a separate vegetable or in a stew
or alternatively lightly mashed to a product closely resembling mashed
potato. For this purpose, *D. alata* is the most suitable yam and is
generally favored (except in Jamaica, where food habits more closely
resemble those of west Africa, and *D. cayenensis* is the preferred
species), and the processing conditions must be kept as mild as possible
to minimize cellular rupture and starch damage, and thus give a light,
fluffy product on reconstitution. The product quality for this type
of use is improved by the addition of 0.5% glycerol monostearate
(Gooding, 1972; Steele and Sammy, 1976b).

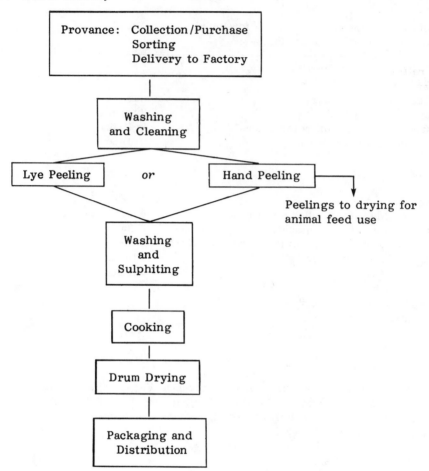

Figure 1 Flow diagram for manufacture of yam flake.

For west African markets, for which both Foutoupret and Poundoyam were intended, the requirement is for a product which will reconstitute to fufu. This is traditionally made by prolonged pounding of pieces of boiled yam (*D. rotundata* is the only species from which good fufu can be made, on account of its starch rheology, discussed previously) in a wooden mortar with a wooden pestle, until a sticky, elastic dough is formed. Processing for an instant fufu therefore involves more vigorous treatments, which will result in a high degree of cell rupture and starch damage (Coursey, 1966; Onayemi and Potter, 1974; Ayernor et al., 1974). Although the two commercial products mentioned, and other experimental preparations, have reasonably closely simulated good-quality fufu when reconstituted, there is still scope for improvement in product quality. The reconstituted product usually lacks the draw (viscosity) of the best fufu, and products have also been criticized for the vigorous stirring in boiling water that is necessary during reconstitution (Onwueme, 1968).

4. Byproducts and Processes

There are no major byproducts from yam processing, except where hand-peeling is adopted. The peel from manual operations, together with trimmings, can be dried and used for incorporation in animal feed, and this was, in fact, done during the operation of the Poundoyam plant in Nigeria. The product was sun-dried, which might present difficulties in a large-scale operation. Appreciable quantities of starch are entrained in the waste water from the cooking operation, and recovery in settling tanks might be feasible, although it has not yet been attempted commercially. This would also have the advantage of reducing the Biological Oxygen Demand (BOD) of the factory effluent.

5. Product Stability and Spoilage Problems

As already indicated, dehydrated yam flake products are stable when stored in sealed packs for several months, or even up to a year, which is ample for normal commercialization. Browning and rancidity have been reported as the main forms of deterioration (Steele and Sammy, 1976b), but did not give rise to problems in the commercial operations mentioned. Although there is a considerable loss of vitamin C during processing, it has been shown that little further loss occurs during storage of dehydrated flakes for up to 3 months (Onayemi and Potter, 1974).

6. Quality Control Methods

The first essential in the manufacture of a satisfactory processed product is the selection of material which is not only of good quality, but is of appropriate species and cultivar. For the type of product desired by Caribbean markets, *D. alata* is required, and for a product acceptable in west Africa, *D. rotundata*. Within the former species, certain cultivars were found in Puerto Rico to be more suitable than others for flake manufacture (Rodriguez-Sosa et al., 1972), whereas in west Africa, cultivars traditionally regarded as the best for fufu manufacture are also best for processing.

Where a nonsticky product is required, as for Caribbean markets, monitoring of the extent of cell damage is of crucial importance; this damage occurs to some extent during all stages of processing, but most extensively in the drum-drying stage, which needs close control. Estimation of free starch with iodine as the Blue Value Index (BVI) is suitable quality control method; an acceptable product is indicated by a BVI of below 200 (Gooding, 1972), although Steele and Sammy (1976b) have suggested that factors other than cell rupture are involved in the development of stickiness. Uniformity of flake size is also important in this type of product (Rodriguez-Sosa and Gonzalez, 1974).

Apart from these considerations, the main quality control requirement is hygiene. Dehydrated yam is essentially neutral in reaction and, therefore, is a good substrate for the growth of food spoilage and food poisoning organisms. Preservation of good factory hygiene and regular monitoring of samples from routine production to ensure the absence of such organisms are therefore essential.

V. RECIPES

As has already been indicated, dehydrated yam products are used essentially as substitutes for fresh yam, and no special recipes, therefore, exist. The difference in food habits between west Africa and the Caribbean as they relate to processed products has also been discussed.

Apart from mashing and pounding, yams may be eaten simply boiled, and cut into conveniently sized pieces. Especially in Melanesia, but to some extent in other yam-growing areas, whole tubers are roasted, usually among the hot ashes of a fire, or among heated stones, or pieces may be roasted together with meat. Occasionally, thin slices of yam fried in oil are eaten, especially for snacks; the taste and texture are often improved if the slices are parboiled before frying. This is not a widespread trational way of preparing yams, however. The manufacture of French fries and chips, which has already been discussed, or of yam cakes or croquettes made from mashed yam formed into balls and fried do not appear in normal tropical diets, but are rather the invention of expatriates resident in the tropics who tend to look on yam only as a substitute for potato.

The culinary practices of most tropical countries differ greatly from those normally adopted by people of European descent. In Africa, particularly, main meals usually consist of two principal components—first, a doughy mass of essentially carbohydrate material such as yam, or alternatively a heap of grain such as rice or maize boiled until soft and again often pounded and, second, a soup or stew containing all the other food items, including meat or fish, often both together, green vegetables, spices, or other flavoring materials, and vegetable oil. In African households the most important culinary utensil, after cooking pots, is a large wooden mortar, with a wooden pestle, which is used for the preparation of the carbohydrate component of the meals, by a protracted laborious process of pounding.

West Africa being the main yam-producing area of the world, most of the yam crop is prepared for food in this manner, the edible product being known as fufu or variously foufou or foutou. The term is also applied to similar products made from other root crops. To prepare fufu, the yams are peeled, inedible parts are removed, the remainder is cut into conveniently sized pieces, and then boiled until soft. The pieces of yam are then strained from the water and pounded using a wooden mortar and pestle, until the cellular and, to some extent, the starch granular structure is broken down, and a stiff somewhat glutinous dough formed. This pounding process can take anything from 15 to 30 min. Before being served, the fufu is molded to for a spheroidal mass, from which portions are detached by hand when eating and used to scoop up the accompanying stew (Coursey, 1967).

In view of this traditional approach to food, in which the yam or other carbohydrate is served as a separate component of the meal to the highly flavored protein-rich stew, it seems to this writer to be inappropriate to attempt the protein fortification of a processed yam product. This has, however, been suggested by Abe (1973), and experiments on the incorporation of soy into yam flours have been conducted (Collins and Falasinnu, 1977) with some degree of success.

REFERENCES

Abe, M. C. (1973). Adaptability of potato drying to yam processing. *J. Milk Food Technol.* 36:456-462.

Adamson, I., and Abigor, R. (1980). Transformation associated with catecholase in *Dioscorea alata* during storage. *Phytochem.* 19: 1593-1595.

Adesuyi, S. A. (1965). A survey of insect pests on stored dried yam and an investigation of the biology of the more important species. *Ann. Rep. Niger. Stored Prod. Res. Inst.* 95.

Adesuyi, S. A. (1978). The application of advanced technology to the improvement of yam storage. In *Yams-Ignames, Provisional Report of International Seminar on Yams, Buea, Cameroon.* Stockholm, International Foundation for Science, pp. 387-398.

Adesuyi, S. A., and MacKenzie, J. A. (1973). The inhibition of sprouting in stored yams by gamma radiation and chemicals. In *Radiation Preservation of Foods.* Vienna, International Atomic Energy Authority, pp. 127-136.

Afable, L. A. (1970). The preparation of ubi powder. *Philippine J. Plant Industry* 35:19-25.

Alexander, J., and Coursey, D. G. (1969). The origins of yam cultivation. In *The Domestication and Exploitation of Plants and Animals* (P. J. Ucko and G. W. Dimbleby, eds.). London, Duckworth, pp. 405-426.

Anon. (1972). *Primer simposio internacional sobre Dioscoreas.* Mexico, Publ. Esp. Inst. Nal. Invest. For., 8.

Anosike, E. O., and Ayaebene, A. O. (1981). Purification and some properties of polyphenol oxidase from the yam tubers, *Dioscorea bulbifera. Phytochem.* 20:2625-2628.

Ayensu, E. S. (1972). *Anatomy of the Monocotyledons, Dioscoreales*, (C. R. Metcalfe, ed.). London, Oxford University Press.

Ayensu, E. S., and Coursey, D. G. (1972). Guinea yams. *Econ. Bot.* 26:301-318.

Ayernor, G. S. (1976). Particulate properties and rheology of pregelled yam (*Dioscorea rotundata*) products. *J. Food Sci.* 41:180-182.

Ayernor, G. S., Brennan, J. G., and Rolfe, E. J. (1974). Rheology as a tool in product development. *Proc. 4th Int. Cong. Food Sci. Technol. (Madrid)* 2:33-35.

Been, B. O., Perkins, C., and Thompson, A. K. (1977). Yam curing for storage. *Acta Hortic.* 62:311-316.

Booth, R. H. (1974). Postharvest deterioration of tropical root crops: losses and their control. *Trop. Sci.* 16:49-63.

Brennan, J. G., and Ayernor, G. S. (1973). A study of the kinetics of retrogradation in a starch-based dough made from dehydrated yam (*Dioscorea rotundata* Poir). *Stärke* 25:276-280.

Burkill, I. H. (1960). The organography and the evolution of the Dioscoreaceae, the family of the yams. *J. Linn. Soc. (Bot.)* 56: 319-412.

Collins, J. L., and Falasinnu, G. A. (1977). Yam (*Dioscorea* spp.) flour fortification with soy flour. *J. Food Sci.* 42:821-823.

Coursey, D. G. (1961). The magnitude and origins of storage losses in Nigerian yams. *J. Sci. Fd. Agric.* 12:574-580.

Coursey, D. G. (1966). Food technology and the yam in West Africa. *Trop. Sci.* 8:152-159.

Coursey, D. G. (1967). *Yams.* London, Longmans.

Coursey, D. G. (1968). Low temperature injury in yams. *J. Fd. Technol.* 3:143-150.

Coursey, D. G. (1972). The civilizations of the yam: interrelationships of man and yams in Africa and the Indo-Pacific region. *Archaeol. Phys. Anthropol. Oceania* 7:215-233.

Coursey, D. G. (1976a). Yams. In *Evolution of Crop Plants* (N. W. Simmonds, ed.). London, Longmans, pp. 70-74.

Coursey, D. G. (1976b). The origins and domestication of yams in Africa. In *The Origins of African Plant Domestication* (J. R. Harlan, J. M. J. de Wet, and A. B. L. Stemler, eds.). The Hague, Mouton, pp. 383-408.

Coursey, D. G. (1978). Root crops and their utilization in West Africa. *The Adaptation of Traditional Agriculture* (E. Fisk, ed.). Canberra, Development Studies Centre Monograph No. 11, Australian National University, pp. 199-212.

Coursey, D. G., and Aidoo, A. (1966). Ascorbic acid levels in Ghanaian yams. *J. Sci. Fd. Agric.* 17:446-449.

Coursey, D. G., and Ferber, C. E. M. (1979). The processing of yams. In *Small Scale Processing and Storage of Tropical Root Crops* (D. L. Plucknett, ed.). Boulder Color., Westview Press, pp. 189-212.

Coursey, D. G., and Martin, F. W. (1970). The past and future of yams as crop plants. *Proc. 2nd Int. Symp. Trop. Root Crops, Hawaii* 1:87-90; 99-101.

Coursey, D. G., and Nwankwo, F. I. (1968). Effects of insolation and of shade on the storage behaviour of yams in West Africa. *Ghana J. Sci.* 8:74-81.

Cruz-Cay, J. R., and Gonzalez, M. A. (1974). Properties of starch from Florido yam (*Dioscorea alata* L.). *J. Agric. Univ. P. Rico* 58:312-316.

de la Rosa, L., and Emiola, L. (1980). Characteristics of *Dioscorea rotundata* polyphenol oxidase. *J. Appl. Biochem.* 2:100-110.

de Vries, C. A., Ferweda, J. D., and Flach, M. (1967). Choice of food crops in relation to actual potential production in the tropics. *Neth. J. Agric. Sci.* 15:241-248.

Diehl, L. (1982). *Smallholder Farming Systems with Yam in the Southern Guinea Savannah of Nigeria.* Eschborn, Germany, GTZ.

Ferguson, T. U. (1972). The propagation of *Dioscorea* spp. by vine cuttings: a critical review. *Trop. Root Tuber Crops. Newsl.* 5:4-7.

Francis, B. J., Halliday, D., and Robinson, J. M. (1975). Yams as a source of edible protein. *Trop. Sci.* 17:103-110.

Gonzalez, M. A., and Collazo de Rivera, A. (1972). Storage of fresh yam (*Dioscorea alata* L.) under controlled conditions. *J. Agric. Univ. P. Rico* 56:46-56.

Gooding, E. G. B. (1972). The production of instant yam in Barbados. Part I: Process Development. *Trop. Sci.* 14:323-333.

Gramshaw, J. W., and Osinowo, F. A. O. (1982). Volatile components of cooked tubers of water yam (*Discorea alata*). *J. Sci. Fd. Agric.* 33:71-80.

Haynes, P. H., and Coursey, D. G. (1969). Gigantism in the yam. *Trop. Sci.* 11:93-96.

Idusogie, E. O. (1971). The nutritive value per acre of selected food crops in Nigeria. *J. W. Afr. Sci. Assoc.* 16:17-24.

Imakawa, S. (1967). Browning of Chinese yam (*D. batatas*). *Hokkaido Daigaku Hobun Kiyo* 6:181-192.

Imbert, M. P., and Seaforth, C. (1969). Anthocyanins of *Dioscorea alata* L. *Experientia* 24:445-447.

Jarmai, S., and Montford, L. C. (1968). Yam flour for the production of fufu. *Ghana J. Agric. Sci.* 1:161-163.

Kawakami, K. (1970). Yams in Japan. *Proc. 2nd Int. Symp. Trop. Root Crops, Hawaii* 1:102.

Ketiku, A. O. and Oyenuga, V. A. (1970). Preliminary report on the carbohydrate constituents of cassava root and yam tuber. *Niger. J. Sci.* 4:25-30.

le Berre, S., Gallon, G., and Tabi, B. (1968). Teneur en vitamine C dans les tubercules et la plantain du Cameroun avant et apres cuisson. *Ann. Nutr. Alim.* 23:31-45.

Martin, F. W. (1974a). Tropical yams and their potential. Part 1. *Dioscorea esculenta. Agricultural Handbook 457*, Washington, D.C., USDA Agricultural Research Service.

Martin, F. W. (1974b). Tropical yams and their potential. Part 2. *Dioscorea bulbifera. Agriculture Handbook 466*. Washington, D.C., USDA Agricultural Research Service.

Martin, F. W. (1974c). Effects of type of wound, species and humidity on curing of yam (*Dioscore alata* L.) tubers before storage. *J. Agric. Univ. P. Rico* 58:211-218.

Martin, F. W. (1976). Tropical yams and their potential. Part 3. *Dioscorea alata. Agriculture Handbook 495*. Washington D.C., USDA Agricultural Research Services.

Martin, F. W., and Degras, L. (1978a). Tropical yams and their potential. Part 5. *Dioscorea trifida. Agriculture Handbook 522*. Washington, D.C., USDA Agricultural Research Services.

Martin, F. W., and Degras, L. (1978b). Tropical yams and their potential. Part 6. Minor cultivated *Discorea* species. *Agriculture Handbook 538*. Washington D.C., USDA Agricultural Research Service.

Martin, F. W., and Rhodes, A. M. (1973). Correlations among greater yam (*Dioscorea alata* L.) cultivars. *Trop. Agric. (Trin.)* 50:183-192.

Martin, F. W., and Ruberte, R. (1972). Yams (*Dioscorea* spp.) for the production of chips and fresh fries. *J. Agric. Univ. P. Rico* 56:228-234.

Martin, F. W., and Ruberte, R. (1975). Carotenoid pigments of *Dioscorea cayenensis. Ann. Appl. Biol.* 80:317-322.

Martin, F. W., and Sadik, S. (1977). Tropical yams and their potential Part 4. *Dioscorea rotundata* and *Dioscorea cayenensis. Agriculture Handbook 502*. Washington D.C., USDA Agricultural Research Station.

Martin, F. W., and Thompson, A. E. (1971). Crude protein content of yams. *Hortic. Sci.* 6:545-546.

Martin, F. W., and Thompson, A. E. (1973). Protein content and amino-acid balance of yams. *J. Agric. Univ. P. Rico* 57:78-83.

Martin, F. W., Cabanillas, E., and Guadalupe, R. (1975). Selected varieties of *Dioscorea alata* L., the Asian Greater Yam. *J. Agric. Univ. P. Rico* 59:165-181.

Martin, F. W., Telek, L., and Ruberte, R. (1974). The yellow pigments of *Dioscorea bulbifera. J. Agric. Food Chem.* 22:335-337.

Misawa, M., and Matsubara, M. (1965). Studies on the manufacturing of the powder of tuber of the yam. *Jap. J. Food Sci. Technol.* 12:23-29.

Neumann, J., Lehongre, G., and Lavollay, J. (1969). Presence d'une orthodiphenoloxidase (stricte) extractible dans le tubercule d'Igname de Chine (*Dioscorea batatas*). *C.r. hebd. Acad. Sci. (Ser. D.)* 268:412-415.

Noon, R. A. (1978). Storage and market diseases of yams. *Trop. Sci.* 20:177-188.

Okagami, N. (1978). Dormancy in *Dioscorea*: sprouting promotion by inhibitors of protein synthesis in bulbils and rhizomes. *Plant Cell Physiol.* 19:221-227.

Olorunda, A. O. (1979). Storage and processing of some Nigerian root crops. In *Small Scale Processing and Storage of Tropical Root Crops* (D. L. Plucknett, ed.). Boulder, Colo., Westview Press, pp. 90-99.

Onayemi, O., and Potter, N. N. (1974). Preparation and properties of drum dried white yam (*Dioscorea rotundata* Poir) flakes. *J. Food Sci.* 39:559-562.

Onwueme, I. C. (1978). *The tropical tuber crops*. Chichester, J. Wiley.

Opute, F. I., and Osagie, A. U. (1978). Fatty acid composition of total lipids from some tropical storage organs. *J. Sci. Fd. Agric.* 29:959-962.

Osinowo, F. A. O. (1977). *The volatile constitutents of yams*. Unpublished Ph.D. thesis, University of Leeds, England.

Passam, H. C. (1978). Dormancy of yams in relation to storage. In *Yams-Igname Provisional Report of International Seminar on Yams, Buea, Cameroon*, Stockholm, International Foundation for Science, pp. 357-370.

Passam, H. C., and Barrett, C. (1977). Invertase in yam (*Dioscorea* spp.) tubers. *J. Root Crops* 3:1-3.

Passam, H. C., Read, S. J., and Rickard, J. E. (1976a). Wound repair in yam tubers: physiological processes during repair. *New Phytol.* 77:325-331.

Passam, H. C., Read, S. J., and Rickard, J. E. (1976b). Wound repair in yam tubers: the dependence of storage procedures on the nature of the wound and its repair. *Trop. Sci.* 18:1-11.

Passam, H. C., Read, S. J., and Rickard, J. E. (1978). The respiration of yam tubers and its contribution to storage loss. *Trop. Agric. (Trin.)* 55:207-214.

Rasper, V. (1969a). Investigations on starches from major starch crops grown in Ghana. I. Hot paste viscosity and gel forming power. *J. Sci. Fd. Agric.* 20:165-171.

Rasper, V. (1969b). Investigations on starches from major starch crops grown in Ghana. II. Swelling and solubility patterns; amyloclastic susceptibility. *J. Sci. Fd. Agric.* 20:642-646.

Rasper, V. (1971). Investigations on starches from major starch crops grown in Ghana. III. Particle size and particle size distribution. *J. Sci. Fd. Agric.* 22:572-580.

Rasper, V., and Coursey, D. G. (1967a). Properties of starches of some West African yams. *J. Sci. Fd. Agric.* 18:240-244.

Rasper, V., and Coursey, D. G. (1967b). Anthocyanins of *Dioscorea alata* L. *Experientia* 23:611.

Rivera-Ortiz, J. M., and Gonzalez, M. A. (1972). Lye peeling of fresh yam, *Dioscorea alata. J. Agric. Univ. P. Rico* 56:57-63.

Rodriguez-Sosa, E. J., and Gonzalez, M. A. (1972). Preparation of yam (*Dioscorea alata* L.) flakes. *J. Agric. Univ. P. Rico* 56:39-45.

Rodriguez-Sosa, E. J., and Gonzalez, M. A. (1974). Effect of flake size on pasting characteristics of instant Florido yam (*Dioscorea alata*) flake slurries. *J. Agric. Univ. P. Rico* 58:219-224.

Rodriguez-Sosa, E. J., Gonzalez, M. A., and Martin, F. W. (1972). Evaluation of ten varieties of yam (*Dioscorea* spp.) for production of instant flakes. *J. Agric. Univ. P. Rico* 56:235-243.

Rodriguez-Sosa, E. J., Gonzalez, M. A., and Parsi-Ros, O. (1974). Effect of pre-cooking on quality of instant flakes from Florido yam (*Dioscorea alata* L.). *J. Agric. Univ. P. Rico* 58:317-321.

Rodriguez-Sosa, E. J., Cruz-Cay, J. R., Gonzalez, M. A., and Martin, F. W. (1973). Shelf-life study of Farm Lisbon yam (*Dioscorea alata*) chips. *J. Agric. Univ. P. Rico* 57:196-202.

Sadik, S., and Okereke, O. U. (1975a). A new approach to improvement of yam, *Dioscorea rotundata. Nature (Lond.)* 254:134-135.

Sadik, S., and Okereke, O. U. (1975b). Flowering, pollen grain germination, fruiting, seed germination and seedling development of white yam, *Dioscorea rotundata* Poir. *Ann. Bot.* 34:597-604.

Seidemann, J. (1964). Mikroskopische Untersuchung verschiedener *Dioscorea*-starken. *Stärke* 16:246-253.

Splittstoesser, W. E. (1976). Protein and total amino-acid content before and after cooking of yams. *Hort. Sci.* 11:611.

Splittstoesser, W. E., and Martin, F. W. (1975). The tryptophan content of tropical roots and tubers. *Hort. Sci.* 10:23-24.

Splittstoesser, W. E., Martin, F. W., and Rhodes, A. M. (1973). The amino-acid composition of five species of yam (*Dioscorea*). *J. Am. Soc. Hort. Sci.* 98:559-562.

Steele, W. J. C., and Sammy, G. M. (1976a). The processing potential of yams (*Dioscorea* spp.). I. Laboratory studies of lye peeling of yams. *J. Agric. Univ. P. Rico* 60:207-214.

Steele, W. J. C., and Sammy, G. M. (1976b). The processing potential of yams (*Dioscorea* spp.). II. Pre-cooked drum dried flakes-instant yams. *J. Agric. Univ. P. Rico* 60:215-223.

Tono, T. (1970). Isolation of dopamine and browning of tubers of Chinese Yam (*Dioscorea batatas*). *J. Food Sci. Technol. (Japan)* 17:447-450.

Ugochukwu, E. N., Anosike, E. O., and Agogbua, S. I. O. (1977). Changes in enzyme activity of white yam tubers after prolonged storage. *Phytochem.* 16:1159-1162.

Waitt, A. W. (1965). A key to some Nigerian variations of yam (*Dioscorea* spp.). *Memorandum 60.* Ibadan, Nigeria, Federal Department of Agricultural Research.

Author Index

Subject Index